RON NASH

RATIONAL THINKING

RON NASH

BELVOIR VALE PUBLISHING

First published in 2009

Copyright © 2009 by Ron Nash

Ron Nash has asserted his right under the Copyright, Designs and
Patents Act 1988 to be identified as the author of this work.

First published in the United Kingdom in 2009
by Belvoir Vale Publishing
49 Fairway, Keyworth, Nottingham NG12 5DW

ISBN 978-0-9562826-0-6

Printed and bound in Malta by Gutenberg Press Ltd.

ACKNOWLEDGEMENTS

My thanks to:-

Gwyneth M Donaldson – for her enthusiasm, dedicated computer work and patience. Without her efforts this book would never have been published.

Dan Roberts – for his work proof reading, his valuable comments and encouragement.

Margaret Wainer – for her literary advice, proof reading and attention to detail.

Tim Hughes – for his artistic flair and the cover illustration.

Richard – for his computer work and his enthusiasm.

Denville – for his comments and suggestions.

Eileen – for her remarkable patience and tolerance during the period I was writing this book.

And also:-

NATIONAL AERONAUTICS AND SPACE ADMINISTRATION

THE JOHN F. KENNEDY PRESIDENTIAL LIBRARY AND MUSEUM

THE DAILY TELEGRAPH

VAN GOGH MUSEUM

For permission to reproduce photographs and quotations.

CONTENTS
(i OF vi)

CONTENTS
(ii OF vi)

CONTENTS
(iii OF vi)

CONTENTS
(iv OF vi)

CONTENTS
(v OF vi)

CONTENTS
(vi OF vi)

FOREWORD

Rational Thinking is the key to Understanding. It enables us to sort the truth from the fallacies, to recognise the misleading, to choose the best course of action in any situation. It can help everyone of us – from handling the simple problems of everyday living, be it money matters and decision making on a personal level to the major decisions in business, politics and world affairs. However, rational thinking is not as easy as it sounds. It involves a certain amount of mental self discipline, a willingness to question established ideas and views, careful analysis of the information available and, above all, facing facts and resisting the temptation to turn our minds away from anything that looks as if it is going to lead to unpleasant conclusions; in other words avoiding self delusion. It is necessary to control ourselves when making decisions and not let emotions blind us to what may be obvious, but sometimes unpalatable, conclusions. Rational thinking is the proper use of intelligence.

The human race in general, unfortunately, has a penchant for seeing what it wants to see and believing what it wants to believe, sometimes in the face of overwhelming evidence to the contrary. There is often a reluctance to face facts. In writing of Global Warming and The Future of the Human Race I have been accused of doom-mongering. I have no wish to do that for sheer sensationalism and would be happy if someone can provide logical, rational, reasons, backed by solid data, explaining why the conclusions put forward are invalid. However, if we refuse to accept rational conclusions because we find them disturbing or distasteful we are merely deluding ourselves. If we adopt a "Lets be happy today; Don't worry about tomorrow" attitude then we are going to create a terrible legacy for later generations.

To handle the massive problems of tomorrow the world will need rational thinking as never before. Either we learn to put aside the petty squabbles between ethnic groups and nations and recognise we are all one species, living together on the only planet we will ever have, and work together to control our numbers or the whole world is eventually likely to dissolve in chaos, thousands of species will go extinct and human life degenerate into a hellish struggle for survival.

I suppose it was to be expected that an Engineer (or Scientist) would write a book such as this since our profession forces us towards rational thinking. Planes fly, ships float, machines work, bridges and skyscrapers stand only because engineers face facts and accept and work with reality. All the developments that have created the modern world, and raised the standard of living of most of the people on the planet, are the results of rational, logical, thinking allied to detailed observation, analysis of carefully collected data and acceptance of reality and the laws of nature. It is the simple fact that there are far too many of us that is the root cause of the major problems we face today and in the future. If there were only two hundred million humans we could, if we were sensible, all live happily and safely, in harmony, affluence and even luxury, in balance with the rest of the planet. Unfortunately that is not the case and we need all the rational thinking we can get to handle our current situation, mitigate the problems of tomorrow and eventually reduce our presence on the planet to sane and sustainable levels.

A friend of mine said this book is 'The Thoughts of Ron Nash'. I suppose he is right but, does it really matter? What does matter is whether I am right or not; whether the conclusions put forward are correct or not, and whether it will encourage or provoke people into thinking for themselves logically and rationally. Am I right when I suggest thousands of lives could be saved merely by changing tactics on the treatment of Cancer? Am I right when I suggest Global Warming is unstoppable and billions of people will be forced to migrate? Am I right when I suggest there will be 20 billion people on this Earth if we don't take adequate action? If so we should think about these things, discuss them and start to do something. I would be quite happy to be shown to be wrong as long as I am shown to be wrong by logical, reasoned and reasonable arguments, backed up where necessary by scientific data. When that happens I shall change my views. What I am not happy about is when people reject the conclusions simply because they don't like them, because of some dogma or some emotional response. The key thing for all of us is to think carefully, face facts and accept logical conclusions whether those conclusions are disturbing or not.

GLOBAL WARMING

Global Warming, almost certainly triggered by human activity, and now unstoppable, is likely to be one of the great factors affecting the future of the human race in the next hundred years and beyond, leading to migration on an unprecedented scale and probably international strife.

Anyone who has lived in the UK as long as I have (I am 78) will know the climate of Britain has changed, and has become warmer, during this period. It is particularly noticeable the winters have become milder, especially in the last 25 years. When I was a child, my friends and I used to toboggan in the snow and skate on the frozen ponds and canal almost every winter. Any thickness of ice more than 3" (7.5cm) would support us but I can remember, in two very cold winters, I drilled through the ice and measured it at over 10" (25cm) thick. In the last 20 years I only remember two years when ice has been thick enough and strong enough to support skaters on an old canal which is near to my present home and, even then, only for a very short time. In the winter of 1946, lakes froze at Christmas and the ice did not completely disappear until the following April. Those old-fashioned frigid winters now seem to be a thing of the past and, I admit, I am not really sorry to see them go.

However, it must be said, that England is not really a suitable place to judge Global Warming. It is too dependent on the vagaries of the Gulf Stream in the sea and the Jet Stream in the upper atmosphere. We must look elsewhere for evidence. When we do, we find that everywhere we turn there are indications. For instance, glaciers all over the world are changing; from Mount Kilimanjaro in Africa to those in Alaska and Greenland; in the Himalayas, Switzerland and the Andes. Many are melting back and even those that are not, or that are actually advancing, have speeded up; in other words their flow rate has drastically increased. Enormous amounts of ice are flowing into the sea from Greenland's glaciers, as I was able to observe for myself during a recent flight to Alaska. An astounding number of massive icebergs could be seen floating in the sea off Greenland. The shadows thrown on to the sea showed how enormous they really were – especially as 7/8[ths] of the iceberg is under the surface of the water.

Fifty years ago, in Alaska and Siberia, the topsoil only melted down a short distance, a foot or so, in the summer. Below this was the endlessly frozen rock-like earth and peat – the 'permafrost'. The stunted trees growing on the tundra had roots only in the top foot of earth; they could not penetrate the permafrost. Now, however, the surface layer thaws out deeper and deeper every summer. The permafrost is melting, all over the Arctic areas of the world. The sea is also warming. The most obvious evidence of this is that species of fish and shellfish, sensitive to water temperatures, are steadily moving northwards year after year.

The great ice shelves in Antarctica, that have been attached to the Antarctic continent for thousands of years, are now breaking away. An occasional phenomenon in the Pacific, that only occurs during exceptionally hot years, El Nino, a reversal of the ocean currents off Peru, is becoming more and more frequent. It has many secondary effects, such as drought in Australia and disruption of the Monsoons in South East Asia. There is also evidence from spacecraft; the weather and observation satellites. Weather satellites are registering a definite, actual, warming trend; the average temperature of the whole planet is steadily rising.

Finally and this, to my mind, is the most impressive of all the evidence, is the reduction of the North Polar Ice Cap. Satellite photographs have shown that the area covered by ice in summer, around the North Pole, has decreased by an amazing 20% in the last 20 years. Very soon, the Russians will be able to sail cargo ships, without being escorted by an icebreaker, from Murmansk to Vladivostok. The long hoped for North West Passage, from the Atlantic to the Pacific, North of Canada, may soon become a reality. *

I personally have been amazed by what I have seen and experienced in Northern Russia and Alaska. During a salmon fishing trip in Russia, last year, on the Yokanga river, which is situated on the extreme north of the Kola peninsula near Murmansk, within the Arctic Circle, air temperatures reached 32°/33° C. The temperature of the water flowing in that arctic river was checked at 22° C. There was not a chance of catching fish of course. Far too hot! I have experienced very similar conditions in Alaska. In both countries I was fishing close to the sea, not in the middle of a continental landmass where temperature extremes are to be expected. The locals confirm that the Arctic appears to be warming up at an amazing rate. I later read a scientific article which stated that, whilst the average global temperature has increased by 0.7° C in the last seventy years, in Northern Russia, Siberia, Canada and Alaska the average temperature has increased by 2° C to 3° C over the same period of time, but more noticeably over the last 40 years. This rise is causing considerable changes to the tundra. No one yet knows why these areas

* NOTE:- Between the writing of this book (2006/7) and publishing (2009), the North Polar Ice Cap has reduced by a further 20% in 2007 alone and both the sea passages referred to i.e. Murmansk/Vladivostok and the North West Passage have become open.

have warmed faster than the rest of the planet, but the fact remains that the sudden warming of the tundra will have far reaching consequences.

It is now generally accepted by most scientists and politicians that global warming is a reality. Arguments rage over what has initially triggered the warming, and there are many scientists who believe solar fluctuations and variations in the Earth's tilt and orbit (Milankovitch Cycles) are the real trigger, not human-caused CO_2 emissions. However, the facts indicate that the planet is now warming rapidly and, most importantly, the warming trend is speeding up, noticeably over the last few years. Whatever the actual trigger that started the warming, there is no doubt that the increase of man-made CO_2 must, because it is a powerful greenhouse gas, contribute to the overall warming of the planet. Analysis of ice cores, from Greenland and the Antarctic, indicate that the CO_2 level in the atmosphere is now at its highest level for over 100,000 years. We are now hearing reports and warnings that increased global warming will bring floods in some areas, through the sea level rising, and, in others, famine due to higher temperatures and lack of rain. A chorus of voices is now saying we must take action to reduce or stop the trend; we must cut CO_2 emissions drastically.

The UK and other Governments have signed agreements committing themselves to reducing CO_2 emissions in the next few years. This sounds sensible and admirable at first, but let us consider the situation rationally before we come to conclusions. First, as regards the UK, the cost of implementing the agreements will be very substantial and include massive investment in wind power, nuclear power, bio fuels, etc. There will be taxation to make us reduce the use of personal vehicles and possibly also to reduce flying and so on. Businesses will be taxed, to make them take action to reduce their 'carbon foot print', leading to higher costs and hence higher prices for the goods they produce. There is even talk of installing special equipment at coal fired power stations to capture the emissions, compress and liquefy the CO_2, transport it and finally pump it deep underground in the hope that it will stay there indefinitely. This last proposal, it is estimated, would raise the cost of electrical power at least 50%. In other words, the cost of reducing the UK output of CO_2 by say 20% to 30% would be enormous. Billions of pounds a year! A number of other developed countries are also considering undertaking similar actions in order to honour their commitments.

As an example of proposals for economising on power – in order to reduce CO_2 emissions – the UK is embarking on a programme to force the substitution of fluorescent mini-tubes for incandescent bulbs in every household. Enormous inconvenience and considerable cost will be caused

– the changing of light fittings and switches (dimmer switches can not be used with fluorescents), the closing of existing factories and the setting up of new ones and so on. There is also the fact that fluorescents contain mercury which will cause problems when the tubes fail or are broken or scrapped. What reduction in energy use will all this hassle achieve? The answer is – about 3% on UK generated electrical power – about the power output of one large electrical generating power station. That means that all the hassle and trouble caused by changing the bulbs will be negated by just one of the 350 coal fired power stations the Chinese will be commissioning in the next few years. There will be absolutely no discernable effect on global warming whatsoever. The whole project is an expensive waste of time and effort. The rational thing to do is to encourage people to use fluorescents, in suitable applications, but to force everyone to adopt them in unsuitable situations, by taking incandescent bulbs off the market entirely, is an overreaction.

Let us look at the global situation rationally and unemotionally. The brutal truth is that all the UK's efforts, and those of the other developed countries, would achieve practically nothing, except maybe the warm glow of satisfaction that at least we had tried. Let us consider the Third World and the developing countries; China, India, Indonesia, South East Asia, the South American countries, Africa, Russia and the old USSR countries. Firstly, China, which has a population of around 1.3 billion people. For centuries the majority of the people of China have known only poverty. They have lived at the limit of survival and on the brink of starvation. Now – they have made the breakthrough to an industrial society. Now – they see the golden gates to a materialist heaven opening before them. They have the bit between their teeth; no one is going to stop them. And can you blame them? They have already cracked the problem of food. Soon they too will have cars, TVs, computers, fridges and all the trappings that we in the West take for granted. In a few years time there are expected to be a hundred million cars in China. When it is considered that, in the UK, with a population of 60 million, we manage to have over 25 million cars, why should China stop at 100 million? If they ever reach our level of affluence that would imply 500 million cars. Ridiculous? Why should it be? We did it! Europe did it! Japan did it! Think of the energy required to make all those cars, plus fridges and TVs, the concrete for buildings, and so on.

The Chinese are planning, beginning 2007, to commission 50 electricity generating power stations a year – roughly one a week – for the next several years, in order to cope with demand. This is in addition to the hydroelectric power from their new dams. (At least that power is 'green'). The new power stations will, of course, use coal. China has massive reserves of coal, and the manpower willing and able to mine it. China has twenty times the population of the UK. In the circumstances, can we reasonably expect the Chinese to adopt energy and CO_2 restriction policies that would drastically reduce their development and industrial expansion? I think not! They may, and probably will, pay lip service to the idea but, behind the scenes, they will press on regardless. There will be few westerners there to monitor their emissions. The other developing 'Third World' countries are likely to do the same. India, with another billion people, is also racing ahead, with an economic growth, at the time of writing, of around 8% per annum. India's economy is expected to double in the next ten to fifteen years. This cannot be achieved without a massive increase in the supply of energy, most of which will come from the burning of fossil fuel. World development and economic expansion will not stop so the only possible conclusion is that all the available reserves of oil and natural gas will be used in the next 100 years, one way or another. All the available reserves of coal will be used in the next 300 to 400 years. (The Earth still has vast deposits of coal).

As the human population continues to increase, so the burning of the forests in South America and Indonesia will continue, thus adding to the release of CO_2 and, at the same time, destroying trees that otherwise would be absorbing CO_2 from the atmosphere. On the deep sea bed, in various parts of the world, exist enormous deposits of a wax like substance – methane hydrate – formed over millions of years as methane slowly percolated through the sea bed from below and, in the extreme conditions of cold and high pressure, combined with the water to produce a solid compound. The sea floor water temperature is only around 3°C to 4°C, and it has been suggested that only a small increase in temperature might cause the methane hydrate to decompose, allowing free methane gas to bubble to the surface of the sea and add yet further greenhouse gases to the atmosphere. This is probably unlikely, but a much greater possibility is that, sometime in the future, human beings, desperate for fuel, will find ways to release the methane for industrial exploitation. There are additional factors that will also contribute to global warming, now that the process has started.

Earlier, I mentioned the rapid warming of the Arctic Tundra. The tundra produces mosses, lichens and a host of small plants, stunted trees, grasses and so on. Over thousands of years the vegetation that has grown, died and rotted, has produced a layer of peat which may be anything from one metre to three metres thick or more. Fifty years ago, a normal situation was that the tundra froze rock solid in the winter, at temperatures from freezing point to minus 40°C. When the spring arrived, the top surface thawed and, by the summer, down to half a metre deep was moist

– allowing the tundra plants and stunted trees to live. As I have seen, the small pines and other trees in that area often blow over in windy weather, because their roots could only grow in the thin, thawed, top layer. Now the thaw is much deeper. Peat that has been frozen for thousands of years is thawing – and staying thawed for a much longer period of time. Peat that is frozen solid in the permafrost, is inert; there is no bacterial activity. However, when the peat is warmed and thaws out, bacteria become active. In other words the peat begins to decay. It rots and, as it rots, it produces CO_2 and methane. Methane, I'm sorry to say, is a much more powerful greenhouse gas than CO_2. About 10 times more so. (Some scientists claim 20 times more). In other words a million tons of methane has a warming effect equal to 10 million tons of CO_2.

There is a staggering quantity of peat in the Arctic Tundra. We are not talking millions of tons, or billions, but trillions of tons. In other words millions of millions of tons. If this vast amount rots, and releases its CO_2 and methane into the atmosphere, it will totally dwarf whatever the UK contributes to CO_2 emissions. It will probably exceed the total human output of greenhouse gases. There are, of course, plenty of natural absorbers of carbon dioxide. The rain forests are often quoted as a classic example, as are the photosynthetic algae and plankton of the seas. Anything green removes CO_2 from the air; including your kidney beans and dahlias. However, the evidence is, the CO_2 is not being removed fast enough; plus there is the fact that – when plants rot or are burned – back goes the CO_2 into the atmosphere again. The biosphere is being overwhelmed. If it was not, the atmospheric CO_2 levels would not have increased as they have in the last 100 years.

Having referred to the methane hydrate on the sea bed, and the enormous quantities of methane that will be released from the rotting tundra peat, the reader may have the impression the methane could be a bigger problem than CO_2. This is not so. CO_2 is a stable gas and it requires an introduction of energy to break the CO_2 molecule (as happens in photosynthesis – sunlight is the source of the energy). Methane, on the other hand, is a hydrocarbon gas (CH_4). It can be burned and has often been the cause of explosions in coal mines. In the presence of oxygen (in the atmosphere) it will eventually oxidise, one way or another, to produce CO_2 and water. Whilst the tundra rots there will be levels of methane maintained in the atmosphere but, when the methane input drops the levels of methane will decrease quite rapidly. CO_2 levels will decrease much more slowly. If it should be that the methane hydrate on the sea bed does decompose and release methane gas (due to the sea water becoming warmer) then, it seems to me, the best thing to do would be to fire it (if we could find no way to harvest it) and burn it off. The CO_2 produced would be less harmful than the methane.

Another, lesser known but very powerful greenhouse gas, produced by human activity, is Nitrous Oxide. Nitrous oxide is produced when bacteria, in the soil, act on nitrate fertilisers used to boost the growth of crops. As more and more of the planet's surface is cultivated for food, bio-fuels and other purposes more and more nitrous oxide will be produced. Calculations have suggested the benefits of growing crops for bio-fuels (to replace fossil fuels) will be completely negated by the additional release of greenhouse gases from the cultivated soil.

Satellite observations have shown that the polar ice, and ice on the mountains all over the world, is melting rapidly. The North Polar Ice Cap, for instance, is just a floating mass of ice which freezes further south in winter, increasing the overall size of the cap, and melts back again in the summer. Recent satellite observations have revealed that, at its minimum in mid-summer, the north polar ice cap has reduced by at least 20% from the area it was forty years ago. Although it has not been said, it is very likely the total area of ice in winter is also less than it was. Unfortunately, not only does the reduction in size of the polar ice cap indicate global warming, it actually acts to increase the warming. Ice reflects sunlight back into space. On a patch of earth, or rock, or grassland the light is absorbed – warming the planet. It also warms the sea if it shines on water. So if we have a patch of rock, instead of ice, in the mountains – it warms the Earth. More importantly, because of the vast areas involved, if we lose the ice floating on the sea, the light warms the exposed water and thereby warms the planet. This is a secondary effect resulting from the original greenhouse warming.

So, if we consider the effects of the melting of the permafrost, the melting of the glaciers and the reduction of the polar ice cap the implication is – we are now in a 'positive feedback' situation. In order to explain, let me turn to an example in engineering. Consider the design of an old fashioned steam engine. Firstly, we have a boiler producing high-pressure steam and a pipework system feeding the steam to an engine. The engine rotates and produces power and, in its turn, drives various kinds of machinery. However, the power requirements, termed the 'load' can vary. Under heavy load, the engine will tend to slow down and, under light load, to speed up. Without any load at all the engine would, if the steam supply was not reduced, speed up to such a degree it would probably 'blow up'. To control the speed of the engine and to ensure that it did not 'run away', i.e. over speed, the designers invented a device termed a 'governor'. This device, which you have probably seen on old steam engines, usually incorporates two or three brass balls spinning around a spindle. The governor is set to allow the engine to run at – say – 1000 revolutions per minute. This speed will be held while the engine is 'labouring' i.e. driving some machine. If the machine is switched off, or disconnected, the steam engine will be inclined to speed up. However, the governor is arranged so that it detects any speed up of the engine and partially closes a valve, to reduce the supply of steam until the engine returns to the correct speed; the more the engine over speeds the more the governor shuts off the steam supply. This is called a 'negative feedback' system. Now – just imagine some idiot connected the governor up the wrong way. So that when the engine speeds up the governor acts to increase the supply of steam. The engine would then go faster and faster until it blew up. That would be called a 'positive feedback' system. A 'runaway' effect. Positive feedback is what we get if the permafrost melts and the polar ice cap reduces. As the Earth warms and the ice melts, more sunlight is absorbed by the sea, so the Earth becomes slightly warmer. More polar ice melts, exposing more of the sea to the sunlight, so the Earth becomes slightly warmer still – and so on. This process is likely to continue until all the north polar ice cap has melted and, in summer, it will be possible to sail all the way to the North Pole in open water. The melting permafrost is also a positive feedback situation; the more the permafrost melts, the more peat will begin to rot and release more greenhouse gas, and so on. What is not often mentioned is that simple water vapour in the atmosphere also acts as a greenhouse gas. As the planet warms, more water will evaporate and the greater the concentration of water vapour in the atmosphere will become, reinforcing the positive feedback situation.

Some people might say – "What a lot of doom and gloom. What a lot of scare-mongering you write". I do not! This is exactly what is likely to happen. You may have read, or heard, that scientists are afraid of global warming reaching a "tipping point". What they mean is they are afraid we are approaching the point at which positive feedbacks kick in. The point of no return. The point at which nothing you can do will prevent global warming. I contend that we have already passed this point, probably about 20 or 30 years ago. Global warming is speeding up faster than would be expected from human CO_2 inputs alone. The accelerated warming of Alaska and Siberia, the accelerated rate of flow of the Greenland glaciers, the drastic reduction of the Arctic ice cap all point to this conclusion. If so, we are on a one-way trip to a Hot Age, as opposed to an Ice Age. The only thing all our efforts to cut greenhouse emissions will achieve, is to slow the process down a little. Considering the other contributing factors, it is likely to be very little.

Scientists have been studying rocks, sea floor deposits and ice cores to try to discover details of past fluctuations in the Earth's temperature over the past million years or so. In central Greenland, and near the South Pole, there are areas where the ice is static and has been built up over hundreds of thousands of years. Cores have been taken from ice up to ten thousand feet thick. Study of bubbles of air trapped in the ice can reveal a mass of information, including CO_2 levels and temperatures. Study of seafloor sediments give similar information. The data has been surprising. The indications are that the planet has been unstable for a million years or more, with swings from ice age to warm age occurring frequently. Also, the time taken for the reversal is very short. The planet is naturally unstable.

Towards the end of an ice age there is a minimum of plant and algal life on the planet to absorb CO_2. Volcanic eruptions will gradually add CO_2 to the atmosphere. The CO_2 acts as a greenhouse gas and the planet starts to warm. At a certain point the ice begins to melt. More land and sea is exposed to sunlight, so the planet warms further. More ice melts. More land and sea is exposed and the planet warms further still. Any peat or organic material previously trapped under the ice melts and rots, adding to the greenhouse gases. The whole process continues until the ice area is at its minimum and the planet is in a warm age. The ice will never thaw completely off Antarctica because of the altitude as well as the latitude. The North Polar sea ice may thaw completely, but not all the ice on Greenland, again because of the altitude. With the planet warmed, plants will proliferate over great areas of land and there will be increased growth of algae and plankton in the sea. They will extract more and more CO_2 from the atmosphere, gradually starting the process of reduction of CO_2. The planet will stay in the warm phase until the CO_2 falls to a critical level, which may take several thousand years or more. When the CO_2 falls to this critical level the greenhouse effect will be reduced and eventually there will be a colder winter, possibly triggered by fluctuating ocean currents. Ice will form on the Arctic Ocean and on the land. This will reflect sunlight and slightly reduce the solar radiation absorption. At this point plants on land and algae in the sea will still be reducing the atmospheric CO_2. The planet will start to cool. Accumulation of ice on land and sea will speed up. As the ice begins to cover land and sea, more light will be reflected and less and less solar radiation will be converted to heat. We now have a runaway cooling effect, which is likely to go all the way to an ice age with the maximum area of planet covered with ice. Plants and algae will be reduced. The amount of CO_2 extracted from the atmosphere will fall. The ice age will persist until something happens to increase the CO_2 level again. Volcanic activity is the most likely source of CO_2 at this stage. Therefore the ice age may be short or long depending on when sufficient volcanism occurs. When the CO_2 concentration has risen to a certain critical level, then the greenhouse effect will start to warm the planet again. The ice will begin to melt off land and sea and, off we go again, in another positive feedback situation, to a hot age.

Once the tipping point is reached, whether towards a hot age or an ice age, it is likely to go the whole way. That is what happens in an unstable system. The Earth's climate is fundamentally unstable. Since we have not long come out of an ice age, it could be argued that we were in a warming trend anyway and all we have done is speed it up to a degree. One thing is sure, at this stage in the cycle, nothing we can do is going to stop the warming trend. It is far too late to stop the swing of the pendulum now. Surprisingly enough, the evidence of the ice cores and deep sea sediments indicates that, over the last million years, ice ages have become longer, the warm interglacial periods shorter, and a number of scientists have suggested that, far from continuing on a natural warming trend, we were due to start a cooling trend to the next glaciation. Our burning fossil fuels and releasing CO_2 may have acted, just at the right time, to boost warming and prevent the start of a cooling trend. Whichever way you look at the situation it is surely far better to have a warmer world rather than a freezing one.

As the world warms, Europe may be in a unique situation. For thousands of years Europe has been far warmer than would be expected from its latitude. An enormous warm ocean current – the Gulf Stream – flowing northeast from the tropics has maintained the North Atlantic at a temperature several degrees warmer than it would be if the Gulf Stream did not exist. The Gulf Stream is, basically, a simple convection current, transferring heat from the tropics to colder northern latitudes. Normally, convection currents are driven by expansion of water as it is warmed, thereby making it lighter, and also contraction of the water as it cools and becomes more dense. Warm water flows near the surface of the sea northwards, cools, descends to the seabed and returns southwards and the cycle is endlessly repeated. This would continue indefinitely, irrespective of global warming, if the water was of the same salinity throughout. Most of the 'push' that keeps this conveyor system operating is caused by the chilled, denser, water in the north falling towards the seabed. The water rising again after having travelled south along the seabed to the tropics remains cold until it reaches the surface, where it is then warmed. There is thus no convective 'push' at the tropical end of the current to keep it flowing. If something, therefore, reduced or stopped the 'push' at the northern end of the current, the current could slow and might eventually cease altogether. Such a situation is quite possible. Fresh water, because of the absence of salt, is considerably less dense than normal seawater – about 2½lbs (1.1kg) per cubic foot lighter. If a sufficient quantity of fresh water were to mix with the saline water in northerly latitudes, so that the additional density, due to cooling, was cancelled out, the cold surface water would not sink and the convection cycle would be disrupted.

As global warming speeds up, enormous quantities of fresh water, mainly in the form of icebergs, will flow from Greenland into the sea. There is also an influx of fresh water from the Arctic ice cap. When brine freezes, salt is ejected from its solution in the water and, also, the snow which falls on the floating ice is, of course, salt free and therefore the Arctic ice cap is frozen fresh water. The melting of the Arctic ice sheet will also, therefore, add fresh water to the sea. It is very likely that global warming will lead to dilution of the cold northern seas with fresh water and lead to a slowing of the Gulf Stream. The amount of heat transferred by t he Gulf Stream is directly proportional to its flow rate. In other words, if the Gulf Stream slows by 30% the amount of heat carried north is reduced by 30%. If Europe was very lucky, the reduction in heat carried north might cancel out the increase in heat due to global warming, and Europe would stay near the temperature range it is today for the next 20 to 30 years. However, if the influx of fresh water was great enough, the Gulf Stream might cease completely, in which case Europe could expect colder, not warmer conditions, contrary to the rest of the world.

If we think the situation through, we realise that the Gulf Stream, in addition to warming Europe, also warms the Arctic Ocean and Greenland. So, if the Gulf Stream stopped, then the Arctic Ocean and Greenland would be cooler and hence the ice would melt less fast. In other words the Gulf Stream, and the melting of the Arctic ice in the North Atlantic, are connected in a negative feedback, i.e. self-controlling, situation. What is really likely to happen is that the Gulf Stream slows, thereby carrying less heat north, and then a balance will be struck between Gulf Stream speeds and the rate of Arctic ice melting. Europe may, indeed, be fortunate. I would point out that when all the Arctic ice cap has melted, and most of the Greenland ice has also gone, the brakes will then be taken off the Gulf Stream and it will speed up again to rates faster than seen before – because of the extra tropical heat that will then exist. So Europe may be cushioned, at first, against global warming and then, later, experience a much faster 'catching up' period until it reaches the global average increase.

Another aspect of a slowing of the Gulf Stream would be that less heat was transferred from the tropics and, hence, the Atlantic tropics would experience some degree of extra warming, for a time, over and above the world norm. This means, of course, that, not only would the land masses each side of the equatorial Atlantic suffer increased temperatures but the Atlantic itself, at these latitudes would experience higher surface water temperatures. Hurricanes draw their energy from the surface of the sea. Let us consider a typical Northern Latitude Hurricane such as the one that recently battered New Orleans. Most Atlantic Hurricanes start, originally, near the coast of West Africa, a little North of the Equator. Breezes blowing over an area of warm surface water cause evaporation and the creation of a volume of water vapour mixed with the air. Water vapour is less dense than air and this is the key to the formation of Hurricanes. The water vapour rises and at the same time, because of the low density, creates an area of low atmospheric pressure. Air begins to move in from the higher pressure areas surrounding the low and the movement of the air causes yet more evaporation. Because of the Earth's rotation, air moving down from the North will be deflected to the West by the Coriolis force. Similarly air moving up from the South will be deflected East. The whole mass of air within the low pressure area begins to rotate in an anti-clockwise direction. Because of the overall drift of air currents in this area the entire low pressure area moves slowly West. If the low did not move, the surface of the sea in that area would be cooled (by the evaporation) and the disturbance would grow to be no more than a localised tropical storm. However, because it moves West, the low moves over fresh areas of warm surface waters, more evaporation takes place, the low intensifies, the winds pick up, increasing the evaporation. We therefore, as the low moves, develop a self intensifying situation which will continue to build while the low is over the sea and continues to suck energy from warm surface waters. Eventually the cyclonic low becomes a full blown hurricane. As soon as the hurricane passes over land it usually begins to lose power as the water evaporation process is reduced or cut off. It would also stall i.e. cease to intensify, if it passed over cooler sea areas. Hurricane events to the South of the Equator (usually called Typhoons) occur in a similar manner but, because the Coriolis forces are reversed, rotate in the opposite i.e. clockwise direction. Since hurricanes are powered by energy taken from the warm surface waters of the sea it follows that Global Warming is likely to produce more violent and powerful hurricanes in the future. It would also seem logical that warmer oceans and warmer air currents will cause more evaporation and, since what goes up must eventually come down, more precipitation. However, whilst there will be, overall, more rainfall it is difficult to predict where such extra rain will fall. There may be a redistribution but I think it more likely that dry areas will stay dry and wet areas simply get wetter.

Considering all these factors – the continuing industrial expansion of the Third World, the inexorable increase of the world population, the burning of the forests, the rotting of the tundra peat, the melting of the Arctic ice cap and Antarctic ice sheet, the increase of atmospheric water vapour, the speeding up of the glaciers – the only possible conclusion is that the process of global warming is now unstoppable and will continue until a new balance is reached – probably in several hundred years time. The only rational thing to do now is to carefully assess the changes in the climate that are likely to occur, and their effects on various parts of the globe and the people living there, and decide what actions need be taken to mitigate the effects. All that the developed nations would achieve, by their efforts to reduce emissions of carbon dioxide gases and, also, sequestration, is a slight delaying – a slight reduction in the rate at which the world warms. Let us consider then the likely effects of the warming on the human race.

One of the most deceptive factors in the understanding of Global Warming is the business of scientists quoting global average figures. More than two thirds of the Earth's surface is covered in water and the average depth is around 10,000 feet (3,077 metres). This represents a colossal heat sink, and it requires an enormous amount of heat energy just to raise the temperature of this immense volume of water a mere fraction of a degree. In other words, the extra heat over the sea, resulting from the greenhouse effect, will be absorbed and result in very little detectable temperature change. The effect on land is very different. Only the surface layer of the land is affected and this warms up very rapidly. The temperature rise experienced on land will be far, far, greater than the average taken over the whole planet. For example, the evidence suggests the average temperature of the entire planet has increased by only 0.7°C in the last 70 years. At the same time, average land temperatures in such places as Alaska, Canada and Siberia have increased by as much as 2°C to 3°C which is roughly four times the global average. When we read that scientists are predicting average global warming will reach 3°C to 4°C by the end of the 21st century, it does not sound too bad; multiply that by 4 and the possible increase on land is stunning. Bearing in mind that it is not everyday temperatures and conditions that kill people, but the occasional extremes of temperatures, and droughts, then it becomes obvious that many high population areas of the world will eventually become, for all intents and purposes, practically uninhabitable. Migration will, therefore, increase from a trickle, as it is now, to a flood of almost inconceivable proportions. Taking into account the expected population increase, many billions of people will seek to move elsewhere. The situation will be exacerbated by the fact that it is precisely the people who live in the tropical countries, who will produce the greater part of the expected population expansion in the next thirty to fifty years. Instead of thinking about how we can reduce CO_2 emissions, and stop global warming, (which is impossible) we should be thinking about how we are going to cope with the change and planning ahead. Consider the impending situation. There are vast northern areas, at present covered with tundra and stunted trees, that will warm up and can then be cultivated. The tundras have the potential to become major food producing areas. The world will be forced to adapt, but the process will not be easy. The northern nations will be inclined to close their borders, and not let in the billions of southerners who will become desperate to move to cooler climates. Obviously these will be very dangerous times and it is difficult to see how a transition can be achieved without wars and bloodshed. Ironically, Europe, where the Industrial Revolution started, and which has triggered the global warming process, may, at least initially, be spared the worst effects.

The final conclusion is that, with the 'positive feedbacks' already established, and taking into consideration the likely CO_2 emissions of China, India and the rest of the Third World in the next thirty years, much of the costly efforts of the industrialised nations to reduce CO_2 emissions (particularly CO_2 sequestration) is fundamentally likely to be a waste of time and economic resources. The most they can hope to achieve is to slow the process down a little – a very little – and it is going to be a very expensive exercise. This is not to say, however, that it will not be worthwhile to improve energy efficiency and create more fuel-efficient means of transport, or to concentrate on renewable sources of energy and bio fuels. On the contrary, I think this will be a very wise endeavour. The reason is – it will extend the period that the human race will have access to supplies of fossil fuels. It will not, however, stop or alleviate, to any great degree, global warming.

You may ask – "where does this positive feedback scenario lead us"? The answer is, the warming will continue until a new balance is reached. The Earth radiates heat energy into space, more noticeably at night, and the warmer the Earth becomes, the more energy will be lost to space. This will continue to occur despite the fact that the greenhouse gases trap more heat. A garden greenhouse is a good example. Despite the fact the glass traps heat, a closed greenhouse does not get hotter and hotter indefinitely. It warms up until a new balance is reached and then settles at the higher temperature. In the case of the Earth, the level of greenhouse gas is not fixed but is increasing, so we can expect the warming to continue to increase at least until the greenhouse gas levels stabilise and start to reduce. It is probable, therefore, that the warming trend will continue for at least the next 100 to 200 years until the Earth reaches a maximum temperature. Once this has happened, it is difficult to assess how long the Earth will take to cool again to year 2000 temperatures but, in view of the enormous quantities of greenhouse gases involved, and the only known way CO_2 can be extracted and sequestrated on a vast scale is by long term biological processes on land and in the sea, then the cooling time is likely to be of the order of 5,000 years or more. We might get a clue if researchers can find evidence, from the last hot age, when CO_2 levels were at the sort of levels we are likely to experience in the next 100 years. It would be interesting to learn how many years it was from the commencement of such a hot age to the next glaciation. I wouldn't be surprised if the time from the start of a hot age to glaciation was found to be 20,000 years or more.

There is evidence that 400,000 years ago, in a previous 'hot' age, much of Greenland was covered in forest, as was a section of the western part of Antarctica. In order for such forests to develop it must have been warm in those areas for a long time, probably for thousands of years. It also gives us an idea as to how warm the planet might be 200 years from now. Maybe, in 150 years time they will be growing crops on Greenland as well as in Alaska and Siberia.

People who quote Venus as an example of what can happen with runaway greenhouse warming are simply scaremongering. Venus, although similar in size to the Earth, is in many ways very different. It is closer to the sun and therefore receives around 30% more solar radiation. The most important factor, however, is that Venus has an enormous blanket of CO_2 rich atmosphere at least a hundred times more dense than Earth's. This constitutes an enormous heat trap, and creates a total blanket of cloud from pole to pole, so Venus's surface is never visible. In contrast, Earth has a much thinner atmosphere and most of the surface is exposed to space, so, despite a limited greenhouse effect, a great deal of heat can radiate away. Global warming, therefore, whilst it will be devastating to us, will not be a threat to life on Earth. Earth has been very hot, on occasions, before. However, before temperatures stabilise, it is probable the entire Arctic ice cap will disappear, much of the ice on Greenland and Antarctica will melt, except for ice at higher altitude levels, and, most importantly, vast areas of land, particularly in India and South East Asia, will become too hot for mass human habitation.

The sea will gradually rise due to the influx of melt water and thermal expansion but the worst effects will not be experienced until late in the 22nd century. When the Earth finally does begin to cool down it will commence another positive feedback scenario – but this time in the cooling direction. To start cooling, greenhouse gases must have been reduced and, as the Earth begins to cool, what ice patches are still left will begin to increase, thereby reflecting more light back into space. Gradually, more and more ice will develop and the area covered in vegetation gradually reduce. This process will inexorably continue until, finally, the Earth is back in an ice age again.

The unpredictable factor that could modify both the warming and cooling phases is massive volcanism. In the warming phase massive volcanism would act to make the warming even worse, but if it occurred during the cooling phase it could, depending on the amount of CO_2 released by the volcano, either reduce or slow down the cooling or, if enough CO_2 were released, even trigger the next phase of warming again. It is believed that, in the past, before human intervention, volcanism was the trigger that moved the Earth from a cooling to a warming phase. Immediately after a volcano erupts there is a short period of cooling due to dust and aerosols in the upper atmosphere. Following this there is a long term warming effect due to the CO_2 that has been released. The volcanism that would cause major climatic change is not so much the relatively small volcanic eruptions we are used to, but the much more massive 'super-volcanic' eruptions that only occur very rarely.

Eventually, when the next cooling cycle begins, and gradually gathers pace, the human beings on the Earth at that time will have no fossil fuels to burn, produce CO_2, and thus stop the cooling cycle. The coal, oil and gas we are burning today took hundreds of millions of years to form.

I recently read that the entrepreneur, Sir Richard Branson, has offered a prize of 12 million pounds to any scientist who can invent a device to remove CO_2 from the atmosphere. Whilst it is already possible to do it on a small scale, (Mr Branson must be unaware of this), as an engineer, I am sure it can never be done on a scale to make any difference and there is, of course, the question of the energy required to make and operate the equipment. It can be reasonably argued that it would be much easier to go for direct capture and sequestration at the point of origin, such as in the power stations. However, sequestration of CO_2, by which I mean the extraction of CO_2 emissions from coal fired power stations, liquefaction of that CO_2, transporting it and finally pumping it, under high pressure, deep underground is not, in my opinion, a viable option. The quantities of CO_2 produced by power stations are enormous. What is not generally realised is that each ton of coal burned produces roughly 2 tons of carbon dioxide (the extra weight is the oxygen that is consumed from the atmosphere). When it is realised that just one, large, coal fired power station can burn 7 million tons of coal a year, the magnitude of the problem becomes apparent.

Forget sequestration. If you want to remove CO_2 from the atmosphere simply plant trees. A billion trees will remove a billion tons of CO_2 in around fifty years and, at the same time, give back half a billion tons of oxygen into our atmosphere. However, to do any good, the billion trees must be in addition to the existing tree population. There would be no benefit if, as you plant your billion trees, someone else cuts down a billion. However, it would still be better than someone destroying a billion trees without replacement. It isn't difficult to plant a tree. Dig a small hole in the ground, insert a small tree, a metre (3.25 feet) high, costing maybe 50 pence, replace the earth and tread it down. A child can do it! If you are really enthusiastic you might increase the tree's chances of survival by adding stakes, ties, rabbit protectors and so on. The easiest is to plant twice as many trees as you originally intended; enough will then survive. The key thing is, they must be planted as soon as they are available in the autumn and be out of the ground for the shortest possible time. Trees planted in the spring usually die.

In the UK we have tens of thousands of miles of hedgerows. Farmers are encouraged to leave a strip of uncultivated land alongside the hedgerows for environmental reasons, so why not plant trees, every ten metres (thirty-three feet), alongside the hedges. Not only will the trees remove CO_2 and replenish oxygen, they will beautify the landscape and reduce the intensity of gales by acting as windbreaks. (It may interest the reader to note I took my own advice 18 years ago and planted over 1000 trees. A small 7-acre field has over 100 trees planted around its perimeter hedge). In actual fact, there are millions of potential trees already in existence in the hedgerows of Britain. Nobody sees them and they cannot develop because they are flailed off in the annual hedge trimming. If the flailing was interrupted occasionally, and the trees allowed to grow, they would spring up like mushrooms. In my opinion the Government should encourage and subsidise farmers to plant trees – or even pass a law forcing them to do so (grants are already available, but few bother). At the present time farmers are paid to leave areas of land uncultivated ("set aside"). Why not encourage them (by law maybe) to plant, say, 5% to 10% of their land with trees. Children would enthusiastically participate, if encouraged. In the end it will not stop global warming, but it would help to slow the onset and we could enjoy the secondary benefits. Since gales will become more intense as global warming increases there would be substantial benefits from the extra millions of trees acting as wind breaks. All green plants, of course, take some of the power of light and, instead of converting it into heat, convert it into chemical energy, at the same time absorbing CO_2 and converting it back into carbon and oxygen. The oxygen is released to the atmosphere and the carbon used to help create the structure of the plant. So plants create a slight direct cooling effect as well as removing CO_2. In the end, of course, the CO_2 removed by the plants will be reintroduced into the atmosphere when the plants rot or are burned.

The truth is, there is no simple solution to the problem of removal of CO_2 from the atmosphere. Current global warming is an inescapable result of the Industrial Revolution and the human Population Explosion and will run its course. Human beings will simply have to adapt and live with the consequences no matter how disruptive and devastating they may be. Simple things like flood barriers and strengthening buildings, bridges and houses to withstand increased gale and hurricane forces could be started straight away. It is the forced migration of billions (not millions) of people that will be the biggest problem the human race will have to face.

A few months after writing this chapter I saw Al Gore's film 'An Inconvenient Truth' to do with Global Warming. I thought it an excellent presentation – enough to convince any reasonable person that Global Warming is a result of human activity. However, like a horse that baulks at the last fence, Gore stopped short of coming to the final rational conclusion – that Global Warming is now unstoppable. It is understandable, however, since Gore has taken upon himself the task of trying to save the World. He thinks that by reducing CO_2 emissions, we can stop Global Warming. He has devoted an enormous amount of time and effort to the cause – travelling all over the World, studying the evidence and giving lectures and presentations in nearly every country on Earth. His message is – 'We must act now to save the planet'. Naturally his mind will not wish to admit he has basically been wasting his time doing all this work over the years but, fundamentally, that is the situation.

It is interesting to note that Gore does, in fact, refer to one of the major positive feedback situations that have already kicked in – the melting of the Arctic Ice Cap – and points out, correctly, that far more heat will be absorbed by the exposed sea than would be the case where ice covers the surface and states that it will contribute to Global Warming. He predicts, as I do, that the Arctic Ice Cap will totally disappear over the next 50 years or so. However, whilst he refers to the heating up of the tundra and the melting of the permafrost – as a symptom of Global Warming – he does not mention the effects of the rotting of the peat and the consequent release of vast quantities of CO_2 and methane – another enormous positive feedback effect. He also mentions the increase of the human global population as exacerbating the CO_2 emission problem but accepts, without question, the proposition, put forward by a few optimists, that the global population will stabilise, in a few years, at no more than 9 billion (a mere 34% increase over present figures). The brutal truth is that if the whole world adopted the Chinese population control rules right now, with the same success as they have had, the world population would still increase to 9 billion over the next 50 years. Since that sort of global population control will not happen, my projection of 20 billion by 2125 is far more likely and could well be an underestimate. The Chinese themselves are even having a rethink. Because of China's success in feeding its population and its economic boom, which means China can now afford to import food, fears of starvation are waning. They are beginning to talk of relaxing the birth control rules. There is now anxiety about the time when China will have a preponderance of old people and there will be too few youngsters to support them and keep the country going – exactly the same thinking that is leading Politicians to say Britain needs immigrants. So – it is quite likely that even China's population figures will begin to increase a little faster in the next few years rather than decrease.

By all means let us adopt many of Gore's suggestions for improving efficiency in the use of fossil fuels but let us do it mainly because it will extend the period such fuels will be available – it will not stop Global Warming and will do very little to slow it down. But let us think very carefully before we adopt the idea of CO_2 capture and sequestration which would be very costly, would entail the use of a lot more energy to operate and would achieve very little with regard to slowing the rate of Global Warming down.

Incidentally, in a recent TV programme on Global Warming, a film showed a number of scientists on top of a large glacier in Greenland. They were investigating why glacier movements have speeded up so drastically. They were standing high up on the glacier, inland, with more than 1000 feet (305 metres) thick of ice beneath them to the rock of the valley floor. The surface ice was melting and where they were standing, streams of water were falling into a hole in the surface of the glacier. They wondered if the running water would go straight down to the bottom of the glacier or go down a certain distance and then track sideways along a flaw in the ice. To check this they had a probe, containing a camera, which they lowered from a cable drum, into the hole. The probe only went down about 100 feet (30.5 metres) before it jammed so they were unable to complete the investigation.

It is not really necessary to use a camera probe to find out. Armed with a few facts, a little rational thought will tell us what will happen and also explain why the glaciers are speeding up. Everybody knows that falling water can produce power; we have all seen illustrations of dams or waterfalls and hydro-electric power stations. What is not quite so generally understood is that all falling water releases energy – whether we tap it or not. Given the weight of water falling over the Niagara Falls in one second and the height it falls I can calculate the energy released in horse power or kilowatts. At the present time a power station, built near the falls, taps off some of this power to supply American and Canadian homes and businesses nearby. The rest of the energy produced by the falls is wasted. If a weight of water falls over a distance it produces a certain amount of energy and the energy produced is exactly the same whether the water falls vertically over a cliff or trickles slowly down the slope of a hill. You may wonder what happens to that energy. The answer is – most of it is converted into heat. (Some of the energy will be converted into sound, some into evaporating some of the water etc). Instead of calculating how much power in kilowatts is produced at Niagara Falls I can, instead, work out how much warmer the water at the bottom of the falls is than the water at the top.

Now, to return to the Greenland glacier. The melt water, at 0°C as it falls into the hole, drops maybe 50 feet (15.3 metres), hits ice, deflects and falls again. When its fall is interrupted, the energy of its fall is converted into heat thus warming the water. The warmed water will obviously melt some of the ice it touches. The water falls another 50 feet (15.3 metres) or so and is checked again. The falling water will generate heat, every time it is checked, all the way to the base of the glacier. Because of this heat input, the falling water will tend to cut rapidly through to the base of the glacier, maybe not vertically but following zig-zag cracks. When it reaches the base of the glacier, what will it do? It will run along the floor of the valley, under the glacier, and flow all the way to the sea, generating more heat as it goes. With a river, on land, the heat generated, as it flows, escapes into the air but under the glacier it is trapped and will act to melt more ice. Glaciers also flow downhill, slowly, and as they do, the friction of the millions of tons of ice grinding over the rocks will also produce heat (not much, compared to the water, because of the extreme slowness of the movement but a small amount nevertheless).

On the top of the melting glacier, which is many square miles in area, there will be many holes with water pouring and trickling down. The water reaching the bottom will accumulate to form a small river. To give you an idea of the amount of heat that can be produced, I calculate that the water trickling down through 1000 feet (305 metres) of ice to create a small river flowing at 20 cubic metres (roughly 20 tons) per second under the glacier will release, during its fall, approximately 60 megawatts of energy. If the floor of the glacier then falls another 1000 feet (305 metres) down the valley to reach sea level then the flow will release another 60 megawatts. (The total – 120 megawatts – maintained continuously for months represents a massive input of heat. Think of a hundred and twenty thousand – one kilowatt electric fire bars operating non-stop under the glacier for the duration of the summer). The flow I referred to – 20 cubic metres per second – is a reasonable flow rate and it is quite probable a melt water river as big as or larger than this, lies under many large glaciers. The amount of energy produced by falling water is proportional to the flow rate and the height through which the water falls. If the glacier flows into the sea no one will ever see the river as it will enter the sea hidden by the glacier. It is normal, on land, to see a small river of melt water flowing from beneath the lower end of a glacier.

Let us now go back 500 or 1000 years or more, when the ice which is now at the bottom of the glacier was originally forming. It was formed when snow fell, high up the glacier, in temperatures down to – 20°C or colder. This would accumulate, compact and form ice before it started its long slow creep to the sea. The mass of ice at the bottom of the glacier, for most of its run to the sea, insulated by all the ice above it, would probably be very cold – at least a few degrees below zero. Ice has a number of properties. One is that it has considerable hardness and strength at temperatures below zero. Melting ice becomes weak. Another feature is that the melting point of ice varies with the pressure. (Ice is slippery because, under the pressure of the blade of an ice skate or sledge runner or ones foot, a thin film of ice momentarily melts and then instantly re-freezes as the pressure comes off. In cold countries, children will be aware that, at 0°C, it is easy to make snowballs. At – 20°C it is not possible, as the hands can not apply enough pressure to cause particles of snow to melt and the snowball to 'stick'. Poor Captain Scott, on his trip to the South Pole, was unfortunate enough to be assailed by abnormally and incredibly cold weather – so cold in fact that the ice and snow would no longer momentarily melt under the runners of his sleds and he and his men found his sled just as hard to pull as if they had been pulling the sled across dry earth or sand). Under the glacier, when the slowly moving ice comes up against a projecting spur of rock, the pressure at the front of the rock builds up until the ice melts, flows around the rock and re-freezes behind it. The rock appears to move slowly through a solid block of ice. (This trick can be duplicated by running a thin wire across a block of ice, supported on a trestle, and suspending weights from the ends of the wire. The wire will slowly move through the block and finally fall out, leaving the block of ice intact). The important thing to bear in mind is that the speed of melting and re-freezing will be much slower if the temperature is below zero. The colder the ice the slower the flow.

So – 50 years ago – before Global Warming, and before the top of the Greenland glacier started melting, the ice at the base of the glacier was probably at – 5°C or colder which meant the rate of melting and re-freezing of the base ice against the obstructing rocks was slower and the glacier flowed, very slowly, to the sea. Now, when snow first melted on top of the glacier a few years ago and trickled down to the base, generating heat as it went, the first thing it would do would be to warm the ice until a considerable layer at the bottom of the glacier was at 0°C. This would not take long because the heat required to warm the ice is very much less than is needed to melt it. As soon as the ice at the base of the glacier is warmed to 0°C the brakes are taken off and the rate at which the glacier flows will be drastically speeded up – which is exactly what is happening. If surface ice melts and water trickles down to the base of the glacier in summer it will not matter how cold the weather gets in the winter, the glacier will still flow fast. The cold will not reach down and cool the base which will remain at 0°C. It can be expected, therefore, that glaciers will speed up at any point below the altitude at which the surface melts in summer.

I suspect a similar effect, combined with hydraulic pressure, was involved in the recent disintegration of the Larsen 'B' ice shelf in Antarctica. Scientists were staggered when the whole enormous ice shelf, an area of 3,250 square kilometres (1,250 square miles), 200 metres (650 feet) thick, weighing roughly 500 billion tons, suddenly disintegrated into chunks and floated away. Many large pools of water were seen from the air, on top of the ice shelf, before the break up. The fact that these pools were blue suggests each pool was deep as well as large, containing millions of gallons of water. If the ice shelf was then flexed by tidal movement or fluctuating currents in the sea and formed cracks in the ice, the water from the pools would flood into the cracks. In addition to warming and weakening the deeper ice, the water would press against the opposite faces of the crack, acting to push the walls apart. The forces generated would be enormous. Let us consider a crack half a mile (805 metres) long and 300 feet (91.5 metres) deep (much larger cracks are quite possible). If such a crack filled with water I calculate the hydraulic pressure, i.e. the force acting to push the walls of the crack apart would be over 3 million tons. It is, therefore, not so surprising that, after large pools of water formed on top of the ice shelf, it soon disintegrated. In future, if large pools of melt water are seen on top of a floating ice shelf, I suggest it can be taken that the break up of the shelf is likely and probably imminent.

THE OZONE LAYER

Many people seem to get confused between the Global Warming and Ozone Layer problems. They are two totally separate situations. The ozone layer is a high altitude layer created by the action of solar radiation on the oxygen in the atmosphere, which protects us from the effects of Ultra Violet light emanating from the sun. The term UV light covers a range of short wavelength radiation just out of the visible spectrum. It is very penetrating and energetic.

UV can penetrate human (and animal) skin and damage the DNA in the body's cells. This can lead to cancer, cataracts of the eyes and other damage. It can damage plants, also, and all sorts of organisms including the plankton in the sea. The UV with the shortest wavelength is the most energetic and the most dangerous. However – whether the longest wavelengths of UV are safe is questionable. (I have always been cautious about the safety of UV 'sun-beds' used for home sunbathing and tanning and I have never used one). If the full power of the UV emitted by the sun was to reach the surface of the earth, we would be in serious trouble. There would be a massive increase in skin cancers, and cataracts of the eyes, in humans and animals. There would be effects on plants; growth would be impaired, plants stunted and crops reduced. Probably the worst effect would be the possible reduction of the ocean plankton, which, of course, is at the bottom of the ocean food chain. Massive reduction in plankton levels, would result in a concomitant loss of fish stocks. High levels of UV might damage plankton, because it can penetrate about fifteen feet (4.5 metres) down in seawater and a lot of the plankton lives in this upper layer of sea. It is obvious, therefore, that the high altitude ozone layer which protects us from the UV is very important indeed.

Ozone itself is a very reactive form of oxygen and, surprisingly, is actually produced in the upper atmosphere by the very UV it is good at blocking. Normal oxygen is in the form O^2, which means it is in the form of molecules, each consisting of two atoms of oxygen. Ozone is more complex and is in a condition where the oxygen is in the form of molecules built up of three oxygen atoms, i.e. O^3.

Years ago people started building gadgets like refrigerators and air conditioning units. To make these work you need a gas in the system, which is alternately compressed and expanded. I could get carried away here on the working of refrigerators but I will avoid that. You can learn about the working of refrigerators and air conditioning units elsewhere, if you wish to do so. Suffice to say, a refrigerator will work better if the gas has certain special properties. The designers found what they were looking for in a synthesised gas called a CFC. CFC stands for Chloro – Fluoro – Carbon and, as the Chloro part indicates, it includes chlorine. So, before being sold to a customer a refrigerator is charged with a quantity of CFC. When the fridge finally wears out, and is scrapped, you can guess what happens to the CFC gas; it escapes and ends up in the 'wide blue yonder'.

Many years ago, back in the sixties, the late, great Science Fiction writer – Isaac Asimov – who happened to have a degree in chemistry among his many qualifications, thought about this and came to the conclusion the CFC gas was a menace. How he came to think about CFC gas and the ozone layer amazes me – but he did! Not only did he write Science Fiction but he also wrote Scientific Articles. So he wrote and published one that said CFC's could destroy the ozone layer. He claimed that the chlorine containing molecule was capable of breaking down the O^3 molecule. Worse than that, he claimed that the chlorine atom in the CFC would act as a catalyst. A catalyst, as you may know, is a substance which causes a chemical reaction, but is not itself involved in the reaction and is not used up in the reaction. The chlorine atom in the CFC molecule would, said Asimov, destroy an ozone molecule, drift away, destroy another and so on, so one molecule of CFC could in time destroy thousands of ozone molecules. Enough CFC gas and you would destroy the whole ozone layer – despite the fact UV from the sun was creating new ozone molecules all the time. "Rubbish!" said the experts, "Scare mongering! He writes Science Fiction anyway doesn't he?" And they forgot about it.

Years later, a satellite was launched carrying various Earth studying sensors, amongst which was a device that could detect – could, in effect, 'see' – the ozone layer and there, to the stunned amazement of the scientists, was a massive hole in the ozone layer over the South Pole. It seems that, in the particular conditions over the South Pole – related to the very cold temperatures – the CFC molecule destroys ozone with even greater efficiency. Checks over the following few years confirmed – without any doubt – the ozone hole was growing. Since there was no argument – the evidence was there – and since the consequences of losing the ozone layer totally would be so disastrous, the Nations of the World got their heads together and CFC's were banned. Incidentally, one of the uses of CFC gas was as a propellant in such things as hair sprays and deodorants; which is why your deodorants and hairsprays are now propelled by propane. Propane sounds dangerous enough to me, but I suppose it is better than CFC's.

Fortunately, in the upper atmosphere, the CFC does get destroyed, slowly, over time, so the ozone hole over the South Pole is growing larger more slowly. It hasn't quite stopped growing yet, let alone started to reduce, but we are on the right track. So now we can all stop worrying! The existing CFC's will slowly disappear; the sun's radiation will produce more O^3 and the ozone hole over the Antarctic will gradually disappear.

I found it interesting to note – on a recent visit to New Zealand – that, each day, the newspapers carried a chart stating the UV situation and quoting how long it was safe to be outside with skin exposed to the UV; some days the time was down to 20 minutes. I concluded that New Zealand must be a little too close to the South Pole. What is less commonly known is that there is a substantial reduction in ozone over the North Pole also. Not a hole as such, but a considerable reduction nevertheless. On a fishing trip to Alaska a few years ago I did not take any precautions; you cannot see UV, remember. I was savagely burned on the face, worse than I have ever been sun burned in my life, although I remember getting badly burned sunbathing as a youth. (Suntan cream had not been invented then!).

So – if you go to New Zealand or Alaska, or anywhere else in the Arctic – you have been warned. Cover up. Slap on the suntan cream or you will learn about UV the hard way!

THE HUMAN POPULATION EXPLOSION

Other than all out thermo-nuclear war, the human population explosion will be the greatest factor influencing the life and well-being of the human race in the next two hundred years. It will be even greater in its impact than global warming or the exhaustion of fossil fuels, minerals and metal ores. The combination of these three factors will create conditions which will drastically affect the lives of every human being on the planet.

People often say – it is impossible to predict the future, but this is, in fact, incorrect – it is an over-simplification. It depends on what you are trying to predict. If you are trying to predict something subject to the whims and fancies of everyday life – such as fashion, the stock market or which horse is going to win the Derby – they are right. It is possible, however, to predict the future of some things that will happen in the far, far future with very great certainty. Some things are in between.

For instance, we can predict with 100% certainty that the sun will burn out and cease to exist, in its present form, in about 5000 million years (it will become a red giant and then a white dwarf). This is because we have plenty of other similar stars of various ages to study and learn from. As an in between thing I can predict – with 90% certainty – that I will be fishing in Alaska, at a certain time on a certain river at a certain place, next July 10th. That is because I have already booked the trip. There can only be a 90% certainty in this because I might have an accident. The plane might crash, I might even drop dead, but there is a 90% certainty I will be right.

Let us consider the human race. In 1948, when the world population was a little over two billion, several students, including myself, using population increase data, calculated that, providing there was no World War Three, the likely world population in the year 2000 would have increased to six billion. It was a very slight underestimate. The human race, in common with all other animals, has a built in desire to reproduce. Most people (not everyone) wish to have children and raise a family. I am reminded of an old song – popular when I was a child (a long time ago I agree). The song went "Roses around the door, babies on the floor, who could ask for anything more – in Happy Valley." My mother used to sing it when I was very small. So people in general want children. Quite natural! Years ago, with very little or no birth control, couples often produced families of 8 to 10 or more; however life was full of hazards. For millions of years very few (an average of about 2) of the 8 to 10 would live to grow up, and themselves have children. Any less than an average of 2 and the human race would have gone extinct. Much more than 2 and the population explosion would have already occurred. In actual fact, between 40,000 years ago and 300 years ago, the average must have been just over 2, since evidence and history shows a slow increase in the human population over this time. However, in the last few hundred years, and particularly in the last seventy, there has been a change. Modern science and medicine have found ways to drastically cut mortality rates, food supplies have been secured and now the chance of a baby growing up to be an adult, and reproducing itself, has been greatly enhanced.

When living things reproduce in the presence of plentiful food supplies and the absence of predation there is a chain reaction; they multiply exponentially; two produces four; four produces eight; eight produces sixteen, and so on. The same exponential effect still occurs at a lower rate of reproductive success – but slower – in humans. At an average of 2.9 offspring per couple then 20 becomes 29 in the next generation. 29 becomes 42 in the second generation. 42 becomes 60 in the third generation. In other words, the population has tripled in only three generations; which is what the human race has actually done in the last three generations. Another three generations like that and there would be eighteen billion people on the planet. Three more and there would be fifty four billion. Three more and we are at one hundred and sixty two billion. Impossible! Of course it is! This is a finite planet. Sooner or later the explosion has to stop, whether we do it voluntarily or not. At the present time the human population of the Earth is over 6 billion (the latest figures suggest 6.5 billion). There has been an increase of around 2 billion over the last 20 years; this is despite the numbers of people all over the world being killed in natural disasters, road accidents, famine, wars and disease and although the birth rate has been reduced by increased use of contraceptive methods.

World War Two ended after the horrific atomic bombing of the Japanese cities of Hiroshima and Nagasaki. The bombs killed something like a hundred and forty thousand people. Of the two, I believe the Hiroshima bomb killed the most – about 100,000. Horrendous! It is a stunning thought to realise that, if a Hiroshima type bomb was dropped on a Hiroshima sized town every morning, and another similar sized bomb dropped on another similar sized town in the afternoon, and this was done every single day, day in, day out, month after month and even year after year, it would not reduce the human population on this Earth. It would not even stop the population increasing. It would slow the increase down, to be sure, but the population would still increase, more slowly. That is the incredible measure of the rate of human population growth on this planet at the present time.

In order to enable you to visualize the immensity of the human population. Imagine you boarded a plane at New York and, as you took off, you saw, gathered together, an enormous crowd of people in a mass a mile wide stretching away into the distance. As you flew you discovered the mile wide crowd continued to stretch into the distance endlessly as you flew, hour after hour, incredibly all the way across America to San Francisco. That would be about 6½ billion people. And if , at San Francisco, you saw a large gate with soldiers passing through it, three abreast, marching at normal speed, endlessly, 24 hours a day, 365 days a year, year after year adding to the enormous existing crowd – then that would be about equal to the current rate of increase.

There is now some evidence indicating the rate of growth may be slowing down a little. Europe, including the UK, is now around the balance figure. The increase in population recorded in these countries is mainly due to immigration. The United States has slowed, although they have just passed the 300 million mark – boosted by immigration – mainly from Mexico. Russia is now in negative territory, the Russian population is actually declining slightly. Instead of being pleased, President Putin is alarmed. How can he rebuild Russia to a Great International Power again, if he doesn't have enough people for workers or the military? So he has offered a substantial payment of cash to any Russian women who produce an extra child after a certain date. Apparently this has, at first, had an adverse effect, as some women who were pregnant, and expected to give birth before the deadline, have opted for abortions so they can conceive again and qualify for the cash. Some of these women are now disillusioned, as they hadn't read the fine print.

The Indian Government has worked hard to increase the use of birth control methods and, at one stage, offered to give a free radio to every man who had a vasectomy. Nevertheless, the Indian population has boomed, to reach an estimated one billion people – from about 450 million in 1945. China is the most important. Starting with about 800 million in 1950, when it was already on the limit of what the country could feed, the Chinese Government saw the danger, decided to take drastic action, and brought in laws limiting the number of children that couples could have. Additional pregnancies, where they occurred, were terminated. A lot of people in the West were horrified at this draconian action and complained about infringement of human rights, the curse of abortion and so on. It is only natural that people (including myself) should be shocked and horrified at the Chinese action. However, if one can set aside the emotional shock and revulsion and think rationally – it made sense, considering the situation the Chinese were in. "Better to have only one child and be happy," the Chinese said, "than to have three and starve." Surely, if you think about the situation calmly and sensibly – they were right. Nevertheless some people will always manage to dodge the rules – at least I assume so in China – since the population has not stabilised and at the time of writing has crept up to 1.3 billion; but it could have been far higher. However, it must be pointed out that 50% or more of the Chinese population increase has been due to the fact that, in recent years, the expectation of life of the Chinese has risen as the standard of living has improved. If, for instance, we consider a situation where a Third World country, having a population with an average expectation of life of 40 years, adopts a birth control system that cut the birth rate to an average of 2 per family, then the population of that country will stabilise. However, it will only do so as long as the expectation of life remains the same. If the standard of living then improves and the expectation of life increases to 60 years then the population will increase by 50% even though the birth rate continues to be controlled. Because of the increased life span, a normal family of four (two adults plus two children) becomes a family of six (two adults, two children and two grandparents). A new balance will only be struck when the expectation of life stops rising. This effect will apply in all countries where the expectation of life is increasing (it has risen by about 15% even in the UK over the last 40/50 years) and will be especially noticeable in Third World countries where expectation of life, at the present time, is particularly low. An immediate draconian world wide restriction to an average of only 2 children per family (even if this were possible) would not prevent the world population increasing substantially – probably to 8 or even 9 billion.

A number of politicians and scientists have taken to saying "The world population will increase to 9 or 9½ billion in the next 40 years and then stabilise". The basis of this remarkably naïve prediction is that they see, in the affluent countries of the world, there is a tendency for the birth rate to drop to balance or near balance figures. Therefore they assume that, when the standard of living of the whole world has risen to this level of affluence, the same effect will occur worldwide. This is simplistic thinking and it will not happen because the planet simply does not have the resources. To raise everybody's standard of living to that enjoyed by Europe, Scandinavia and the USA would require the material resources of not one but three or four planet Earths. In the next 40 years the standard of living of the Third World may rise – but not much. Three quarters of the world's population are doomed to remain in relative poverty. There will be no reason for them to change their ways.

At the present time population growth in South America, Africa, Indonesia and other Third World areas continues unabated. Currently, the Roman Catholic Church shows no sign of a change in attitude towards birth control, and I recently read of a peasant farmer in Botswana who was proud to have 3 wives and 18 children. (What will happen if his eighteen children, in their turn, multiply at the same rate and produce eighty children? His small plot of land won't be able to feed them all). In South America the population of Colombia, for instance, is doubling every 22 years. I have read, on a number of occasions, in the past and even quite recently, that Thomas Malthus 'got it wrong'. Malthus predicted that the human population would increase, without limit, while there was sufficient food, and the expansion would only finally be stopped by starvation, pestilence and or war. Malthus will only be proved to be wrong if the human race voluntarily and deliberately stops the increase by birth control methods, otherwise he could still, at a later date, be proved right. Let us assume – as I think is reasonable – that the amount of land available for agriculture, in the future, will stay roughly the same as it is today. Considering Global Warming what we lose in the South we gain in the North. So the question becomes – how many people could we feed now – if we had to. Maybe 12 billion? However, we may be able to boost food production using Genetic Engineering and improved techniques. Let us be optimistic and say we could possibly feed 20 billion. Even if the rate of expansion is slowing, we are now working from a base of 6½ billion people. On top of the simple birth rate calculation there is now the factor that people are living far longer than they used to do. Apart from the fact that older people, people who do not work and produce, are a burden on the young – there are many extra mouths to feed. Allowing for this, it is reasonable to expect we are likely to reach the 20 billion maximum figure in about 120 years. That is – allowing for the slowing in the population growth rate that we see today, but if we did not take additional steps to slow the expansion rate further. That means, there could be a number of people alive today who may live to see the Earth approach its absolute maximum population. Better, I suppose, than when it seemed quite likely I would see the world's population problem solved quite drastically. (See under WAR AND NUCLEAR WEAPONS). When the maximum population is reached, whether it is 20 or 25 or even 30 billion, further expansion will cease. If we don't take the necessary action then nature will do it for us.

So far we have not considered what the quality of life would be with 20 billion people on the planet. I for one, am very glad I was born when I was and have lived in a good time. When the crunch comes, and the planet is at its limit, things will get very stark. To put it simply –

when a man has the choice between seeing his family starve or killing a member of an endangered species, the endangered species no longer matters.

It so happens that I have, personally, seen an example of this sort of thing. I lived through World War 2, as a boy, and remember talking to a friend of my father's. Times were tough and food was very scarce. (Rations were incredibly small. We would think nothing today of eating, in one day, amounts that, in 1942, had to last for a week). My father's friend told me later, "I had nothing to put on the table for Christmas for my family, so I didn't mess about. I went to the lake and shot a swan and we had him for dinner." In England at that time the killing of swans was taboo. They were the 'Kings Bird', legally protected. When the chips are down, human survival will come first.

I sometimes think that, in 500 years time, when people have been forced to adapt, and forced to limit the size of their families, through laws, ostracism or starvation they will probably accept a restricted family as perfectly normal and sensible. They will probably look back at the "Population Disaster" and wonder how we could possibly have let it happen. If we think about the political aspect of all this – there are tremendous problems. It is likely that, to achieve controlled reproduction, (instead of nature taking its course) draconian laws will have to be instituted in many countries. To do that – I fear – would need either a dictatorship or an authoritarian form of government, such as the Chinese have today.

Any politician in a democratic society who said, "Vote for me. I will bring in laws to force you to control your family", would be committing political suicide. No democratic politician will ever touch the subject with a barge pole. It is too sensitive and provokes violent emotional reactions; it goes against natural instincts. The drive to procreate is primal. I admit I am really surprised that the Russian population is in decline even considering the demoralization, the deprivation and the poverty.

It does not matter if my calculations are slightly askew, as it will merely take a little longer, or slightly less time, to reach saturation if we do nothing about it. It could reasonably be argued that there are already far too many people on the Earth right now. Think of the problems the 6½ billion are creating. The problems of pollution, destruction of forests, over fishing, loss of habitat and CO_2 emissions are bad enough already. The industrialisation of China, India and the Third World would make these problems far worse in the next fifty years, even if the population was miraculously stabilised at its present level. With the increase of population that is likely to occur, the planet will be in a terrible state in fifty years from now – even if there is no problem with food or energy supplies. Sometimes I reflect on the situation and think – "if there were only 200 million of us on the planet it would probably be able to maintain us indefinitely and, at the same time, there could be all the marvellous diversity of habitat and species that existed before the industrial revolution."

Consideration of the global population problem is very depressing but, do you prefer to face the facts, or stick your head in the sand? Let us accept that at some point population must, and will, be controlled. By all means, if necessary, help people to have one or two children, but recognise it is selfish and anti-social to have more. It could be argued that people with more than two children are helping to wreck your grandchildren's future. Let us at least recognise the magnitude of the population problem and start to do something. The problem is not going to go away.

At the present time, the Third World countries are the ones where the population is still exploding. No wonder there is poverty, starvation and disease. Everybody in those countries would be better off if the birth rate could be reduced. This is the real key to any improvement in nourishment, well being and a decent standard of living. Let us not shy away from this fact. Let us have the mental courage to face it and try to do something about it. Educate the people. Explain how they will all be better off if they have fewer children; they successfully did it in China. Send endless supplies of contraceptives free (it will cost us less than feeding the burgeoning millions to come if we don't). One understands perfectly well the desire to alleviate the starving and poverty of people in the Third World. However, if the population explosion continues, then the starving million today will become the starving 10 million tomorrow; in which case, you could argue, the sum total of human misery in that country has increased 10 fold. We should stop criticising the Chinese – and look seriously at how they have managed to drastically reduce the rate of population increase there.

If the Chinese had not taken action, and the population there had increased as it has in Indonesia, or Africa, or South America, the population of China would now be well over 2 billion and many of them would probably be starving. The Chinese had the courage to look the problem in the face and take action. Let us do the same if it is at all possible. We MUST face up to the fact that human overpopulation is the root cause of all the major problems facing the human race today. It is causing global warming, the stripping and impoverishment of the seas, the pollution of the Earth, the destruction of species and the burning of the forests. No politician in the West will have the courage and the nerve to say so, because of the political dangers. Somehow the message has to get home, and the public must be made aware and recognise the need for action; otherwise nature will take its course and there will be suffering and death on a scale almost beyond comprehension.

THE FUTURE OF THE HUMAN RACE

NOTE: This Book was written in the winter of 2006/7. By the time it was published, the Recession predicted was rapidly developing. However, no attempt has been made to modify or rewrite so it gives a clue as to the value of the rational thinking used in writing it.

To be able to predict the future of the human race we don't need a crystal ball. We don't need to pore over the ramblings of Nostradamus. What we need is a knowledge of history, an understanding of human nature, careful analysis of the data available and an application of rational thought.

As I write, in December 2006, the state of the World, by which I mean the general condition of the Human Race, looks, to me, to be basically good. (Many young people might be inclined to argue about this, but remember, I lived through World War Two, The Cuba Missile Crisis, The Cold War, etc). There is still some degree of strife and unpleasantness – and always will be, while human beings are on this Earth, but, in my opinion, things are as good as or better than they have ever been. Most of the people on the planet have sufficient food. There are no major wars. There is no immediate danger of Thermo Nuclear War and the standard of living of most of the World's people is steadily rising. Some would say – "What about the people starving in Ethiopia? What about Darfur and Iraq and terrorism"? It is true there are a number of problems in certain areas but this does not change my opinion.

Let us remember that, in World War Two, so many people were killed that it averages about thirty thousand dead for every single day of the five years of real war (the war technically lasted nearly six years but most of the first year was the 'phoney war' when hardly a shot was fired). Later, in the Cuba Missile Crisis, we came within a hairs breadth of wrecking the entire planet and destroying most of the human race. Following this, during the Cold War we were, for years, on the brink of nuclear disaster. In comparison, therefore, at the present time, the people of the Earth are far more secure and prosperous.

To attempt to formulate the future, we must consider the various factors and trends that exist today, and extend and extrapolate in order to deduce the probable conditions of tomorrow. One of the most important factors must be the number of people that will exist in the future. At the present time we have a population which has grown from approximately 2 billion in 1945 to 6½ billion in 2006. China introduced a drastic form of population control a few years ago but, despite this, the nation's population has continued to slowly increase, but at a much-reduced rate, to a figure of approximately 1.3 billion. India has made efforts to reduce population growth rates, by encouraging contraception and voluntary sterilisation, but with limited success, and the population is now around 1.1 billion. Indonesia, South East Asia, Africa, Mexico and the South American countries have rapidly expanding populations. The population growth of the USA, Japan and Europe has slowed to slightly above balance figures and, remarkably, the Russian population is in slight decline. However, the fact is that two thirds of the nations of the Earth are still experiencing rapid population expansion and are likely to continue to do so, though at a declining rate, for the next 50 to 100 years.

Considering the drive of the human race to procreate, and the fact that expansion of population is unlikely to be restricted by shortage of food, (Genetic Engineering and agricultural development make it likely that up to 20 billion people or more could be fed) then it is reasonable to assume the World population will continue to increase, but at a declining rate, until a peak level is finally reached. (I have analysed and written about the population problem in detail in the Chapter – THE HUMAN POPULATION EXPLOSION – elsewhere in this book). Extrapolating from the present, and allowing for a gradual slowing of the rate of increase, I calculate the following: 2035 – 9 billion, 2050 – 11 billion, 2070 – 13 billion, 2100 – 17 billion, 2125 – 20 billion. It is quite possible that these figures may be underestimates, but I am assuming that, after 10 billion, the World will wake up to the seriousness of the population explosion and start to take drastic action.

Some optimists have suggested the expansion of the population will tail off more rapidly as the standard of living of the Third World rises, and peak at around 9 billion people. They think that, since birth rates tend to fall in affluent countries, this will also happen in Third World countries as standards rise. I am convinced this is extremely optimistic and the truth is, the Third World will never reach the standard of living of the highly developed countries such as the USA, European countries, Scandinavia and Japan. The planet simply does not have the resources to permit it.

When I suggest the planet could feed, in the future, 20 billion human beings or more, (See Chapter – GENETIC ENGINEERING) I am not suggesting there will be a steady, uninterrupted, increase in numbers until the maximum is reached. There will be mistakes, there will be local disasters – droughts, floods, crop failures, plant diseases and even that old menace – a locust plague – is not impossible. So it is to be expected there will be variations in the food supply from year to year. In certain areas people could starve or come close to starvation. However, these minor disasters will be manageable. It is a question of organisation, priorities and distribution. New and better crops, new and better methods of cultivation will be introduced. More land will be switched to food production.

At the present time we have a situation where the affluent countries of the World are over consuming. Taking into account waste and deliberate overeating they are consuming roughly twice the amount of food they really need, leading, of course, to ill health and obesity. The fact is, the Earth today could feed a further billion people without producing another extra ton of food per annum if food supplies were distributed purely on a basis of need. To feed the 20 billion plus that I anticipate will exist in the future I visualise a World where food production is organised on a planetary basis; where every hectare of productive land will be used with maximum efficiency to produce food – as will the sea. In the end, food will be more important than bio-fuels or anything else that can be produced by cultivation.

More people can, of course, be fed if meat is cut out of, or reduced, in the diet and there is even the possibility, pointed out by the late science fiction writer – Isaac Asimov – of producing food by growing yeast in large fermentation vats using various kinds of feedstock, including grass, to grow the yeast and then processing the yeast to produce various imitation foods – as is done on a limited scale today using soy beans. However, I am doubtful if the public would be happy eating 'ersatz' food for long. (Ersatz was a term used in Germany during World War 2 to describe awful imitation substances such as coffee made from acorns). Finally there will come a day when it is simply not possible to produce a greater annual quantity of food, when the planet has reached its ultimate limit and the maximum number of people that can ever live on Earth at the same time has been reached.

One of the features of a high standard of living is the high consumption, per capita, of raw materials used in the production of the goods and services associated with the standard of living. In America, for instance, statistics indicate that the average American, living the average lifetime, consumes, indirectly, over 500kg (1102lbs) of copper, 300kg (661lbs) of lead, 300kg (661lbs) of zinc, 40kg (88lbs) of nickel, 100kg (220lbs) of chromium and so on. At first these figures look startlingly high but then I look around my house and think of all the metals and materials used in producing the house and all the equipment and gadgets contained in it; boilers, refrigerators, cookers, radiators, TVs and so on. Then I think of the cars, lawn mowers, electric drills and other devices I have used and scrapped in my lifetime, not to mention thousands of drinks cans, bean tins, bottles, etc. Maybe the figures are not so surprising after all. What is clear is that even at current rates of consumption the World's reserves are being depleted rapidly and, as China, India, Brazil and other Nations develop, the rate of depletion will escalate. At current rates of consumption, reserves of copper, for instance, are expected to be exhausted in the next 40 to 70 years. However, as the demand from China, India, Brazil and the rest of the World increases, the time to exhaustion of the copper reserves will probably be reduced to 40 years or less. A similar situation applies to most of the other metals and minerals used in a modern civilised society. The planet simply does not have enough resources to permit the 6½ billion people, living on the Earth today, to all have the same standard of living as the Americans do at the present time, let alone the 9 billion that will be living thirty years from now.

At the present time, World consumption of oil is around 85 million barrels per day of which the United States of America consumes 20 million barrels. Consumption of oil is, of course, closely linked to the standard of living. To enable everyone on the planet to consume oil at the same rate as the Americans it would be necessary to boost World oil production to no less than 440 million barrels per day i.e. a five fold increase which is, of course, a manifest impossibility. In actual fact, discoveries of new oil and natural gas deposits are already tapering off and the World's major oil fields are struggling to increase capacity. It is likely that maximum oil production of no more than 100 million to 120 million barrels of oil per day will be reached in the next 20 years and, after that, production will inexorably decline. By 2100 A.D. nearly all the World's recoverable reserves of oil and gas will be exhausted. At the time of writing there are still, however, enormous reserves of coal, and despite the pollution and CO_2 aspects of using coal, it will, as oil and gas stocks decline, be increasingly used as a primary fuel and also for conversion into liquid fuels, chemicals, rubber and plastics. There are also enormous deposits of brown coal and peat, which are hardly touched at the present time but, as other fuels are reduced, these too will be exploited.

As I write there is now a hiatus in the building of nuclear power stations, mainly because of public opinion over the perceived hazards of nuclear waste. However, as the need for energy becomes more pressing, these worries are likely to be thrown aside and massive expansion of nuclear power generating facilities are likely to take place. As an Engineer, knowing something of the problems, I would be surprised if Fusion Power becomes a practical reality in the next fifty years.

It is now generally accepted, by most people, that Global Warming, triggered by human activity, is a reality but, whilst relatively minor effects such as increased Hurricane activity and more frequent El Nino events happen, it will probably be 20 or 30 years before the more serious repercussions begin to occur.

Let us consider what is likely to happen in the next twenty years. Taking into account the various factors, it is reasonable to assume the 'Good Life' will continue for most people with economic expansion and a steady improvement in the average standard of living – with maybe a couple of hiccups, such as recessions, along the way. I think the Chinese Economic Boom, for instance, is likely to suffer a setback. On reflection it is almost a rerun of the Japanese experience of 20 to 25 years ago when they flooded the World with Japanese goods and their real estate and stock exchange prices rose to insane levels. The trouble is, in any boom of that description – everyone gets carried away on a tide of enthusiasm and euphoria. Money is thrown around like water, "Invest in this! Invest in that! Lend here! Lend there! Don't worry about security". As a result land values and property prices go sky high. Money is loaned to non-viable businesses without second thoughts. Finally there comes a correction – as it did in Japan. (Even now, after nearly 20 years, the Nikkei-Dow and real estate prices are only a fraction of what they once were). I think it quite probable we shall see a similar repeat of the Japanese set-back in China. This does not, of course, mean the Chinese economy will crash back to the conditions of twenty years ago. Far from it, but the brakes will be applied. From the present runaway growth the economy may experience zero growth or even contract slightly for a time – before resuming expansion at a more modest pace. A Chinese correction is likely to affect the entire World economy to a degree. Overall global growth will probably slow a little.

Here, in the UK, we are creating our own problems. The housing market is overblown and the average level of personal debt very high so a correction is likely in the next few years. The market is now such that house prices may fall – maybe 5% to 10% and then probably stabilise for a few years. If house prices do fall, there will be repercussions. People will default on mortgage payments. Houses will be re-possessed. Confidence will be dented. People will reduce their spending. Shops and businesses will suffer. Unfortunately a similar situation exists in the USA and various other countries such as Spain. A correction in one country might trigger corrections in others in which case we might see a serious World recession but not, I think, too shattering. The Financial World has learned lessons from the past. Governments and Financial Institutions will take action to prevent a slump or World Depression.

Terrorism will, of course, go on. However, the most important terrorist organisation – Al-Qa'eda – has received a massive set-back. I am of the opinion President Bush was right to declare "War on Terrorism" but, if you think about it, surely war had already been declared. I have described the full extent of the Al-Qa'eda plan in detail in the Chapter 9/11 AND THE BUSH/BLAIR RESPONSE. In my mind – if we consider the full extent of the five plane plan – that all added up to a determined and serious attempt to decapitate the United States of America as a nation. Could anyone reasonably suggest there should be no major response to an attack of that magnitude? It was only by luck that the fifth plane was delayed to such a degree that the hijacking team abandoned the attempt and fled, and only the magnificent courage shown by passengers and crew of the fourth plane prevented the attack on either the White House or the Capitol.

Al-Qa'eda had, in fact, been killing Westerners in bomb outrages for years, including blowing up the U.S. Embassies in Kenya and Tanzania in 1998, killing over 200 and injuring 4,000, without serious retaliation. They had even made a previous attempt to topple the twin towers using a truck load of explosive strategically placed in the car park under one of the towers. This failed but if such a manoeuvre had succeeded, up to 20,000 people or more could have been killed. Even after this attempted atrocity still no serious action was taken against Al-Qa'eda. As a result they became bolder, more confident and more ambitious. Way back in the Nixon era, a certain Colonel Oliver North said he thought the most dangerous man on the planet was someone called Osama Bin Laden. Everyone wondered who this unknown man Bin Laden was!

When I see films of President Bush, I am forced to admit I have been inclined to think like nearly everyone else. He does not give the impression of being too bright. (Upon reflection, maybe we are all being fooled. There must be more to George W Bush than the bumbling 'country boy' we are used to seeing on TV. Maybe, behind closed doors, his 'Aides' see a different President). Nevertheless, I am of the opinion that his declaration of "War on Terrorism" was the only thing to do. If there had been no massive reaction to 9/11, the next Al-Qa'eda attack might well have been a nuclear bomb, or a nerve gas or biological attack, (it still might be – if some rogue nation supplies them with these weapons). High explosive bombs are bad enough, and kill many people, but are not as devastating as it would be if half of London was sprayed with Anthrax one dark night, or a nuclear bomb detonated in New York harbour. President Bush's and the World's, reaction was right. Many people, however, are short-sighted, and say "Look at the soldiers being

53

killed in Afghanistan and Iraq. Pull the troops out!" They don't appear to grasp that the action so far taken may well have prevented a devastating nuclear, biological or nerve gas attack. (Bear in mind there was evidence, around the time of the Twin Towers attack, that Al-Qa'eda were interested in crop spraying planes). The drastic response to the 9/11 attack will also have made rogue states a little more cautious about giving terrorists the weapons of mass murder. Colonel Ghaddafi of Libya, for instance, has seen the writing on the wall. He used to support terrorism. Now he has decided he wants none of it and Libya is switching to being friendly to the West. Nevertheless, sooner or later it is possible, and maybe even likely, that terrorists are going to get hold of a nuclear bomb, or fifty kilos (one hundred and ten pounds) of Anthrax or, maybe, a dirty bomb (radioactive material spread by conventional explosive) or a quantity of nerve gas. It may well be that only after a third city is devastated by a nuclear weapon will the World really decide that International Terrorism cannot be tolerated. It might also focus the minds of leaders that the planet will never be totally safe from nuclear disaster, until the last nuclear bomb has been dismantled and destroyed.

There are only two really dangerous rogue states at the present time – North Korea and Iran. I doubt if Kim Jong il, the leader of North Korea, would ever change if left to himself. Having been brought up under his fanatical Communist father – Kim il Sung – he will have been thoroughly indoctrinated. However, North Korea is in a desperate economic situation with its people on the brink of starvation. In the circumstances he may listen to his Chinese friends. Maybe the Chinese will invite him to China and show him what is happening today. They might even say, "Be pragmatic! If you can't beat em – join em", and it is not impossible he will decide to do so. After all – look what happened to the USSR! They have switched from Communism to Capitalism. At one time that would have been quite unthinkable.

Cuba is not a menace, and as soon as Castro and his guerrilla friends are dead, Cuba will turn Capitalist. The major problem is Iran; this might not be so if they did not possess one of the World's largest deposits of oil but that gives them Power and Money. Also, they are filled with religious zeal and are hostile to the 'West'; a very dangerous combination. It is the Iranians who are now financing terrorists in Afghanistan and Iraq and supplying them with bombs and weapons. Without Iranian interference everything would quieten down. Terrorists need money, and supplies of explosives and weapons. Without doubt Iran is going to be a tough problem to tackle and will probably take ten years to resolve.

Incidentally the Al-Qa'eda and Iran situation is a classic example of irrational thinking. The attacks on America and the West are basically prompted by religious fervour, with what can only be a long term ambition of converting the West to Islam. Nothing else would really satisfy them. Obviously (to us that is) they could never, in this day and age, convert the whole of the Western World to Islam, so the attacks are fundamentally futile and might, quite possibly, result in military action to take over Iran and change the political situation. The only logical course of action for the Iranians is a policy of co-existence. Anything else is, in the end, likely to be self-destructive.

The activities of North Korea and Iran, particularly their interest in nuclear weapons, whilst worrying, will never constitute a global threat such as a major nuclear war. I think it is probable that, if North Korea comes in out of the cold and joins China in co-operating and trading with the West, Iran, finding itself isolated and increasingly ostracised by the rest of the World, will see sense, recognise the futility of what it is doing and eventually cease to support and sponsor terrorism. Maybe it will take a change of Government before there is a change of policy but I think it will happen.

The final conclusion on International Terrorism is that because of the anti-terror actions already taken – the military actions in Afghanistan and Iraq and also the intensified security activities at airports, seaports and international boundaries – we are likely to see vastly reduced (but not totally eliminated) terrorist activities in the West for the next ten years or so. What activities do occur are likely to be small scale and suicide actions using relatively small quantities of improvised explosives. The unpredictable factor, at this time, is how the situations in Iraq and Afghanistan will be finalised. If the international community (mainly USA and Britain) stick with the job and do not leave until stable, safe, democracies have been created then that would be fine. However, if political situations and pressures change, leading to premature removal of troops and advisers, then the Taliban (backed by Iran) are likely to re-take Afghanistan, the Al-Qa'eda camps might be reinstated, the Taliban and Al-Qa'eda would proclaim that the West has been defeated and there is a risk that, with their renewed confidence, they will then plan larger and more drastic terrorist actions against the West. In this situation there would be a real risk of a truly devastating nuclear, chemical or biological attack. Let us hope the West is fully aware of the dangers of premature withdrawal – particularly from Afghanistan.

The greatest threat to the planet, and the survival of the human race, is likely to develop around 2020 to 2030, when China has developed to match the USA in economic output and military strength, and decides it is time to take Taiwan back as a part of Greater China. The situation then could match the danger that existed in the 1980s stand-off between the USA and the USSR during the Cold War. There could again be a confrontation that would threaten the planet with thermonuclear war. Let us hope that some sort of peaceful transition can be arranged, in a similar manner to that achieved with the peaceful transfer of Hong Kong. Unfortunately, the situation in Taiwan is far more complex, and the deep-rooted antagonism of the Nationalist Chinese on Taiwan towards the Communist Chinese mainland would be very difficult to overcome. It is hard to see how this situation will be resolved without strife. However, since the World has come so close to nuclear disaster in the past, I feel that lessons have been learned and nuclear weapons will not be used. Nevertheless, it will be a very dangerous time.

By 2030, assuming World economic growth averages 3% per annum (at the present time it is over 4%) then Gross World Product would have doubled. Even allowing for drastic improvements in the efficient use of energy and the introduction of bio-fuels, more nuclear power stations, hydro-electric schemes and wind and wave power, it is extremely likely that production of oil and natural gas will not be sufficient to satisfy demand. Shortages will mean increased prices, all the more so because supply is in the hands of just a few nations. As in the early 1970's there will be far reaching financial disruption.

Despite the worries over Global Warming, coal mining is likely to be increased to compensate, both to provide fuel for power stations and conversion of coal to liquid fuels, rubber and plastics. Full scale exploitation of tar sand and oil shale deposits is likely, despite the downside aspect that roughly a barrel of oil will have to be burned for every barrel made available for use.

The global population will probably have reached around 8.3 billion by 2030. Because of the advances which will be made possible by Genetic Engineering, I foresee no difficulty feeding such numbers. This, of course, means the population will continue to increase, but probably at a slower rate, because of improved birth control methods and growing awareness of the population problem.

Pollution however, will be an increasing problem. More people means more waste, and a higher average standard of living means more rubbish for disposal per person. Human waste can be handled by building the necessary treatment plants, but there are insidious and less obvious forms of pollution. For example, existing sewage treatment installations do not remove traces of Oestrogen resulting from women taking contraceptive pills. Oestrogen is not a persistent chemical, like DDT or PCB's, and does degrade slowly over time but, because of the continuing input, a continuous level of oestrogen is maintained in the environment. Only now, after a number of years, are the effects of oestrogen in the water of rivers and lakes becoming apparent. Frogs, other amphibians and also fish are being affected. For instance, I noticed, years ago, that spawning frogs exhibited an imbalance in the sexes. It was normal to have four or five males competing furiously for every female. However, in the last few years this has changed. In my garden, where a small pond for frogs has been filled with water from the domestic supply, there are now several females to every male, resulting in some of the frogspawn being infertile. I recently read of tests being carried out in Canada over the last few years. The researchers found a pristine, pollution free lake, full of fish, in the wilds of Canada. They checked the fish populations and then introduced oestrogen up to the levels found in our domestic water supplies. Over the next few years the numbers of fish declined rapidly. Apparently the males became 'feminised' by the oestrogen in the water – even at extremely low levels. It would appear to be having the same effects on frogs. There have also been reports of a decrease in the average human male sperm count in the last few years. Maybe it is not only frogs and fish that are being affected.

If World economic growth were to continue at an average of 3% per annum, then by 2045 the Gross World Product would have tripled compared to what it is today in 2006. However, it is highly probable that there will simply not be enough energy and other resources available to permit such a degree of expansion. Energy and commodity prices will go sky high, leading to massive World wide economic repercussions, disruptions and strife. People in the Third World will see the standard of living they coveted, and very nearly achieved, slipping from their grasp. People living in the developed nations of the World will begin to see their standard of living being eroded. Fuel costs, food costs, product costs will all inevitably escalate faster than their incomes. Attempts to force pay rises to compensate will simply fuel inflation and exacerbate the situation. There is likely to be large-scale civil unrest. Vast areas of arable land are likely to be switched from the production of food crops to the production of bio-fuel crops and this in turn, is likely to lead to food shortages and increased prices.

Nations will frantically build nuclear power stations – ignoring the waste disposal and future decommissioning problems. The Athabasca Tar Sands (an enormous area of Canada, where oil from an immense underground oil deposit has leaked and soaked into the upper layers of sand and shale) will be exploited along with similar deposits wherever they are found. As stated earlier, one of the problems with extracting shale oil is that, for every barrel of useable oil that is produced, it is necessary to burn another barrel or more to produce it. It is necessary to mine the shale, bake off the oil and then get rid of the residue. The CO_2 output will be enormous, with all its implications for Global Warming, but it will be done. It is likely Greenland and Antarctica, will eventually be tapped for oil – if it can be found there. (It would be most surprising if it was not). Forget conservation! The need for oil will override it.

Wind farms and wave energy schemes will proliferate. Incidentally, since wind speed increases with the height above ground and power increases as the square of the diameter I expect wind generators to be built taller and larger, both on shore and off shore. It would not surprise me, in the future, if wind generators are built 800 ft (243.84 metres) to 1000 ft (304.8 metres) high. This means, of course, it will eventually be almost impossible to be anywhere in the beautiful hills and dales of Britain without having the view besmirched by the necessary but monstrous, endlessly twirling, wind generators. However, as we, today, have become used to electricity pylons and overhead wires, I expect the people of the future will get used to it.

In tropical, dry and desert areas enormous solar power stations will spring up, with square miles of glass or plastic trapping the sun's heat. The hot air generated will be trapped, and funnelled into giant chimneys, half a mile high, fitted with turbines. (This is not my idea – it is already on the drawing boards).

My own idea of what I think would be of immense value is a cheap, simple, solar panel anyone could buy and use – like a thin, roll up, carpet you could lay out in the sun and plug in. Instead of spending scores of billions of dollars sending men on a mission to Mars, why not spend at least some of it trying to create this cheap solar panel? It may not be possible – but why not give it a good try.

Around forty years from now I think the dark clouds will begin to gather. The World population will probably be over 10 billion. The oil supplies will be failing. The seas will be impoverished. Many metals and minerals will be in short supply. Global warming will be beginning to be noticeable. El Nino will probably become semi-permanent, drastically changing the climate, and hence the rainfall of South East Asia, India and Australia. The Gulf Stream is likely to slow down, as the Arctic Ice Cap and Greenland glaciers melt, affecting and cooling the climate of Europe and Scandinavia or at least moderating Global Warming effects. However, there should still be no real problem in feeding the people of the World. Advances in agriculture will be made; crops will be improved; Genetic Engineering will enable crops to be grown in areas where they could not be grown before. There will be far more overcrowding in cities – with more urban strife. Waste disposal will become a massive problem.

More people will begin to migrate from regions such as India, Egypt, Central Africa, South East Asia and Central America. Global Warming will mean these areas will gradually become too hot for general human habitation. At this point there is likely to be great resentment by people in fuel starved countries that have to buy oil at massively inflated prices from those few nations still having oil supplies. The situation will result in too much of the World's wealth being in the hands of a few nations and individuals. Nearly all businesses, services, hotels, transport systems and infrastructure in the buyer countries will be owned by the oil suppliers. (How else could the oil be purchased? Trade will not be enough!). The oil suppliers will continue, as they do now, to use the oil wealth to purchase businesses and real estate. They will be well aware that real estate is far more secure than a Bank balance. In addition, the purchase of assets gives the money back to the buyer nation so that they can buy yet more oil.

In my opinion OPEC (Organisation of Petroleum Exporting Countries) should not exist. OPEC is a Cartel and was created to control the World's oil supply and, fundamentally, to restrict supplies and push up prices; to hold the World to ransom you could say. They did this very successfully in 1973, doubled and quadrupled the price of oil, causing massive inflation and recession throughout the World. Fortunately, following this, because of the discovery of new oil fields that were not under OPEC control, the price of oil gradually fell and the World economy recovered. However, as oil becomes more scarce the major oil supplies will again be in the hands of the few and excessive monetary exploitation will again be possible. Many nations have the good fortune to have special natural resources within their borders. In some cases it is oil or natural gas, in others – coal, copper or rare metals and some countries simply have very fertile land and good growing conditions. All these nations should benefit from their good fortune but should not seek to exploit the situation excessively by forming cartels to push up prices and extort money from the rest of the World. It could, in the long run, become a dangerous game. Nations and peoples impoverished by the unavoidable purchases of excessively expensive oil may become resentful of the exploitation by affluent, oil rich, countries and demand some form of retaliation or retribution. If everyone adopted a cut-throat policy why not create OGEC (Organisation of Grain Exporting Countries)? Restrict the production of grain and force prices sky high. If this was done there would be a Worldwide howl of protest and indignation (and rightly so). OPEC, so far, seems to be able to get away with it. But, for how long?

Although most people now accept that global warming is inevitable, they are not unduly worried because of the figures they see quoted. A 4°C increase by the end of the 21st century does not sound so bad. However, averages can often be misleading, and especially so when global average temperatures are under consideration. When one realises that more than two thirds of the entire planet is covered with water, and the average depth of the sea is around 10,000 feet (3,077 metres), the water represents an enormous heat sink. It takes an immense amount of heat to raise the temperature of the sea even a fraction of a degree. The situation on land is different. Land heats up far more rapidly. What this means is – if more solar radiation is trapped by greenhouse gases – the effect on the sea will be very little, and slow to take effect, whereas, on land, the effect will be far more pronounced. As an example – as I write, the global average temperature in the last 70 years has only risen by about 0.7°C yet, in Alaska, Canada and Siberia the local average temperatures have risen 2°C to 3°C or more. It is probable, therefore, that a rise in average global temperatures of 3°C or 4°C may well mean that, in certain land areas on the globe, the average local temperatures may rise by 10°C or more, and these temperatures we are talking about are averages. Temperatures on land fluctuate far, far more than sea temperatures fluctuate. For instance, the 3°C average increase in temperatures in Alaska and Northern Russia that has already occurred have led to my experiencing amazing 32°C temperatures occasionally, on my fishing trips in the Arctic. It is not average temperatures that kill people and destroy crops but the occasional heat wave and drought. What a 3°C or 4°C global average increase in temperature really means is that parts of the planet, such as India, Egypt and South East Asia, where people are now, sometimes, living close to the human tolerance limit, will become all but uninhabitable. Instead of the 40°C to 42°C they now have to occasionally live with, they may be afflicted by the sort of temperatures at present associated with America's Death Valley.

The cost of fuel and power and the need to conserve energy is likely to prevent air conditioning becoming the norm in most dwellings in the hotter countries of the World. Those people that have the means and opportunity are likely to emigrate to cooler climes. The increasing migration will cause resentment, from people living in cooler countries, against the influx, leading to calls for more control of immigration and the closing of borders. Trouble, up to the level of serious wars, may ensue.

By 2050 the general standard of living on the entire planet will start to fall since standard of living is inexorably tied to availability of oil, metals and other natural resources. On a more mundane level, non essential travel is likely to be restricted. The engines of personal vehicles may be restricted to 1 litre capacity or less. (You can get anywhere you wish to go with a 1 litre engine – it is merely a question of gearing and speed). Maximum vehicle speeds will be lowered and vehicles designed to a minimum drag coefficient. Higher taxes on fuels and travelling will be introduced and private aircraft might be restricted or abolished altogether – at least for all but VIPs. Sailing for recreation will probably be more popular than ever and fairly large commercial sailing ships (of ultra modern design – not the old wind jammers) may once again traverse the seas. The pressure for recycling will become intense. Anything that can be recycled will be recycled. It is likely that heavy penalties in the form of fines will be imposed on anyone caught burning items or materials which could be recycled. All machines, large and small, will go to special repositories for careful dismantling and recycling. Packaging of goods will be drastically reduced and the use of disposables, such as plastic bags, actively discouraged. The old-fashioned brown paper bag may make a come-back. It is likely that waste tips created before 2000 will be 'mined' to retrieve metals (particularly copper) and anything that could be reused. Newspapers will be reduced in size or abolished and news, articles and information disseminated electronically. From 2050 onwards towards 2100 the problems of energy supply, depletion of natural resources, global warming, overcrowding and, finally, food production will gradually become worse.

At one hundred years from now I would expect the human race to be in serious trouble. The population will probably be approaching eighteen billion. The oil and gas reserves will be exhausted, as will many of the metal and mineral reserves. The Earth does, however, have enormous reserves of iron and aluminium. There will still be coal and peat, and humanity will be forced to continue to exploit these resources. Apart from energy, these fuels will be essential for production of chemicals and conversion into liquid fuels, rubber, plastics, pharmaceuticals, etc. All mineable coal will eventually be mined. Unmineable coal will be fired in situ and turned into extractable gas. (This is called 'Underground Gasification of Coal' and involves drilling holes down to and through coal beds, setting fire to the coal and then pumping a calculated supply of air in so that, whilst combustion of the coal continues and maintains high temperatures, there is insufficient for total combustion and a combustible gas is produced which can be piped off and used as a fuel – either for domestic use or for generation of electrical power). It is even possible to use the gas for conversion to liquid fuels, rubber, etc. Whilst underground gasification techniques have yet to be perfected, the potential is so great I feel sure they will be and this exploitation of inaccessible and unmineable coal beds will eventually take its place as one of the common sources of fuel and power in the future.

I still think it will be possible to feed a World population of eighteen billion, but waste and pollution problems will be enormous. Global warming will be intensifying. The burgeoning population will make it quite impossible to prevent atmospheric CO_2 levels increasing. My conclusion is that the current hopes of Politicians and Scientists, that CO_2 levels can be prevented from going above 450 ppm, are just wishful thinking and levels will probably go to 600 ppm or even higher. The heat, and change of climate, will be the biggest problem, not rise in sea levels, though this will affect many nations to some degree – particularly Bangladesh.

Late in the 21st century, billions of people will become desperate to migrate to cooler climates. We are talking of the order of 3 to 4 billion people or more. There would be room for them in Alaska, Canada, Europe and Siberia, but what will be the reaction of the indigenous people of these areas? It is highly likely that when the people of these areas, including the ones that have already migrated, realise they will be swamped and totally outnumbered by the enormous wave of immigration, they will close their borders and refuse admission. Most people are sympathetic to other people in distress and will do their best to help, particularly if they themselves are secure but, in a situation where they have already had to accept restrictions and a lower standard of living, and will know that more immigration and crowding will lead to an even lower standard of living, people's attitudes will harden. We will, therefore, have a very dangerous situation where the Southerners are desperate to move North and the Northerners are desperate to stop them. What will happen then is anyone's guess. I can only rationally deduce that such a situation will arise.

A civilised and sensible way to solve the problem would be for Northern Nations to simply sell large tracts of land to the desperate Southern Nations. This may sound very radical but it is not without precedent. On 30 March, 1867 Russia sold the territory of Alaska to the U.S.A. for 7.2 million dollars in gold (about 200 million dollars worth in today's money). I do not know if Russia did this to forestall possible conflict or simply because they needed the cash. (It is an interesting fact that there are still a few communities of residual Russians, living the old pre-revolution way, in villages on the Kenai peninsula of Alaska, to this day. They live happily, mind their own business and are left alone). However, it would seem a practical solution to the problem if the Northern people were reasonable and willing to seriously consider the predicament of the Southerners. The Northerners would benefit from the payments; definite boundaries to the transferred land would be fixed and the Southerners would have somewhere to go and start a new life without having to go to war for it.

It is probable that, when the tundra areas of the World have warmed up and are properly cultivated, they will be found to be extremely productive. It will be necessary to add lime (to neutralise acidity) and various fertilisers but the rich organic base of the soil should ensure heavy and sustained cropping capability. The peaty fens of East Anglia in the UK are a good example of the productivity of such areas. There is, however, a substantial downside to the cultivation of peat lands and that is – massive production of greenhouse gases caused by cultivation. In the Anglian Fens the surface levels of cultivated peat areas have fallen dramatically over the last 100 years or so; in some cases as much as 2 to 3 metres (6.5 to 9.8 feet). This is due, not to removal or extraction but solely due to oxidation and decomposition of the disturbed and exposed peat. Cultivation of peat lands leads to increased release of greenhouse gases from those areas.

At some point in the late 21st century a 'sea change' will have to occur in the economics of nations and businesses; economic growth will have to stop, and stop forever. The planet simply does not have the resources for endless expansion. Industrial output will have to stabilise or reduce. Both businesses and Governments will have to come to terms with the fact that further economic growth will not be possible. Economic growth automatically means more consumption and this is a finite planet. Cessation of all further growth and expansion will cause many serious problems and repercussions. The idea and culture of growth is so deeply ingrained into every level of society – from the worker who expects some degree of a rise in his pay and his standard of living every year, the business man who strives to build his business ever larger and Governments whose Budgets are always based on the expectation of growth in the economy leading to higher tax revenues. At the present time as soon as the economy slows to 1½% or 1% annual growth there is dismay. (2½% to 3% is considered the norm for developed countries). Zero growth is stagnation – totally unacceptable. The only thing considered worse is an outright Recession. Recession – where there is actually a fall in GDP for two consecutive months or more – although the fall maybe no more than ¼% or ½% – is reckoned to be a total economic disaster.

The adjustment, therefore, from the present culture of economic expansion and growth to the final inescapable situation of static conditions (stagnation in present day terms) or steady contraction, will be a long arduous and difficult process. It will play havoc with the economic system and devastate the stock markets whose life blood is the gambling associated with expansion and growth of businesses and profits. For a stock broker there can be few things worse than a business that is static, with steady turnover and profits, year after year with little or no change, no unpredictability.

Governments will have to change their ways. It will no longer be possible to make mistakes, overspend and underestimate, and rely on the anticipated growth of the next 5 years to put things right. Initially, in the first years when growth has finally stopped, I expect Governments will fall back on that old trick – Inflation. With Inflation we will have a situation where in monetary terms the economy appears to expand and the worker appears to get a pay rise and there is still scope for adjustment – where one group actually does get an increase at the expense of another – but this cannot go on forever. The period of adjustment – to final acceptance that economic stasis or contraction is, and will be in the future, normal, will be long hard and painful. With no further overall growth possible the only way businesses could grow would be by taking someone else's market and customers. Business competition could become utterly ruthless and brutal. Governments would have to be vigilant to prevent monopolies and cartels being created.

As I write there are over 6 billion people alive today. I am very much aware I am lucky to live in a nation with one of the highest standards of living on Earth. No more than 1 billion people enjoy such a standard of living and the other 5 billion can only dream and aspire to do so. It is a brutal fact that they can never all catch up. The resources of the planet are not enough to permit that, even for the 6 billion living today, let alone the 15 to 17 billion that will exist later in the century. For example, in the UK today there is roughly one car for every two people. If everybody on the planet had the same standard of living there would be about 3 billion automobiles. Allowing for travelling, electrical devices in the home, central heating, food consumption and so on – total energy and consumables production would need to be quadrupled just for the 6 billion alive today. It is not possible. No matter how much they dream, the Third World nations will never be able to match the standard of living enjoyed by the few. The possibility of 20 billion people enjoying the standard of living we in Britain enjoy today is quite out of the question.

Fortunately, it is not really necessary to be affluent to be happy. All a family really needs is food, a roof over their heads and the basic necessities. If the people of the Earth all accepted this, then 10 to 20 billion could live in harmony and reasonable happiness. Sadly, human nature being what it is, there is more likely to be massive strife.

At two hundred years from now things will be dire. The population will probably have reached, or be near, its peak and I think it may even go as high as thirty billion. I still think it might be possible to feed even as many as 30 billion, providing there is co-operation and everyone pulls together but meat would be a rare or non existent luxury. People would eat imitation meat, made from plant or bacterial protein but hardly distinguishable from the real thing; some people may even say better! All the gas and the oil will be gone – every last extractable barrel coaxed from the ground by the ingenuity of man. There will be coal mines in Greenland and Antarctica. Both coal and uranium will probably still be available – uranium only if it is used carefully and not wasted. (Hundreds of tons of uranium anti-tank shells were fired into the desert in the recent Iraq war despite the fact that depleted uranium could still be used to generate power in a suitably designed reactor). Wind farms and wave power installations will be everywhere. Heat pumps will become commonplace. (A heat pump is a device to transfer heat from one place to another. Basically, it is a refrigerator run in reverse. We might, for instance, use 10 kilowatts of electrical power in simple electric fires to heat a building but if, instead, we used the 10 kilowatts to run a reverse refrigerator system, we could extract heat from a nearby stream or river. We would, in effect, refrigerate the river. The heat removed from the river would be transferred to the building. In this way, we can transfer 5 or 6 times as much heat into the building as would be created by simply using the electricity to run electric heaters. It sounds like something for nothing but it is not. We are merely taking heat from one place and transferring it to another. Heat pumps have been built, and used, and they work as I have described). Every possible source of hydro-electric power will be exploited. Visible waterfalls will be a luxury – only allowed to flow on special occasions. Even the smallest streams will be exploited.

Bearing in mind the many different possible sources of energy on this Earth I do not think the primary problem 200 years from now will be energy. I am more inclined to think the greatest problem will be shortage of raw materials – many sources of minerals and metals will be exhausted although the planet has vast amounts of iron and aluminium. Problems of waste disposal and pollution, however, are likely to be immense.

By 2200 global warming is likely to have reached the point where most humans will have abandoned tropical countries. Current projections suggest the World will have warmed by around 4°C by 2100 but there is no reason to believe it will stop there. On the contrary, as more and more CO_2 is pumped into the atmosphere during the 21st century (despite all the efforts to prevent it) and, as the feedbacks from the rotting of the Tundra peat, and the effects of the exposure of more sea and land, instead of ice, intensify, it is very likely global warming will continue into the 22nd century. (See Chapter – GLOBAL WARMING). If we assume only a further 3°C global average increase by 2200, at which point the global climate will probably stabilise, with CO_2 levels at their maximum and global ice cover at a minimum, then many tropical countries will probably be uninhabitable, for all practical purposes, and the people forced to emigrate because of the heat. There really will be no alternative. The areas available for cultivation will have moved North. As the Tundra warms, vast areas of Alaska, Canada and Siberia will become available for cultivation. In addition – genetic engineering will enable crops to be grown in colder, and also drier and hotter, conditions, allowing even more land to be exploited. Think of the potential of genetically engineered, frost resistant, potatoes for instance. Nearly all fish for human consumption will be farmed fish, either in cages or in the wild sea.

At the present time, no one really seems to have grasped the tremendous potential of salmon, particularly in North Atlantic and North Pacific rivers but, possibly, all over the World. Massive farms could be set up, hatching and rearing small salmon to smolt size, and then releasing them into the rivers to migrate to sea. There, they will feed and grow and, when mature, come obediently back to their river of origin, like sheep to their home farm, to be harvested. In South America there were no trout or salmon in the rivers until a few brown trout were introduced, a few years ago, for sport fishing. The trout thrived and a few migrated into the sea, where they grew enormously and returned to their home rivers weighing anything from 4 to 30lbs (1.8 to 14kgs). These were trout mind you! Think what would happen if salmon were introduced! The trout proved what rich feeding grounds for salmon exist in South Atlantic and Antarctic waters. If South America and the Falklands were developed as salmon fisheries in the way I have described, it could become one of the greatest salmon producing areas in the World. All that would be needed is to set up massive salmon hatcheries; the fish will willingly come home when they are mature. As proof of this, a few years ago, in America, baby salmon were placed in a 20 metre (65 feet) diameter concrete tank and reared to smolt size. A gate was then opened which allowed the smolts to swim out into a canal which, after a mile or so, connected to a river and hence to the sea. After 3 years adult salmon came back up the river, into the canal and through the gate, right back into the concrete tank.

If enormous salmon hatcheries were created and the smolts introduced into the rivers, just a few miles up river from the sea (they have to have time to get the smell of the river programmed into their brains in order to enable them to find the home river again on their return) and protected from predators (by culling the predators in the last few miles of river and in the estuary) then millions of tons of salmon could be produced, and harvested for food quite easily and cheaply. All that would be required would be an International Agreement making it illegal to net salmon on the high seas, which, in effect, would be stealing someone else's property. The reason salmon, at the present time, are reared in cages, with all the problems of overcrowding and disease, is simply because it is the only way of keeping control and preventing the fish being stolen. Salmon have a colossal potential as a human food resource if properly exploited.

It may also be possible to seed the sea with fertilisers to produce more biomass. It has been found, for instance, that a very small amount of iron based soluble compound can cause an algal bloom over a considerable area. Such a bloom, provided it is non-toxic, can act as the base of a food chain. A cheap and simple way to do this would be to have an automatic dispenser fitted to every commercial ship that sails the seas. The blooms would also help to remove carbon dioxide from the atmosphere. Large areas of sea will have to be designated World Wildlife Areas, with no fishing or exploitation whatsoever allowed, if large species are to survive.

At some point there must come a Worldwide acceptance that no further increase of population can be allowed and efforts should be made to not only stop further growth but to reduce the total World population. With an issue so basic, so fundamental, so instinctive as the procreation of children, the human race is likely to fly in the face of reason and ignore the repercussions until it is manifestly impossible to continue to do so. Only when the Earth is impossibly overcrowded do I expect the need to restrict population to be universally acknowledged and accepted. In general, the human race only learns very slowly from its mistakes and disasters. Social Evolution is a long, painful and slow process. Only the application of rational thinking and a willingness to face facts gives us a chance to mitigate or avoid the disasters of the future but I have a feeling that emotion will rule and a population disaster is almost inevitable. Only when confronted with the inescapable stark evidence of disaster will the human race face and accept the fundamental necessity of controlling its numbers. In most things I am optimistic but where Population is concerned I fear that only when the entire race has experienced and suffered the hell that can be created will there be a universal acceptance, forever afterwards, of the vital necessity to control our numbers.

Even if the human race does the sensible thing and acts to control the population voluntarily i.e. through birth control, there will be considerable problems to be surmounted. At the present time the policy of Government in the developed nations, is that the work of the young supports the old. In the UK, for example, there is no such thing as a pension fund for the State Pension. The State Pension is paid for, week by week, directly out of the taxes taken from the working population. As the numbers of old, pensionable, people increases, the financial burden on the young increases. The UK Government has tried to offset this by allowing mass immigration of people of working age. Eventually, if the population of the whole World is to be balanced or reduced, this manoeuvre would not be possible. Fewer and fewer working people would have to support more and more old people. It follows that, in the future, active older people would simply have to work for a longer period of time. Retirement age would have to rise substantially and the greater the average expectation of life the higher the retirement age would have to be and the value of pensions reduced.

The logical way to achieve a practical solution would be to have a differential tax system to encourage active retired people to continue to work. They should receive the basic pension whether they work or not but, if they work, the additional income should be taxed at a reasonable but reduced rate for the first 5 years after retirement age, a lower rate still for the period 5 to 10 years after retirement age and no tax at all for periods more than 10 years after retirement. (A person who works contributes to the GDP and helps support those who do not work even if they pay no direct tax. They will still pay tax through VAT and other indirect taxes). These measures would create escalating incentives to encourage older people to continue working as long as possible. Many people would be willing and even happy to work way beyond their retirement age if there was sufficient financial incentive. Work also keeps people mentally and physically healthier.

In the end, strict control of family size will have to be rigorously enforced. The peoples of the World will, eventually, have to accept this. If not, the World would degenerate into violence, anarchy, chaos and starvation. The Chinese Government should be commended for having the courage to tackle their population problem head on. India has tried very hard to control the population by encouraging voluntary contraception methods but with limited success. However, at the present time, India's population is still rapidly increasing. It would, of course, have increased even faster without their efforts. Generally, the Chinese Government is castigated. Their action is said to be Authoritarian and Draconian (indeed it is) and to contravene the human right to have children. In my mind, the Chinese Government had the courage to face the brutal facts. The Chinese had the World's worst population problem and they had the sense, the will and determination to do something about it. I cannot see how a Democracy would ever be able to bring in strict laws on population control, as the Chinese have done. It is noticeable that Politicians discuss such topics as Global Warming, Help for the Third

World, The Need for IVF, and so on but never, ever, a squeak on the Population Problem. At some point, also, the Roman Catholic Church is going to have to change its stance. The question they have to face is – is it better to have two well fed, healthy, happy children – or a dozen desperate, starving children, with distended bellies, begging for food?

As spelled out in the chapter on Global Warming I am convinced that, as I write, Global Warming has already passed the tipping point; the point of no return; that we are on a one-way trip to a Hot Age. For a number of my earlier years, I held the view that what the human race was doing with the burning of fossil fuels was beneficial. Hundreds of millions of years ago the World was much warmer than today, with immense forests and both land and sea teeming with far more life than exists at the present time. Gradually, over millions of years, billions of tons of carbon – one of the key elements of life – was slowly locked up in sediments. On land, rotting trees and plants laid down the layers that would become coal and oil. In the sea, endless generations of diatoms lived and died and their shells, containing calcium and carbon, fell to the seabed to gradually form the enormous deposits of chalk and limestone. Slowly, the carbon available for life was reduced and, at the same time, atmospheric carbon dioxide levels fell. Geological evidence shows that, slowly, the planet's temperature also fell and, in the last few million years, ice ages have become more and more frequent, with shorter and shorter interglacial periods. A few years ago a number of scientists stated that, on the basis of past evidence, we were, in fact, overdue for another ice age. To my mind therefore, it seemed that the re-introduction of some of the locked up carbon, back into the system, would have the effect of bringing the planet back up to warmer conditions and, at the same time, provide the carbon for a substantial increase in the biomass. I think this analysis was, and is, quite valid, but unfortunately it appears probable that the release of CO_2 will go too far. At least, too far that is, for the health and happiness of the human race. It is reasonable to suggest, however, that this will still be preferable to another ice age. The sudden acceleration of global warming in the last 20 years strongly indicates that at least one secondary 'positive feedback' event has already commenced. This could well be due to the warming of the tundra areas of the World. Trillions of tons of peat, which used to be locked up in the permafrost, is now melting and, in doing so, is rotting and releasing CO_2 and Methane. As warming gathers pace, vast areas of land and sea presently covered with snow and ice, which reflects solar energy back into space, will clear, allowing more solar energy to be absorbed and create yet another positive feedback effect.

The really big question is – at what point does global warming stop? The answer is – when greenhouse gas levels in the atmosphere stop rising, when most of the World's ice has melted and when the amount of solar energy reaching the planet, and being trapped, is balanced by the amount of heat being radiated back out into space by a warmer Earth. I do not have the facilities, but some Researchers, armed with Super Computers, may be able to give us an idea of what that level might be. I have a feeling that the answer will be startlingly high to our way of thinking, but not so high as to threaten life on Earth.

Some pessimistic scientists have referred to the runaway greenhouse effect on Venus and suggested it could happen here. Let us then, for a moment, consider Mars and Venus. Mars has an atmosphere with a high CO_2 content but is extremely cold. It is further away from the sun, but the main reason there is very little greenhouse warming effect is that the air is so very thin. Venus, on the other hand, is closer to the sun than Earth but the reason its temperature is so staggeringly high is not so much the extra solar radiation, but that the radiation is trapped by a tremendously dense blanket of CO_2 laden atmosphere. Venus's atmosphere is over 100 times as dense as Earth's and most of that atmosphere is carbon dioxide. Earth, however, has a relatively light blanket of air with only a small percentage of CO_2 and, though the greenhouse effect exists, there will be, nevertheless, a lot of heat escaping into space. Earth will not become another Venus.

How long it will take for Earth to reach its maximum temperature is open to debate, but I would guess probably two hundred years. The rate of increase, of course, is likely to decline quite rapidly after the first 150 years. As to how long it will be before the Earth cools back to the conditions of today, will depend on how long it will take for CO_2 levels to be reduced (there are other greenhouse gases of course such as methane, nitrous oxide, and even water vapour, but the geological evidence indicates CO_2 is the prime cause of Global Warming). No matter how many trees were planted, this would only cause a temporary reduction in CO_2 levels, since the carbon in the trees would almost certainly be recycled by later rotting or burning. Only total sequestration – as happened in the chalk and coal deposits, will truly work. It is probable, therefore, that the Earth is likely to stay considerably warmer than today for a long time. Maybe five thousand years or more. Human beings will have to get used to a warmer Earth for a while. When the Earth finally does start to cool it will, of course, enter another positive feedback system with more ice reflecting more energy back into space, and so on until, eventually, the World will be back in another ice age.

The conclusion therefore is that, in 200 years time, despite global warming, there will still be plenty of land where people might live and cultivate their crops. It will simply be on another part of the planet. All that is needed is sufficient tolerance and co-operation. If we had been unfortunate enough to have plunged into an ice age, it would have been a far greater disaster. Both living space and the land available for cultivation would have been drastically reduced. The human race would have been forced to live mainly in a narrow band around the equator. The main problem of global warming will be the need for people to migrate and the reluctance of those already living in cooler lands to permit this migration. In the event there is likely to be massive civil unrest, to say the least.

In my population projections I am assuming the Governments of the Nations of the Earth will behave in a cooperative, intelligent and civilised manner. I do not, of course, expect the public to do likewise. There will be a lot of strife, killing and terrorism. If Governments do not behave sensibly, there could be any scale of wars you care to imagine. Wars could wreck agriculture and trade and plunge half the planet into mass starvation. Billions could die. You could then tear up my population projections. However, I am not naturally inclined to be pessimistic (neither am I foolishly optimistic – I try to be realistic). During my life I have seen many things turn out better than expected. I have no desire to predict apocalyptic visions of nuclear wars, or millions dying of starvation, just for sensationalism. However, the basic facts of global warming, finite resources and the inexorable increase of the human population, are inescapable and inevitably lead to the predictions put forward in this chapter.

In thirty or forty years from now the average standard of living must begin to fall. It will not necessarily be the disaster most people think. It is mainly a question of psychology and adaptation. I remember a time when it was difficult even to get enough to eat. When I walk into a modern store I stare at the goods available – especially at the immense range of chocolates and sweets on the racks. Back in 1942, during the war, when sweets simply did not exist, as children we used to go out and eat cattle peas growing in the farmer's field, and gooseberries – half grown and bright green; so sour you could not keep your face straight when you ate them. We used to gorge on apples and pears in the autumn. Oranges and bananas – what were they? At home we had gaslight – no electricity; linoleum on the floor – no carpets. We had a small fire in the stove in the living room, around which we crowded on cold nights. If it blazed too much, Dad would go out and get a shovel full of slack (very small pieces of coal and dust) to throw on the fire and slow it down. Coal was expensive! Central heating? Only school had central heating! In the winter my bedroom window was sometimes coated with ice and you could see your breath in the bedroom. If it was very cold I would take a hot water bottle to bed. It was amazing how luxurious my old bed was, on cold nights, once I had warmed up. We had a radio but no television and enjoyed a trip to the cinema once a month, or less maybe. After the war, in 1950, things were much better. We still had rationing – even five years after the war ended, but the rations were bigger and things were far better. During the war they even rationed clothes; so many coupons for a pair of trousers, so many for a skirt, and so on. By the mid 1950's the World was great. Food was off ration. You could buy sweets. We had Rock and Roll. Fantastic! I got around on my bicycle quite well. Hardly anyone had holidays. So what! If you were lucky, you might earn enough to run a second-hand motorbike, but not a car. Cars were for doctors and the well off. So, we were happy – and why not? We had the war in Korea, the insurgency in Malaya and the Mau Mau in Kenya. Not enough to really worry about; not after World War Two! So you see, it really is only a question of psychology and adaptation. All you basically need to be happy is love, good health, enough food, a roof over your head, a job and a few fun things – the local dance, the pub, a few friends. You don't really need a holiday in Tenerife or Spain, or wherever, every year. You don't really need two cars, or two televisions, or a 'Four by Four' to take the kids to school. (During the Second World War I cycled about four miles to school, and four back, five days a week. In the winter I walked, sometimes in a foot of snow or more; this was between the ages of ten and sixteen years. I remember the ice on the frozen canal being ten inches (twenty-five centimetres) thick. (I bored a hole in the ice and measured it).

      If people in the UK today had to go back to living as we did in the 1950's they would probably think it was the end of the World. It would not be. It is merely a question of adaptation. When there are twenty billion people on the Earth, everybody will simply have to adapt to a lower standard of living. The logical thing to do is to accept the situation, and not behave irrationally by going on strike, or rioting or making war. However, I am forced to admit, from what I have seen of human nature, I expect there will be trouble! Some people will no doubt commit suicide. In their situation I would not. I would adapt and enjoy life and be happy, in the knowledge that I was lucky to be alive and a member of the human race. (I might have been unlucky enough to have been born a pig on a farm, been killed at an early age and strung up for bacon. After all, it is only the luck of the draw that we had the good fortune to be born human!) When there are twenty billion people on the Earth, the children born then will be as happy as can be – if they have love, food, warmth, clothing and can play with their friends – as long as they have never known anything different. However, if their parents make the mistake of telling them how marvellous it used to be, they will probably make them unhappy. Far better to tell them how lucky they are. Tell them how awful it used to be; with the wars, the starvation, the pestilence, the hatred. Just don't tell them about the birds, the whales, the bluebells, the deer on a highland hill in the morning mist. Let them be happy in the World that is. Not was!

So, I believe the World could feed twenty, or maybe even as many as thirty, billion people – with the advances (yet to be made) in Genetic Engineering. However, I do not believe we could continue for long at that level. The Earth would end up half a mile deep in waste, and pollution would sour the entire planet. Sooner or later there has to be change. The Earth is a finite planet. There simply has to be a limit to the number of people who can be alive at any one time. It is self-evident it is only possible to keep so many fish in a pond, or so many rabbits on an acre of land.

A couple of years ago I witnessed a remarkable demonstration of the power of exponential multiplication – and its inevitable consequences. I drained down one of my ponds for cleaning, removed the fish, cleaned the pond and refilled it. Then I went away for a few weeks without reintroducing fish. When I returned, the pond was green and the water was like soup. I knew the reason for this was the excessive multiplication of a single-celled swimming alga. I also knew that water fleas (daphnia) eat this kind of algae and, (in the absence of fish which, in the normal course of events, would eat the daphnia) wondered if the daphnia would multiply, consume the algae and thereby clear the water. I obtained some live daphnia from a local pet shop/aquarium and introduced about two teaspoons full of live daphnia to the pond. After 10 days I walked down to the pond to see if anything had happened. What I found was almost incredible. The pond water was no longer green but clear; the algae had been replaced by countless millions of water fleas. The whole pond seethed with them and I found it hard to believe that just two teaspoons of water fleas could, in such a short time, have exploded into the teeming mass before my eyes. A fascinating demonstration of the power of unrestricted exponential breeding and multiplication.

I came back again 3 weeks later and the pond was clear and empty. Upon careful inspection there were just a few water fleas still around. The billions had gone – starved to death. For those readers who are not mathematically minded I will explain that 'Exponential' means increasing in a simple progression such as continuously doubling or tripling the numbers. For example starting with 2, doubling to 4 then doubling to 8, then 16, then 32 and so on, or 3, 9, 27, 81, etc. It can be seen that the numbers take off rapidly. For instance, if there are plenty of nutrients, bacteria can double in 20 minutes. So, starting with only 2 bacteria then, after just 12 hours, there could be over 250 billion.

Since human beings now dominate the Earth and have no predators to fear, we can, if we choose, multiply like the water fleas, to the absolute limit of what the planet can feed. If we do that, the World is likely to be ruined in the process; hopelessly impoverished by the demands of the teeming millions. In any case there must be a finite limit to human numbers. There must come a day when to feed more finally becomes impossible. Whether we choose to limit our numbers voluntarily or not, there has to be a limit. A rational, sensible, intelligent race should be able to accept the facts and take the necessary voluntary action. Sadly, at the present stage of human development, I fear this will not be the case, and it is more likely to be a breakdown of organisation, biological disaster, starvation, or war, that will eventually terminate the expansion and reduce the numbers. We are approaching the crest of the wave of the industrial development of the World and the multiplication of the human race. We may reach numbers of 20 to 30 billion but, after the wave breaks, things will never be the same again. Many people will scoff at my projection of twenty to thirty billion people living on this planet, but remember, I have already seen the population climb from two billion to over six billion in my lifetime. Another lifetime like that and we would be approaching twenty billion.

In a thousand years from now I believe all will indeed have changed – whether we are sensible or not. Looking 1000 years ahead must, of course, be speculation but it is still, if we are careful, speculation based on facts and reasonable assumptions. The World in 1000 years from now will still be a 'hothouse'; the planet will be impoverished; many species of animals and plants will have gone extinct. There will be no oil, gas or coal. The human race will still be here but the numbers will probably have been drastically reduced. However, I do not intend to speculate here on wars, starvation, disease or other apocalyptic possibilities. Maybe people will be rational and cut the population sensibly, by birth control but, I confess, I doubt it. However, I foresee a future in a thousand years time where there are only 500 million people or fewer on the whole planet. A people who live together in harmony. Happy in simple things. With simple homes and simple possessions. A people who know and accept, without question, the necessity to keep the population at a static level – a level the Earth can sustain for a billion years. When they read the history books they will shake their heads in disbelief. How could such an insane population explosion have ever been allowed to happen and the crazy profligacy; the thoughtless plundering of land and sea; the terrible waste and loss of diversity on this fabulous planet. In a thousand years time no one will frantically strive to build a business. No one will talk of Expansion and Growth. No one will talk of Conquest and Empire. No one will bore holes in the ground for oil or gas or coal. They will be a simple people. They will have to be. They will co-operate. They will accept and work with each other and the Laws of Nature. They will live a simple life and they will be happy.

In a million years' time people will probably have changed very little. Maybe their brains will be 25% larger than ours. They will, however, have matured and will know the futility of strife. They will discuss problems sensibly and rationally, and all will abide by the majority decision. No violence. No Terrorism. No Hatred. Just Common Sense and Rational Thinking.

IN THE BEGINNING

For thousands of years, from the time the human race developed the ability for some degree of philosophical thought, people have pondered on the mystery of existence and how everything began. They attempted to explain the wonders and terrors around them, by inventing myths, religions and beliefs. For example, there is a myth in India postulating the Universe as being an endless cycle of Creation, Life and Destruction – over and over again. I was brought up as a Christian and I read the book of Genesis which described the Creation, "In the beginning God created the Heaven and the Earth ………….. and darkness was on the face of the deep ……………. and God said, let there be light …… " and so on.

One of the magical things about living at the present time, is that we have discovered so many scientific facts and now understand more than anyone ever has, in the history of the world. My brother agrees with me; if you have a curious mind – what a wonderful time to live. We now know that the Universe was not always as it is today; that it started in a stupendous explosion, known as the 'Big Bang', and developed gradually, over billions of years, to reach its present state. Remarkably, there actually was a dark age, and a moment when the first star flared into life and there are some scientists alive today who think the idea of the Universe exploding, existing, contracting, collapsing and exploding out again is a possibility. Scientists can now describe, with reasonable certainty, the conditions that existed in the early Universe, back to a time that was less than a millionth of a millionth of a second after the moment of creation – the Big Bang.

We now know what was created in the Big Bang; simple gases, i.e. hydrogen and helium, and a trace of other light elements. We know how these gases condensed into stars, and how the stars created a great many of the elements in the furnaces of their interiors. We also know how supernova blasts created the rest of the elements and scattered the materials into space. These would, in turn, condense to create the next cycle of stars, such as our own, with planets, some of which are capable of gradually creating and nurturing life. We understand, to a very great degree, the development of Life on Earth to the level we observe today. How fascinating that we have managed to learn all these things.

However, there are a few problems; a number of details that it is very difficult to understand. For Life to exist on this Earth, there are a range of remarkable situations that are vital. So many things in the Universe have to be 'just right', or life could not exist. Conditions in a star have to be exactly right to create the carbon which forms a substantial part of our bodies. Another vital factor is that water has to form ice which floats instead of sinks. Most liquids contract as they freeze; wax contracts as it solidifies and metals do the same. Water is different. When water solidifies it expands and, because of this, ice floats. If it did not, the Earth would long ago have become a ball of ice. If water behaved as most liquids do, and contracted as it froze, the ice would sink to the bottom and stay there. In warmer seasons, the ice would not completely melt as it does when on the surface; some would remain. Next winter – more ice would be added until, eventually, the whole lake or sea would be frozen solid from bottom to top. There is another remarkable factor in the strange manner in which water behaves. Liquids normally contract steadily as they cool; all the way down to the moment when they solidify. Water does not. It contracts to 4°C and then, remarkably, expands slightly, as it cools further, until reaching the point at which it freezes. So water at 3°C is less dense than water at 4°C. Because of this phenomenon, the transfer of heat in water by convection stops when the entire body of water cools to 4°C. Both of these features of water help to insulate the surface and prevent the body of water from cooling to freezing point and becoming a solid block. As a result, liquid water has always been available on our planet, which has allowed life to exist and evolve continuously over billions of years. There are so many of these absolutely vital details that it is a major puzzle – an enigma. If just one of a dozen or more critical details was different – we would not be here. What are the odds against such an apparently 'fine tuned' Universe happening by accident?

When told about our Universe and the Big Bang a child might reasonably ask. "What was before the Big Bang?" I once heard a scientist on TV, who was asked this question, say, "There was no 'before the Big Bang'. Even time itself was created in the Big Bang." But some men think differently! If there was no time – nothing could happen. If time stopped in the Universe all action and movement would freeze; not a single particle could change. Everything would be as if it had been photographed – a moment frozen in time. One of the men with different ideas is Alan H. Guth. Professor of Physics at M.I.T. Both he, and others, have pondered the child's question. Maybe there was a form of time; perhaps slightly different to ours, but time nevertheless and, if so, things could happen. I cannot go into Guth's reasoning too much here – any more than I could go into Einstein's 'Theory of Relativity' too deeply; if I did so with everything discussed in this book, it would be a foot (30cm) thick, or more! However, I can give you a brief summary of Guth's ideas. (Should you be deeply interested – I suggest you obtain his book, 'The Inflationary Universe'). Guth speculates that there was a bigger bang than our Big Bang; a vastly, enormously bigger Bang, in a Super Universe, and the rate of expansion of this Super Universe is fantastically greater than the rate of expansion of ours. There is evidence, and reason to believe that, when our Universe first exploded, it expanded at an immensely faster rate than it does now. There is reason to believe that it expanded millions of times faster for a minuscule moment in time; maybe – for a moment – similar to the natural rate of expansion of the 'Super Universe'.

Take a break! Leave this book and pour yourself a drink. Try lemonade or Cola – or even champagne. Notice how thousands of bubbles explode into being when you open the bottle and take off the pressure. Guth speculates – and backs it with mathematics – that the conditions in the Super Universe are such that it explodes outward, with incredible speed and, as it explodes, it generates little bubbles of energy. Each bubble explodes separately, at a slower speed, into a Universe, maybe like ours but, possibly, incredibly different. Imagine, if you will, a swimming pool full of champagne, with the pressure taken off. There would be a great many bubbles. Try to imagine the Solar System entirely filled with champagne or the whole of our Universe filled with foaming champagne! Even in this last scenario, the number of bubbles/universes would be absolutely nothing compared to the figures Guth visualises. If Guth is right, the Super Universe may have been expanding for, say, a million of our years or more, before our Universe was created. It may still be exploding outward at an incredible speed – fantastically greater than the speed of light, right now, as I write, having continuously exploded outwards for the fourteen billion years our Universe has been in existence, creating incalculable numbers of micro knots of energy – which will expand into universes – as it goes. The number of Universes would approach infinity. If you sat on a chair saying, one million million million million million ....million, for the rest of your life you would never match the figure. In those Universes there would be differences; some with light, some with no light, or with light but the speed of light different; some with elements similar to ours, some with water that sinks as it freezes, or where ice floats. Some of the Universes would be unimaginably different to ours. When you have the number of Universes approaching infinity – any possible combination of conditions and situations will arise somewhere. Occasionally you will have one that is just right for Life – as ours is. I have a feeling that Guth is right – in principle if not in detail. It is a more convincing scenario than anything else I have been presented with.

In saying that I have a feeling that Guth is right – in principle if not in detail, what I mean by that is that I think it very likely there are millions of Universes besides ours, whether Guth's scenario is right or

78

not. My reasoning is as follows:- On this Earth we find ourselves on the perfect planet. It is the right size, it is the right distance from the sun, it has the right amount of atmosphere, right temperature, liquid water and so on. Early philosophers, thousands of years ago, thinking there was only one planet – Earth – could only conclude it must have been planned by some Super Being. Today we know there are billions of stars and very probably billions of planets so – every so often there is a 'freak' planet that is perfect for life and we, of course, are on one of these. Similarly, if we find ourselves to be in a 'freak' Universe where everything happens to be 'just right' the simplest and most logical explanation, to me, is that there are probably billions of other similar but different Universes and we are in one of the few that happen to be suitable for life. With regard to the question of where did the Super Universe come from? Guth is even working on that.

If you are inclined to reject the idea of a Super Universe creating myriads of Universes such as ours from virtually nothing – merely micro-energy fluctuations – then I draw your attention to two remarkable features of our own Universe i.e. the one we live in. Firstly:- The mathematics of this Universe indicates that a gravitational field is, in fact, a negative energy field. Objects in a gravitational field are 'pulled in' to the centre (almost like a film of an explosion run backwards). On a cosmological scale it can be shown mathematically that the total gravitational energy in the Universe (total negative energy) is exactly equivalent to the total positive energy in the Universe – represented by all the matter (stars, planets and ourselves) plus radiation such as light etc. Therefore, the sum total of everything in this Universe appears to be zero. Secondly:- There is evidence that, on a sub-microscopic scale, the vacuum of this, our own, Universe is foaming with incalculable numbers of micro knots of energy. Every single cubic millimetre of space in our entire Universe is seething with activity. The energy fluctuations in the vacuum continuously create pairs of particles – one with positive energy and one with negative energy. These particles 'pop' into existence, exist for a very short period of time, then cancel each other out (their total combined energy is zero) and disappear. Near infinite numbers of these 'virtual' particles exist, momentarily, throughout the Universe, all the time. Now, maybe, Guth's ideas don't seem quite so impossible. In the Super Universe the vacuum would be seething, in a similar manner to ours. Instead of producing virtual particle pairs, whose sum total energy is zero, the Super Universe might be producing temporary positive energy/negative energy anomalies that explode into Universes such as ours. Instead of the extremely short existence time of the virtual particles in our Universe maybe the 'short' existence time in the Super Universe equates to trillions of years of our time. Maybe, if our Universe ever collapses back on itself, as some scientists think may happen, then instead of 'bouncing' i.e. exploding back out again, it will simply disappear – as our virtual particles do. If one thinks of the hope of Life, in the far, far future, the loss of our Universe would not matter as trillions of other Universes, some of which would be suitable for life, would be exploding into existence as ours disappears.

If you think these remarkable speculations are too much, possibly bordering on the absurd, pause to consider what has been discovered in the last few hundred years. It was not so long ago when human beings considered the Earth was the centre of the Universe. Diagrams exist showing the Earth as the centre of the Universe with Sun, Moon and planets all rotating about the Earth, and the stars shown as small sparkling objects, on a spherical fixed shell just outside the Solar System. Galileo was risking his life when, in the face of religious dogma, he declared the Earth was not the centre of the Solar System and stated, correctly, that the Sun was at the centre and the Earth was a satellite of the Sun. Faced with the threat of the Inquisition, he recanted; an action that was fully understandable in view of the alternative.

We now know that the Solar System is merely a minuscule part of our Galaxy – the Milky Way – and that there are more than a hundred billion Suns in this one Galaxy alone. The distance from the Earth to the Sun is a little over 8.3 light minutes. The distance across the Galaxy is roughly 100,000 light years. In other words three thousand, one hundred and sixty million times larger than the diameter of the Earth's orbit. We also know the distance we can see out into space, at the present time, is 13 billion light years and the limit of the visible Universe will be 14 billion light years radius – 28 billion light years diameter – which is two hundred and eighty thousand times larger than our Milky Way galaxy. Also, we have discovered that there are roughly a hundred billion other Galaxies; and our Universe goes on, far beyond the volume we will ever see.

Nature, for want of a better expression, is not afraid of large numbers or large dimensions; and who are we to say what is large and what is small. When we consider the stunning expansion of our ideas of the size of our Universe, in the last few hundred years, then Guth's ideas of a Super Universe become more acceptable. The brain begins to realise that, because the concepts and numbers are stunning, this does not make them impossible. If Galileo had suggested, not only that the Earth was not the centre of the Universe, but that the Earth was less than a speck of dust in the totality that was our Universe, his suggestions would have been dismissed as the ravings of a lunatic.

It is almost impossible for the brain to grasp the real immensity of the Universe we live in. If we consider the number of stars, for instance, with say a hundred billion stars in a galaxy and around a hundred billion galaxies, that implies around 10^{22} stars in the visible Universe. To give you a clue as to what that figure really means let us consider a grain of coarse sand as being about 1 cubic millimetre. Then one cubic metre would be one billion grains. To have a quantity of sand with as many grains as there are stars in the Universe you would have to cover the surface of the entire UK with sand 50 metres (164 feet) deep or, if you are American, cover the entire surface of California 25 metres (82 feet) deep. As if that was not stunning enough, we are also now aware that, when our Universe first came into being, the entire Universe, with all the energy and matter represented by the myriad Galaxies and stars we see today, was far smaller than the size of a single atom.

(Some scientists have suggested the Universe exploded out of a Singularity. I am not a cosmologist or a great mathematician but, on the basis of the maths I do know, I cannot see how this conjecture can be correct. The word Singularity means 'of zero size'. Mathematically it is not possible to explode (expand) anything from zero size. If I write .000001 cm it means one millionth of a centimetre. If I write 1000000 it means one million. Multiply the first by the second figure and what do we get? One centimetre! Just imagine I had a strip of paper from here to Australia (or all the way to the Moon or Mars for that matter) and I printed two rows of noughts, one above the other, along the whole length of the strip. When I have finished I print a decimal point at the front of the top row and a 1 cm at the end. I then print a 1 at the front of the bottom row and another 0 on the end. The top figure represents a size which is utterly incomprehensibly small (but it is not zero). The bottom row represents a figure which is utterly incomprehensibly large (but it is not infinity). Multiply the one row by the other and what do you get? One centimetre! Multiply that 1 centimetre by a figure with a 1 at the front and just 30 noughts behind it, which I can do across the width of just one sheet of notepaper, and we are talking of a size much bigger than the total diameter of the observable Universe. Now, perhaps, you have some grasp of what the words zero and infinity really mean. And zero even multiplied by infinity is still zero. Nothing can be expanded from zero size).

So, in the beginning, the Universe was an almost incredible sub-microscopic fireball at unimaginable temperatures and pressures. Unimaginable but not incalculable. Scientists can work out the conditions that existed a mere one millionth of a millionth of a second after the beginning. As the fireball expanded, some of the energy was converted into particles, including the first building blocks of matter – the quarks. As the Universe expanded and cooled further, the quarks grouped together to produce protons and so on. Eventually, at the end of the fiery 'genesis' phase, the Universe contained only the very simplest of substances – hydrogen, helium and traces of other light elements. So, after the initial phase of creation, the Universe was simply filled with great clouds of gas. Nothing else existed. However, small density fluctuations existed in the great clouds of gas and, over millions of years, local concentrations developed which collapsed under the effects of gravity. In the interiors of the concentrations the heat of compression built up, until nuclear fires were ignited and the first stars flared into life. Most of the first stars would be far more massive than our Sun, and would race through their thermonuclear lives at a far greater pace, creating in their interiors many of the elements we need for life on Earth. When thermonuclear fusion ended, these heavy stars would collapse and, in collapsing, generate a final immense blast of energy which would explode most of the star and throw much of the material that had been created in the interior into space. In the brief cataclysmic moment of a supernova explosion, the heaviest elements – gold, uranium, platinum and so on were created, to be thrown out with the rest and scattered as dust across space. Only a collapsed final remnant of the star – a neutron star or a black hole – would remain. The dust and gas, spread through space by the supernova explosion, would drift, and mix with hydrogen clouds left over from the initial burst of star formation and, in a second wave of collapse and star creation, would produce stars like our own Sun with planets formed from the remnant materials of the older supernova.

So – everything we see – mountains, rivers, plants, animals, and our friends – are all formed from materials created in the furnace interior of a star, and blasted into space by the detonation at its ending. A Miracle of Creation indeed!

LIFE AND EVOLUTION

From time immemorial human beings have wondered – "Where have we come from? How have all the living things we see, come to be?" Legends and myths were created and people pondered. Now we need ponder no longer. The 'Book of Life' is there – written in the rocks. All we need to do is to bother to read it.

We can follow the evidence back to the first human beings and back and back to when the very first simple animals crawled in the ooze of an ancient seabed. Further back still, to a time before the animals, when we find evidence of colonies of bacteria (stromatolites) on a distant seashore. And even further back, to a time nearly four thousand million years ago where there are still traces of single celled archaic bacteria. What we cannot yet do is know how the first living cell was created from inert chemicals in the early sea. All we can do is speculate on the distant origins. However, we know for sure it happened because we have proof. If it had not – we would not be here! Taking the information from the rocks and the knowledge we now have about cellular construction – particularly the details and instructions encoded in the DNA – we can now deduce a history of Life on Earth and better understand what is going on at the present time and where it is likely to lead in the future.

Life on Earth probably started from one of the simple chain molecules that often form when chemicals are dissolved in a solvent, such as water. Atoms of various substances link together – attracted by electrical forces to form molecules that may be very simple – sometimes comprising just a few atoms but, occasionally, more complex, possibly containing hundreds of atoms, to form the single smallest molecule of a particular compound. Some complex molecules have the property of attracting other, similar, molecules and locking together – almost like Lego bricks. These can form chains and loops and other arrangements. Benzene, for instance, has a molecule where the chain has extended, looped and formed into a ring. In a vast warm sea, bombarded by heat and radiation, this type of reaction can easily happen. One such chain is RNA or, to give it its full name, Ribo Nucleic Acid. This particular chain has the property of attracting other nearby atoms to join together, in the same pattern, alongside the original chain – in the same way you might form a chain of Lego bricks, red, blue, yellow, green, and so on and then attach more blocks alongside with red against red, blue against blue, etc. The bonding of the atoms along the chain is stronger than the side-to-side bonding, and the second chain may strip away from the first and float away on its own. The process may be repeated. What you have is a simple self-replicating molecule.

In a similar way, other molecules link together to form sheets – think of a film of oil on static water. If such a film is formed and then agitated – say by pounding waves – the film can be broken up. It can then form globules or sometimes bubbles. We therefore could have an active and violent primordial sea, with trillions of pieces of RNA floating around, and molecular films being pounded by the waves to form bubbles – some of which will end up containing a little chain molecule of RNA. This in itself would be nothing remarkable but, in the vast oceans of the early Earth, the numbers of these bubbles existing, simultaneously over the whole globe, must have been immense. At the same time, the Earth was being bombarded by energetic radiation, such as ultra violet from the sun, and other hard radiation – x-rays and cosmic rays from space. Gamma rays are also produced by the natural rocks of the Earth, which happens to this day. (Granite is quite radioactive, a fact which can be easily checked with a Geiger counter). Energetic photons of ultra violet radiation can also act to trigger changes and modifications to molecular structures. No one knows how, but, somehow, the whole assembly of lipid bubble plus RNA must have become self-replicating – the building block of the first form of life! It only needed one, out of the countless trillions of bubble/RNA assemblies in the world's oceans, to be modified to do the trick, and the self-replication would spread, as a chain reaction, through the oceans of the world. Eventually, the sea would become a soup of these microscopic, self-replicating RNA/bubbles. Some people are sceptical, but it is pointed out that, in the world's oceans today, it is estimated there are roughly 2×10^{28} living bacteria and microscopic organisms. That is, 20 thousand million, million, million, million. In the original primordial soup, that was Earth's early ocean, there would be far more, and this soup had all the time in the world – maybe millions of years, for the freak event to occur which produced the first truly living cell. It only needed one – to start the endless chain of life that culminates in modern life forms.

In this Universe anything that is remotely, remotely, possible is likely to occur somewhere, because of the sheer numbers involved; the immense numbers of atoms and molecules, the immense numbers of stars and planets in this galaxy and the immense numbers of galaxies in the Universe. Every possible variation in conditions – heat, cold, pressure, solid, liquid, radiation, magnetic fields, electric fields, lightning, exist. Somewhere, freak things can and do happen all the time.

However, all this is, of course, speculation. There is no evidence from that time. All we know for sure is that life does exist on this planet and there is fossil evidence indicating it has progressed and evolved here from primitive single cellular life to modern complex animals and plants over an extended period of nearly four thousand million years. Therefore, somewhere on this Earth or somewhere else, life did, somehow, start from inert chemicals, perhaps in a process similar to that I have described.

I mentioned the possibility of life starting somewhere else. The idea of life being brought to the Earth in meteorites or comets or even in cosmic dust is called Panspermia. Panspermia cannot be ruled out as impossible but I regard it as less likely than that life started spontaneously here, on this planet. I suspect anyone trying to create life from inanimate chemicals in a test tube would be wasting their time. In all the vast oceans of the world it may still have taken a million years or more for the first spark of life to appear. Somehow it did and we are here as living proof.

Scientists are very keen to search for evidence of life on Mars and, possibly on moons such as Titan and Europa. Ideally they would like to find actual living cells that they could take into the laboratory and study. If, for instance, they found life forms, such as bacteria, on Mars that had a similar construction and genetic mechanism (RNA and DNA) to our Earth bacteria it would strongly indicate some link – some common ancestry or origin. It would suggest possible transfer from Mars to Earth or Earth/Mars. (Remarkably a piece of rock from Mars – blasted into space by a meteorite impact on that planet – was discovered on the ice near the South Pole, proving that such a thing can happen). If, instead, they found what was undeniably life but with a different structure and genetic code it would immediately suggest separate genesis, indicating that life in the Universe is probably common and can be expected to be found on any planet or moon in any solar system, which has suitable conditions.

So – when the first self-replicating life form on Earth appeared, it would then multiply, in a chain reaction, until all the world's oceans were saturated and all the nutrients in the water used up. Because of the nature of chain reactions, this would occur remarkably quickly (in geological terms), probably only a few thousand years or less. When all the chemicals in the sea had been used up, there would be countless trillions of cells floating around, which could not replicate because of the shortage of nutrients. However, radiation and variations in the environment would destroy some of these primitive cells and turn loose their component molecules to be acquired and reused by other cells for self-replication. This situation may have applied for thousands or millions of years until, eventually, a modification took place which changed a cell, in such a way that it could cause the destruction of a nearby cell itself and take its components for self-replication. At this point, evolutionary life could be said to have started. The new, more complex cells would rapidly destroy all the old type cells and fill all the oceans until only the new cells existed. Then, the only way for the improved cell to replicate would again be to destroy a similar neighbour to obtain the necessary nutrients. The endless chain of living, killing, reproduction and defence commenced, that brutal competition that continues unabated to this day.

From that point, nearly 4000 million years ago, the destruction, new assembly and endless occasional modifications have finally resulted in the incredibly complex life forms that abound on this planet, including you and I. At some point, probably billions of years ago, a more efficient self-replicating molecule was created – the double strand helical molecule known as DNA (De oxy ribo Nucleic Acid). This molecule can form chains, billions of molecular assemblies long, and can be copied with remarkable accuracy. At some point, probably around 700 million years ago, the seas must have been full of highly complex solitary cells of life endlessly warring and competing for nutrients – the chemicals of energy and self-replication. Eventually two cells, instead of trying to destroy one another, must have worked together to destroy a third. This must have proved very effective, and led to more and more cooperation of larger and larger groups of cells, acting to destroy single cells and then other smaller cellular groups. Cooperation must have eventually extended to the situation where some cells of the group did one job, and other cells another, to more efficiently achieve what no single cell could possibly do. Here we now had what could be called an organism. To work together effectively the cells had to develop signalling systems – possible with the tremendous potential of the DNA molecule.

With better, and bigger, cooperative groupings of cells, various developments took place. The first animals describable as such, were probably no more than mobile lumps of slime, crawling about the rocks of the seabed, but with chemical weapons such as enzymes to attack and destroy other organisms.

It is interesting to note that, at this present day, there exists a very primitive form of life called a slime mould, which is a form of fungus. In the presence of nutrients – food – the fungus merely spreads like other common moulds into a large patch of goo. However, when the food is all used up, a remarkable thing happens. The great mass of similar fungus cells begins to change. The goo breaks up into smaller pieces, and then each small piece gradually gathers together and forms a shape similar to a miniature garden slug. Then, amazingly, each little group of fungus cells begins to cooperate. Various cells form the base, other cells form the front-end, others the rear, and so on. The little slug then becomes mobile and crawls off to search for food elsewhere. Incredible! But it actually happens. If the little slug finds more food before it runs out of energy, it then changes back to being a normal fungus and spreads and consumes the food in a new cycle. If it does not find food it eventually gives up, reverts to fungus mode – puts up a stalked fruiting body, a miniature mushroom you might say, produces spores to blow on the wind – like many other fungi – and dies. Fascinating! Is this a clue to what the very first animals on this Earth were like?

After a truly immense period of time – about three thousand, four hundred million years – at roughly 600 million years ago, the breakthrough to complex multi celled organisms was made. The new DNA double helix chain molecule could be programmed to reproduce any combination of cells and chemical devices imaginable. The result is called the Cambrian Explosion when, suddenly (that means over a few million years), an immense range of different organisms, animals and plants appeared. It was as if the groups of cooperating cells were experimenting, to see which arrangement worked best to ensure survival. Mobile organisms – animals – abounded in all sorts of weird and strange configurations. Other organisms formed plants. All large organisms (which means anything big enough to be seen with the naked eye) used the double strand DNA molecule as the basis of life. The evolutionary battles for survival between all these different experiments resulted in the most bizarre and weird configurations being weeded out. Only the most efficient and successful survived to carry on to develop further.

At some time – probably about 450 million years ago – certain groups of animals became fixed in their basic arrangements. One group became jellyfish, another crustaceans, another fish, and so on. So the process of competition, killing, reproduction and modification continued. In the very early stages of evolution, change must have depended on chance mutations; modifications induced by radiation and chemical actions. Nearly all changes induced in this way would merely be damage, and would result in the early death of a cell, or it's becoming less competitive than its neighbour. Very rarely, a mutation would be beneficial. It is probably because of this, that early evolution was so slow. Nevertheless, a single modern bacterial cell has evolved to be an almost unbelievably intricate life form. The evolutionary development, required to achieve the complexity of a single bacterial cell, is probably as great as, or greater than, the development from single cell to complex modern animal. It is easy to overlook this fact.

As life developed, a new way to speed evolution came into being; sexual reproduction. In the early days – one cell might develop a mutation that conferred a slight advantage; another might develop a different mutation – again giving a slight advantage. In some cases a combination of the two mutations might be far more effective. Sexual reproduction, by which genes from one cell were mixed, in random combinations, with genes from another cell, soon selected the most effective arrangements. Sexual reproduction speeded up evolution. (Single bacterial cells often conjoin, temporarily, with other bacterial cells to swap genes). With the development of multi cellular animals and plants, the problem of gene transfer was difficult but, eventually, the system of sperm transfer of genes to eggs was perfected. Primitive plants developed in the sea, and in shallow waters, using light to achieve photosynthesis.

The early Earth probably had an atmosphere of nitrogen, carbon dioxide, methane and ammonia. The first life forms would have had to survive and evolve in these conditions. Some bacteria from this era – anaerobic bacteria – survive to this day. At some point photosynthesis evolved, where sunlight was used to trigger chemical reactions – the breaking down of carbon-dioxide and the splitting of water molecules to produce hydrogen and oxygen. The hydrogen would be used to create carbohydrates and the oxygen ejected as waste. In this way, the conversion of the original atmosphere to an oxygen rich atmosphere began. In the early days the sea was rich in dissolved iron compounds. These, reacting with the new oxygen, produced insoluble iron oxide compounds, which were precipitated to produce the iron rich rocks we see today. At one time the sea was probably red from pole to pole – not blue, as we now know it. The iron would combine with nearly all the oxygen freed by photosynthetic bacteria and algae, and very little would be retained in the atmosphere, until all the iron in the sea had been converted and deposited on the sea floor. It would take a very long time for life to produce enough oxygen to combine with and precipitate, all the iron from solution in the sea – probably millions of years. Levels of free oxygen in the atmosphere and in the sea water would remain very low for nearly all of this time and would only increase very slowly. This gave time for life forms to adapt to the new conditions and, finally, metabolise the previously poisonous oxygen. Oxygen is a very reactive gas and rapidly combines with other elements. Oxygen will be a very significant marker when we are able to detect other 'Earth-like' planets. The presence of free oxygen in the atmosphere would be a strong indicator of life on that planet. (The oxygen on this Earth is continually being replenished by living things, through photosynthesis. If, somehow, life was suddenly, totally, destroyed then the oxygen in the atmosphere would slowly disappear).

One of the side effects of an oxygen atmosphere is the generation of a high level layer of ozone, which, fortunately, is very effective in blocking ultra violet radiation coming from the sun. On this Earth a high level of UV radiation would have made it very difficult for life to colonise the land. So, gradually, as UV was blocked by the new ozone, life came out of the sea and edged on to the land. Mosses developed around the margins. Even today some primitive plants still use the swimming sperm means of gene transfer. Gradually, over time, the first land plants developed new methods, at first – spores and then a modified gene transfer system, pollen, which would carry on the air, or be transferred by insects. These changes enabled plants to spread far and wide. The first sea animals began to come onto land to exploit the food potential of the plants. Animals like millipedes and woodlice were probably the first. Gradually, insects developed and swarmed onto the land. New methods of breathing the oxygen rich atmosphere evolved. Fish began to crawl up the beaches and mud flats – as mudskippers still do today – to feast on the insects, but having to return to the water frequently.

Fish can, in fact, take oxygen from the air, if the gills are kept moist and the air is allowed to flow over them freely. (Many people do not seem to realise this and think that fish will suffocate rapidly in air in a similar manner to the way we do in water. When I was a youth I saw a pike, (a large predatory freshwater fish) which had been out of water on the bank for five or six hours, recover completely when returned to the water. It was a damp November day. The fish's gills stayed moist and it was able to take oxygen from the air). The ancient fish gradually developed some form of lungs. Interestingly enough, a large sea fish existing today (the Tarpon) has a modification to its swim bladders to enable it to breathe air. It has developed a type of lung tissue and, under stress, breathes air as well as water. I was amazed when I first caught Tarpon. The fish came to the surface near the boat and gasped – like a dolphin – every few minutes while it was on my line. The fish was taking oxygen from the water with its gills, in the normal manner but boosting its power and stamina by breathing air at the same time. I visited the International Game Fish Association in Miami and was told baby Tarpon retreat to brackish, low oxygen, water to escape predators and had evolved this lung tissue – which continued to exist and function in the adult fish. It is probable that fish, similar to the modern mud skippers, developed a similar trick, to enable them to stay out of the water for longer periods of time.

Gradually the first land animals, like newts and frogs developed; then came the lizards and true reptiles. Mosses developed into ferns and giant horsetails and then the first trees. About two hundred and eighty million years ago, there was a devastating mass extinction event, which wiped out around 90% of all species on the Earth. Recently, geologists have discovered an enormous crater in Antarctica under the ice, which is suspected of being the site of a meteorite or comet impact – perhaps the one that caused this, the Permian Extinction. We shall have to wait until the scientists drill down through the ice, and obtain samples of the rock for dating, before it can be confirmed. If the impact crater in the Antarctic is confirmed and if its date matches the date of the Permian Extinction then it is probable the impacting body was a comet. We know the one that caused the Dinosaur Extinction, sixty five million years ago, was an asteroid because it left a calling card. Asteroids are known to be rich in a rare element – iridium – and scientists found there was a thin layer of iridium rich deposit, sixty five million years old, over the entire planet. Since there is no similar deposit associated with the Permian Extinction, any large impacting body, at that time, is most likely to have been a comet. (Comets are, of course, mainly ice but a comet impacting at 70,000 miles (112,651 kilometres) an hour would cause the same damage as an asteroid of the same weight. A ton of ice would have the same impact energy as a ton of rock or a ton of iron.

Life gradually recovered and there came about an age of cold-blooded reptiles. At some point, probably 210 to 220 million years ago, a breakthrough to warm blooded animals was made. Warm blood confers numerous advantages, the most important being enhanced metabolism, activity, stamina and speed, and the ability to operate efficiently in a range of temperatures. This gives warm-blooded animals an enormous competitive advantage in normal conditions. The downside is the need for far greater quantities of food – most of which is used for the purpose of keeping the body warm. Most people think that, in the sea, only whales and dolphins have warm blood, but this is not totally correct. Certain species of fish – Tuna fish, Swordfish and some sharks such as Mako are also warm blooded, to a degree. These fish do not have a controlled body temperature as most land animals do, but simply maintain body temperature well above ambient, i.e. the surrounding sea temperatures. Such fish are fast predators that need extra speed and stamina to catch prey. (Swordfish have been clocked, stripping line off a reel, at speeds up to 70 mph (113km)). For water breathing animals, keeping warm is more difficult than for an air breather. Water conducts and strips heat from the body far more rapidly than air does. To cope with this, warm-blooded fish have an efficient 'heat exchanger' system, to prevent blood losing heat through the gills; a contra flow heat exchanger system as good as any an engineer might contrive.

From the warm-blooded reptile on land, two species evolved; one was the superbly efficient type of animal generally termed Dinosaurs, the other is the mammals. (I have explained why I am convinced Dinosaurs were warm blooded in the chapter – DINOSAURS). To reduce heat losses in cool climates the mammals evolved, and converted the original scales, inherited from the fish, into hair. Some of the dinosaurs converted the fish scales into a new, elaborate form, which became feathers. Members of both species which adapted to living in warm areas of the Earth, simply kept a leathery skin. Of the two – dinosaurs and mammals – the dinosaurs were undoubtedly the most efficient and successful.

Mammals, although they did not go extinct, clung on, but were forced down by unremitting predation into small, specialised, mammal variants, mainly insect eaters, hiding in rocks and boulders, or burrowing in the ground and relying for survival mainly on an enhanced ability to breed rapidly. Dinosaurs dominated the entire planet – on land, in the air and even back in the sea. Their ability to differentiate into new species and take over all available niches was unsurpassed.

A great many people think it is only mammals that produce live young. This is incorrect. Some snakes produce live young, as do some fish, for example Manta rays and several species of shark. The young are attached to the mother, and are fed through an umbilical cord in a similar manner to mammals. The word mammal simply means milk feeder; nothing to do with producing live young. There actually is an egg laying mammal still in existence – the platypus – a primitive mammal in Australia. Some dinosaurs also produced live young.

I am not a palaeontologist and I know there is still much controversy about land dinosaurs, pterosaurs and marine reptiles. However, from what I do know, I am inclined to conclude they were all variants of the extremely adaptable animals whose land representatives are called dinosaurs. For want of a group name and to keep this book simple I have therefore, linked Land Dinosaurs, Pterosaurs, Archaeopterix, Ichthyosaurs and Plesiosaurs under one group heading – Dinosaurs. (See Chapter – DINOSAURS). (Some people would raise their eyebrows at my inclusion of Ichthyosaurs and Plesiosaurs as part of an overall warm blooded 'Dinosaur' grouping but there is evidence that they were descended from Dinosaur type land animals that returned to the sea. This immediately raises the possibility that they too were warm blooded. After all, land mammals returned to the sea, in a similar way, to produce the whales and dolphins and they have retained warm blood despite making the sea their permanent home). The ichthyosaurs and plesiosaurs living in the sea solved the problem of reproducing in the sea, in the same way as modern dolphins and whales, by producing live young. Primitive animals like turtles have never solved the problem. A 20-ton marine dinosaur could never have crawled up a beach to lay eggs, as turtles do (some marine dinosaurs are believed to have exceeded 100 tons). Fossils of plesiosaurs have been found with fossilised baby plesiosaurs inside them.

The idea of dinosaurs as lumbering, brainless, limited creatures is hopelessly inaccurate. This view was simply generated because the first dinosaur fossils found were the most massive of the dinosaur range – mainly enormous herbivores and the accompanying large predators. Large herbivores, even today, are not usually noted for brains or sophisticated development. The elephant, of course, is an exception. The highest level of development of the dinosaurs was probably that of the small and medium sized raptors. The fossilised skeletons of some of these, indicate remarkable brain development. It is interesting to note that one of today's descendents of the dinosaurs – the parrot – has been found to be amazingly intelligent – almost as intelligent as a dog or chimpanzee, despite having a brain no bigger than a walnut. Many birds show remarkable capabilities.

The incredible range of birds now existing on this planet – all descended from one feathered dinosaur survivor of the great extinction at the end of the Cretaceous period – is testament to the amazing versatility and adaptability of the dinosaur species. Indeed, a version of the large, dangerous land dinosaurs almost made a comeback, just a few thousand years ago, developing back from the birds. In Argentina the fossilised remains of a massive, Moa size, bird with an enormous predatory beak – but still without teeth – was found, dating back only a few thousand years. The beak was so powerful it would have been capable of chopping through a mans leg as easily as a pair of scissors would cut through a straw. However it was too late. Once the mammals had taken over the world, there was no going back. Land dinosaurs had the disadvantage of laying eggs. Eggs and young could be destroyed, once mammals had gained the upper hand.

Having considered the evidence, I am of the opinion feathers probably evolved, originally, for insulation, i.e. thermal protection against heat loss in cold climates. The small, feathered dinosaurs would, of course, be attacked by predators and the ability to run at high speed would have been a primary defensive adaptation. In this situation, the proto-bird would run on its hind legs and use the feathered front legs for balancing. Air would catch the feathers and assist in balancing. Gradually, the feathers would evolve to become more efficient for the balancing process, until an aerodynamic configuration resulted. This would develop, until a burst of speed would enable the animal to leap into the air and glide a short distance. Then, flapping of the primitive wings would extend the glide. From this situation it was only a matter of time to achievement of true powered flight.

Some people argue that flight was achieved because of a proto-bird living in trees and gliding from tree to tree – like the modern day 'sugar glider' – a type of gliding squirrel. I personally think not! My reasons are – many birds today rely on running speed to evade predators and only fly when running is inadequate, or fly into trees to escape predators. That is what the pheasants in my garden tend to do. Also, it is noticeable – on islands where there are no effective predators, birds often lose the ability to fly. Then they sometimes grow larger; heavy weight and flight, however, do not go easily together. The 'Dodo' comes to mind – a type of king sized, flightless pigeon. Everything on its island was fine until a major predator – man – arrived. Rapidly the Dodo went extinct; as did the Moa in New Zealand and the Elephant bird of Madagascar.

I was extremely impressed when I first saw flying fish near Florida. Previously, I was of the impression that flying fish, to escape predators, developed a burst of speed, leapt from the water and glided twenty or fifty yards before dropping back. I was amazed to see a flying fish leap from the water, glide a few yards and then start to flap its large wing like fins to extend the glide. The fish actually flew – powered flight – for 150 to 200 metres (488 to 650 feet). I think birds on land would have passed through a similar stage. (I remember, in New Zealand, at dinner one night, chatting to a lady. Somehow the conversation got around to fish and I told her about the flying fish I had seen when I was fishing near Florida. She listened with a little smile on her face, and when I had finished, the smile was still there. I asked her if she believed me. "Of course not"! she replied, "I'm not that stupid"! I smiled and left it at that. One day she may discover I was not lying). I think it is more likely to be bats, the flying mammals, that would have evolved from tree dwelling animals like the sugar glider, that learned to glide and finally fly, and also the pterosaur type of flying dinosaur. Both of these animals are, and were, very ungainly on the ground. Many birds are very efficient runners. The pheasants in my garden can run like the proverbial 'roadrunner' – like rockets; faster than I can run! They fly to cover longer distances, or to get into trees to roost at night. Around the garden they prefer to run; if trapped or surprised they fly.

200 million years ago the dinosaurs reigned supreme. Nothing on the planet could compete with them. If you look at the evidence with an open unbiased mind, you begin to realise how dominant the dinosaurs must have been. If there had been only mammals descended from the warm-blooded reptile precursor, then mammals would have totally taken over the planet. You might have had whales, dolphins, elephants, tigers, mammoths and possibly something like homo-sapiens, a hundred million years ago. It did not happen! Why? Because the dinosaurs were simply

superior to mammals. It is the only possible conclusion. To restrict the development of mammals, as they did, for a hundred and forty million years, they must have been dominant and superior for all that time.

Only one thing could stop the dinosaurs and, after a hundred and forty million years of total domination, it finally did. A massive asteroid came from space and struck the Earth at a place called Chicxulub on the Yucatan peninsula of Mexico. (I have described the enormity of the impact in the Chapter DINOSAURS). From the ruination of the planet just a handful of species survived. The disaster gave the mammals the one chance for domination they needed. In the immediate aftermath, the surviving mammals used their one great weapon – the ability to reproduce at breakneck speed, to flood the planet and conquer the remaining dinosaurs with sheer numbers. After the disaster the Earth would initially explode with insect life which, in turn, would fuel the mammal population explosion. If there were mammals big enough to kill the dinosaur young and eat the eggs, in other words – rat-sized mammals, the few remaining dinosaurs would be doomed; swamped by sheer numbers. Only the feathered, flying dinosaurs, perhaps living on islands the mammals could not reach, survived.

Being related to the dinosaurs, the mammals too had enhanced potential for development and diversification. So mammals finally, after 140 million years of domination by the dinosaurs, took over the Earth. In order to survive predation by the now dominant mammals most of the birds stayed small and, when possible, nested in inaccessible or mammal free areas; a practice which has continued to this day.

I have noted, in the last few years, it has become fashionable for some scientists to say that mass extinctions have been beneficial; that they have been a stimulus to evolution. I do not subscribe to this view and suspect half the reason for saying such a thing is because we – Homo Sapiens – now exist. They believe, and I agree with them, that without the Chiczulub asteroid impact that wiped out the Dinosaurs we would not be here. Massive extinction events, of whatever cause, have undoubtedly changed history and spurred rapid evolutionary change in whatever life forms survived. After all, the planet is suddenly theirs with a million and one niches available to them that were not there before. Species that had been, hitherto, not very successful suddenly prosper. However, can a mass extinction that wipes out 70% or more of life on Earth really be called beneficial. After an extinction event, evolution continues, on an impoverished planet, and what we see today is testament to the resilience and adaptability of life. However, it is not necessarily better or more advanced than it would have been and I am more inclined to the view that mass extinctions, every time they occur, simply set back evolution by many millions of years. A massive asteroid strike, for instance, puts a bomb under the Darwinian principle of survival of the fittest. The strike may allow the survival of the less fit for various reasons including sheer luck.

A Chiczulub size strike right now, as an example, would, very likely, exterminate the human race and all the other large animals and take us back to the stage where rats and mice were the most important survivors. The planet would, in effect, be taken back to similar conditions to those which existed after the Chiczulub strike. If massive asteroid strikes were more common – say every 20 million years or so, evolution would probably be stalled indefinitely. If the human race, as is quite possible in the next 200 years, managed to cause the extinction of 70% of large animal species on the planet, would the scientists still say "Mass extinctions are, in the long run, beneficial"? I doubt it! Finally I will point out that in the sixty five million years of evolution since the Dinosaurs were destroyed, only one animal can really be said to be superior to the Dinosaurs and that is ourselves. There is not another animal alive on the planet today that the Dinosaurs could not have successfully competed with.

Nevertheless the speed of change and evolution of life, in the last sixty five million years since the Great Dinosaur Extinction, is remarkable, compared to the slower rate of evolution in the previous 3900 million years. I have thought about this carefully and suggest simple Darwinian Evolution is inadequate to properly explain it. By simple Darwinian Evolution, I mean waiting for mutations and occasional improvements to accumulate. I feel there are other factors at work to drastically speed evolution. Perhaps we inherited far more than just warm blood from our warm-blooded reptile ancestors; the built-in ability to adapt.

Let us consider the facts. Human beings, for instance, have an inherent ability to adapt – without waiting for mutations or aberrations. A classic example is adaptation to high altitudes. Let us imagine that the Earth's atmosphere was slowly being lost so that, over thousands of years, we lost, say, 30% of our atmospheric pressure. The air would be thinner; it would be more difficult to extract enough oxygen during breathing. According to simple Darwinian Evolution, mutations would occur, here and there, and some would have a better, more efficient, oxygen transfer system. Because of this, their survival rate would be better than the norm, their numbers would gradually increase and the species would slowly evolve to the new type, with improved oxygen transfer. However, what is reality? Reality is that the human race could evolve much more rapidly, and could change to cope with such conditions almost immediately. An example of this, is the rapid adaptation of an ordinary human being to high altitude, where the condition I described can be experienced after a few hours climbing. Experienced mountain climbers are very well aware of their adaptive capabilities. Before tackling the highest mountains, they spend weeks or months "acclimatising". They climb up the mountains to 16,000 ft (4,923m), stay there a few days and come back down. A week later they then go up to 17,000 ft (5,230m), stay a few days, and so on. In response to the short term oxygen deprivation the body responds. The spleen enlarges and produces more red blood cells, so as to extract oxygen more efficiently from the rarefied air, and carry adequate supplies for the body's metabolism. By the time these climbers tackle Mount Everest, their blood is very different to yours and mine. They have far more blood cells, and their lungs become more efficient. When they come down and live in the normal low level conditions, their bodies will re-adapt to low-level conditions quite rapidly. If they stayed at high altitudes, the adaptation they experienced would become permanent – as it is for people who continuously and normally live high up in the mountains of the Andes, or Tibet. Humans don't need to wait for mutations to cope with that problem.

It is not really remarkable that Ethiopian and Kenyan runners do so well in long distance athletic events. Their oxygen transfer and transport system has become more efficient than the norm, because they were bred and born at a higher altitude. We all know that if a man over-stresses his muscles time and time again, those muscles will develop, to an amazing degree, to cope with the extra loading. What is not so well known, is that bones will also react and develop. Bones are actually living tissue, not just a stony framework. Built into the bones is a sensor system that detects stress. If bones are overstressed, then more bone cells are added until the stress is at an acceptable level. It is possible to look at the skeleton of someone who died in the middle ages and say – "This man was an archer"! The bones of his arms are thicker and stronger than normal – to cope with the stress of pulling an English Longbow. (The force required is a lot greater than the average man today could apply).

It was quite predictable that, when man stayed in zero 'G' conditions for long periods of time in the Space Station, there would be trouble. The sensors in the bones detected low stress and signalled for removal of bone cells. (The body only builds the skeleton it needs and no more. For example, long periods in bed can cause bone loss). For human beings on a long space trip – to Mars for instance – in order to retain normal bones and body tone, either artificial gravity (a rotating system of some kind), or violent regular exercise, would be needed.

The human body then, is very adaptable. Other animals are too. I remember reading about a large, refrigerated, food storage plant somewhere in the U.K. Mice managed to get in, survive and breed. In a very short time, the mice became little powder puff balls of fur, to cope with the cold. They did not wait for Darwinian Evolution. They adapted – fast! Even some fish can also adapt – surprisingly rapidly. I sometimes fish for pike – a large predatory fish – on the Norfolk Broads in England. Some of the pike have exceptionally broad, flat heads. The reason is – some of the Broads are full of bream – a large flat-sided fish – on which the pike feed. In order to swallow these, the pike develop the distinctive head.

The common brown trout is also remarkably adaptable. In small streams, with very little in the way of food supplies, the trout will mature and breed at a mere 9 or 10 inches (230mm to 250mm) in length. Transfer these fish to a richer, larger stream and, in a couple of generations, you have large plump trout. In a chalk stream, with plenty of insects, the trout's mouth is small. Transfer them to a lake, where there are many small fish, and the trout will develop a large, sometimes enormous, mouth for catching the rapidly moving prey fish. Placed in a large river near the sea, the brown trout can undergo an even more remarkable change. Under normal conditions, in fresh water, the fish has to have a protective layer of mucous on its skin to prevent osmosis. Fresh water develops an osmotic pressure, which tends to drive the fresh water into the fish, to dilute its saline body fluids. If its protection system fails, the fish becomes dropsical and dies. In the sea, there is a reverse osmotic situation. A sea fish has to prevent its body fluids leaking out to join the more saline sea. The trout has the remarkable, built in, capability of adapting from fresh water to seawater; it can even handle a reversal of osmotic pressure.

A classic example of this capability occurred quite recently. A few years ago, settlers introduced common brown trout to rivers in Argentina where, previously, there were no trout. Within a very few years, some of the trout had gone down the river to the estuary, and into the sea with its rich feeding grounds. The trout, which would normally, even in a good river, only have an average weight of a few pounds, grew enormously and returned to the home river to spawn, weighing anything up to 30lbs (13.6kg). The Argentinean rivers now provide the finest sea trout fishing in the world. No waiting for Darwinian Evolution there!

If we consider land animals, the most adaptable seem to be mammals and birds, which, between them, totally dominate the planet. (Marsupials are mammals too but with a pouch in which the young can grow). So, if we go back to that warm-blooded reptile precursor, you really could say, its descendents inherited the Earth. For a hundred and forty million years, it was the dinosaurs as the primary warm-blooded animal, with the mammals as back up. For the following sixty five million years, it has been mammals as the primary animal, and dinosaurs (the birds) second rank. Some people may argue that warm-blooded mammals and warm-blooded dinosaurs are an example of parallel evolution. They could be right. However, I am inclined to think, with the first dinosaurs and mammals existing at the same time, it is much more likely they descended from a common ancestor. It would not surprise me at all if, one of these days, someone discovers a fossil of a small, dinosaur-like, animal with fur instead of feathers; one of our early ancestors.

Now! Let us consider the salmon very carefully. The salmon can tell us a lot about modern evolution, ageing and the power of genes. In Alaska, Canada and the USA, five species of Pacific salmon enter the rivers to spawn and die. With these salmon there is one hundred percent mortality. In Europe and Northern Russia the Atlantic salmon behaves similarly, but with less then one hundred percent mortality. Some of the fish recover, go back to the sea and then return to the river to spawn again, and sometimes even for a third spawning. The salmon is a descendent and relative of the trout; no question about it! When Atlantic salmon have been in the river for a time, after returning from the sea, but before spawning, they begin to look like trout again, with spots and similar colouring. Pacific salmon do not, but they have one distinctive feature that marks them, unquestionably, as being a form of trout – the Adipose fin. This is a little fleshy, degenerate, fin on the back. Only trout and trout relatives have it. Trout that go to sea and return – Sea Trout in Europe, Steelhead in the Pacific – do not die after one spawning. They return to their home river, and spawn over and over again – usually until they are finally killed by predators. It is reasonable, therefore, to believe the forerunners of the salmon would do the same.

Let us consider what would happen if we had a 50/50 mix of salmon coming up a river to spawn; 50% salmon that spawned once only and 50% that spawned twice or more before dying. It is immediately obvious that the group that spawned only once should gradually die out. The salmon that spawned two or three times would out-breed them. The salmon that produced twice, or three times, the offspring should inherit the river, according to the Darwinian 'survival of the fittest'. Let us also remember that the first salmon would follow their trout ancestors and spawn over and over again, as sea trout and steelhead do. So the trait of once only spawning and dying evolved into the system – not out; defying the normal laws of Darwinian Evolution. Experts say the salmon die in order to fertilise the river (so that the baby salmon can thrive) and, as it seems to be the only possible explanation, I have no reason to disagree with that, but, how could it possibly evolve?

Let us go back to the development of the first single cells in the sea. Initially, it would be simple Darwinian Evolution. Every cell for itself. Competition, reproduction, death. Brutal survival of the fittest. Then came co-operation, which produced the first organisms. In this situation cells had to give up independence for the common good; even to die on demand – as in Apoptosis (Programmed cell death). The future of the organism is more important than the future of any individual cell. (Occasionally the original individual cell drive, for survival and reproduction, breaks through and we have cancer). The genes in every cell of a modern organism have the ability to control the cell, even unto death.

Now! What if the future of the species is, somehow, recognised as being more important than the survival of the individual organism. Somehow, in the evolution of the salmon, maybe through the semi starvation of the fry (the baby salmon), in the home river, it has been recognised, even into the genes, that the death of the individual salmon would fertilise the river, lead to greater survival of the fry and, therefore, in the end, create an overall increase in the number of the species. The greater the numbers; the more barren rivers that can be colonised; the safer the future of the species. It is a profound thought, and at first seems very unlikely – but I cannot see any other explanation for a phenomenon that seems to defy common sense and the usual Darwinian Laws of Evolution. After all, it must have been similarly recognised, in the evolution of the organism, that cells must be killed, on demand, for the good of the organism. We know that happened; it is a proven fact or we would not exist.

The killing of a cell (Apoptosis) is achieved by the activation of a specific gene. When this gene is activated, a special enzyme is created which, literally, chops the inside of the cell to pieces. The killing of the salmon is achieved by a deliberate switching on of an ageing gene. The salmon ages at a fantastic rate, degenerates and literally falls to pieces, as soon as it has spawned. It is the Atlantic salmon that gives us the clue. Sometimes, an Atlantic salmon manages to switch off the ageing gene. It recovers, grows new teeth, regenerates, goes back to the sea and regains all its old life and vigour, returning to spawn again and again.

The implications of all this are indeed far reaching. If there is recognition, somewhere in the genes, that the species is more important than the individual, it could explain why we age at all; why we display the signs of age – fairly early on. It could also explain the phenomenon of producing mules – thus preventing hybridising that may harm the species. Obviously, if this is so, then, in the branching of the evolutionary tree, there must be a mechanism that recognises when a variation is sufficiently different, and advanced enough to warrant protecting. I suspect that, somehow, the subconscious mind itself may be involved – with power to affect organisms down to cellular level; maybe even to the genetic level. How else could hereditary memory be created? We know some form of hereditary memory exists.

Consider the Cuckoo! The young bird is reared in a different bird's nest. It does not know its parents. It cannot be taught anything by them, yet it knows how to migrate – to fly to Africa as its parents did. It knows, after it mates, that it has to lay its eggs in other bird's nests – and only specific birds at that. We call it instinct. Instinct is just another name for hereditary memory. Even in humans, I suspect some degree of hereditary memory exists, besides the deeper instincts. Racing drivers often produce sons that take to car racing like ducks to water. Lester Piggott, as a youth, was predicted to develop as a great jockey. He had a talent, and expert horse riders existed on both sides of his ancestry. Even I, immediately took to using carpenters tools as a boy – it was in the family – a long series of carpenters, blacksmiths and wheelwrights. On mother's side, incidentally, the name was Archer, but I haven't yet found out if I am good with a bow and arrow. I have concluded that evolution of advanced life is more complicated than we thought.

Before Darwin, there was a man named Lamarck who thought animals simply evolved to suit a need. If the giraffe wanted a longer neck to reach the high branches it simply gradually grew a longer neck – over many generations, maybe. After Darwin, people ditched Lamarck's ideas; they were considered childish! Too simplistic! Now, however, I am not quite so sure! Darwinian Evolution works; there can be no doubt about that, but is it the entire explanation? The salmon goes against it. Maybe Darwinian Evolution is only part of the picture, or it needs to be extended. Maybe Lamarck wasn't entirely wrong. What about the mouse that felt cold in the refrigerated store? It developed its 'powder puff' coat much faster than Darwin would have expected. Lamarck would not have been surprised.

No doubt we still have the principle of survival of the fittest but, in advanced animals, it may be the survival of the fittest species that matters most, not necessarily the fittest animal or fittest cell. Obviously, the survival of the fittest animal will also contribute to the fittest species – which is why many animals, such as deer, are programmed to fight amongst themselves and select the best genes. A contrived situation if you think of it – where natural selection by predators alone is not enough.

However, deer are still programmed to die of old age. It is detrimental to the species if they live too long. A high turnover rate is better for evolution. Salmon still fight savagely on the spawning beds for the right to fertilise the female's eggs. I am simply saying, I think there are far more facets to evolution than we have yet realised. Ageing and mules being merely part of the picture; in-built adaptability being another; the killing of salmon to fertilise the river – another. It is certainly not a question of waiting for the odd mutation to turn up, not any more, though the occasional mutation will, of course, be tested by the system.

It should be understood that my comments imply no criticism or suggestion of any failings of Charles Darwin. What he deduced from his own observations and the extremely limited knowledge and information available at the time and in the face of deeply entrenched views on the origins of mankind and other species is a testament to the brilliance of the man. In his day there was no knowledge whatsoever of DNA and chromosomes and the structure of cells. Today there is fantastically more information and data easily available for me and others to consider. In my mind – Darwin was a genius. If he could deduce, 150 years ago, that every living thing on this Earth is descended from a common ancestor, he had to be.

I referred earlier to brown trout having the ability to leave rivers and go to sea and return as Sea Trout. Brown trout mainly live in Atlantic rivers. Pacific rivers have a different trout – the Rainbow trout, and that too sometimes leaves the river, goes to sea and returns, greatly enlarged, in a form that is known as a Steelhead. I have been told that the US Department of Fish and Game recently reclassified Steelhead as a species of salmon. If so, I think they are wrong. Attempts have been made to introduce Steelhead into new, non Steelhead, rivers, by transferring eggs, but with mixed results. In some rivers the Steelhead eggs produce, not Steelhead, but simply the original rainbow trout. This suggests the Steelhead version of the rainbow trout is produced by the river conditions, not the genes. In one river the rainbows may decide to go to sea, in another they may not, depending on the conditions. If this is so, then the Steelhead is a sea-going rainbow trout. It has not yet evolved into a true salmon. When Steelhead have truly evolved into salmon, then the eggs will always produce Steelhead no matter where they are hatched – as true salmon do.

Some people talk about ageing as if it was some form of wearing out – like a machine. This is incorrect. A living body is a cooperating mass of cells. Cells die all the time and are replaced. Millions of blood cells die and are replaced every second. There would seem to be no reason why the new cells cannot be as efficient and active as the old. The reason they are not, is because they are programmed not to be. Ageing is genetically built in. Obviously this does not apply to germ cells, i.e. the eggs and sperm. These produce young vigorous cells that cooperate and develop to form the new baby – who is also programmed to live for a limited time. The life span of an animal – or plant for that matter, is programmed in the genes. (See the chapter on AGEING). If we consider the DNA – that incredible double helix molecule – on which every detail of the construction and function of an animal or plant is programmed – the information on it has been slowly accumulated over 4000 million years. The DNA incorporates all the information necessary to produce the basic stem cell, in all its complexity: the information for diversification of stem cells into all the different cells of the body; the information for the function of all the different cells; the information on how the cells shall be arranged; the information as to how and when certain cells must die (without apoptosis the body would never form its final shape); the information as to how the various parts of the body shall cooperate to achieve final function and the information as to how long that organism shall be allowed to exist if it is not destroyed by predators, disease, accident, etc.

Researchers have traced the function of many genes in the DNA chromosome, but there are many they have not. They tend to refer to these as 'junk DNA', as though it is trash that has accidentally been duplicated but should not really be there. I would not dream of leaping to such a conclusion; I would simply wonder what the mystery DNA was for. Maybe there is a lot of spare information – like a library – being held available for reference in extreme situations.

I remember reading that the first dinosaurs had a certain bone structure in the shoulder area. Later, the dinosaurs evolved a different structure. Then, when birds evolved, the original bone arrangement was reintroduced – as it was more suitable for flight. Whales have, occasionally, been caught with rudimentary hind limbs and human babies have, occasionally, been born covered in hair or with a small tail. These aberrations are sometimes called 'throwbacks'. What they prove is that the genes for the earlier stages of the animal have not been destroyed but only suppressed. Maybe, if the need ever arises, they can be re-activated. Also there is the storage of hereditary memory – instinct. There is a lot more information that needs to be stored on the DNA than just "how to build an animal". Even traits of character are inherited. Some people think that character and what a person becomes, is dictated by the environment. Some believe it is all in the genes. I remember reading what a sensible man, John Moore, who created Littlewoods Pools and Littlewoods Shops once said, "The character of a person, in later life, is the result of the interaction of his genes with his environment". That, I think, is a perfect summing up!

In human evolution there are developments that are difficult to explain. For example, the evolution of the voice box, and rearrangement of the mouth and throat area, to permit complex speech and communication. I have read that the original chimpanzee arrangement is much safer, with air passage and throat passage widely separated. The new arrangement in our species is far more dangerous – with a considerably greater risk of food getting into the air passages, causing possible choking and death. Obviously the new development, the change in the arrangement, would have to proceed considerably, before human speech and communication became possible. One would expect Darwinian Evolution to block the development of a more dangerous arrangement. The benefits of better communication would only affect evolution later.

I speculate as to whether the sub conscious mind can, somehow, over time, recognise a need and influence evolution, as it appears to have done in the salmon, which raises the question – at what point in evolution did some form of sub conscious evolve? Dogs and cats dream – as anyone who has kept them will testify. I have personally experienced problems with a schizophrenic dog.

Incidentally, many people seem to believe that only homo sapiens is conscious. I suppose it depends on the definition of the word conscious. I prefer "awareness and perception". If people include the very advanced brain functions including a perception of morality (very tricky ground) then they would be right. Let us stick to awareness and perception. Few people would deny that advanced animals – cats, dogs, dolphins and so on, are aware and perceive their surroundings.

Let us now consider the chain of evolution. Do you think your parents were conscious? And their parents? Now, carry on back! At what point do you say the progeny were conscious and the parents were not? I have little doubt the dinosaurs and primitive mammals possessed awareness and perception.

I have spoken to people who did not believe fish could feel pain. As anglers, some are hypocrites and simply say fish cannot feel pain to excuse their cruelty. Others not so. They genuinely think fish cannot feel pain. One said to me, "They cannot feel pain because they have no pain receptors". Pain is such an obviously necessary survival requirement, that I feel sure it must go back to the most fundamental animals. Pain – the recognition and signalling of damage – must be as fundamental as hunger and the urge to procreate.

I suggest a form of consciousness must go way, way back, to the early stages of animal evolution. I suggest many emotions – hunger, lust, anger, aggression, fear, a feeling of pleasure, even love and jealousy go a long way back. All these are evolutionary traits that help the survival of the species. Even an earwig will look after its young and birds self sacrifice to an amazing degree for their chicks. "Instinct" you say. Of course it is! But what else is the human desire to reproduce and look after children? Instinct! But it manifests itself in feelings of love and affection; the reward for being self-sacrificial. Some people scoffed at some of Henry Williamsons stories. 'Tarka the Otter' comes to mind. They said Williamson anthropomorphised too much. In other words he suggested animals had feelings like us. He writes, "Tarka had never felt so happy". Why not? The otter is a fairly close mammalian relative. A pet parrot will soon let you know if he is happy or not! Also, it is well known that animals get jealous. Anyone who has a dog, before they have a baby, had better watch out! In my opinion, human beings are just another animal branch on the tree of life. The top animal I grant you – but an animal nevertheless. The emotions and feelings we experience evolved long, long ago – before humans, as such, existed. A cat will come to you, not just for food, but to be stroked and fussed and for the sheer pleasure of knowing it is wanted. Dogs, obviously, from their behaviour, get great pleasure just from pleasing humans. They recognise the tone of voice and the human smile just as we do and, also, human body language. There is nothing more unhappy and dejected than a dog that is abandoned and knows it is not wanted.

I am sometimes amazed at what people will say about other animals. I visited a Raptor Centre once – a zoo with owls, hawks and eagles. One of the owners gave a demonstration – flying a bird – and said, "Of course, birds have short memories – only a few days". I said nothing. I thought of the pheasants that come into my garden. They were originally hand reared by a gamekeeper. If you go to them before they have been released and shot at, they will come rushing to you, like a flock of hens, hoping to be fed. Then they are turned loose into the woods. The next thing they know is they are being shot at and blown out of the sky. The survivors remember, only too well! They never trust people again. Even the cock pheasant who has been in my garden for two years, and comes to feed, every day, on bird food put out for the doves, never ever trusts me. He keeps his distance and sidles behind a tree if he sees me. This is a bird that used to come rushing to a human for food. There is nothing wrong with his memory, I am sure!

The potential of the DNA molecule is truly incredible. Let us consider ourselves. Somehow, by reference to different sections of the

DNA code some cells become skin, others hair, teeth, finger nails, and so on, all organised with incredible precision. The greatest marvel of all is the human brain – trillions of cells cooperating to produce a self-assembling, self-wiring, self-signalling computer, of staggering complexity and performance. Somehow, out of this immense mass of cooperating cells – which are prepared to die on demand for the good of the group – comes the remarkable feeling of 'I am'. The mass of cells which is the brain, in contact by various means of signalling – electrical and chemical – in order to be efficient for survival and reproduction, produces the ultimate effects – consciousness and the recognition of the perfect cooperation – not as 'we are' (as you might expect a group to do) but as 'I am'. The feeling that this group of cells is one thing – a person. So there you are! The end result of thousands of millions of years of evolution; the end result of thousands of millions of years of endless competition, murderous killing, immense suffering and ruthless, brutal, warfare. For you to be alive, your DNA chain must stretch back, in an unbroken line, right back to the first breakthrough, the beginning of Life, four thousand million years ago. It could be said that, in reality, you are four thousand million years old. The fact that you are alive proves that your ancestors survived volcanoes, ice ages, asteroid strikes – everything that, over and over again, destroyed most of life on Earth. Through it all – your line survived.

It is also sobering to realise that, since all macro life – living things big enough to see with the naked eye, uses DNA as its basic copying tool, then we are all related – all connected back to some common ancestor, thousands of millions of years ago. This means that you are not just related to chimpanzees, but literally, to everything you can see; rabbits, fish, whales, insects, trees and grass, toadstools, even the lichen growing on the rocks. A dandelion is just a long lost relative. It is interesting to note that the chlorophyl molecule – the green compound that is the stuff of life for all green plants – is a close chemical relative of the haemoglobin in your blood that allows you to breathe.

If you consider animals, there are some amazing demonstrations of the power of DNA. The butterfly's egg turns, not into a butterfly, but a larva – a caterpillar – with its own special construction and function. When the caterpillar has reached its final level of development it pupates. Its skin turns into a simple shell – a container – and inside, the caterpillar's body dissolves until there is nothing but a soup of cells. Then another part of the DNA blueprint is triggered, and the cells reassemble into something that looks nothing like the caterpillar at all - the butterfly. How such a dual existence system evolves I have no idea! Some animals – particularly parasites, have taken this genetic trick to extremes. I believe there are parasites with no less than five different modes of existence – and with the ability to procreate and multiply in more than one condition. An incredible demonstration of genetic flexibility.

Many people think Homo Sapiens has reached the pinnacle of evolution. I do not! Evolution will not stop. It will continue while life continues – perhaps for another billion years – on this Earth, providing an Asteroid or Comet, of sufficient size, does not intervene, or if we do not destroy ourselves. In my mind there is no reason why human beings should not continue to evolve. (At the moment we are practising negative evolution but that is probably only a hiccup). I see no reason why, in a million years or so, the average IQ would not be as great as, or greater than, that of Leonardo Da Vinci. I choose Leonardo Da Vinci because it is generally recognised that he was an unusual individual, in that he was not talented in the usual sense. He was simply far more intelligent than the rest of us. That meant that, whatever he was interested in, he was utterly brilliant in doing. He was Scientist, Biologist, Engineer – you name it. (I think he only produced paintings to make a living).

There is, of course, no reason why the Da Vinci level of intelligence should be the limit. In millions of years we could end up with a fantastic, total and instant-access memory, an incredibly fast deductive brain and creativity beyond our dreams. We could evolve to be as far ahead of Homo Sapiens, as we now are ahead of chimpanzees. There really could be "Homo Superior".

We have already conquered the Earth. The biggest danger now is not an asteroid or comet strike, by far the greatest danger will come from ourselves. With Genetic Engineering, we have already circumvented the species barrier, and this has been done without even knowing how the barrier works. It has been done by simple experimentation. Scientists will discover how to beat ageing; they will do it if it takes a thousand years, but I really expect them to do it in the next fifty. We will soon be in a position to re-engineer human beings themselves; to make us stronger, more agile, less prone to disease. They will eventually beat cancer – but this may take a hundred years. It will be much more difficult than people think. We will be able to live longer – maybe to 150 years.

The greatest danger is that some irrational, aberrant individual or group will create an unstoppable disease. Imagine a cross between the common cold and HIV or H5N1 flu. In the worst case, the human race could be devastated – causing a collapse of civilisation and the loss of, maybe, 95% of all knowledge. The human race might be thrown back to the Middle Ages. I think a biological disaster is more likely than a nuclear one. Sometimes, I have speculated, maybe humans will go back to a primitive existence and, thousands of years from now, civilisation will slowly return and the 'new' scientists might rack their brains trying to explain the colossal concrete runways, at places like Heathrow and Gatwick, and how we could possibly have travelled the world in enormous flying machines or even, as legend had it, walked on the moon and created weapons with the power of the sun. Who knows? Ten million years from now will come – as surely as the sun will rise tomorrow morning.

DINOSAURS

A great many people think of Dinosaurs as massive stupid lumbering creatures, hopelessly primitive, doomed to die out anyway even if the asteroid strike hadn't finished them off. The term Dinosaur is commonly used to describe people with antiquated, stupid and outmoded ideas. However, if we consider the evidence available today, rationally, logically and unbiased we may come to very different conclusions.

When the first enormous fossilised bones were found (far larger than any land animal that exists today) people were stunned. The sheer size of the animal was overwhelming. Certain features suggested a lizard-like ancestry; so the animal was called Dinosaur, which means Terrible Lizard. I am inclined to think it was a mistake! The name suggests all dinosaurs were huge and many people have that impression to this day. The truth is that the original massive dinosaur was just one of an immense range of highly developed, warm-blooded, extremely versatile animals, far removed from the cold-blooded lizards and crocodiles. It is probable that dinosaurs and mammals were descended from the same precursor – the first warm-blooded reptile.

The first dinosaurs discovered were certainly impressive. There were the immense brontosaurs (now called apatosaurs), the eighty to one hundred foot (twenty-five to thirty metres) long Diplodocus with its ridiculously small head and Tyrannosaurus Rex, believed, when it was first found, to be the greatest predator the world had ever seen. (Later they found another predatory species – even bigger). Then, as palaeontologists searched all over the world, they discovered dinosaurs had been everywhere – and ranged from small bird size specimens up to sixty-ton monsters. The truth was, dinosaurs had dominated the entire planet – more than mammals dominate today. Dinosaurs were obviously an amazingly variable and adaptable species. On land, the variants ranged from fast lizard-like animals only centimetres long to the enormous herbivores. A great range of predators existed – from chicken size all the way up to T Rex and beyond. Some wolf size specimens had large brains and probably hunted in packs. Some adapted and went back to the sea. A whole range of marine dinosaur relatives evolved – from small dolphin size ichthyosaurs (fish like) to whale size specimens. Plesiosaurs were somewhere in between. These marine animals must have solved the problem of reproducing in the sea, as mammals such as porpoises and whales had to do later. Other dinosaur relatives developed wings and took to the air. There were two kinds; the first, the Pterosaurs, had leathery wings – like bats. Most people immediately think of the enormous

Pterodactyls, but in fact there was an immense range of Pterosaurs from the size of your hand all the way up to the enormous Quetzalcoatlus with a wingspan of 15 metres (49 feet). Every imaginable variant existed – as they do in birds today. There was even a Pterosaur version of a flamingo, with shaped beak and a filter system for capturing plankton. A second type of flying dinosaur evolved – with feathers and wings – the forerunner of the modern birds.

The realisation gradually came that dinosaurs and dinosaur relatives had totally dominated the entire planet. Then it was discovered that mammals had lived on the Earth at the same time as the dinosaurs. In the ancient rocks – the same age as the rocks with the dinosaur fossils – were discovered fossils of mammals. However, nearly all the fossils of mammals were very small, mostly shrew, mouse and rat sized. I believe the largest ever found was no larger than a domestic cat. The inescapable implication is – the mammals could not compete with the dinosaurs. The predatory dinosaurs were too fast and efficient. Dinosaurs ruled the Earth for a hundred and forty million years and, in all that time, the mammals failed to do anything better than merely survive. Small predatory dinosaurs were probably just as lethal to small mammals as terriers are to rats today.

For many years scientists argued over whether dinosaurs were warm-blooded or cold-blooded animals. They studied the skeletons to see if there was any indication there. People argued about the Stegosaurus – the multi-ton herbivorous dinosaur with staggered rows of bony plates projecting from its back. Study of the fossilised plates indicated they were endowed with a rich supply of blood vessels. It was proposed that the plates might have evolved to absorb heat from sunlight – which would make sense if Stegosaurus was cold blooded. If, instead, it was warm blooded, and lived in a hot climate, the plates could act as radiators, to dissipate heat on the breeze. In Africa today several animals have evolved enormous ears for heat dissipation – desert hares and mice and, of course, the African elephant. As soon as I learned that mammals lived at the same time as dinosaurs I had no doubts. Dinosaurs were warm-blooded. They had to be; otherwise the mammals would have taken over the world or, at least, part of it. The mammals would have spread into the colder areas of the planet – where the dinosaurs, if they had been cold-blooded, could not have operated. Cold-blooded dinosaurs would only have been able to operate efficiently in a warm climate. (There are no crocodiles in Alaska, Siberia, or Europe, except in zoos). There are a few reptiles in colder countries – lizards, newts, and snakes – but they are small and they go torpid in cool or cold weather. Their survival then depends on their hiding away and not being found by warm blooded mammals or birds. No large cold-blooded reptile could compete, in cold conditions, with wolves, leopards and tigers let alone polar bears. In cold weather, cold-blooded animals have little energy. Body cells work far more efficiently if they are warm. Snakes and crocodiles bask in the sun to get warm and then they are dangerous, but cold, they are nowhere nearly so active. To compete with the mammals successfully, over the whole planet, for all that time, dinosaurs <u>must</u> have been warm-blooded. Otherwise, if this had not been so, in the colder areas of the Earth mammals could have multiplied, grown bigger and slowly evolved to compete with the dinosaurs. They would at least have been able to grow large and dangerous in the colder zones – maybe to the size of bears, tigers or larger, but we find no fossils; nothing bigger than a rabbit. The dinosaurs must have been everywhere, and so, for a hundred and forty million years, the dinosaurs held the mammals down.

Then, one day, came the asteroid. The energy released when a twelve kilometre (seven and a half mile) diameter asteroid struck the Earth, at a speed of probably 70,000 miles an hour or more, would be enough to reduce the planet to a smoking cinder. The miracle is that any land animals survived at all, but, somehow they did. Today only the relatives of just one dinosaur remain – the birds. It is very unlikely that only one, out of thousands, of species of dinosaur, survived the holocaust. I suspect a number of smaller dinosaurs probably survived – as did mammals. The mammals survived during the age of dinosaurs in the same way as mice and rats survive today. Their survival strategy was breeding capacity. After the asteroid strike, when all the large dinosaurs had disappeared and only a few small ones survived, the breeding capability of the mammals would come to the fore. There would be a population explosion. Rats today breed far faster than birds. The remaining small dinosaurs would have been overwhelmed by a rising tide of mammals – that would attack the young and eat the eggs. The remaining dinosaurs would be wiped out, all except one small, flying, feathered dinosaur that nested and bred in inaccessible places such as cliffs and offshore islands.

There were a number of puzzles with the dinosaur fossils. How could an animal like a Diplodocus grow to such an enormous size? Its head was so ridiculously small. Today we know that many birds that eat vegetation, seeds and nuts have a special adaptation. They simply grab the food and gulp it down. They do not chew the food as most mammals do – especially herbivorous mammals. Chickens feed rapidly, throwing the food down, even if the seed or corn is bone hard. The food passes down the gullet and is then stored in a pouch (the crop) from where it is passed in a steady stream to the gizzard to be pulverised and then on into the gut for digestion. The gizzard is a special organ which incorporates a powerful muscle. The bird swallows grit and small stones, which are then retained and incorporated in the gizzard. When food passes through the gizzard, muscles contract and move, to produce an action which grinds the food against the stones and grit – a very powerful substitute for chewing. Remarkably, among dinosaur bones, piles of rounded stones have occasionally been found. The herbivorous dinosaurs had gizzards, and that was why diplodocus did not need a large skull. The Diplodocus's head was not much smaller, compared to its body, than the head of an ostrich is to its body.

Another interesting feature of birds is that they have a far more efficient breathing system than mammals do. Mammal breathing is basically simple. Pull air into a convoluted bag and puff it out again. The bag, which is subdivided and called the lungs, is filled with millions of little sacs (alveoli) but the principle described is, nevertheless, basically correct. In the bird, although, to an observer, breathing appears to be similar to mammals, it is actually far more complicated. Modern research has shown that when the bird inhales, the air does not go directly to the lungs but is channelled into a complicated arrangement of air sacs, which, remarkably, extend even into cavities in the bones. In the next cycle, air from these cavities is then transferred to the lungs as more air is introduced to the cavities. Finally the air is expelled from the lungs through the windpipe and ejected. Instead of the mammalian in/out simple breathing, the birds have a continuous flow, one-way air system. Combined with a contra-flow blood circulation system this produces a far more efficient oxygen extraction arrangement than is possible in mammals.

At sea level, the bird respiration system is said to be over 30% more efficient and in thinner air (or low oxygen air) very much more efficient (as much as triple at altitudes of 9750 feet (3000 metres) and above). This is supported by confirmed evidence of geese migrating over the Himalayas – flying at well over 20,000 feet (6100 metres) at heights where many human beings would die from oxygen starvation. The record, I believe, is 37,000 feet (11,280 metres) when a Griffon vulture was struck by an airliner. (Incidentally, although I have seen no reports I can, as an Engineer, deduce that it is extremely likely that the contra-flow oxygen transfer system is backed up by another contra-flow heat transfer system – otherwise birds would lose far too much heat in cold conditions).

Research has shown that dinosaur bones in the Jurassic and Cretaceous periods, large and small, have a similar hollow bone structure to birds, indicating that even the large dinosaurs had the more efficient, bird type, breathing systems. Birds also have a different sleeping system to mammals. Sleeping, when consciousness is largely switched off, can be a dangerous time for many animals. In mammals the entire brain is affected during the sleeping period, leaving the sleeping animal vulnerable to attack. Birds, however, have evolved a safer system. When birds sleep, only about half of the brain enters the deep sleep condition; the other half stays awake. After a time the situation is reversed and the other half of the brain rests. The bird, therefore, is always reasonably alert. If this ability was general to Dinosaurs this, again, would be an evolutionary advantage over mammals.

It is interesting to note that, recently, a sample of protein was extracted from a fossil T Rex bone. The protein is the same as that found in modern domestic chickens. There is little doubt, therefore, that the whole range of dinosaurs and modern birds were, and are, simply variations of the same basic animal. It has been found that birds even have better and more efficient eyes than mammals. The retinal area at the back of the eye is a slightly different construction giving birds better acuity and perception. It is believed the best vertebrate eyes belong to hawks, eagles and vultures.

For many years, the idea persisted that dinosaurs were pea-brained lumbering monsters. The term 'Bird Brain' has often been used to describe something or someone who is stupid. Many birds are in fact, anything but stupid. Tests have suggested some parrots may have an intelligence to rival dogs. (All the more remarkable when you consider the size of a parrot's brain compared to a dog).

Until recently it was considered that only human beings had the ability to 'think things out'; to solve problems by thought alone; to conduct 'thought experiments'. Recent experiments with Ravens have shown they are capable of solving problems by 'thinking it out' and not making a move until they have thought about, and decided, the correct sequence of actions to solve a problem. Other types of crow have demonstrated amazing feats of memory; able to hide up to 1000 caches of food and accurately remember where every one is. I would have difficulty remembering 10 or 20. Not bad performances for 'bird brains'!

Fossils have been found of small predatory dinosaurs (wolf size or slightly larger) that had skull cavities indicating the raptor had a brain about the same size as a modern dog. Considering the performance of some of the small-brained birds of today, maybe Velociraptors really were as clever, and as cunning, as described in the book 'Jurassic Park'. There is evidence such raptors did hunt in packs. Hunting in packs requires intelligence, co-operation and foresight. With the more efficient bird type breathing system these predatory dinosaurs would have been lethal indeed. Very probably able to outrun, and have more stamina than, any predator today. These small dinosaurs had multi-toed feet with claws; so, of course, do we. Our ancestral claws have simply reduced to finger and toe nails.

The conclusions to be drawn from all this are very thought provoking. The dinosaurs were warm-blooded; they had an efficient breathing system; they evolved to fill just about every niche available. They out-competed the mammals for over a hundred million years. We know some had evolved large brains and it is highly probable the raptors with the large brains hunted in groups. This behaviour encourages the development of large brains for thinking tactics, and for communication – as in wolves, wild dogs, chimpanzees and humans. Even today there is a bird (Harris Hawk) that will sometimes cooperate with several other Harris Hawks to hunt and kill prey.

The conclusion is that there is no reason to think the Dinosaurs would not have continued to rule the world – to this day – if it had not been for the asteroid catastrophe. They would have continued to evolve. If the raptors had not been wiped out, their descendents might have reached the moon millions of years ago. People have laughed at this suggestion but, think about it! If two intelligent extra terrestrial beings had visited the Earth seventy million years ago and, after seeing the raptor dinosaur with the dog sized brain and the little rat sized, scurrying, furry mammals with a brain no bigger than a bean, and the one ET asked the other "Given fifty million years of evolution – which one do you think is the most likely to develop into a highly intelligent, creative animal, capable of building a machine to fly to the moon"? I am sure ET would vote for the dinosaur. After all it was bipedal, it had arms and hands and it had a large brain. It had only to grow a little larger, stand upright, triple the size of its brain and, if necessary, develop five fingers. (The change from three fingers to five is a very minor evolutionary adaptation. For instance we have people with six fingers and toes walking about the Earth today). All you need to do, then, is place a spear in the little dinosaur's hands and he is halfway there. Who would back the little mammal?

If it hadn't been for the asteroid, a descendant of the dinosaurs might have been walking on the moon twenty million years ago. The little mammal had a far, far, greater evolutionary distance to cover. We, of course, are descended from the little mammal. We probably developed from small mammal to lemur, to monkey, to ape, to primitive man, to Homo Sapiens.

People laugh at the idea of an upright, intelligent descendant of the dinosaurs, something like us but with basilisk eyes – something out of Sci Fi – Star Trek perhaps. In my mind, it would have been, undoubtedly, perfectly possible, in sixty five million years. After all, we did it from starting as a shrew or a cat-like mammal. Can you imagine a mouse evolving to land on the moon? It probably took us thirty million years, or more, just to reach the level of the raptors with brains and, after all, they were our cousins. It might well be that, if descendants of the dinosaurs had reached our level, they might have looked and behaved remarkably like us. They might have lost their tails (we have). Their skin might have been free of scales, or fur, or feathers (we only have small patches and traces of hair and fur) and they might have had big appealing eyes – like owls – not lizard eyes. Who knows?

After life crawled out of the sea, land animals developed that were cold-blooded. Somehow, because it gave greater competitive efficiency, warm-blooded reptiles evolved. From those warm-blooded reptiles both mammals and dinosaurs evolved. This is far more likely than that mammals evolved from a different ancestor. We have the interesting situation that an egg-laying mammal survives to this day – the platypus. Warm blood gives an animal a great advantage over cold-blooded animals. More flexibility; more energy; the ability to operate more efficiently in the colder areas of the world and so on. There can be, however, one great problem. When there is a food shortage, the warm-blooded animal starves far faster than the cold-blooded animal, because up to 80% of the food is used to produce heat. Some cold-blooded animals can survive for up to a year or more without food, providing they have reasonable reserves to start with. In general, most warm-blooded animals would not survive for one third of this time. Some, of course, have developed the trick of hibernating – which immediately places them at the same disadvantage as the cold-blooded animals. They can only get away with it if there are very few, or no, active predators to take advantage. If there were, even a hibernating Grizzly bear might be dead before he had time to wake up.

Incidentally, it is interesting to speculate whether the various legends of dragons, all over the world, stem from someone finding dinosaur bones. The head looks roughly right; the body is also right and some dinosaurs even had leathery wings. People have sometimes wondered about the remarkably small arms on Tyrannosaurus Rex. I would point out that the evidence available shows that a lot of dinosaur species constructed nests for their eggs and young. In the Gobi Desert masses of nests, with fossilised eggs, have been found close together; as flamingos do today. Dinosaur eggs and young were very small relative to the size of the adults. Is it possible a Tyrannosaur might use its very small arms to feed youngsters, which might be no bigger than a chicken. A six-foot (1.8 metre) long mouth full of enormous teeth might make things a little tricky! Mash the food up with those enormous jaws and then delicately feed the infants with those dinky little arms! I wouldn't be at all surprised!

I was watching a pheasant in my little wood recently. It was scared and ran like the proverbial 'road runner'. It did not wobble from side to side. It ran – at terrific speed – smoothly, as though on wheels. Ostriches can also run fast and smoothly. In BBC animation programmes T Rex is usually shown lumbering around. Come on BBC! Study birds a little. They don't usually rock and roll from side to side as they run. My guess is – T Rex travelling smoothly, in an attack sprint, at 40 miles an hour, or better. It is very easy to underestimate reptiles and similar animals. Having seen films of crocodiles slowly shuffling across a sandbank, on their bellies, who would believe they can move like lightning when they attack, or rise up on their legs and run, on land, as fast as a man, if they consider it necessary. T Rex did not have those enormous hind legs for nothing. I have seen an illustration showing what T Rex might have looked like in feathers. When I heard about it I thought it would be ridiculous but in actual fact the illustration didn't look crazy at all. Feathers and hair are, of course, adaptations of scales. On chickens it is usual to still have scales on legs and feet. There is, however, a fancy chicken – a novelty bird with feathers on its legs and feet right down to its toes. Genes are nothing if not flexible.

I have speculated on how the enormous species of Pterodactyls – the ones with 30ft (9.2m) and even 50ft (15.3m) wing spans, managed to fly. Is it possible the air was more dense in those days? Perhaps some researcher will find out. If it was, say, 30% more dense it would make a great deal of difference to the effort required – particularly to get airborne – and thermals would be more powerful, making it easier to soar. I remember, years ago, when people flew in low powered, piston engined, propeller-driven aircraft, they used to send the planes out to Nairobi in Kenya for flying tests, before they certified them to take passengers. Nairobi is 5 or 6 thousand feet (1538m or 1846m) above sea level where the air is much thinner and a compounding effect was the reduction in engine power due to the air temperature. If the plane could take off, with full load, at Nairobi it could do it anywhere. I read that it did, however, need nearly double the length of runway to take off. Modern jet planes have so much spare power there is no problem. All planes however have a 'ceiling', at which there is not enough air to support them at the speed they are travelling. If the air was more dense 70 million years ago, the easier it would have been for the giant Pterosaurs to fly.

The evolution of the dinosaurs was cut short by a catastrophe of enormous proportions. A major asteroid impact. Consider then, if you will, the asteroid strike. The immense rock – a mini world (although only a very small cosmic body – as things go) sailing through space, serenely, as it had done for billions of years and then, one day, that most unlikely event – a collision occurred. By a rare fluke, the Earth was in the wrong place at the wrong time; a not impossible happening considering there are, in fact, millions of asteroids of all shapes and sizes drifting around the sun in perpetual orbit – sometimes disturbed into a new orbit by collisions, or the gravitational influence of another body. We know it was an asteroid, and not a comet, by the tell tale iridium left in the debris – a thin but clearly discernible layer found in rock strata all over the world. The speed of the collision – the relative speed between the asteroid and the Earth – depends on a number of factors. Was the asteroid travelling around the sun in a direction similar to Earth's, or at an angle? Was it travelling in the opposite direction? We do not know! The Earth is steadily cruising around the sun at 66,000 miles an hour. The asteroid, in an elliptical orbit, would probably be travelling at a similar speed. The speed of impact could have been as high as 130,000 miles an hour or more or as low as 25,000 miles an hour, but not less (because of Earth's gravity pull). The energy released when a mass, be it one gram – as in a small bullet, or an asteroid weighing trillions of tons, is proportional to the square of the speed of impact. If the asteroid hit at 70,000 miles an hour, as was likely, instead of a minimum 25,000 miles an hour, the energy released would be nearly eight times as great. If it arrived at 130,000 miles an hour the energy would be 27 times as great.

Imagine then – the asteroid, estimated to have been about 7 miles (11.2km) in diameter and weighing roughly one million, million tons, impacting the Earth. The immense ball of rock, as it touched, would plough into the atmosphere which, having no time to move out of the way (the asteroid would only take about one and one third seconds from contact with the first layers of air until it reached the sea) would be compressed and heated until the pressure reached millions of pounds per square inch – exploding out in a gigantic shock wave. Then, the sea would be subjected to incalculable pressures and heated until it was at incandescent temperatures. (If the sea, at point of impact, was a mile deep (1.6km) then the asteroid would slam through the sea to the sea bed in about $1/20^{th}$ of a second – less than the time it takes you to blink your eye). The exploding sea would blast out – pushing back the surrounding water in a colossal wave – probably several miles high. The asteroid would plunge inexorably, barely slowed – into the body of the Earth. The rock of the Earth itself would be forced out of the way, in the same way as the air and water and heated to millions of degrees. The rock would vaporise and explode and there would be a similar effect with the Earth as with the sea. An immense blast of vaporised rock and vaporised asteroid would push out an enormous wave of rock and debris, away from the path of the asteroid. The asteroid would continue to plunge deeper and deeper, slowing as it went. The energy released would be so great that almost the entire mass of the asteroid (and a similar or greater mass of the Earth) would be vaporised. Every gram of the asteroid would release vastly more energy than an equivalent weight of TNT.

At an impact speed of 70,000 miles an hour the entire asteroid would crash through the air, the sea and disappear into the Earth in less than 2 seconds. It would carry on down until all of its energy was converted into heat, shockwaves and the momentum of the exploding debris. It is difficult to estimate how deep it would penetrate before all of its energy was dissipated. If it came in vertically or at a steep angle (evidence indicates a steep angle) it would almost certainly penetrate into the mantle; trillions of tons of white-hot gas and debris would explode outwards. The shock wave, racing through the Earth, would mean that animals and trees thousands of miles away would be thrown into the air. Even on the very far side of the Earth – opposite the point of impact – the shock wave would arrive, having travelled through the very centre of the planet. Even here, earth, rocks, trees and animals would be thrown high into the air. The immense white-hot mass of gas, steam and vaporised rock would blast out, from the point of impact, condensing and cooling as it went; spreading out steadily until it covered the entire Earth. The sky would turn into an immense red-hot oven. Everything on the ground – probably for half the planet or more would be roasted. Everything – trees, plants, animals, would burn.

We know the asteroid struck in the sea just off the Yucatan Peninsula of Mexico at a place called Chicxulub. There is evidence that vast areas of North America were sterilised of animals and plants. The ground was cooked metres deep – even destroying deep buried seeds. The immense heat of the blast would cause vast quantities of the atmosphere to burn. The nitrogen and oxygen would combine, depleting oxygen levels and creating acidic compounds. (This happens, on a small scale, with every lightning flash). Rain that eventually fell would be like battery acid. The ozone layer would be totally destroyed. Plutons all over the World, would be shaken and possibly broken open. A pluton is an enormous reservoir of molten lava deep within the Earth. To get an idea of how vast a large pluton can be, consider the Hawaiian Islands in the Pacific Ocean. The sea around the islands is over 10,000 feet (3076m) deep. Millions of years ago a pluton, deep under the seabed, broke through, a volcano formed, and gradually grew, and enlarged until it formed the first of the Hawaiian Islands. The seabed gradually moved over the pluton, which then formed another volcano and another island. All the Hawaiian Islands have been formed in this way, from the one pluton and, at the present time, the pluton is still pouring out lava from the volcano Kilauea. It is probable there is still enough lava in the pluton to create several more islands in the future. The Canary Islands in the Atlantic have been formed in the same way, as has the whole of the large island of Iceland.

There is, in India, an enormous area over 500,000 square kilometres (nearly 200,000 square miles) covered with old lava that is up to 3 kilometres (1.8 miles) thick, the Deccan Traps. This area is almost directly opposite the Chicxulub impact site. Some of it has been dated to around the time of the strike. I have written in this book of the power of shock waves. I think it quite possible a massive shock wave could have travelled through the centre of the Earth and burst open a gigantic reservoir of lava – a pluton – in the Deccan area. The enormous amount of heat, lava, gas and dust released by the eruption – and probably other eruptions around the world – would have vastly added to the destruction caused directly by the asteroid impact. It is not remarkable that the dinosaurs and many other species became extinct. (Even coral reefs all over the world were massively damaged and destroyed). The miracle is that any animals survived at all.

If you think I exaggerate, consider what happened when comet Shoemaker Levy impacted Jupiter a few years ago. Jupiter is vastly larger than the Earth. The comet broke into pieces before impact. Jupiter is a gas planet, not solid like the Earth and is believed to have only a very small rocky core. Many scientists said we would see nothing when the comet pieces struck Jupiter or, maybe, just a twinkle of light. In the event there were massive flashes when the pieces struck. Some of the pieces caused explosions so large that Earth sized scars were visible on the surface of Jupiter for months.

If you are sceptical about the possibility of a shock wave passing through the Earth and blasting millions of tons of earth and rock skywards on the opposite side of the globe I suggest you obtain one of those little novelty desk top toys that incorporate about seven steel balls suspended on threads from a wire frame. The balls are arranged in a line, touching each other, each ball independently suspended and free to swing along the axis of the row. When you swing the end ball out, with your fingers and then release it, to swing back and impact the next ball, the only other ball to react is the end one the furthest away from the impact. This ball kicks out, swings away from the rest, then swings back and impacts the last but one ball. Number one ball then kicks out again and the process repeats for a remarkably long time before the action finally stops. The centre 5 balls of the row do not appear to move. What is really happening is this. When the first ball strikes the number 2 ball the impact creates a mini shock wave. This shock wave travels through ball number 2 and, because it is touching number 3, the energy of the shock wave is transmitted, through the point of contact, causing a shock wave to travel through ball number 3. This is repeated through balls number 4, 5 and 6. However, when the energy of the shock wave reaches ball number 7, no further propagation can take place so the energy of the shock wave is expended kicking number 7 ball away from the group. When number 7 falls back and strikes number 6 the whole sequence is repeated. Some energy is lost each time a ball is displaced, by noise, air friction etc, until, finally, all movement ceases. Exactly the same thing would happen if the centre 5 balls were replaced with a solid steel bar to transmit the shock wave. By now you will have realised that the Earth will act like the solid steel bar or the row of steel balls and the final layer of earth and rock at the far side of the planet will be hurled into the sky when the shock wave arrives.

Let us consider Plutons such as those affected by the shock wave created by the asteroid impact. These reservoirs accumulate over millions of years and tend to rise mainly from the mantle. Sometimes the rock above the pluton cracks and lava moves up the fissure and reaches the surface. We have a volcanic eruption. When a pluton is forming, it is usual for a massive amount of water and gases to accumulate within the lava mass. It is dissolved in that mass – like the carbon dioxide in a bottle of soda water – and maintained in the dissolved state by the pressure. If a pluton is undisturbed for a long period of time this situation builds up. When, finally, a crack occurs and the lava moves towards the surface of the Earth, pressure is reduced. The lava then explodes into fragments, some of which may be as fine as dust, and, mixed with the gases, blasts from the vent of the volcano at a velocity which can approach the speed of sound.

The classic eruption of this kind, which is called a 'Plinian Eruption' (because it was first described by the Roman historian Pliny), is the eruption which destroyed the Roman city of Pompeii in Italy. The effect of the lava exploding out of the volcano vent is very similar to what happens in a small, solid fuel, rocket motor. The whole top of the pluton can gradually explode into gas and dust and rocket up through the vent in a colossal column, sometimes reaching as high as the stratosphere. The gas is usually steam and CO_2, but there can also be sulphur dioxide and other gases. Although the pressure which kept the water and gases dissolved in the lava has been released it has, down below, at the top of the pluton, only partially been released. The remaining pressure is sufficient to support the roof of an immense cavity, which forms as the exploding lava escapes. Eventually, when enough gas has been released, pressure gradually reduces until the cavity above the remaining pluton collapses. The ground caves in. The collapsed crater is called a Caldera.

Now – imagine a situation similar to that above, where a pluton – a small one in the case I am going to describe – has built up a quantity of lava containing enough gas and water to explode the lava, if the pressure was released, but where a plug in the top of a volcano vent is maintaining the pressure. The volcano begins to give way, and is on the verge of an eruption, when suddenly the side of the volcano falls away in a landslide, suddenly reducing the pressure to the point where the lava can explode. That is what happened at Mount St Helens in Washington State, USA a few years ago and was vividly recorded on film. Because the landslide, which released the pressure, was on one side of the volcano, the blast of gas, ash and dust came out sideways and swept over the countryside causing massive devastation. The exploded rock of the pyroclastic flow still contains the heat that was in it when it was liquid and red-hot. The flow of dust and gas looks dangerous enough, but the reality is far worse, because the dust cloud is at temperatures of anything up to a thousand degrees. Years ago on the Island of Martinique in the Caribbean a volcano, Mt Pele, erupted, producing a similar pyroclastic flow. The cloud rolled towards the sea but, in the way, stood a town, St Pierre, with 20 to 30 thousand people. Everyone died except one man – deep in a dungeon at a local jail. Everybody else was literally fried.

Having discussed plutons in some detail, let us now come back to the Dinosaurs and the Deccan Traps. The pluton that released the lava that became the Deccan Traps must have been truly immense. Imagine now – this colossal pluton containing enormous quantities of gas and water dissolved in the hot lava. Suddenly, the shock wave from the asteroid impact simply rips and smashes the overlying rock off the pluton,. The pluton would instantly explode – in a blast maybe millions of times greater than at Mount St Helens. That would probably be the worst volcanic eruption on the planet at that time although other plutons throughout the world might also have been ruptured by other shock waves. Shock waves do not dissipate easily. They reflect, refract and reverberate. The whole world would have been racked by earthquakes and tsunamis. The entire planet would have reverberated like a gigantic bell.

So there would be the immense blast of the asteroid strike compounded with volcanism on an unimaginable scale. Together with the smoke of burning biomass, the whole world would have been covered with an enormous blanket of choking dust and gas. The planet must have been reduced to a smoking ruin. The dust from the asteroid explosion, the smoke and dust from the volcanic eruptions combined with the smoke from the burning forests (probably 80% of the entire planetary land surface biomass – trees, grass and other plants would burn) would blanket the world from pole to pole. There would be pitch darkness for months. Temperatures would plummet. Everywhere but the tropics would freeze. When the dust and smoke finally cleared, the ozone layer would have been destroyed and there would be intense U/V radiation. Because of the combustion of oxygen and nitrogen in the fireball, the burning of the biomass and, above all, the cessation of photosynthesis on land and sea for a year or more, oxygen levels would plummet until there might be as little oxygen available at sea level as there is now on mountains at 3000 metres (9750 feet). Then, as the air gradually cleared, global temperatures would soar because of the massive increase in carbon dioxide due to the conflagration and massive volcanism.

Increased volcanism would continue to take place for hundreds or thousands of years after the initial impact. Forests and land biomass would take many years to regenerate. There is evidence, in North America, that all trees were wiped out and the area was finally colonised by ferns, whose spores can blow on the wind. Nothing more complex than ferns existed for the best part of a million years. It is remarkable that any land animals other than insects survived the catastrophe at all.

One can only speculate on why birds are the only dinosaur survivors of the asteroid strike holocaust. Since they survived, it is only reasonable to speculate that, although it would be expected all the large dinosaurs would die, it is probable quite a few of the smaller predatory or scavenger dinosaurs would survive. However, on this Earth, we commonly note that dominant species breed slowly. Prey species often adopt the policy of prodigious reproduction; sharks produce few young whereas prey fish breed by the million. On land the fox produces a few cubs a year; rabbits, rats and mice produce large litters at frequent intervals. (In the absence of predation and with plenty of food a single pair of rats can generate a colony of up to a thousand or more in just twelve months). Birds normally produce from two to twenty chicks a year, rarely more. It is probable that dinosaurs did not breed at anything like the rate of the small mammals. Land dinosaurs laid eggs. (There is evidence Ichthyosaurs and Plesiosaurs in the sea produced live young). So, after the disaster, there would be only a few dinosaur and mammal survivors but, after a short time, insect life would explode, feeding on animal remains, which would, in turn, permit the small mammal population to explode. After a year or so the surviving dinosaurs would find they were massively outnumbered – swamped by mammals. No matter how many mammals the dinosaurs killed they would still have their eggs destroyed. Laying eggs was probably their Achilles heel. Birds probably survived by nesting on islands free of mammals.

The big question mark is why the flying Pterosaurs disappeared. One would think that if birds survived, possibly on islands, the Pterosaurs would have done the same. Given the fact there were thousands of different species of Pterosaur – from bat size upwards – it would be reasonable to expect them to have a far greater survival potential than birds which, so far as we know, were small, inefficient and rare. We must, however, remember that, after the initial effects of the asteroid strike, there would be a period of intense cold, extending over the whole planet, lasting for months, if not a year or more, due to the immense quantities of dust and smoke blocking the sun. It is noticeable today that birds can withstand the cold far better than bats. Maybe birds survived the cold better than the pterosaurs because of their feathers, and then survived the onslaught of the mammals because of their inaccessible nesting sites. Speculate as we may, it is unlikely we will ever know.

Shortly after I wrote about the possible link between the dinosaur destroying asteroid impact at Chicxulub, Yucatan, and the enormous volcanic lava deposits (The Deccan Traps) in India, I picked up a copy of New Scientist and browsed. This was in December 2006. In it was an article on a gigantic new asteroid (or comet) impact crater that had been found under the Antarctic ice, (using ice penetrating radar) even larger than the Chicxulub crater. They speculated that this crater might be linked to the great Permian mass extinction two hundred and fifty million years ago. To prove the age of the Antarctic crater, scientists will have to drill down through half a mile of ice and get rock samples for dating. The writer of the New Scientist article also mentioned a colossal outpouring of lava (The Siberian Traps) which occurred around the same time. Perhaps they were linked? They studied the globe carefully and decided it looked unlikely. The Siberian Traps were a little too far from opposition to the Antarctic crater, but then they realised – two hundred and fifty million years ago the continents were in a different position from where they are today, because of Tectonic Plate movement. A computer was used to "run the clock back" and see where the continents were at the time of the impact. Sure enough, the Siberian Traps were in the right area at that time roughly opposite the Antarctic impact site. Obviously, I am not the only person who thinks about shock waves!

The Siberian Traps and the Deccan Traps are enormous volumes of lava. It is true the lava did not flow all at the same time; there are layers; but how immense were the first eruptions? (Some scientists have suggested that volcanism alone was enough to cause the extinctions – without related asteroid impacts). The colossal outpouring of dust and noxious gases from the volcanoes might have been enough to blanket the Earth and block out the sun, so extending the period of darkness after the initial asteroid strike. If impact and volcanism were related, i.e. at the same time, it is no wonder the dinosaurs died.

Shock waves can be immensely powerful. A focussed shock wave from the detonation of a few pounds of explosive can drive a hole through 30 centimetres (1 foot) of solid steel. A similar focussed shock wave can be used to detonate an atomic bomb. The most extreme example of the power of a shock wave is an exploding star – a Super Nova. When a large star finally exhausts its nuclear fuel it collapses. The result of the collapse is the formation of an immense shock wave, so powerful it causes most of the material of the star to explode into space.

When the asteroid struck it would create a single enormous explosion – like millions of H bombs – all going off at the same time in the same place. This would create a colossal shock wave, much of which would travel right through the centre of the Earth. When this had travelled through the Earth, and reached the far surface, it would blast millions of tons of earth, rock, trees and other detritus skywards. If you ever learn there is going to be an Asteroid strike on this planet – don't be clever and bolt for the point the greatest distance away from the impact – the opposite side of the Earth. It definitely would not be the place to be! The safest, if you could say such a thing, would probably be at 120° to the point of impact. However, there would be nowhere at all – on the entire planet where you could escape the red-hot debris raining from the sky; some would travel one thousand miles before falling back; some would travel all the way around the world and pound the earth and debris that had just fallen back from the shock wave effects. "Go deep down in a mine", you say. The mine would probably be crushed by shock waves travelling through the Earth. Some of the debris from the impact explosion would be blasted into space and fall later, plummeting back into the atmosphere. The small, semi-melted, stones called Tektites are believed to have been formed in this way. Some of the debris would be blasted into space at such tremendous speeds that it would be thrown completely away from the Earth altogether. Chunks of the Moon have been found in Antarctica and even, also, pieces of Mars. (We know this from analysis of their composition). So the dinosaurs were probably struck by the direct effects of the asteroid impact – and the after effects of the volcanism. If a similar strike occurred now, human beings would have no more chance of survival than the dinosaurs did. Even in the Space Station you would be very lucky to survive the hail of debris. Almost certainly you would not.

At the present time probably the worst possible place for an asteroid strike would be the Madagascar area. Almost diametrically opposite Madagascar lies Yellowstone National Park in the USA. It is known that, under Yellowstone, lies a gigantic pluton of molten lava. There has been no eruption for millions of years but the last eruption to occur there was an enormous 'super volcanic' eruption which covered most of the USA metres deep in volcanic ash. If a large asteroid or comet were to strike in the Madagascar area the shock wave would probably 'blow off' the overlying rock at Yellowstone and trigger an enormous eruption possibly resulting in something like the Deccan or Siberian Traps.

Fortunately, impacts of the magnitude of the one that killed the dinosaurs are very, very, rare. No impact of this magnitude has occurred since. However, as scientists have gradually come to understand the real menace of an asteroid strike, more attention has been given to the possibility of an impact affecting the human race. Although the probability of a major impact in the next 100 or 1,000 years is extremely low, it is not impossible. Astronomers are now using the latest equipment to search the skies, and are creating a database of large asteroids that occasionally cross the Earth's orbit. If we could spot an asteroid that would eventually be on a collision course with Earth, providing we had enough time, we might be able to deflect it and so prevent disaster. Even a quite small asteroid, say – 100 metres (325 feet) diameter, would be capable of wiping out a large city. It seems prudent, therefore, to do what we can to prevent such a happening.

ENVIRONMENT

The greatest environmental change ever to affect this planet –
more far reaching than the effects of ice ages or even the devastating
effects of asteroid strikes and volcanism – must have been the changing of
the atmosphere of the Earth. Originally the atmosphere of the early Earth
is most likely to have been a mixture of carbon dioxide, methane, nitrogen
and possibly ammonia. The life forms that first evolved must have been
adapted to those conditions. Remarkably, even today, there are survivors
of that era. Anaerobic bacteria are commonly found in the oxygen free,
methane producing, lower layers of bogs and in the sediment and sludge
at the bottom of ponds and lakes. Colonies of primitive life have also
been found, on the deep sea floor, that can metabolise and live on
methane.

When photo-synthesis first evolved, where the energy of sunlight
was used to crack water and CO_2 molecules – producing hydrogen and
oxygen and then using the hydrogen to make hydro-carbons, the oxygen
was a waste product. In effect oxygen was a pollutant – and an extremely
dangerous one for most of the life forms that existed then; a pollutant so
powerful it would change the planet, and the future development of life on
Earth, for ever. Oxygen is so reactive it would, in any degree of
concentration, have acted as a potent poison. (Oxygen is lethal to
anaerobic bacteria).

So – life had produced the first major pollutant. Fortunately, the
sea was full of vast amounts of soluble iron compounds and this combined
with, and soaked up, the oxygen as fast as it was produced and would
have kept the amount of oxygen in the atmosphere at very low levels for
millions of years, giving life time to adapt and evolve into different forms
that could handle and metabolise oxygen. This meant the new life forms,
using oxygen, could produce far more energy and were the direct first
ancestors of oxygen breathing animals that live today including you and I.
When the soluble iron compounds combined with oxygen the resulting
compounds were insoluble and were precipitated out, slowly, over
millions of years, creating the enormous ironstone deposits we see today.
Therefore, what seemed to be a monstrous, planet wide, pollution disaster
turned out to be beneficial in the end. It probably resulted in the
extinction of perhaps 97% of the bacterial types existing at the time, but
the process would be very slow and dead bacteria did not leave much in
the way of fossil evidence. After all the ironstone was deposited, the
oxygen content of the atmosphere slowly climbed and there is evidence it
went as high as 28% at one time (as against 21% today). It would be very

125

unlikely that oxygen levels could go higher than 28% as the slightest spark (or lightning flash) would cause a raging fire in anything combustible.

Gradually life evolved, from bacteria and primitive plants, to animals, and then the fossil record shows there were other environmental changes, far more sudden and violent. As complex life proliferated and advanced, the second most drastic change of environment, again caused by life itself, occurred. Not as permanent as the change to an oxygen atmosphere had been but extreme nevertheless and lasting for many millions of years.

In the sea countless trillions of small planktonic animals created shells and skeletons using calcium and carbon taken from solution in the sea water. When these died the remains fell to the sea bed and gradually accumulated, forming the enormous limestone and chalk deposits we see today. In the process vast quantities of carbon were removed from the sea. Since the CO_2 enters the sea from the atmosphere the atmospheric concentration of CO_2 was gradually reduced. At the same time, photosynthetic cells and minute plants also extracted carbon from the sea to create their tissues and again their remains fell to join the ooze on the sea bed and are believed to be the source of the vast oil deposits found around the world today. Despite a steady input of CO_2 from volcanic eruptions the CO_2 content of the atmosphere slowly fell until a critical situation was reached where the greenhouse effect was insufficient to keep the planet warm. The sun, at this time, actually produced less heat than it does today – so the greenhouse effect was very important. The planet began to cool and plunged into the most extreme, the most extensive ice age ever.

It is believed, on the basis of available evidence, the ice may have spread to totally cover the entire planet, from pole to pole so that the surface of the planet may have been a complete ball of ice. From space, Earth must have appeared to be a frozen, lifeless planet but, underneath the ice, the sea did not freeze. There would always be heat entering the sea from underwater volcanoes, hot seeps and the sea bed being warmed slightly by conduction from the hot rock of the mantle below. Life therefore, continued despite the drastic change of environment but would be greatly reduced in quantity because of reduced light and because the supply of CO_2 from the atmosphere would be cut off. It is believed this 'Snowball Earth' continued for millions of years until, eventually, volcanoes gradually increased the atmospheric CO_2 level to a point where a global warming phase kicked in. As life recovered and multiplied the CO_2 extraction process would again occur and a series of glaciations and warm ages have continued to this day but no subsequent glaciations have ever been as extreme as the first.

Incidentally, scientists are particularly interested in Jupiter's Moon – Europa which appears to be, on the outside, like 'Snowball Earth', a lifeless ball of ice. They think there is a liquid water sea under the ice which may contain life. Remarkably it was discovered that, even at the coldest place on Earth – the South Pole – there is an enormous lake of liquid water (Lake Vostok) ten thousand feet (3,077 metres) down under the ice. It has probably been there, undisturbed for millions of years. Russian scientists have drilled down and are almost ready to break into this lake. They, and many other scientists and biologists, will be very interested to find if life exists in this lake. If I was a betting man I would lay odds that it does.

Asteroid strikes and massive volcanism have also affected the Earth causing sudden catastrophic changes of atmosphere, temperature and climate. (I have described an asteroid strike and volcanism effects in detail in the Chapter – DINOSAURS). The history of life on Earth is punctuated by a series of mass extinctions and sudden environmental changes. This is an active planet, active in many ways; the movement of tectonic plates (Continental Drift), volcanism, ocean currents, air currents, glaciers, the effects of the seasons and the constantly changing effects of life itself. Environmental change, therefore, is in the nature of the planet. Stability is only to be found on a dead planet such as Mercury, or a satellite such as Earth's moon. For the last few hundred thousand years, the main environmental changes have been caused by ice ages and the interglacial warm periods between. The next big worldwide environmental shock will be the changes induced by global warming, resulting from human activity. (See Chapter – GLOBAL WARMING). All life on the planet will be affected, to greater or lesser degree.

In the sea, everything, from the plankton and corals to large fish and whales, will be affected by the increasing temperature. Ocean currents such as El Nino and the Gulf Stream will be affected which will, in turn, affect the amount of nutrients brought up from the deep sea and, indirectly, affect the food chain. Changes in habitats and migration of species will occur (there is already evidence of warm water species moving north). On land the steady increase of temperature will modify habitats. Rainfall may decrease in some areas and increase in others but, overall, the amount of rain can be expected to increase because of increased evaporation. Some deserts will expand, others decrease. Low lying coastal areas will eventually be flooded because of slowly rising sea levels. An indirect effect of all this is that evolutionary pressures will intensify – as they do during any period of rapid change. Polar bears, for instance, will have to change their behaviour (as I feel sure they will) or risk extinction. For many animal species the problems of environmental change, due to global warming, will be compounded by the impact of human activity – deforestation, the cultivation of the tundra, over fishing of the seas, and so on. For humans, the environmental changes will be such that mass migration is likely to take place. In the past, human beings have, of course, had to deal with global and local environmental changes, particularly during the ice ages.

A lesser known and local change, which must have affected the European area a few million years ago, was the time when the Mediterranean Sea dried up. In the 1960's, when sonar had been developed adequately, ships began echo-sounding and recording the profile of the sea bed to produce detailed underwater maps. It was then we learned about the mid Atlantic ridge and other features.

As part of the survey, ships carried out an echo-sounding survey of the Mediterranean. Everything went well, and they produced their maps, but a slightly puzzling thing was that they seemed to get a double echo from most of the Mediterranean sea bed – something that occurred nowhere else. However, it was dismissed as an unimportant anomaly. A few years later, an engineering firm was contracted to build a large structure near the mouth of the Rhone river in Southern France. Ideally, they would have liked to have bored down through the earth to solid rock and build concrete piles (columns), extending from the rock to the surface, to support the structure. They drilled, but did not find solid rock where they expected to. They drilled deeper, and yet deeper. It was found that, at the mouth of the Rhone, there appeared to have once been an enormous ravine, which went down way, way below sea level and which was now filled with sand and river deposits. Quite a puzzle!

The Mediterranean is very deep, much of it 10,000 feet (3,077 metres) and more. Despite this, scientists lowered equipment down and took cores from a number of points on the sea bed. The double echo was explained! A good deal of the floor of the Mediterranean was covered (under the surface layer of sediment and mud) by a thick layer of salt. Eventually somebody put two and two together and realised the remarkable answer to the questions of "Where had the salt come from?" and "What had caused the ravine at the mouth of the Rhone?" The Mediterranean had, at some time in the past, dried up. They concluded that some upheaval, some earthquake perhaps, had lifted up the sea bed and closed off the Straits of Gibraltar. A gigantic natural dam! This must have stayed in place for a million years or more and, during that time, the Mediterranean had evaporated until the entire immense basin was empty, except for a few lakes fed by rivers such as the Rhone, the Ebro, etc. (It is believed the Nile did not exist at this time, being created later as a result of earth movements in the Rift Valley area of Africa). The total evaporation of the Mediterranean may sound unlikely but it is a fact that today the Caspian Sea which, in reality, is only a large lake, completely evaporates the entire input of the mighty river Volga and other, smaller, rivers. It is also a fact that there is always a current, from the Atlantic to the Mediterranean, through the Straits of Gibraltar showing that the evaporation from the 'Med' is considerably greater than the inputs from all the rivers including the Rhone and the Nile.

So, at one time, the Mediterranean dried up and there was an enormous cavity – a depression in the Earth's crust – 10,000 and more feet (3,077 metres) deep below normal sea level. The evaporation of all that amount of water, and the mass it represented, must have slightly altered the balance of the Earth. More importantly it meant the removal of a colossal heat sink. (The Mediterranean must act today to substantially cool the whole of Europe and produce lower temperatures, even in North Africa). With the Mediterranean Sea area reduced to a gigantic, blazing hot, dust bowl, the average temperatures in Europe must have soared. Also the rainfall in that area would probably have been drastically changed. It is interesting to note that there is evidence in the UK that lions and rhinoceros once roamed here; maybe not so surprising!

Eventually there was another upheaval at the Straits of Gibraltar and the dam broke, the waters rushed in and the Mediterranean was filled again. It has been estimated the waterfall that ensued, at the Straits, was probably 1000 times bigger than Niagara. The Niagara Falls drop 167 feet (51 metres); the Gibraltar Falls tumbled thousands of feet to the valley floor. There was probably an initial, colossal, waterfall and then gigantic cascades. What a spectacle it must have been! I wonder if any of our (very primitive) ancestors saw it. When the Mediterranean re-filled, the climate of Europe would again be drastically changed. The flooding of the Mediterranean cannot, of course, be linked to the legend of Atlantis because it happened millions of years ago.

Incidentally, there is evidence the Black Sea area was once separated from the Mediterranean in a similar manner and, instead of the Black Sea, there was a large fresh water lake, considerably smaller than the current Black Sea area and below existing sea levels. There are believed to have been human settlements around the lakes shores. Around 6 to 7 thousand years ago something, probably an earthquake, broke the land 'dam' that existed between the Mediterranean and the lake, and sea water cascaded in, to flood the low lying land around the lake and convert the lake into the Black Sea. The inundation may be the basis of the legend of the Biblical Flood. It also occurs to me that maybe a settlement or ancient city on the western shore of the lake may have been flooded, giving rise to the legend of Atlantis.

So we can see that environmental change is in the nature of the planet, and the environmental changes we worry about today are relatively minor compared to the great changes that have occurred in the past. However, human beings are the first and only modern animal species capable of massively affecting and (if we consider the ultimate – thermonuclear war) practically wrecking the environment of the entire planet. With capability should come responsibility. We have a responsibility to preserve the planet, both for our descendents and for other life forms.

On a planetary scale the most important action we should take is to control the human population. Deforestation in South America and Indonesia, for instance, will not cease while the population continues to increase. Also, no country with an expanding population can be expected to prevent an increase in overall CO_2 emissions. Population increase automatically means an increase in the area of cultivated land and space used for habitation, leading to a reduction in the remaining natural habitat. Without population control all other efforts to try to conserve habitats will, in the end, be futile.

Since man evolved and became the dominant animal on the planet and especially since the numbers of human beings escalated, first into the millions and then to the billions, he has acted in a manner which has affected and changed the environment. However, it can be said, that all animals do, to a greater or lesser extent. For example it is believed a lot of African grasslands – the Savannah – have been created because elephants routinely push over and destroy established trees so that they can feed from the lush, untouched, top-most branches. This effect is then backed up by the grazing of types of deer which efficiently eat, and destroy, tree seedlings and saplings. Because of this behaviour there now exists thousands of square miles of grassland which would otherwise be forest or scrubland.

On a much less obvious scale we have the effects of insects, of various types, on different kinds of plant life. For instance, in the UK, we occasionally see a metre high bushy plant, with spikes of purple flowers (Purple Loosestrife), along some of the less disturbed river banks. It cannot be said to be rare but, to most of us, it is not common either. A few years ago someone must have taken some seed to the USA. The plant grew, thrived and spread, to such an extent that it became a plague in some areas. Scientists investigated and found that, in the UK, a small beetle a couple of millimetres long, often attacked the Loosestrife and kept it in check. They took beetles to America and – problem solved.

A similar thing happened when Prickly Pear cactus was introduced to Australia. In a few years there were vast areas of the cactus and there were fears it would get totally out of control. Scientists investigated to see why the cactus did not run riot in its native land. The reason was the controlling effect of a small moth, and its voracious caterpillars. The moth was introduced to Australia, and again – problem solved.

Both of these situations were, of course, created by the intervention of man – and solved by the intervention of man. However, it is often not so simple. Man creates a problem, introduces a pest or predator to correct the situation and the pest or predator runs riot, in an unpredicted manner and becomes a bigger problem than the one it was intended to solve.

Occasionally there have been situations bordering on the ridiculous. Years ago, humans colonised a fairly small island in the Pacific. Rats came with the ship and devastated the islands wildlife. Having practically wiped out the wildlife, the rats then started on the islanders' domestic chickens and ducks. To control the rats, snakes were introduced (pythons). The snakes multiplied and polished off the rats and then, of course, started on the chickens. To eliminate the snakes, mongoose were introduced. As you can guess the mongoose eliminated the snakes and then they too, started on the chickens. I have no idea what happened next.

Incidentally I saw a film of how the mongoose handled the pythons. The pythons, unless they are hunting, stay up on branches of trees. The film showed a mongoose climb a tree and approach a python on its branch. The python assumed a defensive posture, the mongoose then flung itself forward, grabbed the pythons neck in its teeth and leaped off the branch. The python's head, and a couple of feet of its body, were dragged down below the branch by the impact and before the python could contract its body enough to grip the branch and prevent it slipping. Then the mongoose, dangling in mid air, began what can only be described as a circus type act. It swung its dangling body, with a twisting motion, so that it began to rotate. Amazingly, the python's head was rapidly twisted totally off its body. The mongoose and head fell to the ground, quickly followed by the dead python's body and the mongoose began to feast. How on Earth did a mongoose learn a trick like that?

A less amusing situation arose in Australia after settlers introduced rabbits for sport hunting. With no natural predators the rabbit population exploded, so much so that large areas of grassland, which could have been used for grazing sheep or cattle, were reduced to near desert. In desperation the Australian Government erected a fence, over

131

1000 miles long, to restrict the rabbit population expansion. Recently, flying over Australia, I looked down and was puzzled by a knife edged straight line on the ground running roughly North/South. On the western side of the line the colour was sand. On the eastern side the colour was brown and green. I then realised I must be looking down on the great Australian rabbit fence. In addition to erecting the fence, Australian and other scientists sought for ways to eliminate the rabbits. They finally came up with a bio-weapon. In the early 1950s, they introduced a viral disease – Myxomatosis – carried by rabbit fleas; the disease was lethal. Rabbits died in their tens of millions but Darwinian Evolution will not be denied. A few of the rabbits had mutations that enabled them to survive. The rabbits that exist today, whilst not totally immune to Myxomatosis, are more resistant and rabbit populations have climbed again – as shown by my view of the fence from the aircraft. The Australians are now experimenting with a new anti-rabbit disease.

While we are on the subject of bio-weapons against pests, remarkable success was achieved in eradicating a pernicious pest (the screw-worm fly), in the southern states of the USA. Most people are familiar with the common meat fly (bluebottle fly). This fly produces maggots that eat meat but only dead meat. The maggots are so selective it has been found that they are beneficial in the treatment and healing of serious flesh wounds. It was noticed, during the Crimean War, that soldiers with maggot infested wounds recovered better, and died less frequently than wounded soldiers without maggots. A common cause of death, in those days, was gangrene – a disease which started in rotting dead flesh and spread to living flesh, and almost always killed the sufferer. It was later found that maggots ate away the dead flesh and thereby cleaned the wound and even secreted an enzyme which helped prevent infection.

To return to the screw-worm fly. A screw-worm fly looks very much like the common bluebottle and its maggots eat meat but there is one big difference. The screw-worm fly maggots will eat live flesh with the same gusto that they consume dead flesh. Screw-worm flies lay their eggs on living cattle and the maggots then eat the animal alive – and carry on merrily when it is dead. The screw-worm fly could, and did, devastate herds of cattle in the USA and elsewhere.

Due to the efforts of scientists and biologists the screw-worm fly was eradicated – totally wiped out – in the USA by a brilliant biological manoeuvre. Screw-worm flies were bred in their billions in laboratories – the maggots feeding on dead meat. Then they were placed, live, in containers, and subjected to a high dose of gamma radiation; not enough to kill the flies but enough to sterilise them – Radiation Castration you might call it. They then released the sterile flies in areas infested with the wild screw-worm flies. The new flies mated with the existing flies, with the result that 95% of the eggs produced were sterile. The screw-worm fly population plummeted. The scientists then repeated the performance and the remaining wild, fertile, flies were overwhelmed by the next wave of sterilised flies. After several introductions of sterile flies the wild population was totally eradicated – 100% wipe out. A great pest control success story! Some people have said "Why can't we do the same thing with malaria carrying mosquitoes?" The answer is, it would work in principle but no one has come up with a practical way to produce billions of live mosquitoes under laboratory conditions. Breeding bluebottles and screw-worm flies was easy. Thousands of tons of bluebottle maggots are produced every year, simply as bait for anglers.

When, in the 1950s and 1960s, a considerable number of nuclear weapons were test fired, above ground, it subtly altered the environment of the whole world, by slightly increasing the radio-active background. There are probably more mutations and cancers as a result. After the Bikini atomic bomb tests, when lagoons were massively contaminated by radio-activity, it was thought that, in the following years, many deformities would be induced in fish, crabs and other wildlife. However, when scientists checked, 5 years later, they found none. Then it was realised that any defective (and thus less competitive) fish and animals had been wiped out by Darwinian 'Survival of the Fittest'!

Closer to home, i.e. in the UK, we have recently experienced a number of environmental changes due to human activities. The whole countryside of the UK is now different, due to the accidental introduction of Dutch Elm Disease. It is estimated 40 to 50 million full sized elm trees (they used to be up to 100 feet high) died in the 1950s and 60s and countless more saplings since. (Remarkably the disease does not totally kill the roots – which keep throwing up new growths – but, as soon as the new trees reach a few metres in height, the disease, which is spread by beetles, kills them). Other tree diseases have now reached the UK. There is a disease killing horse chestnut trees (bleeding canker) and another killing sweet chestnut trees. (The infected tree seems perfectly OK – it simply does not wake up in the spring). 'Sudden Oak Death' is killing oak trees and half of my Mountain Ash trees (Rowan) have died of a form of blight.

I have been involved with fish since I was a child, both through angling and, later, keeping fish in ponds. When I was a child the UK, ponds, lakes, canals and rivers teemed with healthy fish. Shoals of large salmon ran up the river Wye and other UK rivers. In the late 1960s, a disease (UDN Disease) appeared from nowhere and devastated the salmon, which have never recovered. Since then we have had various diseases decimating other kinds of fresh water fish.

The source of most of these diseases (not UDN) is quite obvious. It is the uncontrolled importation of diseased fancy fish (mainly Goldfish and Koi Carp) from the Far East. Whereas live animals imported into the UK are subjected to checks and quarantine, fancy fish are not. A fish dealer of my acquaintance tells me he travels to the Far East, orders lots of fish which are shipped live, by air, in polythene bags to the UK. He then drives his van to the airport, signs a few forms and then loads his fish, straight from the plane, into his van and drives home. Fortunately, he is a responsible man and will not sell his fish until they have been heavily medicated and quarantined by him for several weeks. Others are not so fussy and I have seen goldfish and Koi on display at Garden Centres, where it is obvious the fish are hopelessly diseased. These fish are bought by people who are not experts and placed in small garden ponds. Along comes a Heron one morning, gulps a diseased goldfish and goes back to his local lake. Result – the fish in the lake become diseased. The worst feature of the Heron who visits me is not the fish he eats but the disease he brings. Every year I have to dose my fish to eliminate disease and, after a few months, the Heron brings me disease again. Time after time!

In a few rivers flowing into the Baltic Sea, salmon suffered from infestation by a small parasite (Gyrodactylus Salaris) which is a skin and gill fluke. In the gills the flukes are lethal. Somehow, flukes were transferred to some prime salmon rivers in Norway and the salmon populations were devastated. In desperation the river board, to try to clean the affected rivers and prevent the disease spreading, completely sterilised the affected river systems by saturating them with Rotenone, which killed everything, all the way to the sea. When they are sure the flukes are gone they will reintroduce salmon, plus insects and all the other river life. In the UK, in order to prevent transmission of disease, there are laws where anglers can be fined thousands of pounds for transferring fish from one lake to another. However, Herons, Cormorants and other fish eating birds are transferring disease all the time.

I would point out that natural accidents – seeds and diseases carried by birds, insects carried on the wind, rats being carried on floating logs, and so on, must have created local biological disasters, similar to the ones described, at various times in Earth's history. In all these cases the disasters play themselves out, over time, resulting in extinctions, new developments and slight twists in the long path of evolution.

Fundamentally, it can be said that the whole planet is, and has always been, in a state of flux. The environment has been endlessly changing as a result of the interactions of plants, animals and the planetary conditions. Today, very few areas of the Earth are in their 'natural' state. So much has been altered by the activities of man. The wonderful and beautiful English countryside I loved as a boy was almost totally man made; the result of the elimination of the original forest, farming practices, the planting, control and coppicing of woods, the planting of hedgerows, the building of cottages and so on. Today much of the UK environment seems, to me, harsher and less attractive with more concrete and paving, high rise dwellings, vast fields, small flailed hedges and, of course, the necessary but hideous enormous wind generators.

In some ways, however, some things are better. Rivers running through large cities such as London were little better than open sewers and many beaches were horribly polluted; these have now been cleaned up. There is, generally, a great awareness of the need to look after the environment, and for conservation, if we are not to lose much of the flora and fauna of the natural world. It is sad when people of basically good intention do not think things through before taking action. For example the 'Animal Rights' enthusiasts in the UK did not stop to think before they released over 1000 mink from the cages of fur farms. (Mink, which are not indigenous to the UK, are murderous, ruthless, predators in the wild). They did not stop to think what damage would be done to the native British birds and other wildlife.

No doubt American grey squirrels were also introduced thoughtlessly to this country. Grey squirrels are predatory, destructive and aggressive. They have displaced our original red squirrels (which are vegetarian and do far less damage), do an enormous amount of damage to young trees – as I can personally testify – and decimate the song bird population by raiding nests and eating eggs and young. They may look very appealing, sitting on a window ledge eating peanuts but, in the countryside, they are a menace.

In the light of our mistakes, it is obvious we must be very careful before we introduce either animals or plants or anything biological into new habitats and, in cases where we have already made mistakes, we must be very careful that our attempts to put things right do not make things worse. We must think and act very carefully, and rationally, in everything we do concerned with the environment.

I sometimes wonder if there is much rational thinking going on in the 'powers that be'. On a fairly mundane level, for instance, most people in the UK like song birds and lament their decline. In order to encourage them, calls for larger hedgerows, more 'set-aside' land and untouched strips around cultivated fields are often made (I am all in favour of this) but a few years ago magpies (a murderous predator of the eggs and young of songbirds) were a protected species. It was illegal to shoot or trap magpies and, as a result, the numbers increased until we were swarming with them; small bird populations were devastated. Eventually, (about 10 years late) the rules were changed and it is now legal to control magpies.

We now have a very similar situation with sparrowhawks. In the last few years the sparrowhawk population has dramatically increased. Sparrowhawks decimate small birds (one sparrowhawk will kill and eat several a day). A pair with two or three chicks can be killing 10 or more small birds a day, so we are talking of thousands a year. A pair of sparrowhawks, nesting nearby, have practically wiped out the small bird population in my garden, orchard and little wood. I used to have a nesting pair of spotted flycatchers in the garden together with robins, wrens, blue tits, dunnocks, chaffinches and so on. In the wood were warblers, chiff chaffs, long tail tits, bullfinches and even the occasional goldcrest. All these are gone. All I find are the remains, in telltale patches of feathers and bits of flesh. Despite soaring numbers, sparrowhawks are protected. No doubt, in ten years time, someone will wake up and decide sparrowhawk numbers need to be reduced.

The proliferation of cormorants are another example of this thinking. When I was a youth cormorants were coastal birds. We never saw them on inland lakes and waterways. Now these ugly birds are everywhere, not in ones and twos but in hundreds. Many lakes have been stripped of coarse fish, but cormorants are protected.

Whether we are considering global warming, the human population, methods of agriculture, the building of roads or any of the myriad things that affect the environment, whether it is on a global or local scale, let us pause and do some serious rational thinking before we take action.

AGEING

How would you like to live to 100 or 120 or even 150? Not as a decrepit old person vacantly gazing around from a wheelchair but active, fit and healthy. It may be that it is not as impossible as it sounds.

Every living thing on this Earth appears to age and die. People, in general, accept it without question. We tell ourselves it is a fact of life but let us pause and consider the evidence very carefully. A mouse, for instance, has a very short life and some insects, even shorter. There are other animals, however, that have remarkably long lives – at least by our standards. The large tortoises come to mind, with life spans of over 100 years. The sturgeon, an archaic fish, well known because of the caviar produced from its eggs, is an amazing fish with no known limit to its size or its life span.

To check the age of fish it is usual to remove a scale and, under a microscope, check the number of growth rings in a similar manner to checking the age of a tree. The sturgeon does not have scales but it does have, on it's flanks, a number of bony plates known as 'scutes'. A scute can be removed, sectioned and the annual growth marks counted. A friend of mine in Canada told me he once caught a large sturgeon of 600 to 800lb (272kg to 363kg) and decided to have its age checked by the scute removal method. It was found his fish was around one hundred and fifty years old. 'Impressive' you may say, but wait! A 600 to 800lb (272kg to 363kg) sturgeon is a large fish these days but, years ago, fish were caught that were far larger. In the 1930s, during the Depression, many sturgeon from the Fraser river in British Columbia were slaughtered for food. Sturgeon were taken from the river eighteen feet (five and a half metres) long, weighing over 2000lb (907kg). One wonders how old those fish were!

Plants too have varying life spans. I once read it was possible for a man to plant a young pear tree in his youth and then outlive it. Some trees, however, such as the Bristlecone Pine in America have been proved to live over 4000 years. In my orchard I have a Bramleys Seedling apple tree. It is a perfectly healthy young tree. The original tree, grown from a seed, has probably died from old age long ago. However, my tree has been grown from a cutting grafted on to a rootstock. In fact it is probably a cutting from a cutting. It appears that, if you do this, you can go on and on, ad infinitum. Apparently the act of cutting and grafting, rejuvenates; coppicing does also, I am told. A coppice stool (where a tree has been cut off just above the ground and grows new shoots – which are cut off every year) can go on living indefinitely. It appears coppiced shoots simply regenerate, and keep producing fresh young shoots for hundreds of years. I also have a plum tree – grown from a sucker cut off a root of a friend's plum tree, which was grown from a sucker cut off a root of his mother's plum tree; which originally grew from a stone planted by a child. (For non gardeners – a sucker is a new shoot growth developing from a nodule on a root. A sucker may pop up anywhere, from close to the parent tree or several metres away. If it is not cut off it will, eventually, develop into a new, full size, tree. Many fruit trees are prone to this). My tree is young and healthy, and produces good fruit. (The original tree grown from the plum stone has died from old age). Incidentally, you cannot do this with a sucker from a tree bought at a garden centre because the plum will have been grafted on to a different root stock. The sucker would produce a different, useless, tree; genetically related to the rootstock, not the graft.

Which brings us to English Elms. I noticed when I was a youth that, although English Elms were glorious trees and sometimes flowered profusely, you never saw an elm grow from seed. Years later I read that all the Elms in England are descendents of one tree, brought here by the Romans. This is why they produce no seed. It also means all the Elms are clones, descended from the original tree and propagated from suckers on the elm roots. So a sucker is exactly the same genetically as the parent tree. That means an elm in this country today (if you can find one – nearly all mature trees have been destroyed by disease) is the same elm genetically as the one the Romans brought here. In other words it is immortal and it will probably go on for the next 10 or 20 thousand years. Strangely, although Elm Disease kills the main bulk of the tree, it does not kill the roots and the elm suckers, while they are still small, do not get the disease and keep producing new elm trees. These are then killed by the disease when they are four to six metres (thirteen to twenty feet) in height, so we shall never get mature trees again while the disease is around. We can only hope that, sometime, it will die out, and England will have its beautiful, tall, elms again. So far, after fifty years, there is not the slightest sign of this happening. I still have young elm trees dying of Dutch Elm Disease every year.

So it seems ageing is not so simple after all. Let us now consider the human body. Scientists have concluded, after careful study, that most of the cells of the human body are replaced every seven years or so. Yet we can live only to – say – 90 years; maximum about 116 to 118 years. Why is it we cannot live forever, if cells are being replaced? (Forget this business about wearing out – like some motorcar – we are talking about a living mass of cells. The motorcar would never wear out if you replaced everything, every couple of years, would it?)

A few years ago, scientists wrote articles about the discovery of a new genetic component of the cell chromosomes called Telomeres. I first read about Telomeres in an article on cancer. The article stated that, back in the 1930s, a sample of living cancer cells had been taken from a patient before she died and had been kept alive in a culture solution ever since. The cancer cells multiplied, and samples were dispatched to medical institutions in various parts of the country for research. The cancer cells continued to multiply while supplied by nutrients, and it was realised the cells did not show any changes – did not appear to age. Investigation revealed the Telomeres. In every living cell of the body, the genetic information is gathered together in molecular packages called chromosomes. Whenever a cell replicates, the chromosomes are duplicated to provide chromosomes for the new daughter cell. It was found the chromosomes had a small extension or 'tail' of genes, extending almost like the links of a chain. When a cell divides (multiplies itself) a few links are clipped off the Telomere chain. The next time the cell divides – a few more are removed. Eventually, after a certain number of divisions, the Telomere is reduced to a critical length, and then some mechanism is triggered that prevents a cell dividing ever again. In other words – by the time you reach 90 years old, the Telomeres are short, and are signalling your cells to cease replicating. (This cannot be the whole story, unfortunately, because, if ageing was purely caused by the Telomeres, then we should stay youthful and active until we were 90 and then keel over and die. Why the cells become less and less efficient as they replicate has not yet been completely discovered). However, with Telomeres, we are at least on the way to discovering one of the secrets of ageing. Cancer cells have developed the ability to repair the shortened Telomeres back to full length and, as a result, the cancer becomes immortal.

If you think about it, whilst individuals age and die, the chain of life of which you are a part is indeed immortal. Your ancestry must go back, in an unbroken sequence, four thousand, million years, to when the first life came into being in the primordial sea. Life is continuous and immortal. Although you, as a person, age, your seed, (your children) have the Telomere clock reset to zero when they are conceived. So far as the survival of the immortal race is concerned, we, its members, are as expendable as the leaves of a tree or a hair from your head. The conclusion is – as individuals, we are all fitted with a time fuse to a self destruct button. The next question is – Why?

Elsewhere in this book I have written about the strange business of mules; where two related species have diverged to a point where it is possible to cross-breed the animals, but the resulting progeny are only sterile 'mules'. As though Nature has said "no going back". Add this to the knowledge of Telomeres and what do you get? I suggest the answer is something to do with EVOLUTION. I suggest that, in advanced animals, and some plants for that matter, a trick has evolved to facilitate or speed up evolution. If animals and plants die off after a short time, there has to be a definite, fairly rapid, chain of succession – which will speed up evolutionary change. If an animal or plant lived a thousand years and cross bred with the local population – young or old, it would slow up the rate of evolution. Young ladies in the prime of life do sometimes marry and have children with older men. However they are warned – by greying hair and baldness and other degenerative signs – that this man is old and past his prime. The average young woman is inclined to marry the average young man – not someone old enough to be her father. Many animals go further – and the males are programmed to have savage battles, not only to get rid of the old, but also to winnow out the best of the existing crop to produce the next generation. In other words survival of the fittest, simply by surviving in the face of predators and general competition with other species, is not enough; even an internal (within the species) battle for supremacy has been created.

I think an accelerated drive for evolution has somehow come into being. The situation with mules tends to support this. Why would it matter if a donkey mates with a horse? If the resulting progeny cannot compete they would fail anyway whether they are fertile or not. It is as if nature doesn't want to waste time. I believe there is something in most animal genes – and some plants too which is pushing evolution; ageing is just one of the tricks to speed the process. If everybody lived to be 1000, and only had two children, in midlife, evolution would slow down. It is noticeable that animals and plants that do, naturally, live to be very old are primitive species; the big tortoises are an ancient species; the sturgeon is a prehistoric fish; bristle cone pine trees are pretty ancient too. On reflection, it would appear that the fastest rate of evolution would be achieved if animals only lived long enough to reproduce and die. Compare the life span of a mouse with that of an elephant. Some insects of course, have very short life spans indeed. (I have heard it said that life span is related to the number of heartbeats in a lifetime, but am convinced this is invalid. As an exception to this proposition, which implies that small animals, with fast heartbeats, have a short life, I would point out that a parrot can live as long as an elephant). I am, therefore, convinced – Ageing is something to do with evolution. I am also convinced that, sooner or later, scientists are going to solve the problem of ageing and enable people to live to 120 years or more. Think what trouble that will cause! Even if we all became 'immortal' it wouldn't mean we would live forever, of course. Motor cars, for instance, are fairly efficient at shortening our lives. I know one almost shortened mine. Incidentally, I read about a billionaire who was fast off the mark when he read about Telomeres; he poured hundreds of millions of dollars into a research facility. I expect he wants them to crack the problem before his personal time runs out!

One of nature's most remarkable 'ageing' situations is that of the salmon. On one of the rivers I fish in Alaska, no fewer than five different species of salmon enter the river to spawn each year. They come into the river fresh from the sea, in perfect condition. Well fed, bounding with energy. As fit and healthy as it is possible to be. They are only four or five years old – from when they hatched from the egg. Many fish can live quite long lives; thirty, forty or more years. (I have a carp I know is at least 40 years old). There appears no reason why these salmon, if they survived predators, should not live for many more years. But No! They swim up the river and spawn, once only, and die. One hundred percent mortality. Millions of them. As soon as they come into the river they start to change, they stop feeding. (They only attack our flies and lures because of residual aggression – from when they were efficient predators in the sea). Then they begin to change shape and colour. By the time they spawn they are unrecognisable from the fish that came in from the sea. I see them as hump backed, deformed, buck-toothed goldfish (no doubt the males look beautiful to the females!). As they spawn they are weakening, and, by the time they have finished spawning, they are ageing wrecks of the fish they once were. They swim listlessly around and you can easily go and pick one up – it lies, hardly moving, gasping in your hands. It is dying of degeneration – literally a speeded up ageing process. Millions of carcases litter the river; the stench is stunning! I have seen this once – and I have no desire to see it again. The Department of Fish and Game experts tell me there is a reason why this happens. The Alaskan rivers, in their normal condition, are very clear and nutrient low. There would not be enough insect and planktonic life in the river, to feed the countless millions of salmon fry that emerge from the eggs. So 'Nature' has found an answer, and the salmon die; to leave their bodies to rot and fertilise the river, and thus cause a boost in planktonic and insect life to feed the new generation. Amazing!

From the air, as you fly across a wilderness of tundra, you see the evidence of a shortage of nutrients. Just moss and fine grass and a few stunted trees just a few metres high. The trees are all 3 to 10 metres (10 to 33 feet) apart – they need the space to get enough nutrients to grow. They grow very slowly, maybe only 3 inches (75mm) a year. The river cuts through this wilderness like a great green snake. Alongside the river the trees are dense and grow to sixty feet and more. Grass is three feet tall, and there are many kinds of wildflowers. When you are on the river, in a boat, it is beautiful. Lush growth, plants, trees, bears, birds, eagles, otters – you name it! It is hard to believe that, just a mile away, there is a semi-barren wilderness. The reason for this river bank fertility is – the salmon. The otters eat the salmon, as do the bears and eagles. Their droppings fertilise the strip of land on either side of the river, and the tundra blooms.

I also fish in Russia, on the Kola peninsula. On these occasions, however, it is for a different species – the Atlantic salmon. The tundra is the same as in Alaska. The rivers are also the same, but the fish are slightly different. They come into the river, and head upstream to spawn, the same as the fish in Alaska, and they also take our lures in the same way. Most of these salmon spawn, and then die, just the same – but not quite all; there is not 100% mortality. All the salmon degenerate and after spawning, are wrecks but, with a small percentage of the Atlantic salmon something remarkable happens. Somehow, a genetic switch is 'flipped' and, suddenly, the fish begins to recover. It grows new teeth and becomes more energetic, and then begins to feed. It is regenerated. This fish is called a Kelt and it is illegal to kill or take a kelt. The kelt recovers its will to live and goes back to the sea. Once more it is transformed into an efficient predator – a killing machine; a superb, lithe, dynamic fish. After a time, it again develops the urge to reproduce. The fish is, of course, much bigger this time. Again it ascends the river, spawns and degenerates and, sometimes – only sometimes, mind you – the 'magic switch' is thrown again, and the fish once more regains it's will to live. The third time it comes into the river it will be a monster, and that is why I fish the Northern rivers of the Kola; for the thrill of the odd monster that gets on my line!

There is, in fact, a terrible human disease (Progeria) which creates early ageing and death – similar to that experienced by the salmon. Fortunately, it is rare. It strikes children as young as 10 or twelve years of age, causing a sudden speeding up of the ageing process. At fourteen or fifteen they can be wizened and shrivelled, as very elderly people might be. Dreadful!

Another remarkable example of the power of genes to 'switch off' or cause to age suddenly and die is to be found in the function of the mammalian placenta. When conception takes place, usually in the fallopian tubes and the fertilised egg travels into the uterus, it bonds to the uterine walls and, as the foetus develops, the placenta and umbilical forms. The placenta invades the uterine wall very aggressively, almost like a cancer. It stimulates the growth of blood vessels and extracts nutrients and oxygen to feed the growing foetus. We are reminded of a cancer's similar ability to stimulate the growth of blood vessels and the extraction of nutrients and oxygen to feed the cancer. The most remarkable thing, though, is the fact that the placenta has a fixed and limited life span; it is on a genetic timer. After nine months, or shortly thereafter, the placenta is switched into self destruct mode. This is usually timed to coincide with the baby's birth and, shortly after birth, the placenta releases its grip on the uterine walls and falls away, to be ejected. However, sometimes the synchronisation of placenta and foetal development is faulty and the baby can be overdue. When this happens there is a risk that the placenta will be genetically switched off, go into self destruct mode and cease to function. The baby can then be starved, particularly of oxygen, leading to the death of the child and stillbirth. It is for this reason that doctors keep a careful watch on any baby they think is overdue and are prepared to take fast action to induce the birth or to conduct a Caesarean operation if there is evidence the baby is in distress or the placenta is degenerating. Again, therefore, we have another example of the power of genes; to switch on the placenta, at the start of pregnancy, to cause it to become an aggressive, cancer like, entity and then, remarkably, at the end of its useful life, it is, almost brutally one might say, destroyed. Having fulfilled their function, the living cells of the placenta are casually discarded. For this to be achieved the cells of the placenta must obey their genetic orders and accept death on demand.

How much more evidence do we need, before there is acceptance that there really is an ageing gene. If I was studying ageing, I would study the salmon. To see if I could discover the 'magic switch' that sometimes turns the salmon back on – and, also, to find the switch that made him suddenly age and die in the first place. I would also study the sturgeon; discover whether it has Telomeres on the ends of its chromosomes and what happens to them; try to find out why it can grow so large – but not appear to age. I would study ancient tortoises and turtles and trees. Do trees have Telomeres? I would study frogs and newts and lizards. To try to find out how they can grow new tails and, in the case of some frogs and newts, how they grow a complete new limb – a leg – if it has been lost or cut off. I would study the newly fertilised human egg and the condition of the genes and telomeres. (The human embryo has its 'clock' set to zero – whether the mother that produced it is young or old). I would study the genetic control of the mammalian placenta. The keys to ageing are there – somewhere. Ageing is a deliberate genetic 'switching off'. The salmon just do it faster than you or I. There is no real reason we could not live to 150 years or more if we can find the 'on/off' switch. If we could find out what makes the next generation of body cells less efficient – older than the previous generation – and change it – the body could repair itself almost indefinitely. The brain can create new neurons (at one time it was thought not); it can 'rewire' itself. If we could find the key, so that new cells were as efficient as old cells, then an old mans hand would be the same as a young mans hand; strong, muscular, with taut elastic young skin. The old man would be as active, vigorous and fit as the young man. Now! I may not wish to live forever – but it would be wonderful to be as active at my age as I was at 21. Maybe they could even get my spine to repair itself – if they could find the key. Make no mistake, if they do – and I think they will, given time, there will be a great many repercussions. Many problems would be created. People would have to work in their old age – after all they would be fit enough. They couldn't expect to have an endless retirement – financed by the labours of the unfortunate young people. They would also have to be realistic about having children. In the end it will have to be, no more than an average of two, no matter how long you live.

I pause, and daydream for a moment. I am 150 years old. Fit as a fiddle. I'll be going to work next week. We have a choice, 10 hours a week or full time for 3 months a year. Not bad! The robots do all the donkey work. Twenty years ago I thought I might call it a day, at 150, and perhaps go for a TERMIN jab, but I am feeling fine. There is so much to do, and see, and enjoy. I look at my hand. There is a pink stump where my little finger used to be; not bad! – in just ten days; it will be a perfect finger in another few weeks. (I chopped the old one off – being careless with a chain saw). I broke my leg skiing last year and now its as good as new; that RE-GEN jab is really something! Look at that young hussy outside my window, jogging in her bikini. I must admit she has a super figure – and she knows it. Downright provocative she is! Someone told me the other day she is only a hundred and twenty! Anyway I am 150, but I really don't feel like packing it in at all. Life is too good. The world is beautiful! There is so much to see and learn. I read the other day they had found a really weird planet around Polaris – and they are going to launch a new spacecraft to Alpha Centauri; there was a planet there worth seeding after all. It would be interesting to know if it succeeds – but they won't find out for at least another 150 years, I don't really want to live that long – but – you never know. Maybe I'll go and have another REJUVE jab; they say its good for another thirty years! Where's my fishing rod? I've just heard the salmon run is better than ever this year. The river is full of monsters – coming up river for the fourth time.

GENETIC ENGINEERING

Genetic Engineering is, to many people, a dirty word or a dirty couple of words. Not many realise the tremendous potential for improving lives and feeding the world.

Apples, pears, plums, grapes, oranges, bananas, potatoes, sweet corn, wheat, rye, barley, rice; not one of the items I have mentioned is natural. All these, and many more, have been laboriously, selectively bred, in other words Genetically Engineered, by man over thousands of years. You may say, "But that's not Genetic Engineering". Pause to think about it for a moment. None of the things I mentioned would exist in nature, as we know them, without the intervention of man. There is no way a wild plant would produce seedless grapes, seedless oranges and bananas. Chickens have been selectively bred to lay far more eggs in a year than they would naturally do and cows, with enormous unnatural distended udders, produce phenomenal amounts of milk. All the plants and animals I mentioned have genetic traits, especially selected for the benefit of human beings. It is true, however, that we did it the hard way; by looking for the odd freak, which had a mutation (a variation) in its genes. We selectively bred these, over and over again, until we had an unnatural fruit or cereal or animal; but one which particularly suited our needs or preference. We even selectively bred dozens of different kinds of dog, working from one original, wolf like, ancestor.

The most remarkable example, of all the selectively bred plants, is probably the sweet corn, or maize. The original, natural, plant has a seed head or 'cob' no bigger than a two-inch (50mm) stub of pencil. Over thousands of years, the Natives of South America selectively chose plants with a slightly larger cob, and bred them until they achieved the remarkable plant we see today; one of the world's greatest food plants. They even managed to breed it so that it would not shed its grains. The seeds stay attached to the centre stem, ripe or not. I have read that, if the human race was somehow wiped out, maize would soon disappear. If maize is neglected and left until the rotting plant collapses and the cobs lie on the ground, the maize grains will germinate in a mass, so close together that they will, in effect, suffocate each other. Without human intervention – the artificial stripping of the seeds and sowing in the ground – the plant would soon die out.

If modern wheat or rice plants begin to suffer from a disease, say a blight, the plant breeders look for a wild plant resistant to the disease. They then cross breed the modern plant with the wild plant – by pollination. The resulting seeds produce a fantastic variety of hybrid plants. Some will be 50% wild, 50% domestic; some will be 99% wild, 1% domestic; some 99% domestic and 1% wild, and so one. They plant acres of ground with millions of seeds. Then they have to laboriously find the one in a million that is exactly the plant they are looking for, which is the domestic plant with just one variation – the gene from the wild plant that confers resistance to blight. They do not want anything else from the wild plant – it would almost certainly reduce crop yields.

Then, a few years ago, scientists investigating genetics discovered it was possible to use a virus to carry genes from one cell to another. More experiments followed. They discovered that, not only could they use a virus, but it was even possible to fire microscopic gold particles, coated with genes, into the centre of a living cell. A shotgun approach you might call it – on a microscopic cellular scale. In some cases, the introduced genes even became incorporated into the chromosomes of the affected cell and the descendents of the modified cell, when it multiplied, all carried the introduced gene. They continued to experiment and discovered something that could change the world.

Over millions of years, animals and plants on this Earth have slowly evolved into different species. Somehow, as life on Earth developed, a genetic mechanism evolved, (See Chapter on LIFE AND EVOLUTION) which acted to prevent cross breeding of animals and plants that had reached a specific point of differentiation. For instance, the racehorse that wins the Derby, a zebra and a donkey, are all species of horse. The variation between a horse and a donkey is just at the break point. It is possible to mate a horse with a donkey and produce offspring, but the offspring are sterile; they are mules. I sometimes see a similar situation when I go fishing. There is a freshwater fish called a bream, and another a roach, which are distantly related. They often breed close to each other; sometimes too close. They produce hybrid offspring, a roach/bream hybrid; quite distinctive and easily recognised. Again they are sterile, as if something in Nature has said – "No going back". So the old fashioned method of Genetic Engineering was limited. You could only develop animals and plants of the same species. With modern laboratory methods, it is now possible to transfer a gene from any animal or plant directly into the chromosome of any other. In all the years, the animal and plant breeders had worked to improve the stock for human benefit; they had always had to work within the limitation imposed by the Species Barrier. It was only possible to breed cat with cat, dog with dog, and maize with maize. That was a Law of Nature!

The scientists, experimenting with transfer of genes, found, incredibly, that using these new techniques they could implant genes – not only from one to another of the same species, but from one species to another. They had, somehow, broken the Species Barrier. Further experiments continued – to see how far they could go with this phenomenon. They found there was now no limit. They could transfer genes, from any cell with DNA, to any other cell with DNA. When you realise that everything on this Earth, large enough to be seen with the naked eye, and many things that can only be seen with a microscope, use DNA as the basic genetic molecule, the implications are truly staggering. Now you could cross anything at all, with anything you cared to choose.

Scientists experimented and successfully transplanted Jellyfish genes into a plant, and then they transplanted human genes into yeast; the type of cells that are used in baking or to brew beer. Many people suffer from Diabetes – a debilitating and life threatening condition. It is caused by a defect in the Pancreas whereby a key substance, Insulin, is not produced in sufficient quantity for the body's needs. It was found, years ago, that Insulin could be extracted from the pancreas of slaughtered pigs and, for many years, this insulin was administered to patients suffering from Diabetes. Sometimes a person's body would react adversely to the pig insulin. It was not human insulin; there was a subtle difference. When the scientists, discovered modern Genetic Engineering techniques, they took a human gene for insulin and inserted it into a yeast cell. The yeast cell was then cultured and multiplied until they had billions of cells. It was simply a matter of brewing up the yeast in huge vats – in a similar manner to brewing beer. As a by-product the yeast produced human insulin. I believe most Diabetes sufferers now receive human insulin – produced, this way – not pig insulin.

Maize is one of the great food plants of the world. Millions depend on it and it is used to feed both humans and cattle. It was found however that, if the cattle were fed too much maize, they did not thrive as they should and became unwell. Careful investigations finally revealed the reason. The maize was deficient in a key nutrient the cattle needed. When this was discovered farmers began to add a special supplement to the feed – to compensate for the deficiency. Whilst this worked, it was expensive and time consuming and it was realised it would be far better if the maize could be made to produce the necessary nutrient in its normal growth and development. So the Genetic Engineers worked their magic, and managed to insert a gene into the maize plants, so that the plants now produced the much-needed nutrient. The maize was now perfect food for both cattle and humans. How could anyone possibly object to these remarkable achievements?

Then, unfortunately, Genetic Engineers began to make their first mistakes. Many crops are attacked by various pests – Aphids, beetles and caterpillars of various kinds. It was normal to keep these under control by spraying with pesticides – a costly and time consuming business; cost is particularly important in the Third World economies. It was known that many wild plants have developed chemical defences against such pests. Would it, therefore, be possible to transfer a gene to the crops that would enable the plants to defend themselves? They tried it on cotton and it worked. Then the question arose, what about other crops; food plants perhaps? In certain parts of the world, maize plants were attacked by the 'corn borer' a type of caterpillar that burrowed into the stem and devastated the plant, reducing or destroying crop yields. It was necessary, in these areas, to spray crops with pesticide. Experiments were carried out and maize plants were genetically modified to resist corn borer attacks. In other words the maize was genetically modified so that it produced a chemical which killed the corn borer caterpillars; which raised the question, of course, as to whether the modified maize would be harmful to humans.

In the case of the cotton, the genetically added pesticide might be in the cotton fibre but we only wear cotton clothes whereas we eat maize. If the new chemical in the maize could kill the cotton borers what might it do to us? Things were getting tricky!

One of the big problems of growing food crops is controlling weeds. Selective weed killers were introduced – to kill the weeds and leave the crops intact. However, the weeds became more resistant. There were other herbicides that would kill the weeds stone dead, but would damage the crops at the same time. How about genetically engineering the crops, so that they were capable of resisting the powerful herbicide? So they experimented and found it was possible; but there was a problem. The genes of a plant are normally transferred in its pollen. Pollen blows on the wind or is carried by insects. The pollen might act to hybridise weed relatives of the crop plant. If it did, the Genetic Engineers might have created a species of super resistant weeds. The Public began to learn of these experiments, and the problems, and suddenly, GM (Genetically Modified) became a dirty word; anything GM was automatically considered to be bad. Demonstrators marched – and waved their placards, "We want no GM food – no GM crops – no GM anything!"

Let us pause and think about the business of Genetic Engineering very carefully. Firstly there is no going back! The Genie is out of the bottle. You cannot un-discover the secrets of Genetic Engineering, any more than you can un-invent the atomic bomb. The potential for good is undoubtedly immense. For example, a lot of food crops need specialised conditions. Many crops are sensitive to frost. Many must have suitably moist soil to grow; a dry spell and they are ruined. However, there are plenty of wild plants adapted to grow in cold conditions, which can withstand hard frosts without damage. They have evolved to stand the frost; something that makes them resistant is in their genes. Other plants can live in desert conditions; something in their genetic make up allows them to survive and grow in conditions very few plants can survive. It is in the genes! It is quite feasible, therefore, that we can now genetically engineer crop plants so that we can grow them in a far wider range of conditions than ever before; frost resistant potatoes, beans, peas, and so on; crop plants that can grow in arid, near desert, conditions, etc. It is this, appreciating the potential of Genetic Engineering, that led me, in this book, to say I believe we will be able to feed twenty or thirty billion people or more on this planet.

It is quite impossible, at this stage, to grasp the myriad things that could be improved for the benefit of the human race. The Potential is almost beyond comprehension. On the other hand it is obvious we must be very, very careful. The implications and ramifications of modifying the genes of anything, must be very carefully thought through and checked, and double checked, by independent scrutinisers, not by Institutions sponsored by business who have a vested interest in some Genetic Engineering Project. Independent Government Monitoring Organisations must be set up – with the power of Absolute Veto over any GM project. We cannot afford to ignore the potential of Genetic Engineering to improve conditions for the human race but, also, we must look very carefully at the other side of the GM coin. Make no mistake – Genetic Engineering can be terribly, lethally, dangerous. GE techniques could produce biological warfare weapons no less dangerous to the human race than are nuclear weapons. There would be one great difference, however. Nuclear weapons threaten the entire planet – and everything living on it. Biological weapons could be tailored just to destroy us, and might leave almost everything else unharmed. It would be possible to produce the most devastating pathogen the world has ever seen. Maybe far worse than the Black Death or the 1918 Influenza. There can be no doubt, Genetic Engineering must be controlled very rigorously indeed.

The danger, of course, will be rogue states. Someone might be tempted, thinking somehow they would escape the holocaust. It is already staggering to realise what was done – even before the advent of Genetic Modification. During the cold war, the USSR produced hundreds of tons of some of the most lethal pathogens on Earth. I have read that, in the event of war, the USSR was prepared to saturate the whole of Europe with Yersinia Pestis (The Black Death). They also had immense quantities of anthrax. It stuns the mind to think that one Nation could consider doing that to another! The West, of course, also had its biological weapons of similar potential. The whole of humanity must be made aware of the terrible dangers. Genetic Engineering is a reality. We cannot pretend it does not exist. International Laws to ban all biological weapons and any form of Genetic Engineering of any type of human pathogen must be created and Quickly!

I have just read, on 16/12/06, that a UK farmer has received threats, because he has agreed to take part in Genetic Engineering trials and plant a crop of potatoes Genetically Modified to resist potato blight. The potato blight was the cause of the great Irish Potato Famine, during which hundreds of thousands of people are said to have died from starvation. It also led to a mass migration of Irish people to the United States. Even today blight drastically reduces potato crops all over the world. Surely, to create a blight resistant potato would be to help to feed the people of the world. The risk that the genetic modification required, to beat the blight, might be harmful to humans in some way would be small, and must be assessed by careful, sensible, investigation and testing – possibly by feeding animals with the new, modified, potatoes. It is quite probable there would be no risk to humans whatsoever. This is an example of the Genetic Modifications I said would enable us to feed 20 to 30 billion people in the future. I have no doubt the farmer would have been threatened, just the same, if he was assisting in experiments to produce GM crops that would help starving Africans, by enabling crops to be grown in arid regions. I can almost hear the protestors chanting, "No GM, no GM, GM bad, GM bad!" The farmer has pulled out of the trials; scared off by the threats. And I don't blame him! These protestors might burn down his barns or firebomb his house. All I can say to the protestors is – please stop and think of the benefits of blight resistant potatoes. It could help to massively increase crop yields; help to feed the world. Please think carefully, and don't protest until you are sure that the Genetic Modifications in question really do carry a risk.

In the 1950's and 60's, the countryside of Britain was massively changed by Dutch Elm Disease, which practically wiped out the beautiful elm trees of Britain. The denuded countryside has never been the same since. Fortunately, the roots are not killed by the disease, and new elm trees grow, but are again ravaged by the disease as soon as they are 3 to 5 metres (10 to 16 feet) high. This still happens as I write. A few years ago an American carried out Genetic Engineering on Elms to try to beat the disease. If he had succeeded, Britain could have again grown these beautiful trees. Elm wood is also a good timber. The American planted a few acres of his modified trees for tests. Anti GM people complained to the Authorities and it was found he didn't have a permit for the GM tests – which, I agree, he should have had. He was ordered to destroy his experimental trees and did so. He also decided he would not bother any more. Although he was, it is admitted, breaking the rules, why wasn't careful consideration given to his project before he was ordered to destroy the modified trees. It doesn't make sense to me! If his trees had been safe – and I cannot see how they could be anything else – I would have been delighted to have planted some here in the Midlands of the UK, which has been devastated by Elm disease.

Surely we must have rational thinking about GM. There are dangers – no question about it – but think of the immense benefits too! Don't thoughtlessly condemn all GM as being unacceptable. The real GM danger is the scientists working in secret to produce some murderous bio weapon. The Protestors are never even going to hear about that! Potatoes, and Elm trees are the least of their (and my) worries!

CANCER

Cancer – a modern plague of the affluent countries of the world (now likely to strike as many as one in three of us) and affecting every nation and tribe on Earth, has proved far more difficult to conquer than anyone imagined. Progress in treatment is being made, almost painfully slowly, but is there anything that could be done quickly that could reduce mortality? Surprisingly, the answer may be – "Yes!"

I first became aware that something called cancer existed, when I was about ten years old. For years, a good friend of mother's, a lady out of the village, had called to see her, and have a chat, almost every week. Then she stopped coming and I noticed mother was unhappy, quiet and subdued. Another friend called and I heard them discussing the absent friend. "She has cancer"! I heard someone say. When I was alone with mother I asked her – "What is cancer"? All she seemed to be able to tell me was that it was a very nasty disease that usually killed people. Later, I read an article about cancer. The article claimed it was not possible to 'catch' cancer as you can catch other diseases – from person to person – because cancer was a situation where your own body cells rebelled and refused to be controlled as part of the body. Instead, they grew independently and aggressively, without regard to any damage or injury this might cause, often leading to the death of the affected person. I was intrigued.

When I was 13 or 14 years old, during World War Two, mother kept a flock of chickens – to produce eggs and, occasionally, a chicken dinner. This was all part of supplementing the food rations we were issued with at that time. The rations alone were hardly enough to live on. (How people managed to survive in the cities is beyond me. If people today were shown the rations that had to last a person for a week in 1941, they would find it hard to believe. They probably now consume more in a single day). So – we had the chickens and I enjoyed many fried, boiled or poached eggs. Every so often the chickens would be replaced by a new flock, as the old ones stopped laying. At one time, I remember, mother's latest new flock began to come to maturity when, suddenly, they began to die, one by one. Perfectly healthy young hens, just coming into their laying prime, began to die, one after the other. Mother was puzzled and quite upset (we needed the eggs). A single dead chicken was a loss and half the flock, far more so.

Another chicken died. I took this chicken, inspected it carefully but could see no indication of what had caused its death. However, I was curious so I got a knife and cut the chicken open. The reason for its death was instantly clear. There was an enormous ball of flesh – a tumour – completely filling the body cavity. How the chicken had lived long enough for the tumour to grow so large was amazing. All its internal organs were flattened to one side. Another chicken died (this was about the eighth or ninth); I opened it up and this time it was full of small tumours – like grapes. A further chicken died – again full of tumours. I found this alarming as well as baffling. I knew tumours were a form of cancer. The articles I had read said cancer wasn't catching. Ten chickens dead began to look as though it most definitely was. I talked to my parents and suggested the next dead chicken should be sent to the Harper Adams Agricultural College at Newport, Shropshire, only a few miles away. This was done and after a while the college reported back. The chicken was suffering from a tumour caused by a specific type of virus – that, fortunately, only affected chickens. I believe they recommended that we should kill and burn the rest of the flock and not have any more chickens on the premises for a certain length of time. It seemed, therefore, that you couldn't catch cancer directly, but you could, possibly, catch a virus that could give you cancer. I found this revelation startling and disturbing. Later, I saw an article about warts; those nasty little growths people sometimes had on their fingers. These could be caught by simply shaking hands, so, apparently, warts were also caused by a virus. I also read about the human papilloma virus (HPV), and cervical cancer.

Years later, my father gradually became ill. He lost energy, and began to puff, rather more than usual, when he tried to work hard. Slowly he deteriorated over time, until the slightest exertion caused him to gasp for breath. Eventually he died. On the death certificate it stated, "Cause of death – Mesothelioma". Within two months of his death the news came out. Asbestos! Asbestos caused a form of lung cancer called Mesothelioma. Nothing else was known to cause that specific type of the disease. My father was a carpenter and used to work on house building projects. In the course of his work he occasionally worked with asbestos sheets. I had seen him sawing asbestos panels with a simple handsaw, and blowing away the dust so that he could see his pencil marks. Asbestos is a form of natural mineral rock, fibrous and very resistant to heat; perfect for making fire resistant panels. Under a microscope it can be seen that the fibres are ultra fine filaments, which can break into microscopic needles. The needles are so fine that, in the body, they can penetrate the actual individual body cells, without killing them. When this happens the cell may survive, but often the nucleus containing the vital DNA – the individual cells, and indeed the whole body's blueprint – is damaged by the sliver of asbestos. Some damaged cells can turn cancerous and, in the lungs, this creates Mesothelioma.

Cancer can also, of course, be caused by various chemicals and certain kinds of radiation, such as gamma rays, produced in nuclear reactors or an atomic bomb explosion or nuclear waste and, in addition, by radiation from space, including cosmic rays and ultra violet. Even radiation from the very ground we walk on can cause cancer. By this I do not mean fallout from Chernobyl – but natural radiation from rocks and substances like radon gas. Granite is quite radioactive – relative to other rocks. People who live in areas where there are large quantities of granite will have a very slightly increased risk of radiation-induced cancer. So we find that there is a whole range of things that can cause cancer.

Cancer itself is a unique disease. Occasionally, in the trillions of cooperating cells that make up the human body, or other animals' bodies, something goes wrong. The control mechanisms, that instruct the body cells to behave as required to fulfil their function as a body part, fail to work properly, usually because of DNA damage. The cell becomes out of control and genetic mechanisms, which would normally instruct the cell to multiply or not multiply, or even to die (Apoptosis), fail to operate correctly. The cell begins to multiply out of control, without limit. It is possible for a tumour to grow so large that its total weight can exceed the weight of the body supporting it; incredible though that may seem.

There are two basic forms of cancer; Benign and Malignant. A benign cancer, or tumour, is simply a proliferating mass of cells. Unless it is in a particularly difficult position, such as within some areas of the brain, it is often possible to surgically remove it. If all the cancerous cells are removed, that is the end of it and the patient is cured. The other form of cancer is called a malignant cancer – and this behaves differently. Very differently indeed! Somehow, the growing cancer develops the ability to use more of the genetic code that is in its cells. More, that is, than the simple, 'multiply', instruction that the benign tumour seems to use. A malignant cancer becomes, to all intents and purposes, an independent, aggressive, parasitic life form. It does, of course, have the whole armoury of human genes available for use – if it should, somehow, become capable of activating them. It certainly seems to use several. It activates genes which produce signalling molecules, that induce the surrounding tissue to grow more blood vessels (Angio Genesis) to supply extra nutrients and oxygen to the developing cancer. Later, when it has grown to a certain size, it uses enzymes to cut holes in the walls of major blood vessels and, through these apertures, it seeds itself or 'Metastasises', which is the term used. It actually reproduces. Small parts of the cancer break off, pass through the holes in the blood vessel walls and spread all over the body. The cancer also has a final trick that is truly amazing. It becomes immortal. That is – it could live almost for ever if it could obtain sufficient nutrients and oxygen and the host did not die. Way back, in the 1930s, a sample of cancer cells was taken from a patient and cultured in a medical laboratory. The culture is still alive today and will probably go on living for another hundred years, or more, if it continues to be supplied with the necessary nutrients and oxygen.

In humans and all other animals, the genetic code of life – the DNA – which exists in every cell, is compacted together in groups, or 'packets', termed chromosomes. In the last few years it has been discovered that there is a small additional 'tail' of genes on the end of these chromosomes. A simple way to think of it is like a chain, with so many links of the chain attached to the chromosomes. These assemblies are called telomeres. It has been found that every time a cell divides and multiplies, a small part of the telomere – like a few links of a chain – are removed. Each time a cell replicates, the telomere is shortened and, when the telomere reaches a certain minimum length, it triggers some signal to stop the cell replicating further. Some people, including myself, think the telomeres are involved in the ageing process; a sort of biological clock that ticks away until, when your time is up, it switches cell replication off. In a newly conceived child, the telomeres will be maximum length. The biological clock has just been started and set at zero. Cancer cells have developed the ability to override this system and renew the telomeres; build them back up to length and reset the biological clock. So far as we know, therefore, cancer cells are immortal; theoretically they can live forever. You may be sceptical of this. Nothing, you may say, can live forever. However, pause to think, you yourself are but one link in an unbroken chain, going back nearly four thousand million years. You may not be immortal – but your genes are. You are born and develop to breeding age; your telomeres have shortened but, when you pass on your genes to a new child, the child's telomeres are reset. In a way, you too are immortal. Only part of the tree of life is lost, like a leaf of an ordinary tree (see Chapter – AGEING).

Suffice to say, malignant cancer cells have remarkable abilities, which is why cancer is so difficult to beat. The body does, however, have its own defence mechanism to prevent the growth of cancers. The immune system acts as a body wide policing system – endlessly checking for invaders – viruses, bacteria, parasites, anything that threatens, or may appear to threaten, the existence of the cooperating mass of cells, which is the body. The immune system also, usually, recognises rebellious cells, (cancer cells), and eliminates most of them. Occasionally a cancer cell evades the immune system and begins to multiply and grow. Anything that weakens the immune system increases the risk of cancer. HIV, because of its ability to damage the immune system, comes to mind. It is commonly associated with the proliferation of a particular form of cancer – Kaposi's Sarcoma.

With regard to my comment about malignant cancer becoming an independent parasitic life form – I have read, in just the last few months, that there has now come to light a remarkable situation underlining this statement. It seems that a cancer has been discovered in dogs that is transmissible from dog to dog. Researchers – trying to find, as they thought, the virus which was the cause of a type of cancer in dogs – decided to check the DNA of the cancer against that of the dog affected by the disease. If it was caused by a virus then the cancer DNA would, of course, be the same as the dog but, they were amazed to find, the cancer DNA was different. They checked DNA from similar cancers in other dogs and made the remarkable discovery that the DNA, taken from samples of cancers of a number of dogs, was the same. The conclusion is that a cancer first developed in one particular dog, and became independent of the dog to such a degree that it became capable of being transferred to other dogs, entirely on its own. It has become a completely independent parasite of dogs; not just the one dog in which it originated. Truly remarkable! A case where cancer is actually transmissible like a contagious disease. Apparently this may not be the only example of a transmissible cancer occurring. Many Tasmanian Devils are dying from a similar outbreak at the present time. There is also, occasionally, a cancer that gives a clue it is somehow experimenting with the genes in the original body cell. When surgically removed from the body, the cancer may be found to contain bits of bone, hair, or even teeth, embedded in the cancer.

Every cancer that may develop in a person's body has the same total set of genes but, if the cells in the brain, for instance, turn cancerous, the original stem cells have already had certain genes turned on and some turned off, to differentiate them into brain cells. (All the cells of the body were originally stem cells, developed by multiplication of the original fertilised egg cell). Bone cells, or cells in the lining of the gut also have certain genes activated and some suppressed – to turn them into bone or gut cells. When these cells turn cancerous, they have started by being differentiated cells. Is this why such cancers can behave in slightly different manner from cancer to cancer; making it more difficult to treat and destroy them?

Many different methods of treating malignant cancers have been devised. The first treatment of course, is surgery and, if the cancer is caught in its early stages, a total cure may be effected. However, if the cancer has metastasised (seeded) the situation is far more complicated. Sometimes, of course, the position of the cancer makes surgery impossible or impractical. In these cases other treatments must be resorted to. Chemotherapy is a relatively crude technique where powerful chemicals, (poisons), capable of destroying cells, are given to patients in sub-lethal doses. The hope is that the cancer will be destroyed while the patient's body still has the capability of recovery. Improvements in this technique involve using carrier chemicals to concentrate the poisonous substances in the cancer. Another destructive method is radiotherapy, where focussed x-rays are concentrated on the cancer; alternatively, a pellet of radioactive material may be inserted into a cancer. The idea in both techniques is to kill the cancer without causing too much collateral damage. With all these techniques one of the great problems is, every single cancerous cell must be destroyed. If just one remains it will re-grow and the cancer, after a time, reappears.

At the present time more sophisticated techniques are being developed; ways to interfere with Angio Genesis (blood vessel growth), to disrupt the telomere repair process, to prevent the cancer perforating holes in the blood vessel walls and, also, to prevent the cancer metastasising. Research is also being conducted into the possibility of inducing apoptosis (the triggering of programmed cell death), to make the cancer cells self-destruct. A further approach is to find a way to attach some form of marker to cancer cells, to provoke enhanced immune system response. All these approaches are very promising, but I think the most important, at the present time, would be to prevent metastasis (seeding). Metastasis is the major problem of malignant cancer and is usually the reason patients cannot be totally cured. If this problem could be solved, it would immediately simplify treatment by localising just one cancer to be treated. I am hopeful that, in the long run, the battle against cancer will, eventually, be won but it will probably take 50 years or more.

A fundamental question now is "Can anything be done immediately to reduce deaths from malignant cancer"? I think the answer is "Yes"! From everything I have seen and heard from friends and relatives, the impression I have is that malignant cancer is not being considered, or treated, as the murderous, aggressive, malignant, parasitic life form that it is. It is as bad as if a parasitic animal had invaded the body and was intent on growing, and reproducing, and killing the victim. The key thing is the reproduction. Once the cancer has reproduced, the chances of survival are drastically reduced. If you consider the situation carefully, you realise that there must be an exact second, of an exact minute, of an exact hour, of an exact day, when the cancer breaks into a blood vessel and releases the first seed cells. In other words, when a malignant cancer is first discovered, it is like finding a ticking time bomb, but with no knowledge of how long the clock has to run before zero hour.

Therefore – and this is the key point I am making – the cancer must be treated like the time bomb it is, and cut out at the very earliest moment possible. If a person has appendicitis, the doctors know it is a race against time to save the patient. I myself have had an appendix operation, and the life of a friend of mine was in the balance when his appendix perforated, just before an operation. The doctors know that, in this situation, they simply must operate fast or the patient will die. No delays are acceptable. I suggest that all cases of malignant cancer, where surgery is possible, should be treated with the same urgency – given the same priority. To delay for a week, or a day, or even a single hour, can make the difference between life and death. Time after time, I hear of cases of people waiting for weeks for treatment after original cancer diagnosis and this after waiting for days or weeks for a biopsy. To work fast would not only save thousands of lives, but is far more efficient. If a malignant cancer is cut out and destroyed before it metastasises, only a few hours of Health Service time, and minimum cost, is involved. If the cancer is given time to seed, then months of additional treatment, at very high cost, is incurred, in addition to the surgery which is carried out anyway; usually, the most the extra treatment achieves is to buy time. The patient is very rarely cured after metastasis. What then, is it better to do? Work fast and cure the patient with the minimum of time and cost, or waste time after diagnosis and then incur ten times the cost, and increase specialists' workloads on extended treatment and, even then, lose the patient. There MUST be fast action. There should be fast action to conduct a biopsy when a tumour is first detected and, when a cancer is diagnosed as malignant, the health service must go into overdrive, as if it was an appendicitis case, and get the cancer out with the absolute minimum of delay. To do this will save countless lives and also save the NHS an enormous amount of time and money. To adopt this policy would, initially, cause, some disruption – less important operations would have to wait – but, within 6 months, the pressure would ease because of the time saved on secondary treatment. The whole NHS would become more efficient and, more importantly, simply by changing procedures, thousands of lives would be saved.

KURU, BSE, HIV AND FLU

Back in the 1950s, Doctors were aware of a rare degenerative brain disorder which was named Creutzfeldt-Jakob disease. They knew the sufferers gradually deteriorated from having their normal mental faculties, until eventually becoming insane or comatose to an almost vegetative state. Nothing was known of the cause and it was considered to be a non-transmissible disease. Then they became aware that there was an island in the Pacific, where a considerable number of the islanders suffered from a very similar disease, which the islanders called 'Kuru'. All the symptoms were the same as those of Creutzfeldt-Jakob disease. The most disturbing fact was that the incidence of the disease on the island suggested it was, in some way, transmissible. Investigation revealed the apparent cause. On the island, the natives had a very unusual attitude to their dead, in that they had a belief that, as part of the burial ritual, the skull of the dead relative should be cracked open and at least part of the dead person's brain should be eaten. It soon became obvious that the Creutzfeldt-Jakob type disease was, somehow, being transmitted by the act of eating a diseased person's brain. However no causative transmissible agent, such as a virus, was ever found.

In sheep, for as far back as farmers could remember, occasional animals sickened and died. Previously perfectly normal animals, slowly degenerated, and died, often staggering and tottering about before final collapse. The disease was called 'Scrapie'. Fortunately scrapie only affected the occasional sheep, and farmers generally accepted it as more of a nuisance, than a real menace to their flocks.

In the 1950s and 60s, there was a revolution in European farming practices, mainly to do with improving efficiency. This applied across the entire agricultural spectrum from intensive rearing of chickens, battery systems for hens, to more efficient agriculture. In the UK vast swathes of hedgerows were dug out and fields enlarged. Dairy and beef herds of cattle became larger, and more efficient means of feeding them were developed. One of the problems of preparing cattle, pigs and sheep for food, has always been the disposal of the offal, or non saleable parts of the animal; the entrails, bones, spine, feet, and all the rest of the parts not useable in normal human food production. So it was decided to cook the remains, pulverise them and mix the resulting mash, as a high protein additive, to food supplements that are normally fed to cattle, in addition to the grass or hay they daily consume. This process, called rendering, was efficiently done using very high cooking temperatures, and pulverising everything – brain, spine, bones, residual flesh, everything. The system worked! It eliminated the waste and the cattle grew fat and healthy. Experts experimented and found it was even possible to include chicken droppings, which still retained some nutritional value, in the cattle feed.

For a while, the system worked well and then, for some reason I do not know, the rendering facilities were given permission to reduce the temperatures used in the processing. The temperatures were still high – well above boiling point – but not as high as they had been. A few years later, Vets began to report a number of cases of cattle suffering from a degenerative disease, very similar in its manifestations to scrapie in sheep. More and more cases appeared, and it was given the name Bovine Spongiform Encephalopathy (BSE). Affected cattle were culled but the number of cases continued to increase. Scientists searched for the causative agent but, for a long time, were unsuccessful. Then came disturbing news of an apparent increase in the incidence of Creutzfeldt-Jakob disease in humans. Careful study suggested most of the new cases were slightly different from the original CJD disease and the symptoms appeared to develop more rapidly. A suspicion developed that the increase in CJD cases in humans, might be linked to the BSE in cattle. Finally a young scientist announced he had found the causative agent of BSE in cattle. It was not a virus, he claimed, but a totally new type of disease-causing agent – an infective protein which was called a prion. A great many people were sceptical. The suggestion that a non-living protein molecule could, in some way, be causing the disease, and, in addition, be an infective transmissible agent, like a virus or bacteria, was almost beyond belief. Repeated tests confirmed that the young scientist's conclusions were correct. Some proteins and enzymes in the body are molecules that owe some of their normal function to the actual shape of the molecule. Alter the shape, and the function of the molecule might be lost, indeed it might even create a molecule which was a pathogen. The prion molecule that caused BSE is such a molecule. It naturally occurs in the body, in functional form, in many animals including humans, though in slightly variant forms. The most remarkable feature though, in this case, is that a deformed prion molecule was found to be capable of triggering a similar deformation in other prion molecules to which it came in contact. When enough prion molecules were converted, they seemed to agglomerate in clusters in the brain, and gradually destroy brain function.

Because of the long incubation time, it was impossible to know how many cattle were infected or how many infected cattle were being slaughtered and entering the human food chain, without anyone being aware of the infectious prion protein being disseminated. It was a number of years from the first recorded incidence of BSE in cattle, before the true threat to human health was realised. The brutal truth was, nearly everybody in Britain who ate beef products, of any kind, had probably eaten beef contaminated with BSE. It was discovered that, in particular, the brain and spinal cord of an infected animal was loaded with infective prions. The main meat of the carcase less so. Unfortunately, in the making of products such as beef burgers, a lot of secondary material including brain and nerve material was ground up and added to the main beef mix. Everybody ate beef burgers. The cooking process – whether it was roasting the Sunday joint, or cooking the filling for beef burgers – would not apply sufficient heat to destroy the prion protein. It was not a living entity like a virus or bacteria. It could withstand far higher temperatures before the protein molecule was destroyed. The horrendous scenario developed that nearly the entire population of Britain had probably been exposed and might, in a few years, develop the human form of BSE. I personally used to love oxtail soup. I think it is highly probable that originally a lot of oxtail, possibly including spinal cord material, would be used in making the soup.

When the danger was realised, drastic measures were taken to cull all infected animals; a test was devised to detect BSE in animals not yet showing symptoms; a ban placed on feeding cattle with rendered offal supplements and regulations introduced, requiring all brain and spinal cord material to be removed from the carcasses of all cattle destined for human food production. The trouble was – the time lag! Before recognition of the problem, and before any action was taken, most of the UK population had eaten meat products contaminated with the infective prions. Scientists and doctors studied the statistics related to the development of the human form of CJD with trepidation. So did I! Miraculously, although the figures increased, they did not take off and, gradually, in the years since action was taken, have declined. It seems that the human form of prion protein is slightly different to the cattle BSE form, and does not easily convert to the deformed kind on contact with the animal version, except in a few unfortunate, susceptible, people where it does occur.

I have read scare-mongering articles suggesting we may yet have a human BSE disaster, but I do not think so. Although there is a long incubation period, the figures for affected people would be climbing, not reducing, if an epidemic was indeed developing. Therefore, the conclusion is we can relax. By a miracle, nothing less, we shall be spared a situation where most of the people of Britain are suffering the horrors of Creutzfeldt-Jakob disease. We have, in truth, been fantastically lucky. Maybe, if any similar situation ever occurs again, we shall not be so fortunate. It is sobering to note that no person who has been resident in the UK after 1980 is allowed to donate blood for transfusions in the USA because of the risk that the donor is carrying VCJD (The human form of BSE).

The 1914/18 war devastated the male population of Europe. An estimated total of 30 million people died. When the end of the war finally came, people danced in the streets; the slaughter was over. And yet, just at this very moment, a new menace arose. A few people developed influenza – nothing remarkable in that – but this was a new, extremely deadly, strain. The influenza took hold, spread across Europe, the USA and the whole world. Incredibly, it killed more people than the Great War. It is generally accepted that around 50 million people died worldwide. Eventually it burned itself out, and the world slowly recovered.

On several occasions since, there have been outbreaks of particularly virulent forms of flu which appeared, apparently from nowhere, infected millions of people, and disappeared again. Fortunately none was as dangerous as the 1918 variant. Scientists investigated and, gradually, it emerged that the 1918 flu probably started as some form of variant, or mutation, of one of the many strains that affect birds. It was realised, that in some countries, particularly in the Far East, people often lived in close proximity to birds, particularly domestic fowl, ducks and geese. In these circumstances, there would obviously be an enhanced risk of a human variant developing. It had been found that bacteria often exchanged genes with other bacteria, almost like a form of mating. Maybe a similar thing might occur with viruses. The most dangerous situation might occur, for instance, if a bird infected with bird flu, was handled by a human being suffering from human flu. In a human suffering from human flu, the mucus lining the nasal passages will be saturated with human flu virus. Any bird flu virus being breathed in, at this stage, would be likely to come into immediate and direct contact with human flu virus in a near perfect culture medium. Hybridization is the most likely way a bird flu virus would be modified so that it could infect humans. That might have been the way the 1918 flu developed.

Recently, scientists decided, dangerous as it may seem, it might be a good idea if, somehow, it was possible to get hold of a sample of 1918 flu virus. In Canada it was known some Eskimos had caught 1918 flu and died, and had been buried in the permafrost; maybe traces of the terrible flu had survived. They exhumed one of these people and did, indeed, find the 1918 flu virus. A careful check of the DNA and it was revealed that it was, as expected, a variant of a bird flu virus.

A few years ago, in the Far East, several people became ill with a new, extremely lethal, form of flu. The virus was investigated and was found to be related to a virulent bird flu virus, notated H5N1 bird flu. It

162

certainly is lethal to birds, wiping out huge numbers in days. Fears arose that, if this particular virus should make the transition to easily infecting humans – by person to person air transmission – the H5N1 virus could be an even bigger threat than the 1918 type. Horrendous scenarios have been projected, with predictions of anything from 50 million to 100 million deaths. However, before we panic, let us consider the situation carefully. The risk from H5N1 is real, unquestionably, but what about the chances of it making the break to becoming a lethal human flu variant. In 1918 nobody knew the source. It is probable that, somewhere, a great many birds were infected – and not culled. Years ago it was said that, in some Far Eastern countries; "If a man eats a chicken either the man or the chicken is sick". People lived in poverty. They could not afford to cull and destroy chickens out of hand. The situation probably existed where thousands of diseased birds were plucked, prepared, cooked and eaten. The very act of plucking and preparing the chicken created a prime chance for the virus to enter humans and, eventually, make the transition. In other words, there might have been thousands of opportunities for bird/human transfer and, in 99% or more cases, it did not occur. Maybe there were a number of the fluke conditions where bird flu met human flu, in the situation where a human had human flu at the same time as he prepared an infected chicken. We simply do not know how easy, or how difficult, it is for the bird flu virus to make the transition.

One thing we do know; the situation now is very different from 1918. We know the danger and we know where it lies. Thousands of birds are immediately culled as soon as H5N1 is detected. People take precautions. Surely the authorities make sure no one with human flu goes anywhere near infected birds. Anyone who catches H5N1 flu is immediately quarantined. As long as we stay vigilant, I shall be surprised if the H5N1 virus makes the break to humans in the next 5 years or possibly 10. This should give us time to prepare; time to study the H5N1 virus thoroughly, and for us to plan and prepare the best response. The greatest risk of an H5N1 variant developing is likely to be in Africa, where starving people are more likely to ignore the danger, and prepare and eat sick birds. Considering Africa, it is almost certain that various diseases – HIV for example – started in Africa. In my mind a great danger is the Africans' penchant for eating Bush Meat. Bush Meat is wild animal – jungle animal – meat including meat from primates. Primates harbour many diseases and, as they are such close kin to man, any disease they carry may be able to transfer to man, with far less modification than would be required for a disease to jump from a relatively unrelated species. The deadly disease Ebola almost certainly came from monkeys. Simian HIV is very closely related to the human strain.

There must always be a considerable risk, while human beings continue to hunt and eat animals out of the jungle; animals free to roam and carrying disease, but not yet seriously sick when they are killed and eaten. What about the cooking? I commonly eat medium cooked steak, and many like it rare. I doubt if there is enough heat applied to kill pathogens in these cases. Sooner or later, undercooked bush meat will be eaten. Some kind of restriction – a taboo if at all possible – should be placed on the eating of monkey meat; or any primate. I realise it will not be possible to prevent the killing and eating of other bush meat, but maybe the killing of primates for food could be stopped, or at least reduced. I understand tons of bush meat are imported into the UK all the time. Surely something could be done about that, otherwise, one of these days, we may find we have another disease, as bad as HIV, Ebola or H5N1 flu to contend with.

THE BRAIN

You are the possessor of the most remarkable, the most complicated, the most sophisticated cellular construct on this Earth and, possibly, in the whole Galaxy – the human brain.

When the first living cells grouped together, around six hundred and fifty million years ago, to form the first multi cellular life, in a cooperative action for mutual benefit and to aid survival in a competitive world, these cells needed a coordinating system. Initially, there would probably be merely a crude, chemical, signalling system to enable the group to engulf nearby individuals, or other cellular assemblies. Gradually, a specialised sub group of cells evolved, whose sole job was to coordinate the actions of the other cells in the overall mass. The first 'brain' had arrived. Over hundreds of millions of years of evolution, the incredibly complex and sophisticated brain that we see in modern animals came into being. Even very small brains – compared to our own – can demonstrate remarkable capabilities.

Years ago a scientist studying bees, noticed a bee that had just returned to its hive, performing a strange dance in front of other watching bees. He eventually proved that the dancing bee was, in fact, communicating with the other bees, telling them there was a good supply of nectar in flowers, maybe a hundred and fifty to two hundred yards away. This obviously involves communicating to the other bees the distance and direction, etc., to the nectar. Remarkable!

Later, it was found, they could achieve something even more surprising. Bees in a hive multiply and, when the hive is becoming overpopulated, they produce a new queen. The new queen mates and flies away, with a large number of worker bees, to found a new hive. In the wild, bees normally nest in holes or hollows in old trees. The new queen flies away, with her followers, and lands on a branch or tree somewhere and waits. The workers then cluster around her in a large protective mass. Later the mass disintegrates and takes to the air in a flying swarm. They then go to a hollow tree, somewhere within flying range, and start to build their new home.

Scientists wondered what happened during the waiting time, when the queen was with the worker bees in a mass on a branch. After much research the truth was revealed. The mass of bees on the branch sent out scouts to look for a suitable nest site. It was found that each scout bee searched the forest, found a hole in a tree and checked it out. It checked the size of the hole by walking all over the confines of the cavity. It checked the height of the entrance above ground; too low would be dangerous. It checked the orientation, i.e. East or West, South or North facing entrance; an East facing entrance would warm earlier, in the morning sun. Then it flew back to the swarm to report. A dozen or more scout bees are sent out to look for a new home. How do they choose which is the best site? They do exactly the same as we would do. The scouts pair off and compare notes. Number one's site is better than number two's. Number three's site is better than number four's and so on. Half the scout bees are eliminated, and then the remainder pair again. Number three's site is found to be better than number one's and so on. They continue to do this until there is only one bee left – which must be the one that has discovered the best of all the sites scouted. When the information has been communicated, the swarm takes off and flies to the new home. All this is truly amazing. The degree of awareness and communication required to do what they have done is astounding; with a brain no bigger than a pin head.

After being stung too many times I hate wasps! I eliminate them ruthlessly wherever I find them. I found a nest in my heather bed, waited until it was dark and all the wasps were home – then I went and puffed a good dose of wasp killing powder down the hole. That was that; the powder was bound to be carried to the queen and goodbye wasps! But not quite; the powder eliminated all the adult wasps very efficiently, but not the un-hatched grubs. A week later I paused at the nest site to check. A small wasp came out of the nest hole. In the absence of further attention and food the surviving grubs were developing into adult wasps, even though they were only half grown.

I noticed that the new wasp was behaving in a peculiar manner. It came out of the hole backwards, and slowly weaved, in a figure of eight motion, just outside the entrance hole. It then backed out a foot from the hole and repeated the figure eights. It then backed to three feet from the hole and again repeated. It dawned on me what was happening. This was a 'first time out' wasp; it was programming its brain with the information needed to get back home; exactly the same as I do when I leave my car in a multi-storey car park. I check where the car is on the floor; check the floor number; check where the entrance is, and so on. I thought - not bad for a pinhead brain! However, when you consider the life of a wasp or bee, it must have this capability, if it is to go wandering off, half a mile from home, looking for prey, or nectar, to carry back to the nest; half a mile must be a long, complicated trip for an insect no bigger than my finger nail.

If an insect can do things like that, it is no surprise to find that rats are very cunning. They have brains thousands of times bigger than a bee. What is surprising is that mice are so stupid!

The peak of brain development on this planet appears to be our own. I say appears to be, since elephants have larger brains and the largest brains on the planet belong to whales. In both cases, I consider these large brains to have evolved in an evolutionary 'blind alley'. There is no way a whale can ever produce a civilisation like ours, because it is confined to the sea, and it has no manipulators capable of handling small objects. In other words, for whales, communication and information transmission, other than by touch, sight and sound, would seem to be out and it could never progress to make tools, weapons, machines and devices. The elephant would appear to have slightly more potential. It lives on land and has a manipulative trunk. However, the trunk, although prehensile, has limited capability. To really exploit the potential of a large and sophisticated brain, you need the equipment and environment to go with it. We obviously have the right configuration. A large ant, say our size, would also appear to fulfil the requirements. If all the whales became as bright as Leonardo Da Vinci it really wouldn't do them any good. Nevertheless, in our dealings with whales and dolphins, we must (and generally do – I think) treat them as similar sensitive, emotional and intelligent beings as ourselves.

The human brain is the most complicated, and sophisticated, living cellular construction on Earth. It is far, far more than a simple computer. However, I am always amazed at what it is possible to do with a modern computer. After all, it is only a relatively simple device basically using on/off switches; yet look what they are able to do with it. Then I reflect that the entire, unbelievable, complexity of the human body is achieved using a DNA code with only four letters. The human brain is not an electronic computer. It is a self wiring device of a complexity beyond our ability to fully comprehend. (At least – it is today as I write) Every neuron is connected, not to one or two others, but to fifty, or a hundred or more other cells, by an incredibly intricate arrangement of wiring. In addition to this, there is also an extremely complex system of chemical signalling, using many different neuro-transmitters.

In the first multi-cellular life forms, the cells would have acted simply as a group of cooperating cells. You might almost say – as a group of bees or termites work together – with each cell really being an independent entity. At some point in development the group subtly changed – until a mass of cells became so coordinated that the group acted as one entity. Cells would, if necessary, be sacrificed for the good of the group. Cells, when ordered to die, would obediently die – if it was for the good of the overall entity. I would guess this occurred around six hundred million years ago – with the advent of the first true animals. This, I think, would also be the time when most senses evolved; the desire for food, sense of touch, detecting prey chemicals (smell and taste), registering of heat levels, detection of damage and development of the reflex to minimise damage (pain), also detection of movement and vibration. Later would come detection of light and, later still, would come infra-red detection (snakes), ultra-sound detection (bats), electro-detection (fish) and, possibly, some we haven't yet discovered. There is of course the desire to reproduce. If you think about it – one of the most remarkable developments of all must be the ability of one single cell (the egg cell) to carry the information and capability of forming the whole, completely organised, group – the complete animal. A biological miracle!

Sometimes I am amazed at the attitudes and beliefs I find in some people. During the course of one of my fishing trips I met a fellow angler. He was intelligent, affable, likeable and good company; we got on fine! Somehow, one evening, the conversation turned to the idea that fish could not feel pain. I, personally, never doubted that they could. When I strike the hook into a fish, the fish usually reacts – sometimes very violently. I am, you could say, being cruel; I will not deny it! However, my hunting instincts, inherited from my ancestors, are still strong although I do not usually kill the fish I catch. I don't need them for food, so return them, alive, to the water, with as little harm as possible. However, I will not try to fool myself, or others, by saying fish cannot feel pain. Logically, any active, mobile, animal must have a system to detect and reduce damage; in other words it must feel some form of pain; if not, it might happily sit there while some other life forms ate it alive. My angling friend would not have it that fish could feel pain. He had seen a programme on TV, he said, that showed fish simply did not have the sensors to feel pain. They do, however, 'spook' he conceded; it was necessary for survival. So when I see a fish leap furiously into the air, jaws wide open, head thrashing frantically, trying to throw my hook out, I think, "That one spooked –for sure!"

When fishing for pike on the Norfolk Broads I often use a lure or spinner. (For non-anglers I will explain. Pike are a large aggressive predatory fish, up to a metre or more long, with a big mouth full of razor sharp teeth). The spinner comprises a flashing metal spoon with a treble hook at the rear. It is cast into the distance and drawn back to the angler. The pike, normally, lie in ambush, not moving until they decide to attack. Very occasionally, by a rare fluke, my line passes over the back of a lurking pike. He ignores the touch of the line, even the touch of the lure when it reaches him but when the hook pricks his skin he instantly lunges away, sometimes hooking himself in the process. I always know if this has happened – merely from the fish's reaction. Normally, when a pike attacks the lure, I feel the 'bump' of the attack transmitted through the line. I then strike, to drive the hooks home, and feel the weight of the fish. There is then a harsh thumping on the line as the pike opens his mouth and shakes his head, trying to throw the offending object out of his jaws. If he fails to do this he then, and only then, starts to rush about trying to break away. If, as I am retrieving my lure, the rod is almost yanked out of my hand and the fish tears away instantly, I suspect the fish is foul-hooked and I am nearly always right. He wouldn't react so violently if he did not feel pain, would he?

While we are on this subject, I shudder when I think of chefs dumping live crabs and lobsters into a pot of boiling water. Surely the things could be killed or stunned first. There must be a way! For those who say they cannot feel pain, experiments should be carried out to check. It should not be difficult to devise tests. For instance, if I asked you to extend your hand, palm downwards on a table, and then laid a thin copper wire over the back of your hand you would not take much notice. You might look at it and merely wonder what it was for. But if I then put a pulse of electricity through the wire and heated it, just for a moment, to near red heat, you would snatch your hand away from the sudden pain, whether I told you to or not. Why not try a similar test on lobsters, with a wire across the tail perhaps. I would be very surprised if the lobster didn't react.

Incidentally, we have an indication in cases of the human disease – leprosy – of what can happen if there are no pain sensors. One of the features of leprosy is that it can affect the nerves and cause loss of feeling. Sometimes leprosy affects the hands and the sufferer loses the ability to feel pain but without losing function i.e. they can still use their hands. It is common to see such people with terribly damaged and mutilated hands. It is not the leprosy itself that does this but, because the person cannot feel pain, they bruise, cut and burn their hands without noticing, often until the fingers are reduced to stumps.

Somewhere, on the path of evolution, appeared the quality we call intelligence. What is intelligence; how do we measure it? We try – but I do not think the tests we call IQ tests can really be considered adequate. IQ tests measure powers of thinking and deduction, usually against the clock; in effect, how fast can you solve this problem? I once knew a man who was an engineer. Some people thought he was stupid, mainly because he was very slow! The engineering firm I worked for were designing new structures and machines; there were many problems to be solved. I used to talk to this man and discuss problems with him. We used to compete, and take problems home with us on Fridays, to see what solutions we could come up with over the weekend. Sometimes, my solutions were better than his. More often than not his ideas were better than mine; he was a brilliant inventor. He had a list of patents to his name as long as your arm. However, he was so slow it was untrue! When I talked to him he would ask me to slow down; go over it again. If he had taken IQ tests where would he have been? He caused me to do a complete re-think of what constituted intelligence. Previously I had thought – the person with the quick mind, the slick wisecrack, the wit, the lightning fast response, the man who did arithmetic twice as fast as I could – they were intelligent. But now; what about our slow friend with the amazing, inventive mind? I no longer worry if my brain is not as fast as the next man – though I should like it to be. I have my own abilities. So - next time someone makes you look a fool, bear in mind you may have abilities that he does not. Einstein was once asked – what did he think was the greatest attribute of the human brain. He replied, "Imagination!" A good answer, but I am inclined to prefer – 'Creativity'. I regard imagination as more of a tool, to help in creativity. When Einstein said he, "Imagined himself riding on a light beam", it was an imaginative trick to help his brain grasp, and assess, the concepts that led to his Theory of Relativity. I shall use a similar imaginative trick, later in this book, to help you grasp the idea of multidimensional time.

Some people have fantastic memories – walking encyclopaedias. However, walking encyclopaedias do not put men on the moon – or invent a television set. The greatest gift of the human race is ingenuity; the ability to think up ways to trap, and kill, that marauding tiger, or grizzly bear – back in the cave days; to invent the spear, the bow and arrow, the woomera, the bolas, the boomerang, and the sling shot. It would not matter so much if it took ten years to think up the bow and arrow – as long as you did – for the benefit of the human race. (Some people might argue about this – but the bow and arrow would enable early man to obtain food he otherwise might not be able to get and, thus, the weapon would aid survival. Man did not need to use it against man). So I have an open mind on what constitutes intelligence. I do not jump to conclusions.

Sometimes I look at plants; they puzzle me. How can a plant be sensitive if it doesn't have a brain? Obtain some seeds of Mimosa Puddica and grow the 'sensitive plant'. Mimosa Puddica has frond-like leaves; touch a frond gently and the leaves fold up before your eyes; knock it hard and the whole frond will fold up and tuck itself away. There is, of course, the one everyone knows – the carnivorous plant – the Venus Fly Trap. That works pretty fast too! A time lapse camera shows bind-weed searching for something to cling to, as do beans and peas.

Another remarkable thing, it seems to me, is that some plants appear to have an ability to learn. If you have a lawn – and neglect it – the dandelions in that lawn will grow with leaves angled upwards at 45°, and the flowers will grow long, upright stems, six inches (150mm) or more long. If you mow the lawn to within an inch (25mm) of the ground, all the dandelion heads and leaves will be cut off. The plant will not die, it will regrow. If you continue to mow it off it will eventually grow differently. It will grow with its leaves held down close to the ground. When it flowers, the stems may only be one centimetre long. After you have mown the lawn a few more times, the whole plant may stay below the level of the cutter. Remarkable! I have sometimes wondered if the reflexes of plants are like the reflexes in those early groups of cooperating cells, six hundred and fifty million years ago, before the development of a true brain.

At one time, insanity was thought to be caused because the sufferers were possessed by evil spirits. We now know it is far more likely to be caused by some sort of chemical imbalance of the brain; something wrong with neuro-transmitters or their receptors. This is, of course, what happens with mind altering drugs. They upset the delicate chemical balance of the brain. (I shift the chemical balance of my brain with coffee or alcohol). If the balance is disturbed too much – the sufferer can go insane.

I remember an unhappy experience with a schizophrenic dog. My brother once had a friend with a big black Labrador dog; a very friendly, playful, likeable dog. He was never bad tempered or vicious. Then – something went wrong; he developed a split personality (if you can use the word 'personality' for a dog). He used to come to our house regularly – play with my brother for an hour or two, and then – go home. A great dog, and it was nice to see him around. Then he changed! He would come into the house and be his normal playful self and then, on one word, he would suddenly change to a savage, snarling beast of a dog. I remember saying something to him, like, "Now – you must go home", or "Get out of the way!" Instantly he changed and I was confronted with a mad dog. The liquid, soppy eyes and friendly face changed into blazing eyes, lips pulled back, teeth bared, a threatening snarling rasp in his throat. I knew, one mistake, and I would be savaged. His owner made that mistake, and ended up in hospital. The poor dog had to be put down. If you waited and did nothing, said nothing, did not move, in five minutes he would flick back to normal. He remembered; he knew he had threatened you. He was so anxious – licking and pawing – desperately wanting everything to get back to normal. I've often wondered what went wrong!

Amazingly, some pathogens are capable of altering the function of the mind. One of these is Rabies! I had an interesting experience in Alaska – on a fishing trip. Arriving back at the camp jetty, after a days salmon fishing, a few small salmon had been left on the jetty by someone, who had been preparing fish but gone away for some reason. As the boat came to the jetty I saw a mink trying to steal one of the fish. I grabbed my camera and climbed from the boat to the jetty for photographs. I clicked away; the mink saw me, possibly because of the camera clicking. Instead of running away it paused and then came towards me. I continued to click away, until the mink was actually at my feet looking at me. At this moment, the man who had been cleaning the fish came back, saw me and the mink, rushed forward and kicked the mink away. He looked at me and said one word, "Rabies!" Then I remembered! Rabies is one of those diseases that will actually alter the behaviour of its host to propagate itself. Rabies can affect the mind! Fortunately I was wearing heavy neoprene waders but, if the guide had not kicked the mink away, it would probably have leapt up and bitten me on the face. Just one bite, or scratch, that's all it takes and you have Rabies! A terrible disease that is 100% fatal if not treated very quickly. I remembered reading an article which said, "Never trust a wild animal which appears to be more friendly than you would normally expect it to be. The animal may have Rabies". I was so interested in taking photographs I completely forgot the warning. That a virus can actually influence the brain, and alter the behaviour of an animal in order to propagate itself, is almost beyond belief; but it does! (After all – a virus is just a minuscule packet of RNA. It only just qualifies as a form of life at all).

There are several other pathogens known (bacteria and parasites) that also have the ability to modify the behaviour of the host in order to propagate themselves. For instance, there is a small fresh water shrimp that normally hides away under stones and detritus in the day, coming out to feed at night. A parasite sometimes infects the shrimp and then attacks fish if they feed on shrimp. To improve transmission the parasite causes the shrimp's behaviour to change so that it swims around in daylight thus increasing the chances a fish will eat it. Another water borne parasite has a life cycle which includes phases in water snails and birds. After invading the snail the parasite causes the infected snail to climb up reeds and stems and wait, in an exposed position, so that the chances of the snail being eaten by a bird are enhanced.

The normal brain is very finely balanced, both chemically and electrically. Any imbalance can have disturbing, and sometimes devastating, consequences. If the supply of just one (out of several) neuro-transmitters, Dopamine, is disrupted, the result is the devastating condition known as Parkinson's Disease. The whole body is affected. Signals from the brain to the muscles become reduced and, sometimes, the whole body can 'freeze'. Occasionally, for some reason, the brain becomes imbalanced and the affected person becomes depressed; a very debilitating condition. Everything becomes doom and gloom and the sufferer feels life is not worth living; it frequently leads to suicide. The Coroner's phrase, "Suicide while the balance of the mind was disturbed", is very apt. It was found, many years ago that, if a massive pulse of electricity was put through the frontal lobes of the brain of someone suffering from chronic depression, it often resulted in a substantial improvement in the patient's condition. Nobody knows how Electro Convulsive Therapy works; but it does!

It stands to reason that anything that could upset the delicate balance of the brain should be avoided. Unfortunately, human beings like to experiment and drugs that affect the working of the brain have been taken for thousands of years; Cocaine, 'magic mushrooms' and Opium to name but a few. Now we have modern drugs; Crack, Ecstasy, LSD and a whole range of others, including Alcohol, if taken to excess. To dabble with drugs is to risk upsetting the fine balance of your brain – possibly for life. Do not do it! There is plenty of pleasure in life. If you 'enhance' it today you will almost certainly pay for it tomorrow. Why risk ruining your life just to find out what taking Heroin is like, or Crack or Ecstasy? You can enjoy yourself at parties without it. Do not be pressured or cajoled into experimenting; be your own person! Be firm! Refuse! If necessary – leave the party! You will be a healthy, laughing, well balanced person while your drug taking friends are in Rehab.

I have never taken drugs, not ever, not even the smallest experiment; I value my life too much! I don't care what people may say. In the past, people have said, "You don't smoke. You don't take drugs. Your life must be boring. How do you know what it's like if you haven't tried it?" And so on. My answer has still been, "No! I am my own person. It is my life. I make the decisions". Let them laugh, or scoff, or sneer! There is no way I would allow myself to be coerced into experimenting with drugs. Fortunately, I have never been trapped by someone lacing my drink or my food! I also suggest it would be wise not to dabble in anything to do with witchcraft and the occult. It is hocus pocus but your subconscious mind is naïve and may react in ways you don't expect and won't like.

In the Middle Ages, in Europe, many people ate bread made from rye. Rye is prone to being attacked by a fungus – Ergot. Ergot produces a chemical similar to LSD; an hallucinogen – and more; it interferes with the circulatory system. The populations of whole villages and towns occasionally went mad. To compound it they sometimes developed gangrene in the extremities; a symptom of Ergot poisoning. It was sometimes called St. Anthony's Curse or St. Anthony's Fire.

True alcoholics sometimes hallucinate; not just pink elephants and white rabbits – but terrifying hallucinations, usually of something they most fear. (Delirium Tremens). Exhaustion can also affect the working of the brain. Native Americans used to dance continuously for twenty four hours or more, without food or water, in order to induce hallucinations. Spitfire pilots in the Battle of Britain sometimes had 'out of body' experiences because of exhaustion.

Experiments in reducing the body's sensory inputs (Sensory Deprivation) showed what could happen if the sensory signals to the brain were interrupted. People were fitted with breathing apparatus and were then lowered into a tank of saline water of exactly the right density to support them. The water temperature was exactly body temperature; there was no sound or light. The brain was almost cut off in its isolation but not quite, of course, because the volunteer would hear, and feel, his own breathing and heartbeat. Soon, however, the volunteer began to hallucinate. The brain – deprived of most of its inputs – began to create its own. They found, in this condition, the brain grasped avidly at any inputs. It was easy to implant suggestions – to brainwash the volunteer. The Chinese indoctrinated Allied soldiers captured in the Korean War. They kept them isolated, cold and short of food. They deprived them of sleep and, after a certain time, began to indoctrinate them with the ideas of Communism. Brainwashing was becoming more sophisticated.

The brain is a mass of intricate circuitry. There are many parallel circuits and, what an engineer might call, redundant wiring. In times of stress or exhaustion or, occasionally, in perfectly normal conditions, it is possible for signals to cross over and go down the wrong wires. (This is an oversimplification, but it will do). Sometimes people see apparitions, ghosts and such like. Parts of the brain 'daydream' all the time. The subconscious is working away without you knowing it. When I was working as an engineer, sometimes a vision of a mechanism would simply flick into my mind. If such signals accidentally track onto the sensory input channels of the conscious brain, the images will appear real for a time. The person may report they have seen a ghost. (If two or more people see the ghost, or film or photograph it, I might sit up and take note. Unfortunately, films and photographs can be faked, and it is amazing what people will do for fame and fortune or even to get their name in the newspapers, or their face on television. I have never seen a convincing film of a ghost anyway!).

You are the possessor of the most intricate, complicated and remarkable organic computer on Earth. It took nearly four thousand million years of evolution to create. Look after it.

Many people seem to have the idea the human brain, as it is today, is at the peak of its development. I have no such views! I expect evolution to continue so that, in due course, the average human brain and mind will be far superior to what it is today. The brain can develop to have far better memory, far better access to that memory, and a massive increase in general intelligence. We already have clues as to what may happen. Occasionally the human race produces individuals of genius; people of phenomenal talent and abilities, demonstrating that humanity has far more potential than many realise. Usually, talented people have heads and brains no larger than normal. It would appear, therefore, that we already possess a brain that is large enough for stunning intelligence. All we need is an improvement in the connections, the wiring or the arrangement. As proven by the rare and occasional Genius this can and will happen. I see no reason therefore why, in the far future, the human race will not advance as far beyond our present level, as we are now ahead of chimpanzees.

Whereas now we spend many hours in debate and argument and, in general, muddle through our crises, I foresee a time when the correct solution to complex problems is immediately, and utterly, obvious to everybody, and rational, logical thinking is normal everyday behaviour. In no way am I suggesting human beings will become emotionless, passionless, calculating machines. However, greater general intelligence would lead to better understanding, agreement, and cooperation, in tackling problems which can affect the well being, happiness and future of the human race and the general good of the planet.

THE SUBCONSCIOUS MIND

The subconscious mind is fantastically important. It has great powers and influences our lives from birth to death. The whole future of the human race depends, to a degree, on our understanding the subconscious and yet it is still a neglected and little studied facet of the human brain.

When I left school, at 16, I began to think about looking for a job. Very few went to University in those days. The general idea was to get to work, and earn some money to contribute to the family finances. Children, at that time, normally left school at 14 years old, but I was fortunate in that, when I took the 11 plus exams, I was awarded a Special Place at a Grammar School. This meant that my parents didn't have to pay towards the Grammar School fees. In any case, they were very good to allow me to go, because it meant they had to forego the contribution I would have made if I had worked from the age of 14. (It's a sobering thought to remember that, even when children left school at 14, it was extremely rare to meet someone who could not read and write). So, unusually for a working class child in those days, I stayed at school until I was 16. University was never considered. (Today, I think how wonderful it must be that almost anyone can go). Between the ages of ten to sixteen I used to like to tinker and take things like ancient sewing machines to bits, to see how they worked and, if Dad or Uncle Bill would supply materials, I would make gadgets, electric motors, little models, my own design of pike fishing lures and so on, therefore the obvious thing for me to do was to go into engineering.

I became an apprentice draughtsman at a local firm that was involved in structural and mechanical engineering. Indentures were signed, and I had to agree to go to Night School regularly to learn maths, mechanical engineering, structural design, electrical engineering, and so on.

After a while, I found that I could devise and invent things and became friendly with a man at the firm who was a natural inventor. When he found I too was inventive he used to invite me to compete with him in solving engineering problems. Often, on a Friday, he would call me into his office, explain what was required, and ask me if I would like to think about it over the weekend and compare notes with him on Monday. Naturally, as an enthusiastic youth, I readily rose to the challenge.

Sometimes I racked my brains for hours but simply could not devise a way to solve a specific problem, no matter how I ran through, in my mind, all the different devices and mechanisms I had learned about in my studies. What was required was something new; something really innovative! I would go to bed exhausted, my brain fizzing with the thinking I had been doing. Then sometimes, the following morning, as I got in front of my drawing board, the solution to the problem would miraculously come into my mind; from nowhere! It happened not once, but time and time again. I began to puzzle about where these new and original ideas came from; then I read an article in an engineering journal, "How to focus your subconscious mind on a problem." I realised that was what I had been doing. I was racking my brain – forcing the problem deeper into my mind and, somehow, the subconscious was working on the problem and producing these new and original ideas. I read how a man named Singer, in the United States, had vowed to invent a sewing machine, but he had come up against an insuperable problem. No matter how hard he tried, he could not crack the problem of machine-making the stitches. One night he went to bed exhausted, and slept. He dreamed – and in the dream saw his sewing machine working. He looked at the needle. The hole for the thread in the needle was in the point; all existing sewing needles had the hole in the tail end. When he woke up, he thought about the dream and realised a hole in the needle point was the answer he had been looking for.

I read also about a chemist who was trying to discover the arrangement of the atoms in the benzene molecule. He simply could not see how the molecule behaved as it did. One night, after working on the problem for days, he dreamed and, in the dream, saw a snake that had swallowed its own tail. He woke up and realised that the dream had given him the answer. The benzene molecule was in the form of a ring with no ends.

I became intrigued by all this and thought about it carefully. The more I thought, and the more I read, the more intrigued I became. I realised that the implications of what I had found out were staggering. I already knew about the subconscious mind of course; nothing special in that. The subconscious, it was generally considered, controlled the various functions of my body and left me to get on with my life but, to me, it did not look as though that was the whole story. I considered the evidence very carefully. If the subconscious could invent new gadgets, complicated devices that would actually work, it seemed to me my subconscious mind must understand engineering. Therefore it must read what I read and hear what I hear, and there must be some form of intelligence there, to use the engineering principles and knowledge to devise something that would actually work; not just dreaming of a magic wand – and 'Hey Presto' – something would happen. Over the years, whenever I needed to pull something out of the hat – my subconscious has usually produced an answer.

Year after year I read interesting things; about hypnosis, mental abnormalities, and mentally ill people hearing voices in their heads. There were films such as – 'Jekyll and Hyde'; about people with dual personalities. I read about psychosomatic disorders and subliminal advertising and, gradually, I came to conclusions. I believe that, at some time in our evolution, a second 'parallel wired', thinking, part of the brain evolved; maybe so that, as primitive man struggled desperately to survive, from day to day, this second thinking entity could take time to ponder over needs and requirements, and finally come up with solutions; the sharpened spear, stone tools, the bow and arrow, the way to make pots, wicker work, clothes and so on.

Imagine a primitive human family, searching and hunting for food in the day, sheltering under an overhanging rock at night. A short distance away is a cave, a much better shelter for the family but, unfortunately, the cave is occupied by a tiger. This animal has already killed members of the family and the leader of the group, returning from hunting, pauses over the evening meal and thinks how good it might be if they could only get rid of the tiger. They would eliminate the danger and could take over the much better cave. He slept and, when he awoke, exclaimed "I have an idea". A few days later and the tiger returns, as usual, in the evening, to the cave lair. Suddenly the ground falls away beneath his feet and he tumbles headlong into a pit filled with sharpened stakes. Soon after, the family move into the cave. Everybody is relieved at the tiger's demise and the skin helps keep the family warm at night. Similar episodes, over the years, ensured the survival of the human race.

There seem to be problems, however, with this second independently thinking part of the brain, sharing the same skull as the conscious mind. It seems, for the mental health of the individual, the subconscious has to communicate indirectly; in dreams, a 'hunch', a 'gut feeling' or the quick flash of inspiration as an idea is insinuated into conscious thoughts. I realised that, to all intents and purposes, the subconscious was a sort of second personality within the brain; that, if one faced the facts, is what the evidence indicated.

The most convincing demonstration of independence, is when the subconscious mind actually disagrees with the conscious. If there is a minor disagreement leading to mental discomfort we say we have a conscience, but the disagreement between the conscious and the subconscious can become much more powerful than that and the subconscious can, occasionally, take drastic action. People are sometimes punished for things they do that, in fact, the subconscious disagrees with.

Years ago I saw an amazing medical programme on Television. It was to do with hypnosis and psychosomatic illness and turned out to far more interesting, and complex, than I had expected.

A man and his wife were being interviewed by two doctors – a psychiatrist and a hypnotist. The case was very strange. Two years earlier the man, perfectly normal previously, had suddenly lost the ability to speak. He could still write, but not speak, not in any circumstances, not to anyone including his wife. He and his wife had been to various doctors, who had examined him and pronounced that they could find absolutely nothing wrong. Finally, someone suggested a professional hypnotist. The man agreed and, in due course, he was examined under hypnosis. Under hypnosis, which was filmed for reference purposes, incredibly, he started to speak and his wife, who had not heard his voice for two years, broke down in tears. Under hypnosis he spoke quite normally and was questioned, and an amazing story came out.

Just before the man had been struck dumb, his mother had died in tragic circumstances, in a house fire. Although not an invalid she was housebound and he used to call in and see her regularly. He had been due to call in and see her, as usual, one night, when he met up with some friends who persuaded him to go to a public house for a drink. The drinks, and the time spent at the pub, extended and he never did go to see his ailing mother that night. That night was the night of the fire. Under hypnosis, he described how he had been blamed for causing the death of his mother by neglect; he had been arrested, taken to Court and a Judge had sentenced him to be struck dumb as a punishment. The Judge was, of course, his subconscious! No one in real life had blamed him for his mother's death. He had not, in real life, been arrested or gone to Court. It was his subconscious mind that blamed him for his mother's death (his conscience you might say) and it was his subconscious that had punished him. The punishment however, was real; in everyday life he could not speak. He had, literally, been struck dumb. As soon as they took him out of hypnosis, he again could not speak. No matter how he tried he was dumb.

At the end of the programme the hypnotist said that, in his opinion, he would have to try to convince the man's subconscious that he was not responsible for his mother's death, and then he might be free to talk again; otherwise he had no idea when the man would regain his speech and return to normal. The TV programme gave every indication of being genuine. Everything was presented in a perfectly serious manner. This was an extreme example of what is called Psychosomatic Illness. Symptoms can range all the way from minor ailments to extreme and rare cases such as the one described. It is even possible for the person affected to become paralysed in one or more limbs and probably the most remarkable of all is a situation, fortunately very rare, where a person can become blind when there is absolutely nothing detectably wrong with their eyes. The most common cause of psychosomatic illness is where there is stress. Someone may have some sort of nagging illness which keeps them off work – usually off a job they hate. It can happen in the stress of war. In these cases, of course, the sub conscious is trying to help – by creating fictitious ailments. The ailments are perfectly real to the conscious sufferer but no medical causes can be found.

There are other remarkable examples of the power of the subconscious mind to directly affect the body. For instance, it is possible for a woman, who is desperate to have a child, to have a phantom pregnancy. (A classic case was Queen Mary the First of England who, in her anxiety to produce an Heir to the Throne by King Philip of Spain, developed a very convincing phantom pregnancy). The subconscious creates all the symptoms of pregnancy – even to a greatly distended abdomen – in an effort to satisfy the longings of the conscious mind.

There is the phenomenon of stigmata. This, occasionally, occurs when intensely devout Christian monks or priests concentrate on their religion so much that they develop marks or, in extreme cases, actual bleeding sores, corresponding to the crucifixion wounds on the body of Christ. In a few rare cases stigmata have been known to persist for many years.

As another example of the power of the subconscious to interfere with and control signals passing to the conscious mind, it has been found it is possible to hypnotise some people into not feeling pain – even to the extent of permitting major operations to be performed without conventional anaesthetic.

Experts in the practice of Yoga, which can be considered a form of self hypnosis, can reduce their heart rate, slow their breathing rate and reduce metabolism to an amazing degree – even to the extent of surviving being buried alive in a small coffin for many hours without any additional air supply.

One of the programmes I saw, to do with hypnotism, was deeply disturbing. It dealt with subliminal advertising and brain washing. On a film, the old fashioned type with sequential photographs, the normal speed is, I believe, 20 frames a second or faster – to eliminate the flicker. The conscious brain cannot distinguish between one frame and the next, so the film seems, to the viewer, to be a smooth progression of action when, in fact, it is not. It was stated that, if an advert was placed on just one frame of the film, which consciously you would only see as a slight flicker, the subconscious could, and would, read it. That advertisement, by influencing the subconscious would also influence you – by the flow of ideas from the subconscious – and that is why subliminal advertising is illegal. If you think about it – how do you find a single person's name on a long list? You run your eye down the list. You don't actually read every name one by one, you 'scan' the list. Your subconscious reads the list much faster than you can and you just 'spot' the name. The survival expert on TV, Ray Mears, was describing how to track wild animals, "You don't actually look in detail for signs. You scan the area and let your subconscious spot the clues."

On the TV programme, they also gave an interesting demonstration of the power of suggestion under hypnosis. A lady was sent into a room where the walls were covered with a number of paintings (reproductions). She was asked to walk around, and choose the one she would most like to see hanging in her home. After walking around and looking at all the pictures, she chose a Constable (as I probably would have done). They asked her why she liked it and she gave her reasons. Then she was hypnotised and, under hypnosis, was told that she would later be asked to walk into the room and choose a picture; she would forget she had previously done this and this time she would choose the Picasso, "because of its bright colours and it somehow impressed her." They then woke her out of the hypnotic state and asked her to look over the pictures. After walking round for a while she chose the Picasso. When they asked her why, she came out with the exact words she had been told to say when she was under hypnosis. Remember – she was now out of the hypnotic trance. They call it Post Hypnotic Suggestion.

One of the most remarkable of hypnotists' tricks is the negative illusion. It is possible to hypnotise someone into refusing to believe something exists – when it actually does. I remember seeing a film of a demonstration. Three chairs were placed, side by side, in the centre of an empty room and three men were asked to go and sit in the chairs for a photograph. The photograph was taken, and the subject who was to be hypnotised (a lady – I remember) was brought into the room, shown the scene and then, with her consent, hypnotised. She was then told, while in her hypnotic trance, that there were only two people sitting in the chairs; the centre chair was empty. She was then released from her hypnotic trance and the hypnotist chatted to her for a couple of minutes. He then asked her how many chairs were in the room, "Three!" And how many people sitting in the chairs, "Two!" The photograph was produced and shown to her and she was asked how many people she could see in the photograph. "Two!" The interviewer then walked until he was behind the man in the centre chair, and placed his hand behind the seated man's head, with two fingers raised. At this point it was impossible for the subject to see the hand or the fingers. The subject was then asked how many fingers she could see raised on the hand behind the centre chair, "Three!" Not only was the subconscious mind censoring the genuine information that the conscious mind was receiving, but it also supplied false information to reinforce the illusion. Other demonstrations of the power of hypnotic suggestion were also given during the programme. I agree that it would be very easy to fake these demonstrations and produce a 'spoof' programme, but the film described was presented as part of a series on the powers of the mind. I have no reason to believe the demonstrations were not genuine. If they were, indeed valid, the implications are stunning.

It seems that, although having remarkable abilities, the subconscious mind is very naïve and easily open to suggestion. If hypnotism can work on a one to one basis in a closed psychiatrists consulting room how do we know it cannot work on a mass audience. When Albert Speer (he became Hitler's Armaments Minister) as a young architectural student, totally disinterested in politics, was talked into accompanying a fellow student to one of Hitler's beer hall rallies, as a break from studying, he found himself mesmerised by the mental power of the man and became a dedicated follower. He admitted to being overwhelmed by Hitler's charisma. Others have also suggested Hitler may have been a mass hypnotist.

It must be remembered that the brain is shut away from everything. It is locked up, like a man in a cell, with no way to know what is going on outside, except by what he is told on a telephone. The brain is enclosed, and the only means by which information reaches the brain is through the nerve connections (wires if you like). A picture forms on the retina of your eye, which registers it like the pixels on a digital camera. Electrical signals pass the information down the optic nerve to the brain, which re-assembles the signals to form the picture. So it is with all the senses; merely signals down wires. My father had his olfactory nerve cut in an accident and lost his sense of smell forever. If a leg is amputated in hospital, the patient can go home and feel an intolerable itching in his big toe; the one on the amputated leg. The brain is getting a false signal from a nerve that has been cut, so the brain thinks the leg is still there. The signals have to be processed before they are finally registered. What if something goes wrong in the processing stage? What if something interferes with the processing? For instance, drugs can interfere; some can cause hallucinations, delusions or visions. The subconscious, also, can interfere.

Now we can understand how people can see ghosts, apparitions, hear noises, feel phantom touch and have 'out of body' experiences. As Scrooge says to Marley in 'A Christmas Carol', "An apparition might merely be the effect of an undercooked piece of potato." It has been suggested that the feeling of 'Deja-Vous' can occur because information (the scene) has taken a second track, a short cut – you could say, to the part of the brain involved in the seeing experience, and a second 'copy' has come in over a second set of 'wires', maybe only one twentieth of a second later. We have the disturbing experience of feeling we have lived through this before; the brain recognising this is the second time this information has reached it.

Remember, the subconscious is suggestible. Now we can understand reports of Alien Abductions, Religious Experiences, Encounters with Demons; which brings us to the subject of Witchcraft. It is possible, literally, to frighten yourself to death. Years ago I remember, in about the 1950s, there was a Cult on a pacific island; the natives believed in Witchcraft and occasionally, people would be cursed. The curse was that you would die in your sleep. Very nasty! The people cursed would then be afraid to sleep. Sleep is absolutely essential, and I believe it is even possible to die of sleep deprivation. Some young people who had been cursed actually died and news of this reached the rest of the world. The Witchcraft seemed to work best on impressionable young men and women. Doctors took a young man, who had been cursed, to a modern hospital in Australia, where they found he was perfectly fit and healthy; nevertheless he sickened and died; nothing they could do was able to save him. I think the Witchcraft business was finally stopped; the authorities probably threatened the witch doctor, shaman, or whatever he was called.

I once saw a TV programme where a native witch doctor (from Haiti I think) was being interviewed. He was asked "Does witchcraft really work?" "Oh! Yes!" he said. "Undoubtedly! But it doesn't work on white people because they don't believe!" I am convinced that the various forms of brainwashing also work by affecting the subconscious mind. By 'brainwashing' I mean everything, from repetitive advertising to religious chanting, and even 'fashion'. When I was 20 years old, young men had their hair cut neat and short. That was the fashion and that was how I liked my hair to be. Later came the 'Beatles' and long hair became the new fashion. I hated it, so I said "I am independent. I don't care if it is the new fashion. I will still have my hair cut as I always have done." Recently, someone showed me a photograph, taken a few years later, and I couldn't believe I had ever really had hair that long!

I remember women's fashion in skirts. At one time they were mid length, just below the knee. Very appealing! Then the 'New Look' came in, skirts just above the ankles. "How quaint! Doesn't look very attractive does it?" A few years later – "Look at that woman in the short skirt. How old fashioned!" Brainwashing can be very subtle; even in fashions of thinking. I remember when everybody thought the British Empire was great. At that time they hanged murderers, shot traitors and caned children. Everybody thought that was perfectly normal; how could anybody think differently? Swearing in public or in front of ladies just was not done. That ladies might swear was unthinkable. Now look at the difference! I personally, definitely preferred it when ladies never swore and there was no swearing in public. (Please don't ask me if I swear!)

Once, sailors slaughtered whales by the hundreds of thousands; nobody thought twice! Just the job for 'Baleen' for making ladies corsets, superb lubricating and lamp oil, and 'Ambergris' for making perfume. Many people believed that everything was put on this Earth for our use anyway! Fashions of thinking have changed, and they will change again. The susceptibility to follow fashion is linked to the subconscious mind. The subconscious mind has tremendous potential – but it has great dangers too. It is there – in every one of us. Be aware of what it can do – for good – or evil. A child's subconscious mind is an open book with blank pages or, if you prefer, a new computer waiting to be programmed. That which is programmed in, in the first few years, will stay in, for life. Hitler knew this; Mao Tse Tung knew it; the Spartans knew it. Be very careful what you put in a child's mind in the first few years. In general if you are brought up Catholic you stay Catholic; if you are taught Muslim you stay Muslim. If you are taught you are a member of the 'Master Race', and other peoples are inferior, you are unlikely to shake it off.

You can program a child for war or peace; violence or non violence; gentle cooperation or vicious sectarianism; to consider animals as there to be butchered and exploited, or to treat animals with consideration and compassion. This programming is done by the child's experience, observation and education. In schools, education may be controlled; teachers may teach tolerance, compassion and reason, along with reading, writing and arithmetic, but what about when the child is away from school. The example from parents, the TV, computer games, teenage gangs and so on. All too often, TV shows mindless violence. A lot of computer games seem to be violent, and there is a great deal of petty selfishness shown in 'Soaps' and films. (I confess – I like murder films and a good war film. My brother and I both agree it would have been very exciting to have been involved in the Pacific Ocean battles of World War Two, with the kamikaze planes coming in and the sky full of flak; even better if you survived! It makes you wonder what our programming was like; and that of the Japanese, of course).

Sometimes I feel uncomfortable at programmes on TV. Are these really suitable for children? Forget the 9 o'clock watershed! Does

184

anyone really think children don't watch TV after 9 o'clock? I hate to think what they punch up on their computers! Don't forget – all this stuff is programming their subconscious minds! If you want a peaceful, tolerant, rational and civilised Earth in the future – you must start with the children.

Stress and trauma can affect the subconscious, sometimes in small ways; the frustration in the traffic jam or the rage when someone dives in and grabs the last parking plot – just as you were manoeuvring into it. The subconscious reacts; boosts your heart rate, and raises your blood pressure. There are also the more long term emotional experiences. The humiliation a man may experience when rejected or mocked by a woman. This can cut deep – and lead to serial killers like the Yorkshire Ripper. Massive trauma, such as 'shell shock', can cause the subconscious to create disabilities, sometimes paralysis, even psychosomatic blindness, to try to prevent a repeat of the traumatising experience.

If, after a stressful day, you sit back, close your eyes and think calm, serene, thoughts; imagine beautiful scenery and tell yourself to relax; your subconscious will respond. Your heart rate will slow and your blood pressure drop. You can, of course, do the reverse. When you are relaxed, measure your blood pressure and heart rate. Then sit back and remember something that made you really mad – really angry. Concentrate on this for five minutes. Now measure your blood pressure and heart rate again. You can also influence your own subconscious in other ways; create a mind block; push out rational thoughts – especially if there is religious fear or moral dilemmas. You can, in fact, brainwash yourself into believing anything. On the beneficial side, you can utilise the power of the subconscious to help you achieve something you want to do. When I was working as an engineer I decided to try to start a manufacturing business; very difficult in those days, especially if you didn't have any business contacts, assets or money. It took me seven years to get going. Sometimes things were really tough. On my own, driving to work, with no one else to see or hear me, I sometimes ranted out loud in the car. I used to shout, "I will and I can and I damn well shall," over and over again. I built up a steamroller Will. Nothing would make me give up! I only used to visit my parents once in six months. On one trip my mother, seeing how gaunt I was getting, said, "Why don't you give up this business idea. Why not just settle for your job?" I looked at her and said, "The only time I'll give up is when I am in a pine box." I had created a drive in my subconscious that simply would not let me give up.

The Army understands the power of brainwashing. It is hammered into recruits, soldiers, over and over again, "You must obey orders! You must obey orders! It is not your job to think!" The officers are taught, "You must lead! You must lead! You must be an example to your men; even unto death!" After World War Two they had War Crimes trials. A lot of the people involved claimed, "We were only following orders!" Inexperienced people, who had never been in the Army, said, "Why didn't you refuse to carry out these orders?"

Years after the war, in America, researchers carried out experiments. People were chosen, at random, from the public. They were employed and paid to do a job. The job, in fact, was torture, but they were told it was simply research. A man who was an experimental subject (although he did not know it) was ordered to sit in front of a control panel and take part in a 'question and answer' session, with another person who was hidden behind a screen. The control panel incorporated an electrical voltage regulator and a push button. A tall authoritative man in a white coat – the Research Controller – stood behind the subject and gave him instructions on what to do. The subject was given a list of questions and answers and ordered to ask the person behind the screen the questions, one by one, and tick off the correct answers. If the person behind the screen gave an incorrect answer, the subject was ordered to push the red button on the console and punish the hidden person with an electric shock. Initially, the voltage set on the regulator was very low, and there was no detectable response from behind the screen when the button was pushed. However, as more questions were asked and more mistakes were made, the controller ordered the subject to increase the voltage. With the pressing of the button, audible gasps came from behind the screen and, as the voltage was steadily increased as the mistakes continued, the gasps turned to screams. (All this, by the way, was being secretly filmed). If the subject became unhappy, and became reluctant to increase the voltage further and press the button, the controller authoritatively said, "Proceed! It is not your responsibility. It is my responsibility. You are to obey orders!" The tests, under these conditions, were carried out many times, with different subjects. It was amazing how far the questioners (the subjects) would go if they were insistently told it was not their responsibility and they must obey orders. In some instances, the voltage was raised to the maximum on the dial – six hundred volts – to the accompaniment of terrible screams. (Not being able to see beyond the screen the subjects did not know they were being fooled). Many of the test subjects were unhappy with what they were doing, were distressed and complained, but, when told to obey orders, carried on. I think there was only one man who positively and definitely stood up, and resolutely refused to continue. I wonder if even he would have refused if, during the war, he had been threatened with a firing squad or a posting to the Russian

Front! You <u>will</u> obey orders! Even a friend of mine, years after World War Two, in Kenya fighting the terrorist 'Mau Mau', semi-jokingly refused to obey an order. He was instantly threatened with a pistol by his British officer. Obey – or else! My friend obeyed! Does anybody really think any soldier, on either side, in World War Two, could have refused to obey an order from a superior officer? They would simply have shot the soldier and ordered the next man to do the job.

Of the Nations of the World, I would judge the Swiss probably to be the most rational and peaceful. They have not been involved in a war for seven or eight hundred years. Whenever there is a serious political decision to be made, they have a Referendum; the people are asked to vote. Not so long ago, there was a Referendum on the idea of reducing the number of hours in the working week. I believe the Swiss voted – NO! In other words, "Leave well alone. We are doing all right!" To change might reduce the ability of the nation to compete (prices of exports and so on). In the UK, I have no doubt the Trade Unions would have instantly clamoured to reduce the working week, and have lobbied furiously. Then, five years later, they would have been wondering why unemployment was on the rise and shouting for something to be done about it. We could do worse than study how the Swiss educate their children.

Recently I picked up a copy of the Daily Telegraph, dated 11th December 2006, browsed, and came upon on article about the composer Howard Blake, (he composed the music for the well known children's Christmas film 'The Snowman'). He describes how he was walking on the beach, when the vital six notes of the 'Walking in the Air' theme song just came into his head. He then goes on to describe how the lyrics came to him, and I quote, "I was crossing Kensington High Street and was very conscious of stepping off the pavement and, suddenly, it came to me – 'Walking in the Air'. I went to the park, grabbed a deckchair and I'd completed the lyrics by the end of the afternoon."

Ernest Rutherford, that famous pioneer of atomic research, was said to have had a fantastic 'intuitive' brain. When conducting experiments to do with the nature of atomic structure he often instructed his students, who helped build and operate the equipment, to make modifications and changes that no one could understand but they often resulted in amazing discoveries. Once, when asked why he had decided to make a modification he said "he didn't know – simply a hunch". He obviously possessed a dedicated and brilliant sub-conscious mind that was thinking of various possibilities and insinuating suggestions into his conscious brain in the form of hunches!

Some people can do amazing tricks working through their subconscious. I know of a man who can be given a very difficult arithmetical problem and he will simply carry on talking. After a minute or so he stops, and says, "The answer to your question is ...." He is always right. He doesn't know how he does it. The answer just 'pops' into his head.

There have been many amazing inventions of the human mind. A remarkable one, indeed, was produced by German scientists in World War Two. They were building the V2 rocket; the world's first ballistic rocket missile. A major problem was how to guide it on its trajectory. Since they intended to produce one (the A4) big enough to strike the United States, the question arose – how were they going to control the missile, so that it would strike its target with reasonable accuracy. They invented the Inertial Guidance System. The idea is basically simple, you could say brilliant, in its simplicity. A metal ball is suspended in all directions by springs. In space, in zero G conditions, the ball would sit snugly right in the centre of the springs. The pressure on all the springs would be exactly equal in all directions. If you moved the device, the ball would sag back against one of the springs. By measuring the deflection of the spring you could measure the push, or accelerating force, on the ball. It is possible, by measuring the push on the ball and the time the push continues, to calculate the speed the ball has been accelerated up to, the direction, and also the distance it has travelled, in a certain time. If you are really clever, it is possible to measure the acceleration of the ball in three dimensions and, if you know the exact place the movement started from, you can calculate the exact place, in three dimensions, the ball is at after a certain time. Obviously, when starting from the surface of the Earth it would be necessary to take gravity into consideration. The German Scientists and Engineers actually managed to do all this. A marvel of science, precision engineering and the ingenuity of man. Today, rockets are guided that way; for many years, aircraft on long distance flights were guided that way (before the Satellite Navigation System was perfected) . Nuclear submarines, a classic example, can set off from base, submerge and cruise all over the world, staying underwater for months, and know almost exactly where they are after that time because of the exquisite precision of their Inertial Guidance System.

I think the subconscious mind must have evolved as some sort of helper. A backup to the conscious mind. There is no doubt of its ability to assist in the battle for survival. I know very well of its capability to produce ideas; however, as with most things of great power there is also a downside. If something goes wrong with the subconscious a person can be in deep trouble. One thinks of madmen hearing voices; serial killers who have a compulsion to kill – sometimes hearing voices, sometimes not; all sorts of hallucinations, delusions and strange experiences. Some people will be horrified and some frightened at the suggestion they are not really alone in their own head. Some will scoff and dismiss the idea as preposterous, denying the evidence of their own experiences. There is no need to be horrified or afraid – the Subconscious Mind is, for nearly everyone, a devoted and dedicated assistant. Only in a rare, unlucky, few does something go wrong and the Subconscious becomes a perverse, menacing and even dominating independent personality or a source of wild delusion.

I have just read of a classic case – the obituary of a woman named Eileen Caddy (Daily Telegraph Page 23, December 19th 2006). She was the founder of the New Age – Findhorn Foundation, in Scotland. The Foundation was described as 'An International Centre for Spiritual Education'. A number of quite normal, intelligent, celebrities joined. The article says she listened to her daily 'Messages from God'. It goes on to say that, one day, she saw with her inner eye the word LUKANO written in letters of fire. By telepathy, she found out LUKANO was the captain of a spaceship from Venus. (If her subconscious mind had been on the ball it would have been a planet somewhere else in the galaxy – somewhere where no one could find out she was wrong!). The obituary goes on to say the spaceship was going to rescue a few humans, in the event of nuclear disaster. She was even told where the aliens would come down, and her husband felled a lot of trees in the area so that the ship could land. The article also mentions she talked to Spirits about growing cabbages. (From the sublime to the ridiculous; her subconscious must have had a quick flash of a page in a gardening book sometime!). She also met the Virgin Mary at a Healing Centre! Need I continue? However, just imagine this sort of thing happening to someone with real power – say Caligula, Nero, Joe Stalin or Hitler. Remember how Rasputin mesmerised the wife of the Tsar of Russia. An understanding of the subconscious mind and its capabilities can explain a great many things indeed.

The subconscious can be very wonderful – and very dangerous. I suppose I have been lucky. I have never heard voices and never seen visions. The only way my subconscious has ever communicated with me is by ideas. Ideas which just popped into my head, or in dreams, or the occasional 'hunch' or 'gut feeling'. Talking of dreams, I remember, when I was in my twenties, reading an article which said some people (it intimated that they were rare) had Lucid Dreams. (Lucid Dreams are where a person knows, consciously, they are dreaming). I found this remarkable; I thought everybody dreamed like that. Ninety percent of my dreams, when I was young, were lucid dreams. I knew perfectly well I was dreaming. If I didn't like the dream I would refuse to accept it and either wake up or switch to another dream. At 78 years of age, I now find I am losing this effect. Only about 10% of my dreams are lucid now. I also find that I usually forget non lucid dreams almost as soon as I wake. Some lucid dreams I have remembered all my life; in near perfect clarity. Through lucid dreams, my subconscious has given me experiences it would be totally impossible for me to experience in real life.

I remember very clearly dreaming that I was working on some mechanism on the stage of the Albert Hall. The place was packed with people; it was time for a concert to begin. Some great singer, such as Gigli or Pavarotti, was going to sing the classics. Suddenly, people at the back of the stage were talking. Someone came to me and said, "The singer can't go on. You will have to go on in his place." I protested, "Don't be silly. I can't sing." (In actual fact my singing voice is quite hopeless). "But you must! Get out there!" I found myself in the centre of the stage in front of a vast audience – all looking at the stage expectantly. The start of a nightmare you may think. I looked at them. Somehow I was not afraid. I opened my mouth and the most fantastic sound issued. I sang the great classics, finishing with 'Nessun Dorma'. I gave them the lot! The power of my voice was tremendous; the notes – perfect! The audience rose to their feet. They roared. They clapped. I revelled in it! I woke up, realising I had had one of the great experiences of my life. Something it would be totally impossible for me to experience in reality. I have never forgotten. I have had many other fascinating and realistic lucid dreams; flying jet fighters; flying balloons to the edge of space and so on. In the lucid dreams I have been amazed at the incredible detail the brain has created – merely for a dream. Unfortunately my lucid dreams are fewer now that I have become older. The Brain is, indeed, remarkable.

I feel it is important that people know about and understand the workings of the subconscious mind – so that they can be fully aware of the potential and the manifest dangers, and understand the need for great care in the education of children. In particular, to raise awareness of the dangers that lie in so many forms of brainwashing and indoctrination. The people of this planet have to learn to live together. The messages the subconscious mind absorbs can either make this possible or impossible. We must study and understand the workings of the subconscious mind – and be aware.

MEMORY

Memory is fantastically more important than most people realise. It is, in fact, the key to all animal life. Without it there would be no past, no yesterday, not even today or five minutes ago. There would be no learned capability, no wisdom, no experience, no recognition. Without some form of information storage, animal life would never have advanced beyond the slime stage.

Even in plants there is evidence of some form of simple memory, as any gardener with a lawn can demonstrate for himself. (Weeds, such as dandelions and plantains, learn to shorten their flowering heads, and flatten their leaves close to the ground, to avoid having them mowed off). It has been found, in laboratory tests, that even single celled, mobile, bacteria display a form of rudimentary memory by migrating towards a better environment, or turning away from a worse one. (Moving towards a better environment indicates that the bacteria are aware that the conditions are better now than they were a few moments ago). For animals, memory is utterly absolutely vital, for, without a memory system, a brain would be virtually useless. Memory is one of the last great unsolved mysteries of biology. We do not yet know how it works. We do not know the exact processes by which the brain stores information – whether it is chemical or, as seems more likely, modification of the cellular and wiring structure or, possibly, a combination of the two. Without memory, a human being would be simply an inert mass of living cells. In fact, it would not be possible to live at all. A computer without a memory is as good as useless.

The brain is locked away in a dark cavern, and the only sources of information are messages from the outside coming in on numerous wires, like someone locked away in a closed room, with only a host of telephones to let him know what is going on outside the room. In the case of human beings, learning, which is the storing and use of information, begins very early on while the foetus is in the womb. The developing brain begins to receive information and also sends out signals. Some – motor signals – result in the first faint movements of the baby's limbs and, sooner or later, an arm movement will result in a thumb touching the mouth. Pressure sensors, on both the thumb and the mouth, register the contact and the brain needs to record exactly which motor signals resulted in the thumb/mouth contact so that, in future, the experience can be repeated. All the signals from heat sensors, pressure sensors, sound, light and vibration sensors, need to be analysed, catalogued and the information stored away for future reference. Some memories and information will already have been pre-programmed in the genes – the instincts. As more and more information continues to flood in, the brain develops, becomes larger and more complex to handle the load.

After birth the flood of information intensifies and, in the first developing years, an enormous amount of data must be handled and stored. The baby learns to understand its surroundings, recognise its parents and perform a myriad of physical manoeuvres. In humans, even walking is a learned experience though, in many animals, it is a pre-programmed instinctive ability from birth. (In actual fact a human baby, at birth, does have a walking reflex but it is lost soon afterwards). Every single thing a child learns as it grows and develops is utterly dependent on memory, whether it is the smile on its mother's face, the sound of the father's voice, or the first faltering grasp of the meaning of words. Without memory none of this would be possible. All actions need memory, from simple actions such as walking, or scratching your nose, to making a cup of tea or doing complex mathematical calculations. From the very beginning the brain has to learn everything from the signals that reach it via the nervous system. Some signals relate to touch, some to smell, taste, warmth, pain, sight, etc. All these signals have to be recognised for what they are, and a record kept in the memory for future reference. The brain of the foetus actually develops to handle and process these signals, as it grows, and some areas of the brain will not develop correctly unless the necessary signals arrive to stimulate growth.

A few years ago, an experiment was conducted on the development of the brain of a rat, as it grew from foetus to adult. Rats have long whiskers, which are sensory organs with an exquisitely sensitive sense of touch. The experimenters operated on an unborn rat foetus and, on one side of the face, destroyed the cheek buds that, later, would have grown into the long sensory hairs. The base of these hairs, in an adult rat, are connected by nerves to areas of the brain specially developed to handle the sensory input. The damaged foetus was allowed to grow and develop and then, as an adult, was killed and its brain examined. Brain development associated with the side of the face that still had hairs was normal, but it was found the brain area associated with the destroyed hairs had not developed; no input – no development.

We can draw a crude analogy between the brain and an electronic computer. Without memory, in various forms, a computer could not function. Memory is essential to hold information for reference and for playback. A computer program is a form of memory, created by human programmers – telling the computer how to conduct certain operations and functions.

The crudest forms of memory can be extremely simple. I remember, way back before computers became generally available, designing a special purpose automatic machine for a factory production line. The machine carried out a number of functions, sequentially, and some of the later processes had to be modified depending on slight variations in the products passing through. The memory system I devised simply consisted of a row of pegs which could be flipped, left or right. As the products passed through a checking station, pegs were flipped and later processing was influenced by the pattern created (programmed) in the row of pegs. It will be realised that a great deal of information can be encoded in a dozen pegs. After all, this book, and every other book in English, is written using 26 letters of the alphabet.

Many insects are obviously pre-programmed – their instincts are a form of genetically inherited memory. However, in addition to this, many display evidence of a good, day-to-day, working memory. Honeybees are a prime example. No matter where they wander, they remember the journey and how to get back home. Not only that but, if they find a particularly rich source of nectar and pollen, they can remember the location, fly back to the hive and communicate the information to other hive members, who then remember the instructions and fly out to exploit the find. "Not bad"! you might say, but they are capable of far more than that. In the wild, when a new queen leaves an old hive, with her retinue of several thousand bees to start the new hive, she flies a certain distance, lands on a suitable branch or twig, and the followers then form a swarm around her. A number of scout bees then fly off, in different directions, to search for a suitable place to build a new home; hollow trees are preferred. Research has shown that the scouts will check the size of the cavity (by walking around it), the size of the access hole, the height from the ground and the direction the access hole is facing i.e. North, South, East or West. All this information is memorised and the scout bees fly back to the swarm to compare notes. They are then capable of sorting out the information and choosing the site best suited for the future of the swarm. The decision having been made, the queen and swarm then depart from the branch and head for their new home. All this is an amazing demonstration of memory and communication, in an insect with a brain no bigger than a pinhead.

Domesticated honeybees still follow this behaviour, if the beekeeper is a little slack, as I know only too well. Twice, in a few years, the scouts from a local swarm chose the roof space of our house as a suitable place for a hive; space, warmth and a South East access to catch the morning sun. After the first swarm was removed (necessitating ripping out part of the ceiling) all access apertures under the eaves on the

South East side were carefully sealed (so we thought), but, a couple of years later, another swarm moved in. More hassle. When, another two years later, a third swarm settled on a branch in the garden, I lost no time in contacting the village beekeeper and insisted he collect the swarm fast, and get it into one of his spare hives before the scouts did their job and decided, once more, our roof was the ideal space.

Birds, in addition to a lot of genetic pre-programming – migration, nest building, chick rearing, etc., also have good day-to-day working memories. I was amazed, at a Raptor Centre, to hear a bird handler state that birds only have a memory of a few days. A parrot doesn't forget how to talk after a few days! I remember once visiting a Gamekeeper's pheasant rearing pens, and had hundreds of hungry pheasants rush to me like domestic chickens, hoping to be fed; totally tame! However, when they have been turned loose, and some of their fellows have been blasted from the sky during a shoot, the rest never forget and never, ever trust us again. I have had a cock pheasant around the garden for over two years. He comes for food regularly, but not while I am still there, and when he sees me walking around he prefers to sidle off behind a tree rather than stay in view. As a survivor of a batch of pheasants, hand reared for the shoot, there is nothing wrong with his memory.

I suppose one of the most remarkable examples of genetic pre-programming is to be found in the cuckoo. The young cuckoo never knows its true parents. First, when it hatches, it is programmed to throw out any other chicks, or eggs, it shares the nest with, so that it has a monopoly of the foster parents' attention and the food supply. Then, when adult, it migrates in the same direction, and to the same place, as its cuckoo parents did. Later, it migrates back to the land of its birth and knows exactly which foster parent birds to search for, and exactly how to go about planting its egg in the nest. Some species of crows demonstrate a remarkable, practical, memory ability. These birds have a habit of hiding spare food away in caches, for future use, and research has demonstrated they have the ability to create up to a thousand caches, and still remember exactly where every one is located. A most amazing feat, which very few humans indeed could emulate. Squirrels are not so good. Fortunately for trees, they forget where half the nuts and acorns they bury are located and, in the spring, I find seedling walnuts oaks and hazels popping up everywhere, even in the window boxes.

Fish, such as salmon, are famous for their homing instincts – pre-programmed into the genes, and backed up by the ability of the salmon to remember, all its life, the exact smell of the river in which it was hatched and reared, (which, if reared by humans, may not be the river of its origin). It would appear that many fish have quite a good working, day-to-day memory, as carp anglers, in particular, can testify. The carp has a reputation for being very wily and clever. Many anglers these days practice 'catch and release', where caught fish are not killed but are returned to the lake. Carp anglers use a thousand and one different flavoured baits to lure the fish, because they know, once a big carp has been caught on a bait of a certain taste, and released, it is likely to shun that taste in the future. The fish also learn to, very carefully, mouth and check the bait for traces of a hook, before they will take the bait into their mouths and swallow it. Unfortunately, they are up against the fiendishly ingenious Homo Sapiens who have invented the 'hair rig' to catch clever carp. With a 'hair rig' the bait does not have a hook in it at all. There is a very fine thread – the 'hair' – which connects the bait, lying on the bottom of the lake, to the hook, several centimetres away, attached to the main line. The carp, having checked there is no hook in the bait, takes it in his mouth and swallows. As he does so the 'hair' pulls the hook just inside the mouth and the carp finds he is hooked. Wits and memory versus wits, memory and ingenuity.

However, it must surely be that it is in human beings that the potential of memory has reached the highest level yet developed on this earth. A healthy 70 or 80 year old has all the memories and experience of a long life and an enormous wealth of learned knowledge, and information, on immediate call. How all this immense amount of data is stored, is not yet known, but there is, as yet, no indication of a limit to the storage capacity. Gradually, during life, as the memories and experience accumulate, the character and behaviour of the individual varies, and is adjusted. At any stage, the sum total of what a person is, at that age, is in the memory. Without it one person would be the same as any other. In fact, without it, there would be no personality at all – simply a mass of cells. That greatly valued human asset – Experience – is based simply on a mass of accumulated memories – particularly of cause and effect, enabling the possessor of those memories to predict the future – the outcome of certain actions and happenings – on the basis that he (or she) has experienced it, or something similar, or learned something about it, before.

Higher animal memories, such as in humans, seem to have a multi-level and multi-stage system. There are the very important, hard wired, inherited memories (instincts) programmed into the genes. Then there is a second level of learned, programmed, automatic behaviour such as feeding, walking, body language, and so on, which extends into the field of driving, sports, warfare and any form of activity that involves training (programming by repetition). There are also experience memories – memories from everyday life – some of which may be useful and others not. In this latter field there is a two-stage system. Experiences are first stored in a short-term memory system and then there is a sorting process. Memories, which are valued, are transferred to a long-term memory capability and others are discarded. There is such an enormous amount of input from the senses to the brain that some must be discarded (can you remember how many cups of coffee you drank yesterday?). Sometimes, I walk to my car and cannot even remember if I have locked the back door of the house, and have to go back and check. However, if I stub my toe on the step the pain makes that experience important, and it is transferred into the long-term memory so that I remember to lift my foot higher next time. Whilst it is easily possible to forget something trivial, that happened only ten minutes ago, some things that happened very early in life are burned into the memory, and can be recalled vividly and in utmost detail. I forget where I have placed my reading glasses half an hour ago, but can instantly call up, like a film, a memory of the giant Airship – the Graf Zeppelin – looming enormous in the sky as it passed over me as a one year old child.

When I was young, I occasionally had flashes of photographic memory – of some place or situation. Photographic memory is exactly what it says. A total picture of a scene might come into my mind, and I could study details of the picture and notice facts I had not consciously registered before. For some reason this ceased as I became older. When we are very young everything is new. There is so much to observe and to learn; a year seems to be forever. An old person claims that the years simply fly by; especially so if they are in happy retirement. So much is routine, happy or not, and there are fewer and fewer things that stand out and are worthy of serious recording. However, no one, young or old who was alive at the time, will forget the assassination of President Kennedy, or the destruction of the Twin Towers on 9/11.

Unfortunately, memory and memory systems can be damaged – by accident – as in physical or chemical trauma; by disease, in the case of Alzheimer's or Creutzfeldt-Jakob disease, or even, deliberately, in the case of brain-washing. I remember seeing a medical documentary film a few years ago, relating to brain damage and memory impairment. A man in his thirties at a psychiatric hospital was introduced as a patient. It was stated that, as a young man of eighteen, he had been out with friends on a binge-drinking spree. So great had been his intake of alcohol that it had caused brain damage, and had totally destroyed the part of the brain involved in short term/long term memory transfer. The doctor stated he had seen, and talked to, the man almost every week for years. An interview was filmed and the time on the wall clock noted. The patient met the doctor, totally without recognition – as though it was the very first time in his life he had seen the doctor. At the end of a ten minute interview, the doctor left the room and, after a twenty minute gap, returned. The patient then met the returning doctor as though he had never seen him before. Nothing had been transferred into the long-term memory and the short-term information had been discarded. The patient could remember only his early life, up to the age of 18. Nothing after the binge-drinking night existed, or ever would exist, except for a brief moment. If the patient lived to be 70, he would only ever know 18 years of life; nothing else would ever exist, except for the ten brief minutes or so in his short-term memory.

My brother and I have had close experience of the effects of damage to the memory system. When I was seven years old my father had a bad motorcycle accident, which he was lucky to survive; however, he was not unscathed. The front of his forehead was slightly caved in. His olfactory nerve was cut which destroyed his sense of smell and ruined his taste. Miraculously, he was not blinded. More insidiously, and only later, did it become apparent that there was some form of damage to the memory system. He could remember his day-to-day life and seemed normal, except that he could not learn anything new. Fortunately he was a carpenter by trade and remembered everything to do with carpentry, so the disability did not affect his work. Gradually, as a teenager, I noticed he could not learn anything new and, at first, was inclined to wonder if he was stupid. However, whenever I got involved in anything to do with the building trade, I found he knew his stuff and wondered how he had managed to learn so much in the first place. Slowly, as I discovered more about his accident, and the functioning of the brain, I realised the problem was brain damage. Later, to dispense with cycling to work, he bought himself a little Honda motorcycle; a very simple, low-powered machine. My brother, Denville, tried it, and learned to ride it in about 5 minutes but, because it was different to his earlier motorcycle, Dad had terrible trouble learning to use it, and finally gave up. We take so much of our learning abilities for granted, it is only when we see someone who has a handicap that we pause to think.

Another unfortunate example of brain damage affecting memory was our mother. All her life she was bright, generally cheerful and capable. She had a good memory, learned easily and took everything in her stride. She learned to drive a car, in her sixties, passed the driving test first time and continued to drive with enthusiasm until she was 87 years old. As she grew older she became a very friendly, affectionate, likeable little old lady, who liked nothing better than to run a taxi service for her many friends. Then she had a stroke, which put her in hospital. However, she recovered remarkably rapidly; no speech problems, no paralysis, no apparent damage. Then she had a car accident; fortunately no injuries – just car damage. The driving was abandoned. At this time she lived alone – a very active, capable old lady. Denville and I lived 80 miles away, but called to see her quite often. To be on the safe side, I asked a friend in the village to keep an eye on her, call in most days and report back to us if she was OK. Then came a disturbing report. The friend went in and found Mother cooking dinner; not just for one – for herself – but for several. When questioned, she said she didn't know where Arthur was (Dad – who had died twenty years earlier) but she was expecting Ron and Den to be home from work for dinner soon (we both worked near home over thirty years before). She was checked out, and had had a second stroke. I spoke to the specialist who said the haemorrhages that caused the strokes were both in the forebrain. In addition to memory damage, the second stroke also drastically altered her character and she became very aggressive, and short tempered, with everybody. After a second stay in hospital she demanded to be allowed to go home, claiming she was perfectly capable of looking after herself. She was allowed to do so, with a Carer going in to see her every day, but when the Carer reported back that she couldn't even remember how to make a cup of tea, and placed a modern plastic electric kettle jug on the cooker to heat it up, like an old fashioned kettle – and almost melted it before the Carer realised what the smell was – it was realised Mother would have to go into a home. I shall never forget the look of bewilderment on her face when I saw her and talked to her. During the conversation I made the mistake of mentioning her age, and she looked at me as though I was insane, repeating the number as if it was lunacy. Then she said, "I'm afraid there's something wrong with my brain box". I held her hand and told her that she had had a stroke, had lost some of her memory, but that it would come back and she would be alright again. I knew I was lying, and it hurt me to lie, but I daren't let her see it was hurting, or she might have understood. Mercifully a third, fatal, stroke took her, so she didn't have to suffer the dreadful condition long. I know someone who was brain damaged by a stroke, was reduced to a similar condition and lived another 20 years.

A good friend of mine had a brother, happily married, who had a motorcycle accident that left him badly concussed. He was taken, unconscious to hospital and, when he woke up, stunned everybody by asking, "Who is that lady?", (his wife of many years) and talked to my friend as if they were both 15 years old. The specialist told them this loss of memory was not unusual with bad concussion, but the memories would probably, gradually, come back in the next six months – as indeed they did, to the family's great relief, except for a few days before the accident. My father lost several days before his accident too.

The greatest and most terrible loss of memory, of course, is related to Alzheimer's Disease. The first symptoms are simple forgetfulness, which could happen to anyone. Gradually, this worsens, and then there can be periods of confusion, such as forgetting where the car is parked or forgetting the way home. This becomes more frequent, and then the short term/long term memory transfer (referred to earlier) may become affected. People may completely forget what happened last week, or last month, but remember things that happened years ago, perfectly clearly. The amount of time lost increases, until nothing in the last several years is remembered, but again clarity is retained for older memories. The worst feature of this stage is that the sufferer does not remember the kindness, the sacrifice, and the effort that friends and relatives have shown over the years. I know of a person who had her mother live with her for years, but her mother's mind was 30 years in the past, and she was convinced she was simply on holiday and would ask, every week, when she was going home. Finally, in the worst cases, all memory disappears. It was said that ex U.S. President, Ronald Reagan, completely forgot he had ever been the President and, sadly, in a later interview, his wife Nancy, when asked if Mr Reagan still recognised her, said, "I don't know".

Brainwashing is a deliberate attempt to destroy a person's original memories and supplant them with new ones, by drugs and the application of physical and mental stress, including beatings, starvation, freezing conditions and sleep deprivation. Experiments have been carried out, by various regimes, intent on changing the views of military or political prisoners. An example of this was when the Chinese, during the Korean War, tried to brainwash British and American prisoners of war into rejecting Western values, and indoctrinating them with the virtues and values of Communism. In some cases they were successful, with a few individuals opting to stay and live in Communist countries when the time came for their release. In most cases, however, people tended to cling to their earlier values. A very insidious way of changing memories is to work through the subconscious by means of hypnotism. People can be induced to forget reality and, instead, remember things that manifestly never happened. There are also a few individuals who self-hypnotise themselves into believing false memories – usually to impress others but occasionally leading to a miscarriage of Justice.

There are many people who think the human race has reached the pinnacle of mental evolution. I am not one of them, and think there is vast potential for improvement of memory and other mental functions.

Imagine having a brain with four times the memory storage capacity and instant, accurate, recall of everything you ever learned; where nothing of importance would ever be forgotten; where you could consciously decide to memorise something and, after reading the information just once, would, forever after, be word perfect. That this is possible is demonstrated by those few, and very rare, individuals who can read a book once, from cover to cover and then, later, recite any line, from any page, word perfect! Or look at a map once and carry it in their mind, photographically, and remember it indefinitely. Evolution, both human and animal, will continue while ever the species exists.

Gradually, I have realised that what a person is, is totally dependent on the accumulation of memories. There is only one copy of memories that make up the life of the individual. Everything that a person is, is encoded in the chemical and structural modifications of the brain. Destroy the memories and that person will be destroyed. When the miracle of the memory pattern, in the structure of the brain, has been erased, that person has gone – forever.

THE LOTTERY OF LIFE

Have you ever paused to think what a fluke, what a miracle of luck it is for you to be alive, a human being, on planet Earth. For a start there are 6½ billion human beings and you are you, unique in all the 6½ billion. This applies even if you are an identical twin. You will only exist as one of the twins. However, although, superficially, you may think you are one in 6½ billion, this is very limited thinking.

Let us delve a little deeper. You came into being from an egg of your mother's which was fertilised by a sperm of your father's. Before fertilisation occurred, there was a race between the myriad sperms released by your father, as only one is allowed to enter the egg, and achieve fertilisation, before the egg changes and all other sperms are denied entry. If the sperm, that was a fraction of a millimetre behind the sperm that created you, had managed to reach the egg a fraction of a millimetre before yours then the person that resulted would have been your brother or sister, not you. On average, a man in his prime releases about 300 million sperm each time he ejaculates. Multiply that by 2 or 3 times a week, for years, and take into account the fact that a woman will release hundreds of eggs in a lifetime. Then, if your parents have two children, the odds of them producing you in one lifetime is of the order of 500 million, million to one; put another way – this is less likely than you winning the UK lottery (14 million to one) twice in consecutive weeks. Obviously, the same fantastic odds applied to each of your parents and their parents before them. If just one of your ancestors had been different, you would not be here. Instead, some other person – a relative – would have existed.

So far we have limited the analysis to human beings, but there are other factors. All life on this Earth is related. Millions of species reproduce using eggs and sperm, and the same DNA code that was used to produce you. All these are also genetically connected relatives. Before you were conceived, you were not given the opportunity to say, "Wait a minute – I am not willing to be born unless I am born a human being – right at the top of the evolutionary tree". You had to take your chance – the same as everything else. There seems to me, therefore, no reason why, when you were born, you could not find yourself to be a mouse, or a rabbit, or a lion on the Serengeti; the odds are, of course, far more likely you would find yourself to be a beetle. None of them asks to be what they are before they are born. So the chances against you being born you, are so immense as to be beyond imagination. (Not incalculable though, for anyone who really cared enough to bother). "This is Rubbish" you may say, "After all, I am here". Quite so! You are living proof that unlikely things can happen, no matter how enormous the odds against them may be.

When I was young, and in my late teens, I sometimes became very depressed. Mostly, it was probably caused by a chemical imbalance because my hormones were not yet fully sorted out after puberty. Generally, I was an enthusiastic, happy teenager but, nevertheless, I had the occasional bouts of depression. As anyone who has ever experienced serious depression knows, everything looks black, everything is negative. Life really does not seem to be worth living. However, I never, ever, had suicidal thoughts. After my first bout of depression, when I recovered, I thought seriously about life and realised what I have previously written here. I hammered into my brain how lucky I was and that, having been so lucky, I must live my life through, and take what comes, and live it to the very end. Only if life became totally intolerable, through extreme pain or suffering, would I consider taking my own life (I do believe in Euthanasia). I found when, later, I became depressed again, I could cling to these thoughts and know the depression would pass, given time. Fortunately, as I became older, the hormonal balance improved and whilst there were occasions when I was extremely anxious or worried it was never the same as the black cloud of depression. I can only hope that, if young people read this book, and it is mainly intended for the young, they will bear in mind the incredible luck involved in their existence, and determine to see it through – come what may. It seems so sad to me when young, healthy people commit suicide in a fit of depression, when all their life is still before them. Even in the blackest times there is still the chance of happiness and laughter tomorrow.

There are other lottery odds, of course. The odds against living in one of the developed nations of the Earth is about five to one. A very important lottery is that of gender, which is simply the lottery of the flip of a coin; a straight 50/50 chance. Whether you are man or woman is decided by the sperm that fertilises the egg. Half the sperms carry the chromosome for males and half for females. I am always amazed by the macho, arrogant, male attitude of some men towards women. I have, however, always been pleased to be male. In addition to being physically stronger, men seem to have more scope to enjoy the more dangerous pursuits of life; there is more freedom in being male. However, I always bear in mind – just the flip of a coin – and I might have been female. The flip of a coin and Arnie Schwarzenegger might have been Helga Schwarzenegger, that famous singer of stage and screen or, maybe, an unknown waitress in a Bavarian cafeteria! A flip of a coin and Marilyn Monroe might have been Jack Dougherty, the famous welterweight boxer!

A flip of the coin and I might have been Margaret Nash, secretary and typist, pattering away on a typewriter or computer in some office! So I always treat women with respect and consideration.

Men and women are not equal, however, they are different; they are complementary. 'Women's Lib' ladies sometimes try to act like men, which is a mistake. Men should act as men and women should act as women; both physically and mentally men and women differ. Apart from the obvious differences, men have more strength, more musculature, more aggression – mainly caused by the simple hormone testosterone – which even affects the very structure and wiring of the brain. Women are more gentle, more emotional, more considerate and lack the sheer muscle power, strength and aggression of men. Both have evolved to form a partnership – with the stronger, more aggressive, males going out to hunt and, if necessary, risk their lives to kill animals and bring back the food for the family. The females, more gentle, considerate and patient, evolved to look after the children and make a happy home. Although things have changed, the change is very recent and, psychologically and physically, men and women remain as millions of years of evolution developed them. Men and women have not evolved to be, and are not, equal, i.e. the same. No one ever suggests, in the Olympic Games, that men and women should compete with one another. Nor in any sport where sheer strength, and aggression, play a great part. However, in other fields where intelligence, creativity and mental talent is considered, there is no reason whatsoever why men and women should not compete on equal terms, as indeed, they often do. I am perfectly happy to discuss technical matters, or any other subject, with an intelligent woman. In argument, I could never, ever, physically strike a woman. This would be the act of a bully, since women are at a disadvantage and do not, normally, have the strength and aggression of men. In physical relationships there should always be respect and consideration. Remember the flip of a coin!

Having stated that the lottery of being man or woman is a 50/50 chance, or the flip of a coin, there is, surprisingly, the rare situation where the coin could be said to stand on edge. I remember reading a comprehensive medical article which, to say the least, surprised me. The article stated that more than 95% of people were indeed either straight male or female, but a few were in a state that could be called 'in between'. I saw a diagram of twenty people in a row. On the extreme left was a perfectly physically normal man and on the right a perfectly physically normal female. In the centre was an illustration of a person who was both male and female – a hermaphrodite. I was surprised to find this was not uncommon, and I also know it happens quite frequently in nature. I remember, on a farm, seeing the farmer with a beautiful calf, and remarking on it. "No!" he said. When I enquired he said it was a hermaphrodite and, sure enough, it was. A few years later a friend of mine bought his children a pet goat – a nanny – which produced two kids. Again – one of the kids was a hermaphrodite. The remarkable thing, about the medical article, was that it showed not only male and female, and the hermaphrodite with both male and female organs, but also a complete range, from a male with the smallest of rudimentary female organs, to a female with the smallest of rudimentary male organs, and all possible combinations in between. Apparently, these physical conditions were sometimes matched by unbalanced hormonal conditions so that, in addition to the physical graduation between male and female, there could be mental graduations too.

Now I began to understand how there could be mistakes at birth, and why people sometimes had sex change operations, and also why some men seemed very effeminate and some women very masculine. Bearing in mind the lottery of life, I treat them as I would anybody else, providing they act in a reasonable manner, and consider myself fortunate to be a simple, uncomplicated male.

I have sometimes pondered the attraction of male and female, man and woman, boy and girl. I think it must go deeper than simple testosterone. All my life I have enjoyed the company of other males (some but not all), as a small boy, a youth and as a mature man, but I have always been susceptible to the attraction of females.

When I was 5 or 6 years old my parents were friendly with a local farmer and his wife and we used to visit occasionally. They had a child – a lovely little girl about my age – and I used to play simple games with her; hide and seek, I spy and tiddly winks. Just occasionally we shyly held hands. I thought she was wonderful. Then there was a break in the visits and mother finally told me I wouldn't be seeing the little girl any more. She had become ill, with a disease called 'St Vitus's Dance' and had died. (The medical name of St Vitus's Dance is Sydenhams Chorea – a type of Rheumatic Fever – easily curable with anti-biotics today). The dice certainly fell the wrong way for this little girl.

I remember, later, when I was 7 or 8, going to a little school at Upton Magna in Shropshire. The classes were mixed and I began to notice a beautiful little girl who sat a couple of rows away from me. She came from the same village – Uffington – as I did. She had lovely long hair down beyond her shoulders and her smile was bewitching. I fell head over heels but worshipped her from afar. It would have been heaven just to have held her hand. Before I had any real chance to get to know her we left Uffington and moved to Sleapford, near Wellington, for Dad's second attempt at running a small holding. (A 'small holding' in those days was a 'mini' farm typically with a couple of cows, a few pigs and chickens and a part of the land set aside for cultivation of vegetables, etc). During the time I 'fell' for these little girls I had no knowledge whatsoever that sex even existed. In those days there was a taboo on telling young children anything about sex (I didn't learn anything about sex until I was 9 or 10 – from other children – and then I thought it was rubbish. Mom and Dad doing that? – don't be silly!) All I knew was that these little girls were wonderful and I just wanted to be close to them and that to hold hands was very pleasant.

After a couple of years at Sleapford we moved again – to the little village of Leegomery, a few miles away. I had good friends there – Ken Murray, Don Westray and others but there were also a few young girls. Occasionally the boys and girls all got together to play Rounders (a simple form of baseball but with a soft tennis ball). There was one lovely slender, lithe, girl who could run like the wind. Then I walked down the village and heard her practising on the piano in their front room. She loved to play Chopin's 'Polonaise in A Flat Major'. Fabulous! I fell for her like a ton of bricks. At that time we had to collect our daily milk from Mill Farm about half a mile away. I used to hang around, in the front garden, watching for my secret love to leave home to go and fetch the milk, then I dashed indoors, grabbed our can and – out, just to get a chance to be close – even to just pass her on the lane. My feelings and thoughts, even at this age, were quite devoid of lust or sexual intent (or so it seemed to me – maybe they were simply suppressed). However, certainly with the earlier girls, my attraction was innocent, so I feel the attraction of boy and girl or man and woman is deeper than simple sexual attraction. Maybe this is why man and woman, in old age, still love each other – even when all sex is gone, I am glad it is so. I am glad there is still some mystery in attraction.

CONSCIOUS COMPUTERS AND ROBOTS

When I was 20 years old, modern calculators and home computers did not exist. Some arithmetical problems we worked out longhand. For multiplication and division of large figures where an accuracy of say, 1%, was good enough we used slide rules. For large figure calculations, where we needed to be very accurate, we used five figure logarithm tables.

In Britain, the currency was pounds, shillings and pence; four farthings or two halfpennies to a penny, twelve pence to a shilling, twenty shillings to the pound, a Half Crown coin was worth two shillings and sixpence, twenty one shillings was known as a 'guinea'; the wealthy sometimes worked in guineas. No one sold a racehorse for a thousand pounds; it would be a thousand guineas! As we grew up, we became used to this money. I knew people who could look down a list of costs in pounds, shillings and pence – and add it up faster than someone could do it today – in decimals, using an electronic calculator. Measurements of length and distance included sixteenths of an inch, twelve inches to the foot, three feet to the yard, one thousand, seven hundred and, sixty yards to the mile. It all worked fine when you became used to it.

Then came the development of electronic calculators and computers and Metrication was soon introduced; distances became metric, as did currency. A modern calculator – and the computer for that matter – simply works in noughts and ones. Calculators and computers work by using millions of little on/off switches wired together. It amazes me what can be done with something that works in such a basically simple manner. I remember, however, that the entire human body, in all its fantastic complexity, is somehow built up from a DNA code that has only four letters. Nevertheless, modern computers work on basically simple principles. The remarkable thing is how many of these tiny switches can be built in a chip no bigger than a domino and often much smaller. Year after year, they have managed to cram more and more into less and less space. However they are approaching the limit; there is always a limit. People talk about Artificial Intelligence and it is amazing what computer manufacturers have already achieved. They now have a computer capable of playing chess and beating the best human player in the world, although it was only a question of how many switches and the programming of the computer.

I recently received a receipt through the post. It had been produced and dispatched by computer. The receipt, which is a legal document which can be produced in Court to prove I have paid a bill, stated that I owed nothing, I had paid nothing, that this was my receipt and we were all square! This doesn't sound very sensible to me but, after all, a computer is only a machine. All this 'hype' about Artificial Intelligence is simply to impress us with how remarkable the programming is. It will never be possible to program existing computers to invent brand new machines and devices that nobody has ever thought of before! Computers simply run programs. It is really a question of how clever the programmers are.

I have been sceptical about AI (Artificial Intelligence) and the possibility of producing really intelligent computers and, as a corollary – conscious computers – real thinking computers. Then I gave serious thought to the possible future development of computers. When computer engineers have finally reached their limit – when they cannot cram anymore components into a single micro chip – what will they do? They will experiment with new circuitry, new devices and new components. Sooner or later – probably later – they really will produce a conscious, thinking, intelligent computer. I saw the film '2001' and, later, '2010'. Arthur C Clarke's computer, 'HAL', was pretty impressive and acted like an intelligent computer. However, he was not really so bright. He killed the crew of the Spaceship travelling to Jupiter. Why? Because there was a flaw in HAL's programming. A computer programmer had blundered. A really intelligent computer would have thought it over – as a man would – and would have decided not to kill the crew. The reason I am convinced human beings will produce a genuine conscious, intelligent, computer (if the human race survives long enough – say 200 to 500 years) is because we ourselves are conscious and intelligent.

Let us go back to the first brains on this earth. They must have been merely primitive control centres; a simple computer, organising the actions of a group of living cells, but nothing more! Millions of years later, from that crude beginning, life has evolved to produce ourselves. We are conscious and intelligent; although I sometimes wonder about some of us – and a lot of people seem to act as though they are programmed! It is, therefore, merely a question of circuitry and complexity. At some point consciousness emerged. Therefore – if computer engineers continue to develop ever more complex computers, and experiment with far more complex circuitry – I think the inevitable result one day (maybe in a thousand years time) will be a genuine conscious, intelligent, computer. When we do that, we shall indeed have created 'life', even though it is only a machine.

However, there will be responsibilities. In the film '2010', the computer HAL, knowing he is going to be left behind in the spaceship when Jupiter becomes a star, tells his mentor, the Computer Engineer, he is scared. The Engineer is sympathetic, and offers to stay with HAL – as he would with a human colleague who was trapped. Being reasonably rational – If I had been the Engineer – I would have thought about HAL's situation (for about two seconds) and then whipped out HAL's computer modules and headed for the air lock. However, if you had really created a conscious thinking entity – you would have responsibilities – at least as much as you would have if you had purchased a dog. The great science fiction writer, Isaac Asimov, realised that, if humans produced reasonably bright robots, capable of some sort of independent thinking, it would be necessary to build in programs to ensure the safety of human beings, and also the safety of the robots. He invented the Laws of Robotics – which would be a good guide for anybody in the future who gets close to producing a conscious computer. There really should be nothing to fear from an intelligent computer; it will have been created by human beings. Only a madman would create a dangerous computer. (There's a thought!).

In the film, 'The Terminator', the super computer 'Skynet' becomes conscious and decides to do away with the human race. Disaster looms! However, as a computer or a computer network, Skynet must need power; somewhere he must be connected to the mains. Why doesn't someone simply pull the plug or, if necessary, shut off the entire mains supply? What about the super-robot played by Arnold Schwarzenegger. Some genius might invent the brain but the main problem would be the power supply. Imagine it – just as the robot is about to 'terminate' the heroine his batteries begin to run flat. He crawls, sluggishly, around the floor, desperately looking for a power point – muttering to himself – "Ah! Heres one! Damn! Why don't they design these things all the same? Those fools back in 3000 AD fitted the wrong plug". At this point the hero – with his shotgun – walks up and blows the plug right off. Then, with a wicked grin, he shoves his shotgun in the robots good eye and pulls the trigger. (Forgive me – I must have a warped sense of humour!). As for the liquid metal robot in 'Terminator 2', where on earth are his batteries? (I enjoyed the Terminator series immensely. I have a trick of switching off my analytical brain until later. Enjoy the film!).

There is no reason why we could not produce a conscious, intelligent computer that is extremely friendly, and which would treat us like Gods if we so wished. The idea of doing us harm would not enter its electronic brain – if the computer engineers have done their job correctly. Pulling the plug might be like killing your dog – or even your best friend.

Robots are very popular in Science Fiction films. Arnold Schwarzenegger in the 'Terminator' series obviously springs to mind –

and the robots in the 'Star Wars' series. However, real robots in use today are, and are likely to remain for a very long time, extremely limited in their capabilities.

Their real potential is in factories where they can be programmed to repeat a long series of movements over and over again – releasing humans from soul destroying repetitive jobs. In that situation, plugged into the mains electricity supply at all times, they are marvellous. Androids – the walking, talking, thinking, pseudo humans we see on the films are less likely to ever become reality. I do, however, think that we shall see very human like androids created in the near future – as sex toys. I find it an unpleasant thought – but I reflect – maybe it is better to have a machine abused than a real living person.

Recently I read that robotic engineers are working hard, trying to produce a domestic robot. A robot capable of doing various household chores. Obviously this entails an enormous amount of varied activities. I think if I was a robotics engineer – left to my own devices, I would be inclined to work on a robot companion for the elderly. A very high percentage of old people wish to continue living in their own homes as long as possible and do not want to go into a nursing home until it is unavoidable. As the numbers of the elderly increase, and will continue to increase, looking after them becomes a major problem. A robot companion would not need to be fantastically mobile and versatile. The important thing is it would need to be a good companion. I would not consider trying to make it humanoid in any way. I think I would work on a robot that would be a little bumbling and likeable – like the little robots in the film 'Silent Running'. It might have a built in tea or coffee maker, a pill dispenser and could be programmed to make sure people took the correct pills at the right time and did not forget. It would be able to monitor heartbeat, blood pressure, breathing rates and so on – and call emergency services if there were signs of distress. It would include a mobile phone, TV controls and such like and would run around the place on wheels – probably two wheels for maximum manoeuvrability. (An efficient balancing system for two wheels has already been invented – the SEGWAY). It could be called by voice or remote control and ideally, should have a very reasonable soothing voice that could be varied according to the mood of the owner and would know when to keep silent. Friendly, patient up to a point but it would disappear if abused (verbally or by thrown objects), then maybe it would have to be coaxed back. In other words it would sulk if abused. (This might help the owner to develop self control – and so become less likely to be unpleasant to other people). Obviously this reflex must be overruled if there were signs of distress. The idea would be to develop a robot that would be likeable – almost like a pet dog. Old people are often unpleasant and abusive to other people – yet remain devoted to their pets. If you really put your mind to it there are a lot of things that could be built into such a device. On no account must it ever be called a robot. They have a bad image. There are too many films about murderous robots. I think to create such a device would be an interesting and worthwhile design project. The greatest difficulties would probably be in the programming. With a household robot there should be no power problem. As soon as it was out of use it would plug itself into the mains and recharge its batteries as it waited.

Power is likely to be a major problem for any robot that does not have frequent and ready access to a power supply for recharging. Any robot is likely to need a lot of power. Batteries are not going to last long between charges. In the next few years I expect to see robotic lawn mowers begin to proliferate – probably trailing power cables but possibly incorporating heavy duty batteries and periodically plugging in to a nearby power point for a recharge. There is no real reason, however, why one could not be designed using a petrol engine to provide the power.

I do not expect to see a really practical, versatile, general purpose household robot for another twenty years but I would not be too surprised to be proved wrong in this prediction. I have no doubt, as computer technology develops, we shall see more and more sophisticated devices and computer chips with enhanced capabilities. Robotic devices will replace people in many situations – they do not get tired and do not make mistakes – if they are programmed correctly. Robotic control systems will be capable of everything from operating your car to controlling power stations and flying your plane to its holiday destination. This latter, controlling and flying the plane – from departure gate to arrival gate – is possible right now but people prefer to know there is a human pilot in the cockpit. Unfortunately, with all computer systems, there is always the risk of interference and even sabotage, by a capable and determined 'hacker' or terrorist. For this reason there may always have to be a human or humans as 'overseers' where there is any major robotically controlled installation. Undoubtedly, extremely, sophisticated electronic 'brains' capable of operating a human like robot will be developed but I think the endless difficulty will be the provision of an adequate, self contained, power supply.

I always marvel at the efficiency of animals and humans as machines. It is incredible the amount of movement and work a human being can do – fuelled by a couple of bowls of rice a day. It is even more remarkable when you consider that two thirds of the food is used simply to keep the body warm. It will be a very long time indeed before any robot can match that, if ever.

SLAVERY

I recently read that the Government had granted a pardon to hundreds of soldiers who were shot as cowards and deserters in the 1914/1918 war. To us, today, the shooting of terrified, shell-shocked men, seems utterly barbarous and brutal but, as with many things, we must take into account the conditions and psychology that prevailed at the time.

The First World War was the most soul destroying, devastating, murderous war the world had ever known. Conditions in the trenches were at the limit of human endurance. For armies to function, and be effective, there simply has to be discipline and control. From the point of view of the Generals, whose job it was to fight and, if possible, win the war, (it was not their province to decide if the war made sense or not – that was up to the politicians), discipline must be maintained at all costs. The first side to allow its soldiers to, independently, decide if they were going to fight or not, would lose the war. With the stalemate of trench warfare, and the endless bouts of slaughter and carnage, leading to very little territorial gains, the morale of troops in both British and French Armies became understandably low. Most soldiers, by 1916 would have preferred to stop fighting and go home.

At the beginning of the war Nationalistic fervour led to hundreds of thousands of men rushing to enlist, volunteering to fight for King and Country. So confident were those first volunteers, that nearly everyone thought the war would be over by the first Christmas. However, when the murderous efficiency of modern weapons, particularly the water-cooled machine gun, led to casualties in the tens of thousands a day and the war bogged down into an endless war of attrition, fought in the appalling welter of shell holes and mud of Flanders, Nationalism and the desire for War gradually evaporated. Most men would, given the chance, have opted to end the war. Gradually, British troops, despite the murderous propaganda, realised the German soldiers were little different to themselves. This led to the amazing fraternisation of German and British troops at Christmas, when carols were sung and British and German men played football together, in no-mans-land. Officers recognised the danger, clamped down and the war was on again.

Back in Britain, the flow of volunteers gradually dried up, and so Conscription was introduced. Any man, of suitable age who was judged, by Army doctors, to be medically fit, was liable to be drafted into the Armed Services. Unfortunately, as long as a person was not judged by the doctors to be mentally deficient, no account was taken of their

211

psychological suitability. By definition, volunteers are enthusiastic, aggressive people, mentally suited to become soldiers – otherwise they would not volunteer. Conscription, on the other hand, pulled in all types, psychologically suitable or not. The result is an Army incorporating a small percentage of men who are utterly, mentally and psychologically, unsuitable to be soldiers. The majority of men conscripted into the forces do seem to be able to cope, but there are bound to be a few who could never be soldiers. These few present Commanding Officers with a dilemma. If these people are allowed to refuse to fight, to back off and stay alive while their comrades die, then the rot would rapidly spread. More and more would refuse to obey orders, or would fake the symptoms that allowed the others to escape. The only alternative, for the Officers, in order to maintain discipline and control, is to Court Martial the men for cowardice, and publicly shoot them, thus presenting the rest of the troops with the sure knowledge that there was going to be no easy way out. At least, if they faced and fought the enemy, there was a slim chance of survival. Any soldier who shot himself, non fatally, in a bid to avoid facing enemy fire, would be Court Martialed for self-inflicted wounds. It is probable that many Officers were, to say the least, extremely unhappy at having to execute misfits, who should never have been in the Army in the first place, but War is War. Discipline must be maintained or the War is lost. They simply could not allow men to walk away and get away with it – no matter how terrified, how shell-shocked, they were.

So, during the period of the Great War, 1914/1918, the British, Court Martialed and shot over 300 soldiers for desertion and cowardice, but managed to maintain control and discipline. At one point the French Army lost control and a part of the French Army mutinied, leading to a very dangerous situation. If the enemy had learned of the mutiny, and had attacked an undefended part of the Front, who knows what might have happened. The French managed to localise the mutiny, hush it up and do some sort of deal with the Mutineers. Later, the ringleaders were arrested and shot.

By 1917, most British soldiers were disillusioned, as were quite a few at home and would have preferred the fighting to stop. A well known officer – Seigfreid Sassoon – who had been decorated for bravery, openly said he thought the war was madness. He was immediately bundled into a rest home – an Institution – and labelled as being mentally unbalanced. My uncle, who was an honest man, said that, by 1916, he had come to the conclusion that the War was crazy and he had no intention of volunteering. He was, of course, conscripted, fought at Passchendaele and was invalided out of the army, full of shrapnel, from which he never recovered.

In 1939, when War was declared on Germany at the start of World War Two, many men volunteered for the Forces but, Conscription was introduced straight away. It continued throughout the War, and afterwards, although it was then reduced from being indefinite to a fixed period of 2 years. It was then referred to as 'National Service.' When my call up came I did not particularly want to go, but I didn't have a choice. I was conscripted!

It makes me smile a little when I see the last night of the Proms. I love it! All those people jumping up and down, waving Union Jack flags, and singing at the top of their voices, 'Britons Never, Never, Never, shall be slaves'! When Nelson won the Battle of Trafalgar, most of the men on his ships had been 'pressed'. In other words the notorious Press Gangs had been out in Portsmouth and Plymouth, usually in the dark, and had grabbed, and forcibly dragged off, any unfortunate men they happened to come across. They would hit them over the head and knock them unconscious, if necessary, and cart them off without bothering to ask if they had a wife and children. Away these luckless men went – away to sea, "Jolly Tars are our men" says the song. I bet they weren't so jolly the morning after they had been pressed! When the ship finally came home, and anchored at Portsmouth, they weren't allowed to leave the ship. A sentry with a loaded musket was set up, with orders to shoot to kill if anyone jumped overboard, or tried to go ashore without permission. If that isn't slavery – what is? And in the First World War –when men stopped volunteering, the Government brought in Conscription. You wouldn't actually be shot if you refused to go, but they would make life unbearable. Conscription sounds pretty close to slavery to me. At least – in the early days – the volunteers were willing to fight. But conscription drags in everybody able bodied enough to fight. Now – however much some people will deny it – it is a fundamental fact of life that all men are not equal. Some men are strong, some are weak, some are fearless. Some are scared stiff but manage to control their fear and fight. However, some people are simply, pathologically, totally mentally unequipped for fighting in wars. They simply cannot stand the shelling, the pressure, the horror and the killing.

No amount of threats will force them to go 'Over the Top'. So they are Court Martialed and shot. It is a necessity of War. Discipline must be upheld, "Can't let these people ruin the morale of the troops. Examples must be made", etc. Obviously – they never would have been shot if they had not been conscripted. They would never have volunteered in a thousand years. They were victims. The Government is now tacitly conceding this was the case. What else, then, is conscription but a form of slavery.

When I was conscripted I wasn't too bothered. We all had to go –
didn't we? (Not quite all because I had a couple of friends who skived out
of it. One, because he suffered from hay fever. So did I – and worse than
he did – but he had a co-operative doctor. It didn't occur to me to try). So
off I went and, I enjoyed my Army time or at least most of it. (Six months
after I was demobbed, I suffered hellish depression because I "missed my
mates"). However, by nature I am inclined to be a bit of an individualist,
a free-spirit, so despite the compensations, there were things I did not like;
such as being told the Army owned me. 24 hours a day 7 days a week.
"You have no rights in the Army" they said, "Only privileges – which can
be cancelled at any time at the Commanding Officer's discretion". And I
had to write a begging letter – I actually had to write saying 'I beg
.... for permission to stay out of camp after 12 p.m.' I ask
you? A grown man! And I could not make arrangements to meet anyone
at anytime in the future with any degree of certainty, because a note could
go up on the notice board, at anytime, saying I was on Guard Duty, Picket
Duty or on manoeuvres over the weekend. When I was in Germany I had
a German girlfriend and remember arranging to meet her on a Saturday
night. Suddenly I was put on a 'scheme' for the weekend. For 'scheme'
read 'manoeuvres'. I couldn't get in touch so I had to ask a friend to go
and meet her and tender my apologies.

I mention these minor irritations in an otherwise easy army life
merely to illustrate I was not a free man. After all I was lucky; I was in a
peaceful Germany when, instead, I might have been in Korea being shot at
by the Chinese – or wandering in the jungles of Malaya playing hide and
seek with armed Chinese Communist Insurgents or (as a friend of mine
actually was), in Kenya, digging 'Mau Mau' Terrorists out of dilapidated
farm buildings. (He told me that, on the white mans farms, the 'Mau
Mau' used to chop the cow's legs off at the knees with their Pangas (big
knives) and let them hobble around. What on Earth did they do that for?
The poor damn cows hadn't done anything!). So I knew I was very lucky
and the snags I mentioned were only a minor inconvenience. Incidentally,
when it was time for me to be demobbed – after 2 years – the Company
Clerk approached me with a form to sign. "Official Secrets Act", he said.
I hadn't realised I knew any Official Secrets worth knowing but I read it.
"Why should I sign this?" I said. "If I sign this I can be clobbered if I so
much as say, Army grub is lousy". "Quite so", he said. "I am not signing
this!" I said, "After all, I was conscripted, I didn't volunteer!" "OK" he
replied and walked away. Three weeks later one of my mates said he had
been told his demob date. So I trotted off to see the Company Clerk to
ask him when my demob date was. "Oh! Yours is in abeyance" he said.
"Why?" "Well – you didn't sign the Official Secrets Act and, until you

do, you will be in the Army until Doomsday". I thought about this, and then swallowed my pride and signed. The point I am making is – deny it or not – Conscription is a form of slavery. Next Proms – there I shall be – singing – "Britons Never, Never, Never shall be, slaves". I'm told it is different in the Army now. Apparently you can sign up, try it for a week or two – say "I don't like that nasty Sergeant" – and bale out again. What is the world coming to?!

If you think about it – being a slave in ancient Rome probably wasn't too bad. As Caligula might have said "You have to keep the slaves happy you know. – otherwise they might slip some powdered glass in your Lasagne". If the slave was very unlucky it might really be 'Hell on Earth'; almost as bad as being a congenital coward in the trenches just before going 'Over the Top' on the Somme. Incidentally, I have sometimes wondered how I would behave myself, in that situation. I can only hope I would manage to handle it in the same way that 99% of the others seem to have done. My Grandfather too, (on Mother's side) experienced a different form of slavery at one time. When he was a small child he was sold to a farmer for £5 a year. Apparently they worked him into the ground until he finally ran off and joined the Army as a drummer boy. He stayed in the Army, educated himself and rose to become a Sergeant Major.

It is perfectly true, of course, that what I have described are less extreme forms of slavery than, say, the Roman Galley slaves chained to their oars or the terrible trapping, enslavement and shipping of Negro slaves to the Caribbean sugar plantations a few hundred years ago. The worst part of the Negro enslavement must have been the almost unbelievable conditions, chained and shackled to ships decks, for weeks on end, crossing the Atlantic and knowing you could never ever hope to escape and go home. Appalling beyond belief, but there are many different levels of slavery, and I repeat my belief that the 'pressing' of men into the British Navy in Nelson's day and the more recent Conscription of soldiers are other examples.

WHAT IS ART?

Art is one of the most difficult things to assess. The very nature of Art – because it fundamentally creates an emotional experience – will always be subject to argument. One thing appeals to one person and something totally different to another. Because of this, the quality and value of Art is mainly a question of opinion, which gives scope to commercial interests, con-men and tricksters.

Years ago, on a holiday trip to Paris, I visited, among many places, one of the great museums of the world – the Louvre. A friend and I wandered around the galleries, paused to join the crowd looking at the Mona Lisa (I confess I have never quite understood why this is considered a masterpiece. Da Vinci's 'Madonna of the Rocks' with the timeless beauty of the Angel's face impresses me far more). Then, looking at the enormous paintings on some of the walls, I came upon one I had never seen or heard of before. A picture of a raft in mid ocean, carrying the survivors of a shipwreck. I checked the inscription. It was 'The Raft of the Medusa' by a French artist – Gericault. I found the painting enthralling. The picture showed an enormous raft crowded with human beings – some dead – some alive – bodies sprawled everywhere. The plight of a group of desperate people who had survived for weeks on a barren ocean. A mass of wretched people – half of them dead – the rest on the brink of death; hopeless, apathetic, doomed! And then, at the very moment of total despair, there on the horizon, unbelievably, is a ship. Rescue! There – is Salvation! The picture captures the miraculous moment when a survivor first catches sight of the ship. Magnificent! I was so impressed I made enquiries. Apparently there had actually been a ship called the 'Medusa', which had been wrecked, in the Indian Ocean, in a tropical storm. The ship had been very badly damaged and had begun to sink, slowly, giving the men on the ship time to assemble an enormous raft, onto which a host of people clambered before the ship finally sank. After many weeks adrift, when almost all hope had gone, they were eventually rescued; at least – some of them were. A number had died and had been thrown, or washed, overboard. The survivors were in a pitiful condition – very close to death. One of the sailors from the ship that carried out the rescue had told the story, and Gericault – an artist – had heard of it. So he sat down and imagined what it must have been like; the suffering, the desperation and the death; the unbelieving moment when someone first saw the ship that would rescue them. Then he painted what he imagined. The painting is as much a creation of the imagination as a great novel or a magnificent building. Not in a million years could I have produced such a painting. I am not an artist, but to me that is art.

In Holland, in 1938, there was an artist named, Hans Van Meegeren. He could paint, and paint well – and he knew it. He had skill and he had talent. However, people didn't wish to know. He was just another artist, an unknown; nobody wanted to buy his paintings. Gradually he became discouraged and frustrated and then really bitter and angry. He decided he would show them! But how? So he thought the matter through, very carefully, and decided what to do. He experimented. He bought cheap paintings that were old; they must be old. Two hundred years or so. Old canvas, with old paint that had soaked into the canvas and dried out over the years, and had developed a myriad of little cracks that went down deep, right into the canvas. He painstakingly scraped off the top layers of paint until he was down to the base canvas – but still with paint soaked into it – and with the little cracks.

Van Meegeren studied. He learned about paints and pigments – and how they were made a couple of hundred years ago. He bought the materials, mixed up the paint, set up his old cracked canvas and started to work. Hans Van Meegeren had decided to become a forger.

Years before, there was a famous artist, by the name of Vermeer – one of the Dutch Masters – who used to paint religious paintings and other subjects. The hallmark of Vermeer's work was the sheer skill of his painting technique. Superb! One of the most realistic painters ever. You would think no one in his right mind would try to fake a Vermeer. However Van Meegeren knew he was good, so he set out to fake a Vermeer. Not to copy an existing picture, but to create a brand new Vermeer; a superb Vermeer. And he did it! First, he had to learn to paint like Vermeer; with superb skill and technique; so good that any expert could see it was a Vermeer! When he had finished his painting, he let it dry and then placed it in an oven he had made, especially for the job, and slowly, over a period of days, baked it. The solvents dried out of the paint and the myriad little cracks, already in the canvas, extended and came through the new paint to the surface. There it was - a signed Vermeer; the right age, the right paint, the right frame, the right cracks, everything! Let the experts look. Let them test. We shall see! But then, just as he was ready, the war came; before he could try it out. All that work for nothing. He put the painting on one side. In 1940, most of Western Europe was conquered by the Germans, and Holland was occupied.

It so happened that the German Air Force General, Field Marshall Hermann Goering was, among other things, a keen collector of art. So somehow, I don't know how Van Meegeren arranged it, Goering was presented with the opportunity to buy a magnificent Vermeer. The painting was checked by experts. They confirmed – it was genuine. So Goering bought it. Success! Despite this, Van Meegeren still wasn't satisfied. He would do it again and, just to prove his brilliance, he would choose a different artist – with a different painting technique. Again he was successful - and again – and again. Van Meegeren must have been a near genius.

The end of the war finally came and, somehow, the authorities learned that Van Meegeren had sold priceless paintings to the enemy. He was a collaborator! They threw him into jail. I think the sentence was ten years. Van Meegeren considered the situation and eventually decided there was only one way out. He put up his hand and said, "I shouldn't be in jail. I fooled Goering. I cheated the enemy. I painted the paintings myself." The authorities laughed. "No way!" they said. However, Van Meegeren insisted and insisted, so finally they took the Vermeer to experts. The experts looked and they checked and they tested – and then they made their report. This is undoubtedly a genuine Vermeer; a long lost Vermeer - never seen before the war; some secret collector must have had it; not only that, but it happens to be the finest painting Vermeer ever created.

It looked as though Van Meegeren was going to stay in jail. He became desperate to be free. "Look" he said, "I can prove it. Give me the materials, allow me to build an oven and I will paint you a new Vermeer." They listened and, remarkably, they eventually decided to allow him to do it. After a few months he produced a painting they couldn't argue with. There was no doubt. Van Meegeren really could produce a Vermeer that could fool the experts. Before this – some of Van Meegeren's magnificent paintings – including his original 'Vermeer', had been shipped to Paris and hung in the Louvre. Where else?! The authorities carefully considered the situation. Van Meegeren had only swindled the Germans so, after a time, he was released. When the experts at the Louvre heard about Van Meegeren's performance, they hurriedly whipped the fakes from the walls and stashed them in the cellar. "No fakes will adorn our walls," they said! Now – and here we come to the real point of this story - in my mind a painting is either a masterpiece or it is not. One minute these experts are saying, "Look at this magnificent Vermeer; a masterpiece, the best of all his work." The next, they are shamefacedly carting it off to the cellar where, so far as I know – it remains to this day. "Forget it," they said, "Let's pretend it never happened!" You won't find any reference to the magnificent work of Hans van Meegeren in the Louvre. However I say, "Either it is a magnificent work of art or it isn't. Please put it back on the walls and let me look at it." I don't give a damn who painted it – any more than I really cared who painted the 'Raft of the

Medusa'. That painting was magnificent in <u>my</u> mind. So, if Van Meegeren's painting is superb – let me look at it. Let me judge. After all, it was not a copy, it was an original in the style of Vermeer. Is the signature on the painting more important than the work? The answer – in this day and age – seems to be "Yes". I now have a simple test for art. I ask myself if I could have done it. If the answer is yes, then the artwork is rubbish; I know I am no artist.

Poor Van Gogh. Only sold one painting in his life, so I believe. I'm not surprised; I've seen better on the local Art Club walls. However, Van Gogh went insane and it shows in his pictures. Even as a child, the Van Gogh prints on the school walls made me feel uncomfortable. Even a child's brain recognises the signs of insanity; the madly whirling stars, the twisted writhing buildings. Now Van Gogh's work can sell for, maybe, 20 million pounds, and for what? A crude painting of a chair in a room, or a bunch of Sunflowers but, it has Van Gogh's signature at the bottom; it is simply that Van Gogh is in fashion.

Now – when I visit the gardens of some British stately homes, (I love gardens – the coolness, the serene beauty of nature, the magic of the trees, the intoxicating scent of the azaleas – I could go on) I find them besmirched by pieces of junk masquerading as art; a stupid metal daisy or a warped metal caricature of a human being. Why don't they include a broken down, rusty, old lawnmower with a plaque – 'The Day Is Done' by that well known artist Barnum. It cost us ten thousand pounds'!

Some 'artist' used 100,000 or so scrap car tyres to form a replica of a nuclear submarine in London a few years ago. Someone, perhaps like me, was so incensed at this being passed off as art, that he poured petrol on the pile and set it alight. I think he was burned to death. Unfortunately, he didn't realise how dangerous petrol is. (NEVER use petrol to light a fire. Use paraffin (Kerosene to American readers)). I have thought about art rationally, unbiased. I still say – anything that is so crude and simple that I could do it myself, is junk. A pile of bricks is a pile of bricks! A dirty, unmade, bed is a dirty unmade bed! Not Art!

Sometimes, very rarely, someone discovers an old master painting in their attic. Lacking in knowledge they look at it and decide to get rid of it, along with the rest of the junk. Off it goes to a car boot sale or something similar. Along comes a dealer who knows a little about art. He looks at it, takes another look and studies it carefully, taking care to be as casual as possible, and checks the signature. The picture just could be a genuine painting by an 'old master'. He says to the person who found it in the loft, "How much do you want for it? Fifty pounds? Hmmm – I'll give you forty. Done!" The dealer then goes away and checks it out. It is, indeed, genuine. The painting eventually ends up at Christies and sells for a hundred and fifty thousand pounds. This scenario, very occasionally, actually happens. I read of such a case once and, in my opinion, there should be a law; in a case like this the original owner should be entitled to 50% of whatever the dealer obtains.

Now, just imagine someone finds, in his loft in his mansion, inherited from his parents, a long lost and totally genuine Van Gogh. (He painted dozens in his lifetime). Maybe he sold one we haven't heard of or, more likely, gave one away. The person who finds the Van Gogh (a painting of a twisted bunch of flowers) is knowledgeable. He knows it is a genuine Van Gogh. He is wealthy and doesn't desperately need to sell it; perhaps he'll just hang it on the wall. Then he has a novel idea. He will paint over Van Gogh's signature (with a paint he can remove later) and add a new signature, say J. Jones. He then offers it for sale, just for fun. He will not sell it of course; any offers will not reach the reserve price. You know – and I know – and he guesses – it would be surprising if he had an offer of more than a hundred pounds for it. If he cleans off the over-painted signature, and gets the painting certified as a genuine Van Gogh, and offers it for sale at Christies – ten million pounds, for exactly the same painting. People are paying ten million pounds for a signature. Van Gogh is in fashion!

Ask me what I would do if I was an art expert, and was offered what I was convinced was a genuine Van Gogh painting, for two hundred thousand pounds. I would rush off, re mortgage the house, and buy it. Forget the fact the painting is of a teapot on a rickety table; the painting is a genuine Van Gogh. I would buy it because I would know that somebody else would buy it from me at, maybe, 10 million pounds or more.

In the eighteenth century there was a man in England who was a thinker and scientist and also an artist. His painting technique matched some of the best of the Dutch Masters. His mastery of light and shadow was superb and the subjects of the paintings unusual and interesting. However, Joseph Wright of Derby is out of fashion, so he is almost unknown. Maybe if he had gone mad and shot himself, experts might have been more interested, but Joseph Wright was eminently sane and sensible and so remains in obscurity. Someday, maybe someone will remember him and take an interest.

Need I comment further on art?

One of Van Gogh's paintings (The Fields)
currently valued at over 12 million pounds.

FREE WILL
AND THE NATURE OF TIME

There seem to be a number of definitions of the phrase, 'Free Will' but, to me, the term Free Will means I am in charge of my own Destiny; that I really can make decisions that affect my future and nothing is pre-ordained; that I really am 'The Master of My Fate'.

I felt sure of this, of course, when I was young. It seemed so obvious. Then, as I grew older, I learned that things were not always as they seemed. The atomic bomb, for instance, seemed almost impossible; so much energy from a little sphere of metal. So I learned a little about Einstein's 'Theory of Relativity'. I had learned a certain amount of mathematics as I studied to be an Engineer and found, to my surprise, that I could follow the theory and the maths up to $E=MC^2$. (It is not as difficult as you may think – to that stage anyway). I also read about 'Quantum Theory'. These theories are amazing, and fascinating, but I found some of the implications disturbing.

According to Einstein's Theory, space and time are connected. If you move in space, you affect time. If you travel in space, it will affect the time-rate. The faster you travel, the slower your time-rate becomes and, if you could ever actually travel at the speed of light, your time-rate would stop. It is not possible for an object with mass to reach the speed of light, but it is possible to get very close to that speed and, if you did, you would find that, while you lived for a week in your spacecraft, the people back home had lived for a year or more. At first this was very difficult to grasp. Time appears to be so non-physical. How can time be linked to something physical – something real, something you could measure with a tape or weigh with scales.

Scientific theories are usually based on a number of definite facts, or, if it is impossible to have proven facts, on reasonable assumptions. Theories enable scientists to make predictions, and do calculations based on the theories, and it is usual therefore to carry out experiments. If the results of a number of experiments agree with predictions, then the experiments confirm that the theory – and hence the assumptions – appear to be correct. Before Einstein produced his Theory of Relativity, scientists had been considering and discussing the nature of light and other electro-magnetic radiation, such as radio waves. There was a lot of evidence that light acted like a wave – like ripples on a pond or sound waves in the air. The question was – what did the light wave ripples travel in? The conclusion was that there must be something in space – not emptiness – so they called the imagined medium the 'Ether'. Some people thought space was just emptiness, light or no light, but others considered the idea very carefully. Finally, it became possible to measure the speed of light and, at this point, some scientists suggested a clever experiment. "We know the Earth is travelling around the sun", they said, "so it must be travelling through the Ether – if it exists. If we set up detectors to measure the speed of light in four different directions, we should be able to measure how fast the Earth is travelling through the Ether". So they set up the experiment (The Michelson/Morley Experiment). The result was a disappointment. No matter which direction they took their measurements, the speed of light was exactly the same. Einstein took this fact, that the speed of light will always be the same, if you measure it, no matter where you are or how fast you are travelling, as one of the foundation stones on which he built his Theory, and also made a number of reasonable assumptions. One of these is that the Laws of Nature will be exactly the same if measured by anyone, anywhere in the Universe, no matter where he is or at whatever speed he happens to be travelling. The amazing conclusions that come out of the mathematics of The Theory of Relativity are that space and time are inevitably connected and that matter – the solid, everyday stuff from which everything is made, including you and I – is merely another form of energy. The fact that this is true was demonstrated when the atomic bombs destroyed Hiroshima and Nagasaki.

The name of the imaginary substance that filled space – the Ether – was dropped. Now it is called the Space/Time Continuum or the Fabric of Space Time or even just Space. At this point I will digress a moment so that the reader may better understand the meaning of 'Space' and 'The Vacuum'. Many people (including myself) found the modern concept of Space difficult to grasp or understand – especially when we learn that the vacuum of Space – far from being total emptiness – is believed by scientists to be a seething mass of activity, with myriad little particles of matter bursting into existence for a fleeting moment and then disappearing again. The implication is that the vacuum, far from being nothing, is somehow charged with energy. Our minds are inclined to rebel. If we have a container, carefully sealed and we take a vacuum pump and pump out every single particle of air and any other substance within the container, our minds tell us the container is empty; there is nothing there. This, however, is wrong. The word vacuum means devoid of matter! Our brains then translate this to mean nothingness. Within this Universe the vacuum is very far from being nothingness. Every cubic millimetre of the entire Universe is filled with something – a sort of universal fluid – bounding with energy.

Consider again our container and vacuum pump. The container is made up of atoms and so is the vacuum pump. We have a mental vision of atoms as little spheres, so something made of atoms must be like something made of trillions of little spheres, stuck together. This, again, is wrong. Atoms are made up of little clumps or packets of energy (protons, neutrons and electrons). There is a small group of these packets in the centre of the atom and other packets outside. For the sake of simplicity consider the atom like the Solar System with the main mass (the protons and neutrons) in the centre like the Sun and the smaller masses (the electrons) orbiting around it like the planets. If you consider the Solar System as a spherical volume of space then 99.999% of the volume is just space with a few bits in it (the sun, planets, asteroids, etc). So it is with the atom. 99.999% of the volume of the atom is just space with a few bits in it (the protons, neutrons and electrons). So we realise that our container and vacuum pump is, in reality, 99.999% space with a few bits in it. Solidity is an illusion.

Now, imagine you are underwater and in front of you is a large wire netting cage. The cage is filled with small wire netting hollow spheres. The water flows through both the netting and the spheres. You are given a wire netting scoop and with this you can remove the spheres from the cage. Eventually, when you have scooped out all the spheres you might say the cage is empty. The water, of course, has stayed there all the time. Consider the cage to be analogous to your container, the spheres to atoms of air and the wire netting scoop analogous to your vacuum pump. The water also has within it a lot of energy, depending on its temperature and, if studied on a very small scale, consists of a lot of small vibrating particles (molecules). The analogy, although crude, may help you to understand how Space permeates everything but it must be understood that, in other ways, Space does not act like a simple fluid medium such as water or gas. However, you may also grasp that our planet – the solid Earth, including the iron core – is also 99.999% Space and that is why neutrino particles sail straight through it as though it wasn't there. Fortunately one in trillions of neutrinos does interact or we wouldn't be able to prove they exist at all. So everything we are used to thinking of as solid is not and Space/Time exists and flows through all substances almost as if it wasn't there. I say almost because matter does affect Space/Time slightly and if there is enough matter the effects can become noticeable.

To return to Relativity and to cut a long story short, the Theory of Relativity implies that, if you travel, you will not only alter time rates, but also change distances and alter masses. At normal speeds in cars, aeroplanes and even rockets, you would never notice it. (Very accurate clocks can, however, be used to actually measure and demonstrate time distortion at these speeds). However, if you speed up to near the speed of light, the effects become more and more apparent. For instance, if you left the Earth in a one hundred ton spacecraft, one hundred feet (31m) long, with a clock on board, and then built up the speed to near the speed of light, your spacecraft would increase in mass from one hundred tons to maybe one thousand tons or more. The length of the spacecraft would reduce from one hundred feet (31m) to maybe ten feet (3m), or less, and your clock would register hours where, back home, the clocks would be registering days. If you think this sounds ridiculous, I would mention that the designers of large atom-smashing machines (such as the Large Hadron Collider at CERN on the Swiss/French border) have to allow for all these effects. This is because they are accelerating particles to 99.999999% of the speed of light.

It takes a while for the brain to grasp and accept the reality of Relativity (it certainly did with mine), but scores of experiments have been done which have confirmed that Einstein's Theory of Relativity appears to be correct. Part of the maths produces the famous equation $E=MC^2$. The incredible implication of this, is that matter – ordinary, everyday material – is a form of locked up energy and there is enough energy in your breakfast boiled egg to blow your town or city completely off the map. The detonation of the atomic bomb over Hiroshima was a stunning demonstration, but, in actual fact, the energy released was only a very small amount (a fraction of a fraction of 1%) of the energy actually there, in the uranium bomb. It is staggering to realise that, to destroy Hiroshima, the amount of matter actually converted into energy was no more than one gram (roughly the amount of matter in a Heinz baked bean). The total energy, actually there, in the uranium of the bomb was roughly equivalent to a thousand million tons of T.N.T. The hen's egg referred to earlier, converted into pure energy, would be equivalent to about 1½ million tons of TNT.

You may say – what on Earth has all this got to do with Free Will? I will tell you! According to Einstein, the Universe is actually four-dimensional. Three dimensions of space and one of time. Note – only one of time. Einstein also contributed to the development of another theory – Quantum Theory – which is concerned with the mathematics and physics of the very, very small. Your computer depends, in order to work, on the mathematics of Quantum Theory. Briefly, Quantum Theory is as amazing as Relativity. Sub-atomic particles do not behave as larger, everyday objects do. Their behaviour is bizarre. A particle may move from position A to another position B, but, instead of travelling from A to B, it 'disappears' at A and 'reappears' at B. There is no definite 'in between' position. If a particle gains energy, it does not start at energy C and gradually increase its energy to condition D. Instead it starts at C and 'jumps' to a new energy level at condition D. (Hence the phrase 'quantum leap'). Even more remarkably, a quantum particle can be in more than one place at the same time. (If you are intrigued and wish to find out more – look it up. There are plenty of books on Relativity and Quantum Theory).

Finally, and this is the important part so far as we are concerned – to do with Free Will – it seems that even time has an absolute smallest component, the Planck Time, which is 10^{-43} seconds; a very short time indeed. So we can subdivide hours into minutes, minutes into seconds, to milliseconds to microseconds and so on, but it is not possible to subdivide below the Planck Time. There is no time shorter.

I pondered this and found it very disturbing. If there is no time shorter, then anything happening must 'jump' from one Planck time to the next. It is as if the Planck Time is the single frame on the 'Film of Existence'. As though everything we see is a sort of running film. If the time in Albert Einstein's Four Dimensional Space-time really is one dimensional, then that is the inevitable conclusion. Einstein himself concluded the Universe existed as one entity – from start to finish – beginning to end – all at once. Like the film 'Gone With the Wind' in its canister or the James Bond film on your DVD. It is all there, beginning to end, and you merely observe it, in the case of the film, or experience it, if it is life. I admit I didn't like that conclusion at all. It meant that we didn't have Free Will; that everything that would happen was already on the film. No matter what you did, it was already fixed. In the same way as if, when you watch the James Bond film the second time around, you know perfectly well what is coming next – although James Bond appears to think he is making decisions. Very disturbing!

Many experiments have been carried out to check if Quantum Theory is correct. They have yet to prove it wrong. In Electronics it has been called the most successful theory ever. People followed up the one-dimensional time thinking and devised the idea of a World Line. For a person, the world line started when he was conceived (not born) and ended when he died. It was all there, like a film of your life. The World Line contained every single moment of your life – from conception to death. Fixed! Surprisingly enough, the great Shakespeare had a similar idea and wrote, 'All the world's a stage, and all the men and women merely players'.

I spent considerable time pondering over this, and it was the understanding of the phenomenon of the evolution of life on this Earth, that finally convinced me there must be a flaw in the concept of one-dimensional time. For billions of years, evolution of life has occurred because of myriads of random mutations, and the interaction of countless living things in life and death struggles, resulting in greater and greater complexity through the mechanism of 'Survival of the Fittest'. Even random occurrences, such as asteroid strikes, have had a profound effect on the course of evolution. The number of accidental, random and interactive events which have led to me sitting in this chair, writing these words, is so immense, so extreme, so unlikely, that I simply cannot believe it is all on some glorified cosmic film.

So, I have a suggestion to make. What if time actually has more than one dimension? What if it has two or three or, for all I know, four? At this point you may say, "What the devil does he mean?" I will try to explain. Consider Three-Dimensional Space; the one we live in. Just imagine a small beetle walking along a very fine wire, stretched from side to side of a square box. As long as the beetle stays on the wire, you can consider him as being in one-dimensional space. He can go forward and back on the same line, but nothing else. He is hopelessly restricted.

Now, just imagine you place hundreds of these thin wires side by side – so that as you look down it looks like a sheet, or at least a mass of parallel lines. Put the beetle on one of these wires and he has much more freedom. He can not only go forward and back, he can go sideways too, crossing from wire to wire, all over the area confined by the box and anywhere he decides to go on that flat surface. He is now in two-dimensional space.

Take him out and add hundreds of sheets of wires – spaced one on top of each other so the whole box is full of wires, say 4mm (1/6in) apart (enough for the beetle to squeeze through the gaps). Place the beetle back in the box. He is now in three-dimensional space and he can roam anywhere he wants to, in the entire three-dimensional space available in the interior of the box. When he was originally on the single wire, you could predict with absolute certainty that, if he walked one way, he would end up at an exact position on the end wall of the box. If he walked the other way, you could predict, with absolute precision, where he would end up on the other wall. As soon as you added another dimension, it was impossible to predict precisely where he would go. The three dimensions were even better. He had far more freedom and you could not possibly predict where he would be in half an hour's time.

Now! – let us consider time. For some reason we seem to be able to go only one-way in time i.e. into the future; we cannot go back into the past. Some scientists have speculated that, under certain circumstances, (sub-atomic), time just might occasionally run backwards. (This is not the same as time travel). In other words, if our beetle, on one wire was stopped from going backwards, then there is only one place on the whole box where he is going to end up if he moves. He is in one way, one-dimensional space. Let us, therefore, consider one-dimensional time as being like one strip of film stretched between the beginning and end of time. You travel along the film and see the film unfolding. During your lifetime the part of the strip of film you experience is your life. Now imagine a whole sheet of these filmstrips side by side, just touching; time is now two-dimensional. At this point you must think of the beetle. What if you could cross from strip to strip? And each strip was a little different.

You could think of it as being like travelling on a road and, every so often, you come to a junction. Your road goes straight on, so you could ignore the junctions. Alternatively you could make a decision and take the side road instead, which would, of course, make your journey different.

If you were in a field on a 'quad' bike, you would have two-dimensional freedom to roam wherever you liked on the field. If you bought yourself a micro-light aircraft, you could then go anywhere you liked on the field, or go up into three-dimensional freedom. Similarly, considering time, if you extended the sheet of film strips by adding many additional sheets of film strips and, if you could jump from one strip to another, you would have fantastically more freedom, like the beetle in the box full of wires.

Some people talk about Parallel Universes with infinite possibilities; where there is an infinity of parallel Universes similar to our own; where every possible variation occurs; where, in this Universe, Adolf Hitler lost the War but, in another parallel Universe, he wins; where you exist, with the life you have known, in this Universe, but an infinity of you's living slightly, or very different, lives, live in the 'shadow' Universes. I must admit I do not like this idea of parallel Universes. If it is valid then, in another parallel Universe, President Kennedy was provoked into ordering a pre-emptive strike against Cuba resulting in World War Three and Curtis-le-May did annihilate the USSR with thermo-nuclear weapons and there is another Earth where a few human survivors are poking about in the radioactive ruins of the planet desperately trying to survive. (I do, however, believe in multiple Universes by which I mean many real Universes, not 'shadow' versions of our own. See Chapter IN THE BEGINNING). The notion of Parallel Worlds is, of course, great for Science Fiction writers. It enables them to invent and write about any sort of bizarre variation of life on Earth they like. It gives them scope, in the same way as time travel and hyper-spatial tubes (such as in the 'Stargate' series) gives them scope. But it should not be taken that any of it represents reality. There is, however, evidence that quantum particles really do exist in this strange, parallel possibilities, situation. When a particle moves from one place to another, it appears to move, not in a single, well-defined track, but to take every possible path, at the same time, from A to B. To keep this book brief, it is not possible to go into the quantum behaviour of sub-atomic particles at great length. If you are interested, get hold of a good book on Quantum Theory.

I think it is this bizarre behaviour of very small particles that has prompted ideas of parallel Universes. However, quantum behaviour ceases as particles, or groups of particles, become larger and large objects display the fixed, predictable, simple behaviour we are familiar with in everyday life. So I do not believe in the parallel Universes idea. I believe there is only one Universe, in which we exist but that the uncertainty, and parallelism, of the quantum world manifests itself in giving us flexibility, freedom of action, 'Free Will,' in the large, everyday 'macro' world – maybe in a similar manner to that I have described. So, if you drive your car from London to Edinburgh, there is not an infinity of shadow Universes wherein you drive on every possible route to Edinburgh. There is only one You – and you simply drive up the A1, but you have the freedom to take any other route you may care to choose, if you wish. You have Free Will. In a Universe with two or three-dimensional time you are free. Free to make your own decisions. You are 'Master of Your Fate'.

I would point out that I am not a great mathematician, a cosmologist, a nuclear physicist, or an Albert Einstein. I am just an engineer – an ordinary person, but I think about things. Maybe I could have accepted that everything that happened in the Universe – the Big Bang, the creation of matter, supernovae, the development of stars and planets, could be consistent with a four dimensional Universe but it was the contemplation of the evolution of life that made my mind baulk at the concept of one dimensional time. The process of the evolution of life, to produce intelligent beings, is so fantastically more complex and unpredictable than any other process in the Universe that I simply cannot bring myself to believe there is no flexibility and that everything is already programmed and fixed as though pre-recorded. Even if scientists prove my idea of extra time dimensions is false I still will believe the same effect exists – maybe through some manifestation of the quantum unpredictability of sub-atomic particles. Time, as they say, will tell. Some scientists may say that my idea of 2D or 3D time, and my analogy of parallel strips of film is just another way of describing the 'Parallel Universes' theory. They could point out that the parallel strips of film – the parallel possibilities – must already exist in order for us to be able to switch from one to another, in the same way as the wires in the box with the beetle have to pre-exist before he can cross over. I cannot dispute that but the big difference from 'Parallel Universes' is that there is only one beetle – not thousands of 'shadow' beetles on all the different wires. All the roads in the UK must exist, before I travel from London to Edinburgh, to give me the freedom to choose one route out of a thousand possible routes but there is still only one me travelling on those pre-existing roads. Maybe the 3D time works like a growing, branching, tree and we create a myriad new opportunities, in the near future, as we go along and make decisions. Maybe, as each decision is made, no matter how large or small, the chosen path grows forward forming new branches of possible futures as it goes and the earlier discarded choices vanish as time moves on.

If I was right and there were, say, three dimensions of time, then this, added to the three dimensions of space, would mean we are living in a six dimensional Universe. If you think this sounds unlikely, consider – some of the cosmologists and great mathematicians are trying to formulate the mathematics needed to explain how the Universe came about and exists. They are now talking about the possibility of our Universe having eleven dimensions.

Earlier, I mentioned the remarkable behaviour of sub-atomic particles, and the fact that a particle could disappear from one place and reappear in another (usually over very short distances). It is not even possible to predict, with certainty, where a particle will reappear. It may reappear where you most expect it to, but sometimes it may reappear in a different position or, occasionally, considerably further away. It is necessary to use the laws of probability to predict where it is likely to reappear. At first, this behaviour seems quite baffling, but it suggests to me we may be seeing an indication that there is another dimension involved.

Let me explain. Visualise a chess board (checker board) with its squares. Now imagine a flightless, shortsighted beetle, sitting in the centre of the board. There is a bluebottle fly sitting on the next square, which the beetle can just see. The fly takes off, buzzes around and then lands again – on another square. To the shortsighted beetle the fly disappeared from one square and, shortly afterwards, reappeared on another. Amazing! The beetle found he could not even predict where the fly would reappear. To the beetle the world was a flat, two-dimensional surface. The fly disappeared upwards, into the third dimension, of which the beetle was unaware.

If we really have Free Will, as I fervently hope and believe, it is interesting to consider the implications. Just imagine – you are leaving the house to drive to town in your car, to do some shopping. Just as you open the car door, you think, "Did I turn the cooker off? I did! OK! I will carry on. NO! Maybe I did not – better go back and check." You have made a simple decision to go back and check. As a result of that decision, you slightly alter your life and the lives of others. As you drive to town, you are held up by a farm tractor that would not have been there one minute earlier, and so on. As you walk through town you are avoiding people – and they are avoiding you. They would not have been, if you had travelled one minute earlier. You have not only slightly changed your own life by going back to check the cooker – you have also slightly altered many other lives as well. The laws of probability suggest the changes will be very small but, in fact, there is a very low possibility the changes could have been enormous. There is a very low possibility you might have been killed in a car crash on the journey. You might, just possibly, have had a car crash and killed someone else, and so on.

The consequences of a simple decision – let alone an important one – are endless. The reverberations of a simple decision can go on, you could say, to the end of time or at least to the end of the human race. To give you an example. When I was around twenty years old I did a lot of studying. I did not go to University so, instead, I worked in my own time, during evenings at college and weekends at home. Sometimes I rejected the studying and cycled off to a local dance. I am human! I liked music and I liked girls. I went to a dance one night and met an attractive young lady, whom I dated and who became my girlfriend. Later, she decided to become a nurse and moved forty miles away to a city where she went to a large hospital for training. Sometimes the hospital had dances. I had a number of friends, as young men do, and told some of my friends about the hospital dances. Two of them decided to come with me. Believe it or not, the two met nurses and married them. They now have children and grandchildren. If I had stayed at home that one night and studied, instead of packing it in and going dancing, then a number of people who are alive today would never have existed; neither would their children, or their children – ad infinitum. I can think of at least twenty people who are alive today because of definite Free Will decisions I have taken. Similarly, if my father had not decided to go to Yorkshire, looking for work, in the Depression of the 1930's, where he met my mother, I would not be here. Maybe you can think of a few of your own decisions, and consequences.

It is possible for one man to change the future of the world with a simple, conscious decision. Adolf Hitler, in his book 'Mein Kampf', writing of his early life, states simply, "I decided to go into Politics." Another man might have changed the world with a single, careless, almost thoughtless action. In his early life Winston Churchill, on a visit to New York, casually decided to cross the street, stepped in front of a speeding cab and was seriously injured. He might easily have been killed.

I believe, with utter conviction, that we do have Free Will. That we are responsible for our own actions. WE ARE THE MASTERS OF OUR FATE. I hope I live to see that confirmed. If there really is only one-dimensional time, as Albert Einstein thought, then the four photographs on the following page represent parts of my 'World Line'. They could be said to be two-dimensional representations of three-dimensional sections of my four-dimensional World Line.

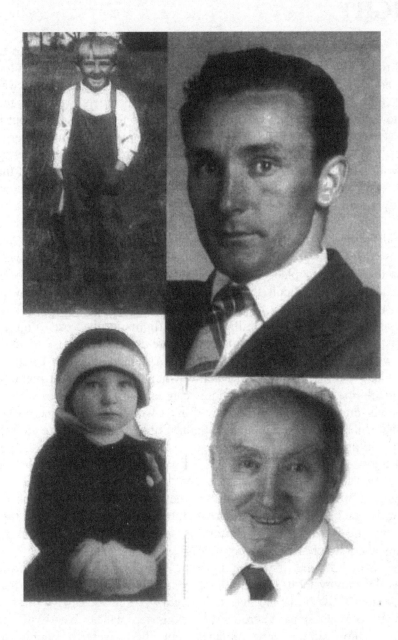

Photographs of the author at ages
18 months, 5 years, 21 and 77 years old.

233

FLIGHT

For thousands of years human beings dreamed of being able to fly. Birds could do it, insects could do it, but man, it seemed, was just too large and heavy. He would never fly. But still men dreamed. There was the legend of Icarus, with wings made of wax and feathers, who flew too close to the sun, so that the wax melted and Icarus fell to his death; but it was just a dream; no human being could possibly produce enough energy to fly. Maybe there might be other ways. Leonardo Da Vinci got very close with his sketch of a hang glider. It was the modern invention of the engine – in particular the internal combustion engine – that finally began to make human flight look feasible.

Today we all take it for granted. We walk aboard a modern plane alongside three hundred other people, grumbling about the delays. We take case after case of luggage with us and we take off and fly half way around the world, to places which, a few years ago, would have been almost impossibly difficult to reach. I read that, in 2004, there were nearly 4 billion passenger flights. Flights, not passenger miles. That implies something like forty million aircraft flights in one year. Figures like this make one realise how fantastically safe modern flying is. Most of us fly without thinking about it – but I do not. On every flight I marvel that a plane with so many people and all their luggage, not to mention sixty to eighty tons of fuel, or more, can take off and power almost effortlessly into the sky. As I sip my drink I wonder what Leonardo Da Vinci and Jules Verne would have thought of this. I know that the aircraft I am travelling in is much better than any magic carpet. No magic carpet would allow me to relax in warmth and comfort, and look out of the window at icebergs floating in the sea off Greenland, whilst I am travelling at 600 miles an hour (966 kilometres) at nearly forty thousand feet (twelve and a half thousand metres) altitude – where the air is too thin to breathe and the outside temperature is minus sixty. This is an almost unbelievable marvel. How is it possible?

As a child, the first flying machine I can remember seeing in the air was the mighty Graf Zeppelin airship; but one could hardly call that flying. Then I saw birds and insects in flight. At the age of five or six I was taken to an air show where I saw various aeroplanes. Nearly all the planes in those days were biplanes, but there were a couple of monoplanes, one of which, I believe, was a Blenheim bomber. There was also a glider. I remember clearly, watching the glider silently loop the loop. I also saw an autogyro – the Cierva Autogyro – built with a body like a plane but with swirling rotor blades above instead of wings. Clearly flying was very interesting.

When I was at school I quickly learned how to fold paper aeroplanes. Some flew well, some did not. I learned to tweak bits of paper at the back of the wings and the tail to get them to fly properly. I learned to 'trim' the paper aeroplanes. I remember Dad buying me a little balsa glider with a lead weight on the nose. It flew quite well until I took the weight off, then it wouldn't fly at all. Flying was obviously not simple. Later I began playing around with bits of balsa making my own gliders. I learned about balance, ailerons, elevators, rudders and trim. At one time I had a little powered model with a propeller driven by a twisted rubber band. In my teens came little diesel engines and we flew models, both control line and free flight. I read about flying; Jules Verne's 'Albatross', with Captain Nemo; the pioneers Otto Lilienthal. Bleriot and Lindbergh. I read the Biggles books, books on planes and war stories. However, I never actually flew myself until my late twenties.

My first flight was with my motorbike, across the Channel, in a crude twin-engine plane called a Bristol Freighter. It roared and vibrated and clattered its way over the sea at about a thousand feet – from Lydd in Kent to Le Touquet in France. It was an experience. I also discovered I could get airsick. My next trip, a few years later, was in a Vickers Viscount – a small four-engine turbo-prop airliner. I spent some of the time marvelling, the rest looking at the inside of a brown paper bag. Thank heaven modern planes fly high and smooth – most of the time anyway.

I never went to University or took a course on Aeronautics, but I read books. Every book and article I read on Aeronautics made flying look complicated. There were wing diagrams, airflow diagrams, reference to Bernoulli's Principle, and the books gave the impression an aircraft only flew because a wing, as it travelled through the air, created a negative pressure (a suction) over the top of the wing. (How on Earth did they manage to fly upside down?). I also read where some scientists had calculated that a bumblebee should not be able to fly because its wings were too small. If so, the scientists involved must have been particularly stupid.

I pondered all this and realised that the first and basic principle of all flight in air, whether it be a mosquito, a bumble bee or a 400 ton Jumbo Jet, is extremely simple. Amazingly the extreme basic simplicity of flight has never, in all my life, been commonly stated, at least not to my knowledge. I therefore spell out, in this book, that the basic principle of all flight in air is – An Object that Flies in Air Does So by Forcing a Mass of Air Downwards thereby Creating an Opposite Reaction. It's as simple as that. Everything else can be considered as Technicalities, in other words – everything else is concerned with the means by which a mass of air is forced downwards and the means to control the resulting flight. That's all there is to it. Push a mass of air downwards, either a large mass slowly or a small mass rapidly, and there will be an opposite uplift force; when that force is great enough you will lift off the ground. That applies to all things flying in air – whether it is a gnat or a falcon or your holiday jet. The only exceptions are rockets, which provide their own thrust and balloons which are supported by a quantity of lighter than air gas (usually hydrogen, helium or merely hot air). Everything else is supported by pushing air downwards.

The bumblebee flaps its ridiculously small wings furiously backwards and forwards, each flap pushing a small amount of air downwards. The bees wing pivots so it pushes air downwards on each stroke, forward and back. To move forwards it simply changes the wing angles slightly so it pushes air backwards as well as downwards. The jumbo jet pushes air downwards by literally skiing on the air.

If you watch a water skier – when starting off he has difficulty, and he sinks deep in the water as the towing boat starts to pull away. He is simply not pushing enough water downwards fast enough. As speed builds up he rises until he is skimming on the top of the water. Because of his speed he is pushing a great deal of water just a small amount downwards. When he slows he gradually sinks deeper into the water until finally, there is not enough reaction force to support him and he sinks.

With the aircraft, it is as if the skis have been extended a hundred feet (30.7m) on either side. As you sit there, eating your meal, the wings, cutting through the air at 600 mph, are just pushing down an enormous mass of air a little; just enough so the reaction force is sufficient to balance the weight of the plane. It takes fine adjustment to get this just right. The speed of the plane, the angle of the wings to the airflow, the adjustment of the wing profile – flaps in, everything streamlined. I marvel at the near perfect control the big aircraft demonstrate. When an aircraft comes in to land there is a problem. At the lower landing speed, the wings would not be able to push down enough air and the plane would fall out of the sky. It would stall. So the wings are modified. Special flaps are lowered at the back of the wings to increase the down push on a smaller volume of air. The leading edge flaps are extended to control the airflow over the wing – the air can only be pushed down efficiently if it flows cleanly and smoothly over the wing.

All the information I learned about shaped, aerodynamic wings was to do with the shape of wings required to push air down efficiently at low speeds. A simple, flat knife blade will work perfectly well if it is

236

pushed through the air at a high enough speed and is angled slightly; which almost exactly describes a supersonic aircraft wing. The problem with high-speed aircraft is the landing speed. High speed aircraft such as Concorde have to tilt the wing, and thus the whole plane, to a steeper angle. The helicopter is the simple skiing type wing rotating in a circle. It is very easy to see the push down process taking place. The vertical take-off Harrier still works on the push down principle. It simply gulps a smaller amount of air into its engine and pushes it downwards at high speed until the reaction thrust equals the weight of the plane and it then lifts off. If a winged aircraft's engine fails, it has to lower its nose and slide down a slope. Gravity then provides the push – replacing the push of the engine. The plane must maintain speed and the wings continue their skiing action. Even a 400-ton Jumbo can glide. It is simply a question of finding the gliding angle. A glider has a very low gliding angle but, nevertheless, has to be on a down slope at all times for the wings to provide lift. The glider only rises when it is in an updraft going up faster than the glider is sliding down. The worst glider in existence is, of course, the space shuttle, which slides downwards at an incredible rate – with just enough excess speed to enable it to flatten out just before it hits the ground. One of the pilots is reputed to have said, "The shuttle has the gliding capability of a pair of pliers".

Birds, of course, having evolved over millions of years, use every trick in the book. They glide, using the skiing technique. They adjust the profile of the wings to suit the speed. Swept back and streamlined for maximum speed, spread out and the equivalent of flaps down for slow speed. Little feathers on the back of the wing signal when they are on the brink of stall. At or below stall speed they switch to a version of the bumblebee technique, with flapping wings pushing pockets of air down and back. In high-speed cruise they use both techniques. Skiing and pushing at the same time. The pushing allows the wings to ski without losing height. Evolution gradually produces near perfection.

I recently saw a television film where a falcon was filmed diving at 180 miles an hour. I have seen a flock of teal come diving in to a lake so fast they made a roar, and had to zoom out and do a circuit of the lake to throw off the speed before they could slow down enough to land. I have seen a sparrow hawk rocket around the house, missing the corner brickwork by inches, before he snatched a blue tit off the bird feeder, with one talon, while he was still travelling at high speed.

With dragonflies I have watched their incredible manoeuvrability and had one, hover, inches above my outstretched hand. I could feel the down draft of air as his wings pushed air down to balance his weight. I have never been able to work out how insects originally developed wings.

Some fly all the time. Some hardly ever fly at all despite the fact they can do so.

An earwig hardly ever flies. Many people have never seen an earwig fly in their entire lifetime. I have! Packed under their minuscule wing cases are amazingly large wings. They can fly and fly quite well. The incredible thing is how such a large wing can be folded over and over – both sideways and, more remarkably, end ways, to finally be tucked up under those hopelessly small wing covers. Ladybirds and beetles all do this sideways and endways wing folding. Like folding a parachute to fit in a rucksack – all by merely shuffling about. The mammals – bats – fly quite well, but without the mastery of birds and insects. Bats fly fast and are manoeuvrable – but I have never seen one glide. I cannot imagine a bat soaring, as I have often watched buzzards and eagles do.

Sometimes I used to think how wonderful it must have been in the early days of aviation – when the pioneers flew those early crude machines – when there were no rules, and you could go and fly anywhere – and no one would worry too much if you broke your neck. But these days, even for light aircraft, there are endless rules; flight rules, air lanes, controlled airspace, flight plans to be filed and you are only allowed to fly from airport to airport. No low flying or fooling about without special permission. I was convinced the golden age of 'seat of the pants' basic flying was over forever when, miraculously, in 1980, something remarkable happened. For years people had flown conventional gliders – with cockpits and long, aerodynamic, wings. Then someone invented a hang glider – very similar to one of Leonardo Da Vinci's sketches. It was possible to launch and fly a hang glider almost anywhere – off hills, mountains or seacoast cliffs. Finally, someone added a small engine. The powered hang glider – which later became ultralight or microlight aircraft – had arrived.

My brother Denville had been flying in balloons for quite a while – we were both in a balloon club near Market Harborough when the first microlight designs were produced. An article describing these first Microlight Aircraft stated that these lightweight machines did not come under any normal Aviation Rules and therefore they could be flown anywhere. Having checked that this was indeed true, and considered the possibilities, I spoke to my brother and suggested we might buy a microlight. Several different designs were on the market – some of which looked decidedly dangerous. There was one design however that we both considered promising – an American design called an Eagle with a canard (tail first) configuration. We learned that a certain Tom Sawyer, flying aircraft at a local airfield, was considering importing Eagles and other microlights, and duly placed an order with him. Eventually about eight or nine other enthusiasts ordered microlights so Sawyer went ahead.

The Eagles duly arrived and Sawyer, an experienced pilot, assembled one and test flew the first machine. He reported that, although the Eagle was slow, it handled quite well and appeared to be a sound design. The next question, of course, was – how were ten totally inexperienced people going to learn to fly microlights, which were, at that time, purely single seaters? We should all have gone to a flying school for lessons first but, remember, there were no rules or regulations governing microlights at that time. You could, literally, buy one, take it to a field and attempt to fly it and possibly – as some actually did – break your neck.

Tom Sawyer had an idea – why not attach a rope to a microlight and tow it down the runway behind a Land Rover. At a certain speed the plane would lift off and rise maybe 3 metres or so, the Land Rover would maintain steady speed, the Eagle would glide along at ten or twenty feet, (3 to 6 metres) and the would-be pilot could become familiar with being airborne. Having perhaps more enthusiasm than sense, I volunteered to go first. The Eagle was set on the runway and the end of a rope tied to the crossbar; the other end to the back of a Land Rover. Fortunately, as we were to find out, Sawyer had a thinking friend who decided to tie a quick-release knot at the Land Rover end. I climbed aboard – in other words I sat in the little kiddies swing seat that was slung from the crossbar. Control of the Eagle was by handlebars connected to two wing-tip rudders and simple body movement, with the seat connected to the elevator. When I was ready, I gave a 'thumbs up' and the Land Rover started down the runway. The speed rapidly built up and, suddenly, the machine seemed to leap off the ground and climb into the sky like a kite. I strove to work the handlebars and keep the thing straight but forgot to pull myself forward to lower the nose. Finally, at 60 to 80 feet (18 to 24 metres) in the air, I remembered the body movement and pulled myself forward as far as I could. The nose immediately dipped and the rope slackened. The danger then was, if the rope tightened up again, there could be a shock that could possibly wreck the machine. Fortunately Tom Sawyer's thinking friend – an ex Spitfire pilot named Ellis, in the back of the Land Rover, saw the danger, pulled his slip knot, and I was on my own, gliding down with the rope dangling. I continued to glide down and, fortunately, had the presence of mind to flare just before I hit the runway. All OK!

Someone else had a go on the towed Eagle. Even worse! The Eagle went up, again like a kite, and then began to swing violently left to right – as kites sometimes do. The rope was hurriedly released, but the

Eagle crashed at the side of the runway with a 'crump'. We rushed to the scene. Miraculously the pilot had nothing worse than cuts and bruises, but the undercarriage was a complete wreck; just a mass of bent tubes. Fortunately – back at our little business – my brother had plenty of light metal tubing, so off he went, came back with a mountain of tube and soon patched up the machine. That evening we had a discussion and concluded it would be far safer to simply crank up the engine and fly the thing normally. Forget the rope!

We knew the principles of flight. We had flown aero models hadn't we? We knew the key thing was not to stall. So we sat in chairs in the office and went over the essentials carefully. Having satisfied ourselves we could handle and fly the machine, we approached Sawyer next day and said, "Forget the rope. Let us just fly it". He mulled it over and said "OK – tomorrow morning early, while there is little wind". Word got around. The next morning, at the runway, there was a minor crowd, eager to see the fun. My brother and I spun a coin. I won – or lost – depending on your point of view, and would go first. Just before I put my crash helmet on and climbed aboard, a gent approached me and said "Is it true what they are telling me. You have never flown a plane before. You have never had any tuition – any lessons in a plane – and you are going to fly – this?" "Yes!" I said. He walked away, shaking his head in disbelief. I climbed into the seat, clipped the strap that held me in, the engine was started and off I went. Everything worked as planned, the microlight flew beautifully, I completed a circuit and landed. Denville walked up, I handed him the crash helmet and he climbed aboard and repeated the performance. Ellis came over, congratulated us and turned to the crowd "You've heard of the Wright brothers" he said "This is the Nash brothers", and we had a standing ovation. Very satisfying!

The rest of the Eagle owners agreed – just flying the thing was a lot safer than messing around with the rope. I think they all flew OK. After that we had a marvellous time flying the Eagle. It was not fast, but a wonderful fun machine and very forgiving. You could do all kinds of tricks in it. If a friend came along for a demonstration I would start the take off run, full power, and push my body as far forward as possible, holding the machine on the ground to build up excess speed, then shove my body back as far as it would go. The Eagle leapt off the ground, soared skyward at 45° then, as it slowed and approached the stall, push my body forward again to bring the nose down. Two or three seconds for speed to start building, then force the left wing down, almost vertical for a smart 270° sweeping turn. They were always impressed! It was better to break the low circle at 270°. If a complete 360° circle was attempted you ran into your own wake and, just above the ground, that could be dangerous. After some of these manoeuvres Denville said he thought I was pushing my luck a little as, during steep banking turns, my wingtip was no more than 2 feet (600mm) from the ground and, later, showed me a video to prove it. I took his advice and resolved that, in future, I would keep the wing tip at least 2 metres (6½ feet) from the ground.

As soon as Den and I had learned to fly the Eagle (the first model with the 220cc engines was rather underpowered). I said to Denville, "What about mother. Do you think she would like a flight"? So we managed to get hold of a spare seat, slung it from the main tube behind the pilot's seat and strapped a sack containing 25kg (55lbs) of sand in it. The Eagle flew. We then increased the weight to 50kg (110lbs). Again I flew the Eagle; rather nose up; a bit unsteady, but I could manage it without stalling. We then invited mother over from Shropshire, gave her a few demo flights, and asked her if she would like to have a go. "Sure" she said, so we fitted the spare seat, inserted mother – in her usual skirt – and off we went. She thought it was great. A bit draughty though! Perhaps she could have a travel rug next time. (See Photo). She used to come for the occasional flight until she was over 80.

Mother and I flying in a Microlight aircraft over Belvoir Castle. She was 79 years old at the time. Note the travel rug around her legs (she was wearing a skirt).

My brother and I practised and experimented. I took the Eagle to a thousand feet, (308m) throttled back, pulled the nose up and held it there. The speed fell away, the machine began to shake and buffet – just before the stall, then it dropped. A controlled stall. This kind of experimenting paid off. In flying slow speed machines there can be a trap near the ground to catch the unwary; the wind gradient. It is possible to have a 30 miles (48km) an hour wind at 400 feet (123 metres), 20 miles (32km) an hour at one hundred feet (31 metres) and only 10 miles (16km) an hour at ground level. Coming in to land the head wind can drop off very quickly in the last sixty feet (18.5 metres). It is also a trap if you take off down wind – as we occasionally did. I remember one evening I was coming in to land with a fair breeze headwind. I came in slowly. At fifty feet (15 metres) the machine started to shake. I knew it was not turbulence and recognised the symptoms. I was on the brink of stall, and descending. I shoved my body forward to drop the nose and opened full throttle to gain speed. I pulled the Eagle out just 4 feet (1.2 metres) from the runway and went around again. I came in a little faster next time. Stall practice paid off!

One day we flew in very windy conditions, just for the experience. I took off and, as I climbed into the wind, the headwind gradually increased due to the wind gradient and at 600 feet (185 metres) I was flying backwards. The wind speed at 600 feet (185 metres) was greater than my flying speed. I then eased back down to 500 feet (154 metres) and the plane was standing still. Wind speed exactly matched flying speed. It was such a novelty I held it there for two or three minutes. Denville said how very strange it appeared to him on the ground. It also answered an old conundrum. When I was a child my father said he had seen a plane standing still in the sky for minutes, engine roaring. Everybody looked at him as though he was mad. Perhaps I wasn't the only flier who played tricks.

Nearly every time Den and I flew we practised dead stick landings, (landing with the engine off). For instance, switch the engine off at 1000 feet (308 metres) and glide in without power. We also practised manoeuvring, turning and throwing the height off without power. Such practise was essential in a plane with an unreliable two-stroke engine.

One day I was flying back home up the M1 motorway. (An easy way to navigate). It was late on a cold November afternoon. (At that time we flew an Eagle with a more powerful 430 cc Cuyuna engine – and we had fitted extra fuel tanks for long range, so we had an endurance of about 3 hours).

Incidentally, when navigating the lazy way, by following railways or main roads it was usual to fly alongside them on the right. Anybody else, following the track in the opposite direction, would do the same so you would not be on a collision course. So I came up the M1 at about 1000ft (308m) until I came to the junction with the M69 at Leicester. Down below was a maze of roads, buildings and power lines. Suddenly cough! cough! no engine! (It turned out it was carburettor icing in the cold damp air. All other aircraft except microlights have heaters to prevent this). I looked around for somewhere to land. There was one small field in the middle of the maze so I headed that way, spiralled down and dropped into the field, then strolled across to Everards Brewery, in full flying rig and crash helmet, and asked if I could use their phone to ring Denville to collect me. They looked at me as if I was a man from Mars! Next morning he sorted the carburettor out, started the engine, and I took off and spiralled up and out again.

A similar thing happened over Melton Mowbray. The engine failed right over the town so I spiralled down and landed in a Recreation Ground belonging to a local pet food manufacturer. Denville did the repairs (drive belt broken) and I took off and spiralled up and out again. We fitted the machine with 'Go Cart' wheels with brakes and, at Denville's suggestion, the brakes were operated by a long lever with a ratchet – as on an ancient Bentley car. It was just the job! You could lock up the brakes, power the engine until the wheels began to skid along the ground, knock off the brake lever and surge forward. We could be airborne in 70 to 80 yards (65 to 74 metres). Emergency landing was even better. Lock up the brakes in mid air. Touch down and skid to a halt. Minimum measured distance – 22 yards (20 metres). I remember flying over the countryside and landing inside the inner area of an Iron Age fort at Burrough on The Hill in Leicestershire. I got out and walked around, and thought how the people who once lived here could never have dreamed that, one day, a man with wings would fly in from the sky and land inside their compound.

I flew along the old Nottingham to Grantham canal – at 300 feet (92 metres), carefully noting the bridges, trees and power lines, and checked that there was nobody about. I then went down and flew along the canal, my wing tip rudder skimming the hedge alongside the canal, my wheels a few feet from the water. I had to lift up every so often to clear the bridges. Sheer magic!

Sometimes, on cross country trips, and before we fitted the long range tanks, Denville or I used to follow in a chase car with spare fuel in a Jerry can in the boot. When short of fuel we simply landed in a farmer's field and tanked up. Most farmers were tolerant and more often than not very interested – I know one who rushed off and bought himself a microlight – but I remember one who complained we were scaring his cows. Scaring? The damn cows used to be a nuisance, crowding round and licking the thing to see what it tasted like. How can animals so stupid be so curious?

We took the Eagle to Shropshire, explored the countryside and visited some old friends. To this day I regret I didn't fly the Eagle along the river Severn and under the famous old iron bridge at Ironbridge. If I had fixed it with Denville to be there with a camera – what a great picture that would have been. After all, if I had flown along the centre of the river, passed under the bridge and climbed out still following the river, nobody's neck but mine would have been at risk. I could have done it in those early days but now, of course, anyone who did such tricks would immediately be prosecuted, presented with a massive fine and have their flying licence confiscated.

So, for a time, we had a lot of fun. Gradually, of course, things changed. We knew they would. It was too good to last. There are always fools who take things to extremes. Someone was reported to have flown a microlight straight across the approach path of a passenger plane coming in to land at East Midlands Airport. Another thoughtless individual went down and 'buzzed' the local foxhunt. Maybe Lord King (at that time the boss of Civil Aviation) or Prince Charles was there. In any case someone could have been thrown and have ended up with a broken neck. Horses are so easily spooked.

Den and I weren't crazy. We used to 'phone Cottesmore Military Air Base and ask if it was OK to fly in the evenings. I remember speaking to the Controller one time and asking him if it was OK for us to fly. "I don't have the legal authority to stop you" he said. "Maybe not" I replied, "But I have no wish to end up wrapped around the windscreen of a Tornado". (At that time Tornado fighter/bombers used to do a lot of low level practice flying in the area). That this was not impossible was demonstrated a few weeks later. I remember taking off one evening, from our little grass flying field, lifting to 250 feet (76 metres) and looking around, doing a 360° scan just to check if anyone else was nearby. What do I see but a Tornado attack aircraft, on a low level practice flight, barrelling in, almost directly towards me, at my height. Not funny! I threw the Eagle on end in a 90° bank and pulled out of his line of flight, in the few seconds I had, and kept going to get away from the hellish turbulence he would create. I don't think the pilot saw me at all; probably looking at his instruments or something. In any case, at his speed (about 400 knots) he wouldn't have had time to avoid me.

The planes that really used to give us the jitters were the American A10 Thunderbolts (Anti-Tank attack aircraft). They usually flew low in threes. Not in formation but spread out over a couple of miles, plunging and diving in simulated tank attacks, flying between 1000 and 200 feet (305 and 61 metres). When I spotted one of those I used to almost twist my head off, thinking – "Where the hell are the other two?!"

We never flew low over farmhouses, only the open countryside and if we spotted a foxhunt we kept away. Rules for microlights were gradually introduced and we had to register the aircraft. We also had to take tests for a Pilots Licence, and so on. Eventually the rules for microlights became the same as for light aircraft. The fun was over, but we had grabbed that marvellous opportunity to fly as the early pioneers flew; by the seat of your pants. No air speed indicators! No stall warnings! No Roll and Bank indicators! Nothing but the wind on your face and being able to see everywhere – even straight down. The nearest thing to the birds.

MONEY

"The love of money is the root of all evil" as the old saying goes (often misquoted as "Money is the root of all evil"). In actual fact money is one of the best inventions mankind ever made. Money is what enables modern civilisation to work. Money oils the wheels of the incredibly complex machine that is modern society. Without money – everything would slow down.

It is possible to run a small society simply by barter. Let us, for a moment, take a trip back to the time when people lived in caves, when they made things and undertook the first agriculture but money did not yet exist.

The man who is good at making shoes makes lots of them. He then has to say to the man who is good at growing cabbages, "Look! How about if I give you a pair of shoes for six of your cabbages". The cabbage man, being a canny individual, says "No! I'll give you 3 cabbages for a pair of your shoes". They eventually settle for 4 cabbages. The shoemaker goes away a bit disgruntled but he really did need those cabbages. "What is the World coming to?"! All that work for 4 lousy cabbages!

It is even possible to have a form of credit system in a barter society. In early summer the cabbage grower says to the shoemaker "I badly need a pair of shoes right now. Let me have a pair and I'll let you have your four cabbages in a couple of months time – when they are ready". The shoemaker, bearing in mind the risk – there is always a risk, giving credit – says "Make it five cabbages and the shoes are yours".

The trouble starts when the man who grows the cabbages already has a perfectly good pair of shoes – and the shoemaker is struggling. He had a similar problem – damm it – when he tried to get a loincloth from that old hag down by the river, her old shoes seem to last forever. Suddenly – things turn even more difficult for the shoemaker – somebody in the next cave has started making shoes too. The shoemaker decides, gloomily, that he might have to move to the next valley – or perhaps he might be able to learn how to make those new fangled bows and arrows. Everybody seems to want them – and the price is through the roof. No chance of the shoemaker getting one of these new gadgets of course – the bow and arrow man said he had enough shoes to last 20 years. With a bow and arrow he could have gone out and shot his own venison, instead of having to go to that lout across the river with the big family. Fortunately – they always need shoes; the kids go through them in no time. How did that bruiser with all the kids manage to get a bow and arrow anyway? There was a disturbing rumour the other day that, if he hasn't got anything to swap, he can get aggressive. It was even said that the bow and arrow man had been threatened – that he might go to his work cave one morning and find the place wrecked. Maybe that's how our friend with the kids got the bow and arrow. It might seem a rather dodgy thing to do, to threaten a man who makes bows and arrows. Funnily enough – although the bow maker has brains he is of a rather nervous disposition. The lout with all the kids knows it! If our bow-maker isn't careful there might be a takeover bid and he will end up working for the lout, and on overtime! Maybe its time to leave this valley and move elsewhere! Anyway, if this sort of thing spreads, where would we be? If we can't swap in a civilised manner, everything will fall apart. Suddenly – some genius invents money.

What is money? It is just a token. Fundamentally – a token for work. The great point is, going back to the shoemaker, if he can make his shoes for money he can now go and get anything he wants, from anybody, whether they want shoes or not. Instead of shoes he gives them the money – and they too can swap the money for anything they want; and so on. Its true there has to be an agreement as to how much money everything is worth, but that can be worked out. Instead of haggling over how many cabbages are worth a pair of shoes, we can haggle over how much money is worth a pair of shoes. You could use almost anything for money really; some islanders in the Pacific used feathers; another island used cowrie shells; we used to use gold and silver at one time, but now we simply use bits of paper, or a few figures on the bottom of the bank balance, or even electronic pulses down phone wires or on radio waves. However, it is necessary to be careful.

The king of the islanders, who used cowrie shells for money, had to stop any old tribesman going out collecting cowrie shells – or you might get somebody saying "You can keep your cowrie shells". So, he would have to pass a law that said, "All cowrie shells belong to the king and must be handed to him – on pain of death". The king would arrange to have the shells marked in some way and then act as a sort of Central Cowrie Bank. As long as he only doles out so many cowrie shells for the right amount of work, the island is economically OK.

The key thing to make the system work, whether the currency is cowrie shells or bits of paper, is that everyone should honour the commitment it represents. For the man who slogs away digging up the road all week, to be rewarded with a few pieces of paper, it is essential, when he goes to the supermarket for food to feed his family, that they should honour his paper and give him the amount of food agreed to be worth two days of his labour. For the business man sitting in his office it is essential that, when he has supplied someone with a thousand tons of coal, his customer will instruct his bank to deduct a certain figure from his bank balance and transfer that figure to the business man's bank balance. If nobody cheats too much, the system will work.

It is interesting to note that, on one of my bits of paper, just under the headline Bank of England, it says "I promise to pay the bearer on demand the sum of Ten Pounds" (many years ago this was in quite large print, but now it almost needs a magnifying glass) and the note is signed by the Chief Cashier. If I went into the bank and handed it over and said, "Can I have my ten pounds please", they would look at me as though I had gone mad or offer me a few coins. If I refused the coins they would probably take the note from me, scrutinise it a little and then, perhaps, give me another cleaner piece of paper saying, "I Promise to Pay the Bearer Ten Pounds". You can almost hear them saying, "Let's get rid of this nutcase". Years ago they used to use real pieces of gold or silver, with the King's or Queen's or Caesar's head stamped on them. They were still just bits of metal – but they lasted longer than the paper. Sometimes any Tom, Dick, or Harry could just dig the stuff out of the ground; in a similar manner to collecting cowrie shells or feathers. You know where you are with a printing press – as long as you keep a lock on the door and don't let anybody else get hold of the printing plates.

A classic example of things going wrong was the 1973/1974 oil crisis. Previously a number of the World's oil producing countries had clubbed together, in September 1960, to form an organisation called OPEC (Organisation of Petroleum Exporting Countries); a cartel, formed so that they could act together to control the World's oil prices. Because the bulk of the World's oil reserves are in the Middle East, the most important members of OPEC are Arab Nations.

Ever since the state of Israel had been created, at the end of World War Two, the Arab Nations had been extremely hostile and vowed to attack and destroy Israel. Israel was supported by the West, mainly America, both monetarily and with weapons. In the spring of 1967, Egypt and other Arab Nations finally decided to act and began to mass their forces for an attack on Israel. The Israelis decided there was no point in waiting to be attacked and, on June 5th 1967, launched a pre-emptive strike. At dawn, swarms of Israeli planes attacked Arab airfields and, in a few hours, practically wiped out the opposition Air Forces. This was then followed up with heavy attacks by tanks and infantry advancing into Arab territory. The International Community managed to get the war stopped before it escalated completely out of control, leaving the Israelis with quite a lot of extra territory as well as prestige. Arab Nations were humiliated and mortified. The whole episode was called the 'Six Day

War'. The Arabs knew that Israel was supported, and supplied with weapons, by the West, and financed mainly by America, and they were enraged – nobody likes being humiliated. So they got their heads together and vowed – next time it would be different.

Over the next six years the Arabs again built up their forces and made sure their intentions were not so obvious this time. In October 1973, when the Israelis were off guard and were involved in observing their religious festival of 'Yom Kippur', the Arabs suddenly struck – in a near reversal of the Six Day War. When the surviving Israeli planes attacked the advancing Egyptians they found their planes blown out of the sky by modern Russian built surface-to-air missiles. On the ground their tanks were destroyed by Russian built wire-guided anti-tank missiles. Suddenly Israel was in a desperate situation. At this point America stepped in and supported Israel, flying in new modern weapons and supplies. The Arab advance was finally halted. Following this the Israelis gradually took the initiative, the tables were turned and the Israelis advanced deep into Arab territories again, as they had in the Six Day War, before the International Community, acting through the United Nations, managed to get the war stopped.

So the Arab Nations had been defeated and humiliated for a second time; both times because of the support of Israel with money and modern weapons supplied by the West, mainly America. In their rage and frustration the Arabs looked for ways to retaliate and damage America and the West and they decided the best way to do it was through OPEC. Drastically restrict oil supplies and force up the price of oil. The OPEC cartel – at that time – controlled more than 50% of the World's oil supply, which made the idea a practical proposition. However, it was a dangerous manoeuvre; more dangerous at the time than may be appreciated today. Oil is the life blood of any modern industrial civilisation. What they were proposing would possibly paralyse America and the Western World. The West might react aggressively; might even encourage and support Israel into conquering and controlling the Middle East. (After all – it could be argued that if the USA and its Allies had not defeated Germany in World War Two then the Arabs would not have had any oil to sell. Hitler would simply have confiscated it). Nevertheless, they decided to go ahead, reduced supplies and doubled the price of oil. They were lucky! Just at that time, the US President – Richard Nixon – (known to some as Tricky Dickey) was embroiled in a nasty, domestic, political mess called 'Watergate' (to do with his authorising the burgling of the Opposition's offices). He was so busy trying to save his political neck, that he had not time to bother about this oil business. The OPEC members couldn't believe their luck. They had doubled the price of oil and no fist waving!

No threats! So they crossed their fingers and cut oil supplies again – and again. The price of oil went sky high. Oil is one of the most important raw materials on Earth. A modern industrial nation simply must have it. There is, as yet, no alternative.

Oil is used for fuel, and to make plastics, chemicals, fertilisers – you name it! So when the oil price went up, the price of petrol, diesel, plastics, etc went up. Factory costs rose, which meant the cost of everything they made also increased. Now, and this is important, if everybody in the West had gritted their teeth and paid up the extra, and accepted the inevitable reduction in the standard of living, there would have been no spiralling inflation. To explain! If society is running along merrily and there is a stable situation, where wages are steady and the prices of everything you buy are steady, everything is fine. The only way you can get a raising of the standard of living – by which I mean a situation where wages go up, and the prices of the goods do not – is by productivity; that is, since money is fundamentally a token for work, by producing more goods or services for the same man hours of work. This applies whether it is the labourer on the street, who now uses a JCB instead of a shovel, or the office boy who uses a calculator instead of doing his sums the hard way, with pencil and paper.

Imagine, if you will, the Government goes mad and says "Yippee! To celebrate the centenary of whatever – all wages will be doubled". Everybody is better off! Your pay is doubled; the plumber's pay is doubled; the train driver's pay is doubled, and the girl in the sweet shops pay is doubled. So – what happens? By the time you follow all these pay doublings down the line, what is the net result? Simple! The cost of everything is doubled and you are back to square one. You have simply devalued the currency. When I said, imagine the Government going mad and doubling the wages and thus causing inflation, in practice they don't actually do that but they are, in the end, responsible for inflation. They are in charge! They allow inflation – and in certain circumstances actually encourage it – usually in small doses because of the hellish dangers. The biggest danger is loss of confidence. People must have confidence the currency will be honoured – and is stable. One of the benefits, so far as the Government is concerned, is that inflation erodes State Debt. It enables them to steal people's money. As an example – people who bought War Bonds (issued by the Government to help finance World War Two) were paid a very low rate of interest, all through a period of high inflation and when the War Bonds were finally redeemed the buying power of the money – in other words its real value – was less than a tenth it was at the beginning.

To return to the OPEC manoeuvre. What actually happened when OPEC raised the price of oil (it was like a massive tax on the West if you think about it) was that prices of everything went up. The people of the West did not grit their teeth and accept the drop in their standard of living. Oh No! Being simple souls they said, "We are not willing to accept a drop in living standards – we have worked long and hard to get it. We demand an increase in wages to compensate". Believe it or not, the Trade Unions went into full cry, and the Government, under Harold Wilson, did nothing to educate the public and tell them how, and why, you cannot do that and get away with it. These people are supposed to be bright – but I sometimes wonder!

The coal miners, there were over 200 thousand of them in those days, led the way, and demanded roughly a doubling of their wages. They didn't need this much, to compensate for the oil related rise in the cost of living, but – if you are going to ask for a pay rise – why not push your luck and ask for double! The Government should, of course, have laughed and said, "Come on! - You can't do this", and explained why. Instead, Mr Wilson, when questioned, during a Television interview, pulled his pipe out of his pocket, carefully packed and lit it before answering, (a ploy he had perfected in order to gain time to try to get his brain working), and then made a lot of mumbling noises, included in which were words to the effect that, "The miners had had it rough for many years. Theirs was a lousy job. They deserved to be paid good wages for a good job", etc, etc.

So the miners got their double pay. Every other worker in the country immediately took their cue and demanded massive pay increases. The result – chaos – and roaring inflation. As you can guess, the author was, at this time, walking around with his mouth hanging open in amazement. Being a curious soul, I had heard about the great financial crash, the great 'Inflation', in Germany in the 1920s, looked it up in the library and read about it. Horrendous! You wouldn't believe it! The German Economy was wrecked after they were on the losing side in the 1914/1918 Great War. On top of this ruin, the victorious French demanded enormous reparation; "They started it! They should pay!" was the cry. (The British – to their credit – did not stick the boot in any more and did not take financial reparations). The result was economic chaos, culminating in the great financial collapse and inflation. If you would like to know how bad inflation can get, I will tell you! When I was in Germany a few years ago (I have German friends there) I was shown a stamp album dating back to the 'Inflation' time. The first stamps were perfectly normal, as you would use when posting a letter, marked 20 pfennigs or so (a pfennig can be translated roughly as a penny). Twenty pence to send a letter – fine! Then it went to 50 pfennigs, then 1 mark, then 5 marks, then 20 marks, and then my eyes really opened. The stamps then went to 100 marks, a thousand marks, a million marks, a billion marks. Unbelievable! You see, it costs no more to print the words One Billion Marks on a piece of paper than it does to print One Mark. That is how insane it became; money was printed by the ton.

When paid, people rushed to the shops to buy something – anything; if you waited until tomorrow morning the prices had doubled or trebled or worse.

There is an apocryphal story about two old ladies who took a sack full of money, in a large basket, to buy something before the money was worthless. They were mugged and robbed on the street. The thieves grabbed the basket, tipped the money out on the street – because it was worthless anyway, and bolted with the basket. It might even be true!

To try to bring order out of this chaos the German Government invented a new currency. A new MARK – which would be worth something. They had limited success. You might say, "Very interesting", and find the story of the old ladies laughable, but the chaos of Germany in the 1920s allowed Adolf Hitler to rise to power. To you and I he might seem a ranting maniac – but, to the people of Germany, he was probably the greatest orator who ever lived. He promised them work; many millions were unemployed. He promised them stability. He promised them power. He promised to give them back their pride. He even – believe it or not – promised husbands, for the millions of women who hadn't much hope because most of Germany's manhood had been slaughtered in the carnage of the war. You might say, "If they could believe that, they could believe anything"! but if people are desperate enough they will grab at anything that gives promise. Hitler seemed to be a Messiah. Many people believe that, if Germany could have recovered from the First World War, without the chaos and the inflation, Hitler would never have come to power. So, you may laugh about the story of the two old ladies and the basket of money, but World War Two wasn't very funny. I lived through it! Fortunately, at the end of World War Two, the Allies had learned their lesson. Instead of crippling the defeated Axis Powers with reparations, America poured money into the defeated countries to help them get back on their financial feet. In Europe it was called the 'Marshall Plan'. Only the Americans could have done it. Britain was on the brink of bankruptcy. The policy worked. All three Nations that formed the Axis Powers in World War Two (Germany, Japan and Italy) recovered and became successful Democracies. The price of revenge after World War One was very high.

Now, let us go back to 1973/1974. A few years previously, the author had managed to start a small manufacturing business and, at the time of the oil crisis, it was expanding nicely. Most of the profits had been ploughed back into the business but I had, nevertheless, managed to save some personal money and put it in the bank. Private money, that is – with taxes paid. So when I saw the way things were going, I sat down and did some careful, rational thinking. The conclusion I came to was that inflation was going to take off – a situation unheard of in the UK before. I decided inflation could well reach 30% in 1974 or 1975 and possibly worse, depending on how the Government handled it. In reality, we reached over 26% inflation, shares went into free fall, losing over 70% of their value, and the situation was only saved from a melt down because the Government went, cap in hand, to the International Monetary Fund – a bank fund – set up by the Nations of the World, in good times, for just such an eventuality. Britain took out a massive loan, which prevented collapse, but inflation stayed in double figures for years. The cure for inflation is a raising of interest rates and a brutal control of the money supply. This usually results in massive unemployment and disruption. (If you want to learn more about it there are plenty of Economics books you can read).

When things began to get really bad, Wilson, of course, having allowed this unholy mess to develop, decided it might be a suitable time to retire and let others, Heath and Callaghan, carry the can. It took a very tough person, Mrs Margaret Thatcher, to clamp down and get a grip on inflation and its consequences. It took ten years, and she is reviled for it, to this day. Anyway, I pondered the situation and decided what to do. The last thing you want in an inflationary situation is money in the bank. Its value will just be whittled away. So I bought gold and copper, and, since I was still living in a small rented flat, decided to buy a house, on a mortgage of course – because inflation also whittles away the value of debts. Gold is always a haven in a financial disaster; the World has loved gold and valued it since the time of the Pharaohs. Copper is a valuable commodity because you must have copper for industry, for electric motors, cables, etc. The house – bricks and mortar – will still be there in ten years time (unless some war or other disaster knocks it down). People must have somewhere to live.

In the event, the price of copper doubled, the price of gold doubled, and I sold them. Believe it or not, the Government then taxed me on 'Capital Gains' despite the fact the inflation was basically their fault. The Arabs raised the price of oil. They did not cause inflation. Inflation was caused by a wrong reaction to this rise, and was permitted by the Government.

The Comedian, Norman Wisdom – being smarter than he looks – bought masses of silver just before the British Government, under Wilson – who else! – devalued the pound in 1967 (in an earlier Balance of Trade Crisis) thus avoiding his capital being devalued by 15%. After devaluation he re-sold the silver and then the Revenue was after him for capital gains tax. "No way"! said our Norman, "I haven't made any gain at all. I have merely protected my initial value". Which was correct – for the price of silver stayed the same over the entire rest of the World. Mr Wisdom was so sure he was right that he went to Court and fought the Inland Revenue. Mr Wisdom lost! The Judge ruled that, according to the Laws of the Land, there was a monetary gain in this country and Mr Wisdom must pay up. This, I presume, is to stop these 'smart alecs' dodging the pain that everybody else has to endure.

To give you a sample of Politicians' double-talk, Mr Wilson is famous for going on television and telling people – because of the Balance of Trade problem he had found it necessary to devalue the pound by 15% but, "This will not alter the value of the pound in your pocket"! Not much! All imports instantly cost 15% more and the man on the street soon felt the effects.

Going back to the house – I paid £2,000 pounds as a deposit and took out a mortgage for £25,000 pounds. Total cost £27,000 pounds. Within a year or two, when inflation had done its work, the value of the house had doubled – if you count the value in the amount of pounds sterling it was worth; not really, because it was still exactly the same bricks and mortar. On paper I had gained £27,000 pounds. So, for an actual outlay of £2,000 pounds I had, in the space of 3 years, gained £27,000 pounds (work it out for yourself). This trick, where you gain a lot of money in a short time by this sort of financial manoeuvre, is called 'Gearing'. You can read about that in an Economics book if you want to. (It could – and sometimes does – work the other way, if the house price falls, for instance). Financial Traders often play around with money using 'gearing'.

For instance, in Copper Futures you can take out an option to buy £100,000 pounds worth of copper on a deposit of only £10,000 pounds – a gearing of ten to one. If the copper goes up 10% you double your money. Unfortunately, if it drops 10% you lose your money. Tough on you if it drops 20%! You cannot avoid the issue as, if you don't sell by a certain date, you have to pay up the full amount.

To give you a clue as to the sort of money these people (Financial Traders) deal in, you only have to look at the case of Nick Leeson. He managed to totally ruin Barings Bank in a few months by losing his gambles (for that is what they are). He managed to lose Six Hundred

Million Pounds in a few months. You may say – where does the money come from that you made on the house? The short and painful answer is, mainly from the poor investors who left their money in the bank during the inflationary period, some of which was loaned to me as a mortgage. Their money is only worth half as much as it was. This is simply one of the effects of inflation. The worst is the 'dog chasing its tail' business of workers clamouring for higher wages to compensate for the higher prices. Some only stop doing this when they have put themselves out of a job. It takes years to really wash inflation out of the system. There is no doubt about it. In the long run inflation is poison.

I would point out that, at the present time, our Chancellor, Mr 'Prudence' Gordon Brown, despite all his talk of 'careful management', has allowed inflationary price rises to run away for nine years in one sector of the British Economy; that is the housing market. In this time the Government has allowed house prices to nearly triple. Soon there will be a price to pay. It will cause trouble. He is not a fool; he must surely know this.

Remember my manoeuvre with the house. Millions of people are pulling that same trick – and congratulating themselves on how much wealthier they are. The Chancellor is a Socialist. He knows full well it is a redistribution of wealth. He is also going to take his cut in inheritance tax and increased Council Tax. Devious people these Politicians! It may not be obvious at first that house price inflation is a means of transferring wealth but it is. Consider three people A, B, and C. Let us assume that, at the start of a housing boom the average price of a house is £100,000. A, has £200,000 available to invest. He could buy two houses but, instead, decides to leave his money in a Bank or Building Society at a low rate of interest. B, and C, have no money but wish to live in their own houses, so they go to a considerate Building Society and obtain 100% mortgages. After a few years the average house price has risen to £200,000. B, and C, now feel wealthy because they each have a house worth £200,000 and only have a mortgage for £100,000. A, finds, although he now has £250,000 in the Building Society (£200,000 plus interest less tax) he can no longer buy two houses. He can only buy one house plus some furniture. Wealth has been transferred from A, to B, and C. It will be realised that there appears to be a discrepancy. B, and C, appear to have gained £100,000 each, whereas, A, seems only to have lost £150,000. (He would have had £400,000 if he had invested in houses). The discrepancy is in the system; the currency has been devalued and it is likely to cause general inflation, sooner or later. You may also wonder why house prices have taken off in the last few years. There has been no 'oil crisis' or similar happening to cause it. The cause is the law of supply and demand

– a shortage of houses coupled to the availability of cheap money. (Easy mortgages at low interest rates). If you have a situation where a seller has something that a lot of people want, he pushes his price up as far as it will go until, ideally, only one person will pay. While the buyers compete the price continues to rise. Conversely, when a number of sellers are offering the same thing, a house for instance, and very few people want to buy, the price drops until buyers can be found.

At the present time, everybody seems to think house prices will go up for ever. They are wrong! They can fall, and probably will sooner or later. Similar house price inflation has occurred, over the last few years, in the USA. At the time of writing, American house prices are falling. As usual with inflation there will be some very unpleasant after-effects. You may also say – "Well! The Government can't do much about stopping that sort of house price rise can they"? You are wrong; they certainly could have done. They have simply ignored the situation or deliberately allowed it to continue. The fundamental cause is a shortage of houses, combined with easy access to finance i.e. mortgages. In this situation buyers begin to compete. House builders love it! If you allow millions of immigrants into the country, then they must have somewhere to live. Also, if you allow wealthy people to buy more than one house, then any extra houses they buy are taken out of circulation, i.e. they stand empty, at least most of the time. House buyers will keep bidding higher for houses (in a shortage situation) if they can easily borrow the money to do so and, especially, if interest rates are low. They also see prices going up and think they cannot lose.

Instead of allowing house prices to rocket over the last ten years the Government should have taken action. Ideally house prices should have gone up, say, 3% per annum in line with general inflation. Many people will raise their eyebrows and say "But house prices have risen because of the law of supply and demand". Quite true! But price inflation can be controlled by increasing the supply or reducing the demand or a combination of both.

The Government should have taken the following actions.
1. Increase the supply.
 Relax planning restrictions – enough houses must be made available, even if Green Belt land has to be used. The MOD also has large areas of land doing nothing. Land must be made available. The only alternative to that is high-rise 'beehive' dwellings.
Stop people buying houses they will not use – and make them sell second houses they already have. Add to the house supply. Make them invest in something else.

2. Reduce the Demand.

Stop Banks and Building Societies offering mortgages under ridiculously easy conditions – this means stop them offering 120% mortgages; enough of a loan to buy the house, and furnish it as well, with little or no deposit. Banks and Building Societies should be forced to demand substantial deposits and mortgages should have a maximum repayment time. Strict rules should be enforced to limit the loan/income ratio.

Increase the Bank Rate. It doesn't actually take much increase to put the brakes on. It makes people think before taking on commitments.

If the corrective actions listed above had been taken seven or eight years ago (it was obvious way back in '98 and '99 that house prices were escalating far faster than general inflation) then we would not have the excessively high house prices we see today. If such actions were taken at the present time – now that property prices are at or near the peak – the result would be simply to make the inevitable correction far worse – and possibly trigger a market collapse. I feel sorry for the young people. Nobody seems to care that house prices are going beyond their reach. The stage is being set for an unpleasant correction one of these days.

As a result of the 1973/1974 inflation I lost my business and tens of thousands of other businesses also went down. Unemployment rocketed, from about 300,000 to over one and a half million, and has now reduced but has never gone down to the pre inflation levels. Because I managed to preserve the value of my personal capital, I was able to start again and employ people and contribute to the economy and the Balance of Trade through exports.

You may think that stocks, shares, insurance and such like are a purely modern creation. You are wrong! The Romans – who were pretty bright – had them too. One Roman – Crassus, is said to have run a fire insurance business in Rome. Apparently he had also managed to gain control of the Rome fire brigade service. Strangely enough – if you didn't insure with Crassus – your home was more likely to catch fire and, usually, it turned out the fire brigade was busy elsewhere. Crassus sounds a little like Al Capone in a toga! On second thoughts, I think most of the others were too; the Romans were the ultimate practitioners of the principle 'Might is Right'. 'Pax Romana' meant you had peace as long as you minded your own business, paid your taxes and didn't cause any trouble.

The Romans of course used money – mainly metal currency – samples of which turn up all over the place – with impressions of the heads of various Caesars stamped on them.

One Caesar couldn't resist playing with the money supply, and thought it a good idea to alloy the gold and silver and stamp out twice as many coins. Result – Inflation! Surprise! Surprise!

With regard to the everyday use of money – yours I mean! – be careful! If you have any spare cash and want to invest it – watch your step. Banks, Insurance firms, Financial Advisers and so on are all businesses. Their prime purpose is to make money. Banks are the World's biggest 'rip off' organisations. Even the Romans would have been impressed! The main thing they do is handle money. They borrow it from you and lend it to someone else. You will be lucky to get a miserly 5% interest from them and they will charge 14%, 15% and higher to the people they lend it to. No wonder they make Billions! They also have a repertoire of fancy little tricks. They offer you a savings account at 5%. If you look carefully in the fine print, you may spot the phrase – "interest rates may vary". Beware! You will put the money in – happy it is a high interest account. They will give you 12 months, if you are lucky, and then drop the rate. A few years ago, this sort of practice became so bad that legislation was passed to make them warn you they were going to cut the interest rate.

I remember, a few years ago, my mother had accounts with one of our major high street banks. I knew she had a little capital, so one day I asked her what she did with it. She replied, "Oh! Everything is fine, I have it in a high interest account with So and So Bank". "Good!" said I. "By the way – when did you invest it"? It turned out she had placed it, in a high interest account, 5 years earlier. The first year the interest rate had been at about 5%, the second year about 3% and the last 3 years about 1¾%. When I phoned up the bank and complained they said "Oh! That's an obsolete account". How can an account be obsolete? The money isn't. No doubt they were lending it out at a high rate. It was another crafty manoeuvre to diddle mother out of cash. If you really complain, and 'play up', they will send you a letter saying they really don't have to do it, but they are sending you a cheque for £50 pounds as a gesture of goodwill!

All this business of 'Caring Banks' and 'How can we help you' is so much eyewash. They are either after your cash, for which they will offer you the lowest rate they can get away with, or they want to lend you cash, for which they will charge you the highest rate they can get away with. With Insurance firms – the adviser (salesman), if he has two products to offer you, is likely to push the one that gives him the biggest commission, rather than the other, which may suit you better. The same applies to Financial Advisers and such. Occasionally, you come across exceptional ones who genuinely give you the best deal, on the principle that a satisfied customer will come back. Bear in mind that everybody has to make a living. Businesses exist to make money and there is no such thing as a free lunch. You will have to pay somehow; otherwise somebody else would have to! Also, bear in mind that anything that looks like 'something for nothing' is almost always a scam.

Incidentally, this reminds me of when I ran the small business I referred to – I was approached with what is now a well-known Nigerian Scam. I received a letter. It said:

MOST PRIVATE AND CONFIDENTIAL

Dear Sir

We are looking for a small reliable business in the UK run by a person such as yourself. The business must be discreet and trustworthy because the transaction we propose is extremely confidential. We have researched your firm and are satisfied that we could do business with you.

We are acting as Agents for a Senior Nigerian Minister who must remain anonymous.

Briefly – a substantial quantity of oil (outside of the OPEC quota) – has been sold privately.

Our client wishes to arrange a transaction whereby the money from the sale of the oil is paid to your firm and then money is to be transferred from your firm to a Swiss Bank Account.

For this service our client is willing to allow you to deduct from the total – 5% for expenses plus 15% commission for services rendered.

The value of the oil that has been sold is forty five million US Dollars.

If you are interested in this proposition would you please let us have your full bank account details and three copies of your Company Letter Heads signed by yourself so that we can set up the deal and effect the cash transfer into your company account.

If this transaction proceeds satisfactorily there may be other transactions later.

Signed ....

Within seconds I am multiplying 45 million dollars by 20%.
Good grief! Nine million dollars for peanuts! However, the Minister can afford this; he's salting away millions in Switzerland; possibly more transactions; I could retire early; I could .... and, at this point,

sanity clicks back in. Hang on a minute – lets think about this! Then it dawns. I know a little about legal matters. I know that you can practically sign your soul away on a piece of toilet paper if you are fool enough to sign it. You can write on a piece of scrap paper that you agree to sell your firm – lock, stock and barrel – for the princely sum of one pound and, if you sign it in the presence of a witness, it is legal. It is quite common to write legal documents, sign them, post them and have them witnessed by someone who is miles away. Who is to prove he wasn't there? These people were even asking for your signature on Company Notepaper, together with full details of your bank account. I lifted the offending letter with two fingers, as one would a filthy rag, and dropped it in the wastebasket. You may be surprised, but I recently read that the money lost to Nigerian Scams is in Billions of Pounds a year. Greed can addle peoples' brains! If anybody ever offers you what appears to be something for nothing – Beware!

With regard to businesses, they are an immensely important part of the nation. They must make a profit or they will cease to exist. The question is – is the profit reasonable taking into account what the firm does? For instance – take a supermarket chain such as Tesco. I shop at Tesco as do millions of other people. You go to the store; they provide free parking space, and there is an immense range of food and goods. The goods are high quality and value taking into account the price you pay. There is an enormous range of choice. Considering the amount of goods commonly purchased on one trip, the payment and checkout is quite efficient; in half an hour you can do enough shopping to last you a fortnight. They also provide work for a great many people. What is their net profit margin? Only 5% or less. How could anyone possibly complain at that; 5p out of every pound you spend.

You may have read that, last year, Tesco made over a billion pounds profit; that is because they have so many outlets and such an enormous turnover. If Tesco in some way, was forced to lower all prices by 10% they would go bankrupt. Compare that to the Banks. What do they do? Basically, they play around with people's and companies' money, and cream off profits all along the way in every financial manoeuvre known to man.

Banks are an essential part of the Nation and, undoubtedly, are of immense value. They bring into this country a vast amount of cash from foreign deals and substantially contribute to the balance of payments. However they do exploit the public and, when I hear of the major banks making profits of 6 to 8 billion pounds a year, each, I think – surely this is too much! Surely they could do the job for half that amount or less.

Unquestionably, it is better for the banks to make excess profit rather than not enough. The last thing we want is for banks to go bankrupt – with all the concomitant, disastrous, consequences. We must have safe, secure banks we can trust not to collapse on us. However, I still think their profits are too high. There are also special cases in businesses. An example is the Pharmaceutical Industry. They have sometimes been criticised for making enormous profits, but remember – they spend astronomic sums on research. Research that sometimes results in drugs that save lives or improve the quality of life for millions. It is true that, if they are successful, they make enormous profits. However, often they spend billions only to see a promising drug fail. I feel we should accept that this is a special case, and not complain too much if they are successful – and very profitable. Better that way than that they should go bankrupt, and the development and supply of new drugs dry up.

Money makes the World go around – as the song said – but what about the personal level? Enough money is essential if you are to enjoy life. I personally know what life is like in poverty. It is a depressing, worrying, frightening situation to not have enough money. I remember, only too well, the hardship and the difficulties my parents experienced, when I was young.

If you are an ordinary person like me, and not a stockbroker or speculator, and you want to dabble in stocks and shares, my advice, for what it is worth is, be careful! I have dabbled, and I have won a few and lost a few. In balance, I have gained more than lost, but there have been painful experiences.

At one time, I decided to look for recovery situations – where a basically good firm has hit a bad patch but there is a good chance of recovery. Way back, I became interested in Rolls Royce, who had made piston and jet aero engines for many years; always a good, sound, solid and reliable firm. There came a time when they needed to spend a fortune developing a new, massive, next generation, jet engine – the RB 211 – and needed a contract with a plane maker for engines to go in its new planes. If they didn't get a contract for supply of the RB 211, Rolls Royce might be finished as a major player in the World's Markets. The American firm, Pratt and Whitney, were also working on this new high thrust type of engine, and already had contracts to supply engines for the DC 10 aircraft and, I believe, Boeing's 747 Jumbo. Rolls Royce were desperate. They decided it was a win or bust situation, and offered to supply RB 211 engines to Lockheed for their new, wide-bodied jet, the Tri-Star, at a price Pratt and Whitney could not match. Rolls were awarded the contract. Work proceeded, both on the engines and on the plane. After a time, it was obvious that the price for the RB 211 engines quoted to Lockheed was hopelessly low. To proceed, and actually supply the engines at that price, would mean Rolls Royce would make enormous losses. Word got out and Rolls' shares plummeted.

It seemed to me there would be discussions; Rolls would claim there had been a mistake; not they, nor Pratt and Whitney could actually make these engines for the price quoted. The price would have to go up, (in that I was right!) and then Rolls Royce would recover; the shares would go up – and I would sell. I therefore bought quite a few Rolls shares. Lockheed, however, were awkward and would not budge. They had a contract, "You made a mistake" they said to Rolls Royce. "Hard luck! You should have been more careful! A contract is a contract. Your problem – not ours!" Then something happened that I had never dreamed of. Suddenly, Rolls announced they had gone bust. A Receiver was called in. All the assets were placed in a new company, called Rolls Royce (1971) Ltd, and it was business as usual. It was all done in 24 hours. Not a man was sacked, not a worker lost his job. It was all done with the blessing of the Prime Minister of the day, Edward Heath. In effect, the Firm was Nationalised.

Now! What was the situation? According to Company Law, the contract with Lockheed was with the old, defunct, Rolls Royce Ltd. Lockheed were now left on a limb. The contract was, for all intents and purposes, dead. Rolls Royce (1971) Limited re-negotiated with Lockheed and agreed to do the job at a new price, which Lockheed were forced to agree to. Their planes, half built, were designed for the Rolls engines. So – everything is rosy! With one quick flash of the magic wand Rolls is back in business and profitable! Hang on a minute, what about we shareholders? I held shares in the old Rolls Royce Ltd; not the new one. We were in limbo. The price, agreed with the Receiver, for Rolls Royce (1971) Ltd to purchase all the assets of the old Rolls Royce Ltd was enough to pay off all the people who supplied Rolls with components. (Must keep them happy!) But the shareholders? Forget the shareholders; no cash for them! At the last minute it was decided to leave just a little cash to pay them something, so they didn't have a 100% loss; just a 90% one. So there we shareholders were – owning practically valueless bits of paper, Rolls Royce Ltd Shares. Painful – it certainly taught me a lesson! I learned a lot about Company Law, Contracts and Limited Companies I assure you.

People seemed to think the letters LTD after a company name conferred something on a business. It does; it means Limited Liability. Limited Liability Companies, and the laws that protect them, were set up to encourage people with money to invest in businesses, which will then contribute to a Nation's prosperity. A Limited Company is a separate legal entity in Law. Let us imagine there is a wealthy person named Jack Jones. He decides he would like to go into business but he doesn't want to take too many risks. He invests part of his cash in a wood working company named Jack Jones Ltd. It is successful. He then decides to go into plumbing. However, being a canny individual, he decides to set up a separate company – Jack Jones Plumbing Ltd. Then he becomes interested in selling electrical goods, and sets up Jack Jones (Electrical) Ltd. At this point you get involved and do a lot of work for Jack Jones Ltd. Eventually, because you know Jack Jones is wealthy, you have worked until Jack Jones Ltd owes you ten thousand pounds. You would have liked to have been paid before the account reached ten thousand pounds but you didn't push it because Jack Jones might get irritated and take his trade elsewhere. Suddenly you hear that Jack Jones Ltd has gone bust and a Liquidator has been called in. You are told that you are a creditor but there is no money left to pay creditors and you have lost your ten thousand pounds. You know that Jack Jones and his wife owned the company and you also know he is still wealthy and his other firms are doing fine. There is, however, nothing you can do. You cannot sue Jack Jones or his other companies. Your debt is owed by Jack Jones Ltd which is an independent entity in Law. Galling though it may be, you have no redress against Jack Jones or his other companies. You should have checked with Companies House (who keep all the Company records) to find out Jack Jones Ltd financial situation, before you allowed the debt to rise to ten thousand pounds. You will, no doubt, be more careful next time!

If a company is badly run or is, say, crippled by competition, as can easily happen, and the Directors run the firm until the firm is insolvent with the assets near zero, then everybody owed money can 'go whistle'! If there are a few assets, which can be sold to make a few pounds, or if the whole firm can be sold for a price, by the Receiver, then there is a 'pecking order' of creditors. Banks and Institutions come first; then the Revenue and Customs; (this does not seem right to me – surely the Revenue should come last! They take enough from everybody when a business is running fine. For instance, when I ran a business they used to take more in VAT alone, than the company made in profits. That is before taking into account income tax, NI contributions, corporation tax, etc); then the general creditors: the Landlord, Service Providers, Component Suppliers, etc. Lower down on the list come the Preferential Shareholders and, finally, if there is still anything left – the Ordinary Shareholders. It is quite normal for the Ordinary Shareholders to get nothing. It does not matter if you have a thousand pounds in ordinary shares or ten million pounds, you still get zero. So – shares might look an attractive investment – they usually are but, beware, you can get your fingers burned – savagely.

In the 1974/1975 recession, over a hundred thousand firms went bankrupt in a short time. If you want my advice on buying and selling shares, be careful; don't be too greedy! Wait until there is a down-swing – a substantial drop in the F.T. Index. Then, when it begins to recover, say by 10% or even 20%, (5% can be a blip) – go in; invest in sound, reliable, safe firms, wait for the shares to rise and, when you have made a decent profit, say 30 per cent, get out! Be satisfied with a decent profit. If you are greedy, and hang on and on, there may come a day when prices will drop so fast you won't believe it and, worse still, you will find it very difficult, or nearly impossible, to get out. Nobody answers phones; computers develop faults; your stockbroker is not available, and so on. Professional Speculators hang on to the last minute; they can afford to. They have contacts, and are in touch with the market 60 minutes in the hour, twenty-four hours a day, seven days a week. They can trade at 2.30 a.m. if they wish to. (Haven't you heard of "out of hours" trading). Those people make their money out of people like you and I – who often lose it!

What about Financial Bubbles? The Dot Com/Techno Financial Bubble, that finally burst in the year 2000, was so obvious that I started a file a couple of months before the crash. The heading on the file is 'RUN UP TO THE DOT COM/TECHNO CRASH'. It is full of newspaper cuttings relating to insane share pricing of Dot Com Companies. You may say, "If that's so, you must have made a killing". You are wrong! I am too rational. I simply cannot bring myself to buy shares that I am sure are ridiculously over-priced – say 4 or 6 times more than a figure that makes sense; I cannot believe that anyone will be stupid enough to bid the shares higher and higher, until they are a hundred times, or more, above the sane price; but they do. When the prices are four times too high I cannot bring myself to buy the shares. When they double again I find it unbelievable; I cannot buy. When they double again I am incredulous. When they double again it is beyond my comprehension; there is no way I could consider buying the shares. Then they double again! When the crash finally came in April 2000 many Dot Com shares plummeted 98% to 99%; nearly all of them fell more than 90%. The experts know the game; they know greed will drive people; they know that sanity goes out of the window and they will spot the signs of a bubble developing, early on. They will buy in, and watch the shares day and night like a hawk. They know the signs that indicate the shares are on the brink of a crash – and bale out – making millions. If you can do that – you are lucky. I can't! However, I feel very sorry for the millions of ordinary people –

who lose half of their pension funds, because the fund managers couldn't resist jumping on the bandwagon. I made very sure my brother's pension funds were not in Dot Coms – or any other shares – months before the crash. (Other shares get dragged down). Being older, I had already cashed in my pension funds for an Annuity.

Many people invest in Bonds, believing them to be safer than shares, which they usually are, but some do not seem to grasp that bonds are simply loans. The safest are Government Bonds which are usually for an extended period of time such as 20 years, 50 years or sometimes more. In other words, the Government asks for loans for a stipulated period and guarantees to pay a fixed rate of interest for that period. Because of the extended period of the bond it is normal for people to buy or sell the bonds, instead of waiting the full period of the bond for repayment. If a bond is issued at, say, 7% interest and, subsequently, the Bank of England rate falls to 5% the price of the bond will go up. Bonds that could be bought initially for £1000 my now be valued at, say, £1200 or £1300. Conversely, if the Bank of England was to raise the bank rate to 8% then the value of the bond would come down. The bond that initially cost £1000 would now only sell for maybe £900. So it is possible, therefore, to make (or lose) money trading in bonds. Alternatively someone may prefer to buy Government Bonds and be happy with the regular interest payments and the knowledge that their investment is secure.

Another, relatively secure form of bond are the short period bonds – with a period of from one to five years – offering interest rates slightly higher than Bank Rate, which are offered by Building Societies and Banks. Whilst it is not unheard of for Banks or Building Societies to go bust, it is a rare event, and these bonds can, generally, be considered safe. Then there are the Corporate Bonds. These are simply loans to businesses. Interest rates offered on these can vary but it must be born in mind the risk is substantially greater. Whilst bonds purchased from old established and sound businesses may be reasonably secure there can be substantial risk with bonds offered by relatively new and, maybe, precarious businesses. If a firm is offering bonds at a remarkably high rate – watch out! You may lose your money! If the business fails and goes into liquidation the share holders and bondholders may lose part or all of their money. This must be born in mind. Not all bonds are safe investments. To emphasise this I will quote from a recent newspaper cutting. "Torex Retail ...... is selling its operating assets .... and will leave shareholders and bondholders losing their entire investment". Be careful then, when considering and investing in bonds. Always beware of grandiose schemes like the 'Channel Tunnel'; the shareholders usually end up being fleeced. Sometimes the bondholders are too.

There have been occasions when the UK has come close to a financial crash and has somehow avoided it. I think it was about 1979/1980 when a dangerous financial situation arose. After the oil crisis in 1974, when oil prices went up more than eight fold, the Arab Nations were awash with cash. What did they do with it? Lend it back to us, or more precisely, British Banks, at a fixed interest rate of course. At that time, the South American Nations (just about all of them) wanted loans. They were willing to pay high interest rates, so our bright boys at the Banks said, "If we borrow 'X' from the Arabs at, say, 5% and lend it to South America at, say, 7% we shall make billions". Nobody said, "As long as they pay up and don't renege on the loans"; so they went ahead. Predictably (at least I think so) after a couple of years the Argentinians, the Brazilians, the Peruvians and others, began to say, "We can't afford to service these loans. Why don't we get together and create a sort of debtors' cartel, and suggest we just might, all of us, default." (i.e. refuse to pay – which meant, not only the interest, but the repayment of the loans as well). The total of the South American loans was hundreds of billions of pounds. (Incidentally, I expect you have heard the old story. If you owe the Bank a million pounds they have got you 'over a barrel'. If you owe the Bank 500 million you have got them 'over a barrel'). I learned about this dangerous situation and I was running a small mail order business at the time. I also learned about the amounts the Banks had loaned to South America. (Don't forget – the Arabs could demand their money back – it wasn't their fault the money had been loaned on, foolishly). Why didn't the Arabs themselves lend their money to South America? Obviously they had more sense! Anyway, I did a few calculations and realised, if the South American countries really did default 'en masse', then my bank would be bankrupt.

I thought about the situation very carefully. Running a direct mail order company, even if you didn't make enormous profits, gave you considerable reserves; we received cash with order and only paid our suppliers on a monthly credit basis. One of the things about direct mail order, therefore, was a great cash flow situation; so I arranged a meeting at the Bank, where I met both the Manager and the Assistant Manager, (probably curious to know what I wanted). I accepted their cup of coffee and said, "I have decided the firm is going to invest in gold". They looked at me as if I had gone out of my mind. I explained about South America. "Oh"! said the Assistant Manager. "Don't you think you are worrying a bit too much over this"? "Well" I said, "I have worked out that if the South American countries all default at the same time, your Bank will go bust". (They looked stunned. I got the impression they had not realised how dire the situation could get). "I just want the gold as an

Insurance Policy". I told them that if the gold did not go up in price they would not hear a complaint from me. If the Crisis was solved satisfactorily business would be OK! However, if the worst came to the worst, we would be covered. I asked them if they could arrange to get the required gold. They said they could and I told them to go ahead. A few days later there was a phone call. "Your firm's gold has arrived – would you like to check it"? So I went in. I couldn't believe it; the gold had arrived by parcel post. Recorded delivery mind you! I picked it up. Gold is very heavy. Heaven knows what the postman thought it was! I had naturally assumed it would be delivered to the Bank by Securicor, in one of their vans along with the usual weekly delivery of cash. No – Parcel Post!

In the event, the Banks negotiated with the South American Nations. In brief they said, "Don't default. You will wreck the Banking System and create financial chaos. If you don't default now, we will write off your loans – completely – over the next ten years". That is what they did – as far as I am aware.

Immediately after the deal the Banks all started massively increasing their charges for everything, large and small. In other words we, the public, paid for their blunders. They made billions of pounds extra profit – and wrote these billions off against the South American Loans. They even gained from it. When the South American financial debacle was sorted out the extra charges stayed. Now the Banks all make billions of pounds profit – and don't have to write it all off. Not bad!

Naturally, when the South American problem was solved, I wanted to get the company cash flow back to normal. Things had been a bit tight. So I phoned up the Bank and said "Would you mind converting the company gold back into cash again". "Oh"! They said, "We don't do that any more". So I had to collect the gold, stash it in a briefcase, go down to London, get a Taxi, walk into Johnson Matthey's Office and dump the gold on a desk. "Would you mind giving me a cheque for this please". "Oh! OK! But we will have to assay it first". "Look"! I said, "As you see on the package, it came from you in the first place". "Nevertheless we must assay it, here is a receipt, send you a cheque later. OK"! So this concluded my foray into the bullion market!

Let me take a moment to tell you of the Brinks-Mat bullion robbery. Crooks found out there would be, at a certain time, a couple of million pounds worth of gold, in a warehouse at Heathrow Airport. They got themselves organised, raided the airport and heisted the gold. I believe the gold bars were stamped, 'Johnson Matthey'! The crooks carted the gold off, bought a little furnace, which they installed down the garden, melted the gold bars and recast them. They then carted the bars

back to Johnson Matthey and said, "Would you let us have a cheque for this lot please". "OK" said Johnson Matthey's clerk, or whoever, "But we'll have to assay it. Let you have a cheque in a few days".
"Fine!" The cheque arrives and the crooks go to the Bank. "Can we put this in our account please". "Sure!". (The cheque was only for a couple of million or so!). The transaction went through. A week later – one of the gang went to the Bank. "Could we call in next week and collect a little cash – in used notes preferably".
"Certainly".
"A quarter of a million maybe"?
"Certainly! Call on Wednesday".
A crook turned up with a black polythene rubbish bag, fills it up with cash and walks off down the street. (You think I joke? Look it up!). The main villain even called his two dogs Brinks and Mat. The crooks were, of course, eventually caught, or I couldn't recount the story. You could not, of course, pull such tricks today, considering the anti-terrorism money laundering rules and checks, but you could then. I thought my games with the company gold were daft enough!

On one of my Russian fishing trips, shortly after the 'Dot Com/Techno' financial crash, I talked to a wealthy American. He had invested heavily in a whole range of these companies; and hadn't got out before the crash. "I'm not worried" he said, "I haven't sold. You only make a loss when you sell. I still own the shares". I thought of the 'Japanese Bubble'. The 'Nikkei-Dow' was at 39,000, before it crashed, 17 years ago. It has never recovered to this day and stands at 16,900 as I write. If you allow for the effects of inflation, assuming only 3% per annum, it would need to be at least 65,000 to be equivalent to the 39,000 it was years ago. 'Bubbles' never recover. I looked at the American and said nothing, remembering that Dotcom shares had lost between 90% and 99% of their value. Sooner or later he would realise and he would sell. He was going to take a hell of a caning. I went to a well-known Fishing Lodge in Alaska, at about the time the 'Dot Com' bubble was bursting. The owner of the Lodge was at the evening meal. "I'm not worried" he said, "America can handle it". However, the number of anglers visiting his Lodge dried up the next year; he went bust and the Lodge is now owned by someone else.

I remember one of my early salmon fishing trips to Russia's Kola Peninsula, just after Russia had been opened up to the West, and President Putin had come to power. The fishing trip had been organised by a Scandinavian group, but most of the fishing guides were Russians with local knowledge of the river. I noticed, as we passed through a local village, on the way to the fishing camp, the village was still, defiantly, flying the red flag, instead of the new emblem. Most of our fishing guides, as you would expect, spoke very little English – just enough to get by and make themselves understood. This was quite acceptable to we anglers, as long as they could operate a boat and take us to the best fishing places. However, one day I had a new guide; an intelligent and educated Russian who spoke good English. I had a memorable day's fishing with him – he really knew the river and the salmon holding places. On the second day he began to question me about the West. "How did the system work?" I looked at him and remembered the red flag still flying over the village, so I put down my rod. He asked my why I was not fishing, so I told him I thought the conversation was more important. He told me the locals were on the brink of starvation, which was why they were always in the woods searching for mushrooms. (Incidentally, I was fool enough to eat several bowls of their delicious mushroom soup, until I remembered Chernobyl. Fungi pick up radioactive Cesium very efficiently. Reindeer eat reindeer moss – a kind of fungus. In Lapland a lot of reindeer meat is too radioactive to be eaten by humans). I said to Sergei, "Soon things will improve. Soon you will have more food, better clothes, more goods and a better standard of living". He shrugged his shoulders, in a resigned sort of way, and said, "In a hundred years!"

I talked to him, and explained that society was like a beehive producing honey. Everybody worked to produce and the sum total of all the people's work was called the Gross National Product. Then it was a question of sharing out the created wealth. Money was just a token for work. In the West, money was also the great incentive to get people to work. I said to him, "Russia is naturally rich. Russia has oil, gas, metals and minerals in vast quantities. These commodities could be sold and the money used to prime the pump of productivity. If Russia could build rockets to place astronauts in orbit, make Mig 29 planes and nuclear submarines, they could also make TVs, fridges, cars, computers and so on. President Putin is no fool, he must understand this. All that is needed is for Russia to create proper trustable business laws, and co-operate with the West on business development, and money will flood in. Russia would rapidly become a wealthy prosperous nation". After two hours we carried on fishing. When we went back to the camp, and the village, I saw Sergei meet his son and daughter with a smile. We fished on for a week. He seemed happier. Perhaps he would talk to others, and help to lift the pessimism, and maybe that red flag would come down. I thought that two-hour chat might have been worthwhile. The next time I went to Kola I was told Sergei was waiting for me. Perhaps even the words of an angler might help – just a little – in the mess that was Russia.

On the downside, I talked to an American who was trying to set up a business there. He was considering packing it in. The Russian Mafia was everywhere. In addition to this, every business had to incorporate a Russian Partner. Sometimes, after a Westerner transferred funds into a new business, the Partner would embezzle the funds and disappear. There seemed to be no redress. If President Putin wants Russia to become prosperous, and boost trade with the West, he will have to sort this out. There must be sound legal laws protecting business. Contracts must be honoured and businesses must be protected from Mafia influence.

I was talking to a friend of mine, when the conversation came around to the question of Foreign Countries building factories in the UK. The Japanese car firm Toyota being quoted as an example. "No"! he said, "I don't agree with it. I want to see British firms, not Foreign". Since, bluntly, British firms had failed in the face of foreign competition, I said I was all in favour of Foreign investment and Foreign firms manufacturing here.

Let us consider Toyota. The firm invests the money (or at least most of it) to build the factory. They then employ British people who get paid good wages and salaries, and put taxes into the Treasury. The firm sells cars here and abroad and the exports help with our Balance of Trade. When the business makes profits – a large percentage of the profits again go to the Treasury in Corporation tax. Often, some of the remaining profit is ploughed back into the business for expansion. Only a very small percentage actually goes to Japan. In Ireland, an enlightened Government understood this, and created a whole range of incentives, to encourage foreign firms to set up businesses and build factories in Ireland; for instance, zero corporation tax for a number of years, and all the help that could be given to assist and speed up the project. Get the businesses into Ireland; milk them later! The result is that Ireland has boomed.

Britain under Margaret Thatcher, opted out of many of the European Regulations, which gave Britain a competitive edge. Many foreign companies built factories here; providing jobs and taxes. Now, under the present Government, we have fallen into the trap of adopting many of the European Regulations; more holidays, shorter working hours, paternity leave, more company taxes, etc. Foreign investment in factories in Britain is reducing rapidly, and Britain's manufacturers are losing their competitive edge. Many manufacturers – such as Dyson with his 'cyclone' vacuum cleaners – have baled out and now manufacture their goods in the far East.

Incidentally – when the Chancellor decided to raid the Pension Funds, and extract six billion pounds a year, each and every year, he was, in fact, adding an extra tax burden on businesses and the public. When there is a shortfall in the Pension Funds, it is the companies who are expected to make it up. The Chancellor does not give any tax back. To cover this, a smokescreen is thrown up; the Pension shortfalls are due to the drop in the stock market. Bad luck; businesses are going to have to make it up! Nobody seems to realise that, before the Chancellor's tax on pension funds, he wasn't giving anybody anything. He was merely letting them keep their own money. The Chancellor taking billions of pounds a year from the pension funds has a double effect. Firstly it adds a massive extra financial burden on businesses, making them less competitive. To try to ease the burden, firms are ditching Defined Benefit Pension Schemes and pushing their employees on to schemes which are less of a drain on the Company resources. Secondly, therefore, retired employees will have reduced pension benefits and Gordon Brown has guaranteed they will have a lower standard of living for the rest of their lives. Incredibly this massive stealth tax has been accepted by the British populace with hardly a murmur. When I remember the tidal wave of protest that erupted when Mrs Thatcher proposed her poll tax I can hardly believe Gordon Brown has managed to get away with this. If the Chancellor reduces taxation (a rare event) political spin says he is "giving away" so much money. He is giving away nothing; he is merely letting us keep a little more of our own money.

Many people seem to suffer from the delusion that the Government is awash with money. All the people who defraud the Government – whether it is false pension claims, false support claims, false unemployment claims, and so on, seem to think it is just the Government they are defrauding. In reality, they are defrauding us – the taxpayers; they are stealing our money; nobody else's. Mrs Thatcher, in an interview, once spelled it out, "The Government has no money" she said, "It simply spends yours". If the people who cheat and defraud the Government stopped doing so, that would be billions of pounds we wouldn't need to pay.

So far, no one seems to have really grasped what a destabilising and dangerous device the modern credit card is. Millions blithely use credit cards with no real grasp of what the figures mean. It is almost as if the card is a flattened pocket version of a magic wand. Wave it around or quote a few numbers and, magically, things appear. The great thing, so far as the consumer is concerned, is that they can go on doing this even though they have no money until, one desperate day, they are told they have reached their credit limit. It was different when people had to use real, physical, money, in notes and coins. Then they could see the hard earned tokens of their labours disappearing and caution became a byword. With credit cards it is too easy to get into serious debt. Another dangerous and pernicious side effect of the credit card culture is the amazing proliferation of crime which, so far, is being accepted almost as a normal facet of a modern society. When, in the past, banks were raided and people were robbed on the street, there was an outcry for action to be taken and stiff jail sentences for these crimes were handed out. Now, incredibly, theft has reached fantastic proportions and nobody takes any notice because it is done through credit card fraud. If, in the past, a gang raided a bank and got away with half a million, it was front page news; the police went into overdrive and the criminals were soon apprehended and locked away. The total losses, per annum, for the whole nation, including bank robberies, burglaries and all other forms of theft was probably no more than two or three hundred million pounds per year. At that time, everybody agreed that monetary crime should not be tolerated. Remarkably, with the common use of credit cards, the annual theft of money through credit card fraud alone runs into many billions of pounds a year. The word billions is not a misprint. I repeat – many thousands of millions of pounds every year are lost to credit card fraud. Because the Banks and Institutions are wedded to the credit card system they have decided to accept credit card losses, due to fraud, as part of normal business running costs. The card holders don't complain because they are reimbursed for each individual loss. In effect the losses are being spread out over all of us, almost like an unseen tax (by increased interest and Bank charges). There are also other side effects. If this kind of stealing is acceptable why should shoplifters feel guilty or benefit fraudsters worry about their misdemeanours? Credit card fraud escalates steadily, year after year. Just how many billions per year will it have to reach, one wonders, before someone in Government takes notice and decides it is unacceptable. Maybe the Government looks upon it as just another means for transfer of wealth. In my mind it is dangerous to condone and almost encourage criminality on this scale. For all its modernity and convenience the ubiquitous credit card has spawned debt and criminality on a massive scale.

In the last nine years there has been a massive housing boom. House prices have nearly trebled, for the same bricks and mortar. This is inflationary. They keep that out of the calculations and tell the public inflation is only 2½%. Inflation is caused either deliberately or, more usually, by default, by the Government. The Government is there to Govern. That is what they are elected to do. They have allowed house price inflation. It could and should have been controlled. Incidentally, when we are on the upswing of inflation everybody thinks it is great; money for nothing. Unfortunately, the price is paid later. Sadly, I have seen it all before. Now, with house prices massively inflated, but general inflation at only 2½% (they keep telling us so) suddenly they realise there is a golden chance to increase taxes. Increase the Council Tax and keep the Inheritance Tax Threshold low. Council Tax is supposed to be the charge levied on householders, to pay the cost of the Infrastructure society needs; for Education, the Police, Social Services and so on. If the Council Tax paid was sufficient last year, then we might reasonably expect it to go up 2½% each year – in line with general inflation. What difference does it make to the Council if your house price has doubled or not – as long as they get the money they need. But No! There is a chance to cash in and they are going to take it! They are going to re-rate your house and increase the Council Tax charge. "Why not?" they will say, "You can afford it". Why should whether you can afford it or not, be anything to do with their spending? If they escalate the Council Tax and obtain extra money, they will simply waste the money in a profligate manner, storing up trouble for the future.

If you sell your house for three times the price you paid for it, it doesn't do you any good if you have to pay the same inflated price for your next house. The only way you can possibly gain is to trade down. I suppose, if you sell up and go and live in a caravan, you might be well off. But who wants to do that? The people who really have my sympathy are the youngsters trying to get on the property ladder. What do they think of a Government that allows such a situation to develop? They probably think it is not the Government's fault and consider house price inflation is just bad luck for them. Think again! It is the Government's job to Govern. It is the Government that has allowed house price inflation to happen. House price inflation is usually followed by general inflation (I have seen it twice before). People begin to scream for higher wages so that they can afford higher mortgages, and so on. At the present time, the only thing holding general inflation in check is cheap imports from China and low cost immigrant labour. Sooner or later there will be a correction. Either house prices will start to fall, or inflation will start to rise or, more likely, a combination of both, and the effects will be unpleasant.

Earlier in this chapter I referred to the possibility of having a credit arrangement in a barter society – where the shoemaker provides a pair of shoes to the cabbage grower in return for a promise of five cabbages at a later date. The extra cabbage, over and above the four cabbages agreed for an immediate transaction, is a form of interest because of the risk involved. The cabbage grower might renege on his promise or his cabbages might be stolen or eaten by deer so that he could not pay his debt even though he had every intention of doing so. In a modern society, lending and borrowing and the giving of credit is done on a vast scale. In fact, if this was not so, modern society would grind to a halt or very nearly so. A vast number of items are purchased on a credit basis. Few people, for instance, save up until they have the full amount to buy a car. Usually they either enter into a hire/purchase agreement with the car sales people or they go to a bank and borrow the money to buy the car. Very few people indeed buy a house outright; nearly everyone borrows the money from a bank or building society, in the form of a mortgage. The house is then purchased, the people move in and then enjoy the benefits of having a house to live in. (It is not generally recognised that, in reality, the house does not fully belong to the householder until the mortgage is paid off. Householders in default of their repayments can have the house repossessed). Buying the house and the car on mortgage and hire purchase agreements, and everything else that is purchased on credit, act as a tremendous stimulus to the economy. It creates a chain reaction of prosperity. The workmen building the houses and the cars can, in turn, afford to take out further mortgages and hire/purchase agreements and provide yet further work for others. It would appear to be a virtuous circle of prosperity. However, there are dangers. Everything depends on trust and confidence. The lender has to trust the borrower to stick to his agreements and not renege on the deals. He also has to have confidence the borrower will continue to be employed and earn money so that he can, eventually, repay the debt plus interest.

This principle is extended until we have businesses, banks and institutions lending and borrowing to and from each other and even Governments who, to try to smooth out the ups and downs of the economy, borrow in lean years and pay back in good years. (At least – they are supposed to!). A whole multitude of financial manoeuvres, all based on forms of credit, have been created. It can be seen, therefore, that there exists a very elaborate, complicated, interdependent structure of finance, underpinning National and Global prosperity. Some would say – a house of cards. I consider that an unduly pessimistic, indeed scary, point of view suggestive of imminent collapse. I prefer an analogy to a brick wall, where the removal of one brick or even a number of bricks will not necessarily bring the wall crashing down. Walls can be propped up, repaired and the cracks plastered over. Governments, Central Banks and the IMF (International Monetary Fund) have to be very vigilant and careful watching the National and World financial structures for signs of weakness and failures and act to prop up the system as necessary. If one person loses his job and fails to pay the mortgage and reneges on his HP debts it is no great disaster. The losses are absorbed by the bank or building society and, in effect, spread in small amount between many people. However, if a great number of people fail to pay (default) or go bankrupt, the losses may be such as to seriously affect the lender and it is possible for some businesses and even Building Societies and Banks to go bankrupt. Obviously, if a number of people stop paying the mortgage and the houses are repossessed it will depress the housing market. If a sufficient number of people can no longer buy cars or goods on HP then some of the workers in the car production factory may lose their jobs and they, too, reduce their spending. The biggest danger is if the majority of people lose confidence and become afraid of losing their money. They then look for secure investments. The worst thing they can do is buy gold, dig a hole in the garden and bury it. Then it is lost to the system. Until it is dug up again it might as well not exist.

In the terrible Depression that followed the Wall Street Crash of 1929, the American President – Franklin. D. Roosevelt – was faced with the enormous problem of getting the economy back on its feet again. He knew that, to do any good, money must be made to work – to circulate. A great many people in the early 1930s, desperate to preserve their capital, had invested what little they had left in gold. Instead of burying it in the garden, where there is always a small chance of someone else digging it up, they played safe (so they thought) and stashed it in deposit boxes in bank vaults. Remarkably, in 1933, in his determination to get the wheels of the economy turning, Roosevelt confiscated (without compensation) all private holdings of gold. A law was passed making it illegal for a depositor to go to a bank and access his, or her, deposit box without a representative of the F.B.I. at his shoulder to check the contents of the box. Non compliance carried the incredible penalty of ten years jail. This was an amazing breach of the property rights of the individual and is the sort of thing you might expect from some dodgy dictator of a Third World country. However, Roosevelt's attitude was that the end justifies the means and, such was his eventual success in rebuilding prosperity, that only a few people finally held it against him. (Even with such Draconian methods it was a long slow process). Incidentally I read where some Financier had recently said "The next Recession will make the 1929 Crash look like a walk in the park". Heaven help us if he is right. If you think a 20% fall in house prices would be a disaster, consider the early 1930s. Houses which previously had cost 5000 dollars sold for less than 500.

At the present time (2006/7) many Governments around the World have been irresponsible (in my opinion) and have allowed Banks, Building Societies, Businesses and the Public to get carried away on a great tide of credit, fuelling a World economic boom. Sensible policies have been abandoned! Whereas, years ago, mortgages would have been advanced at levels up to 3½ times the borrowers annual salary, Banks and Building Societies have advanced loans as high as 5 or even 6 times annual salaries and up to 120% of the value of the house (i.e. enough to purchase the house and furnish it as well). People have also been encouraged to borrow substantial sums, either on credit card accounts or as direct loans, for purchase of cars or consumer goods, often with nothing or very little offered as security. The good side of this has been rapid economic growth and expansion. The bad side is that there are great numbers of people with levels of debt they will struggle to service over the next few years and many who have no realistic chance of ever paying back their debts. We are now reaching a point where, at the very least, further borrowing has to be curtailed. This alone would create some sort of recession but, if it should be compounded by large numbers of people repudiating their debts, the situation could become very serious with large scale economic damage – businesses failing and unemployment rising. It is difficult to predict how far a correction could go. So much depends on the reactions of Governments, businesses and people.

In addition to the Worldwide credit boom there are massive imbalances in trade between Nations and budget deficits within Nations. America, for example, has enormous trade deficits, particularly with China but also with many other countries. This is compounded by large internal budget deficits. All this is particularly worrying since America is a prime powerhouse driving the World economy. We, therefore, have a situation which, at worst, could result in a global depression with massive economic disruption and mass unemployment. However, in my lifetime, I have seen a number of dangerous economic situations develop which, in the event, have turned out to be less damaging than I feared at the time. There is no doubt in my mind the current situation must end in some sort of economic downturn – probably in the next two to three years. My personal reaction will be to avoid shares and place any spare cash I have, only in the largest and most secure Banks and Institutions or in Government Bonds.

WEALTH

A great many people think it is wrong for a single individual to possess enormous wealth. Maybe they are right – but, does it really matter so much? Personally, I have never worshipped money but, as a child, I saw and experienced the soul destroying effects of poverty and this decided me, at a later date, to try to make money, by setting up and running a business. I did not dream of immense wealth – all I wanted was enough to be able to live without perpetually worrying, to have enough to live reasonably and happily, to indulge some of my fancies and, in my retirement, have a garden with flowers and ponds with fish and dragonflies. Maybe enough also to pursue my interest in angling and go fishing for salmon in Alaska. Probably the Billionaire says something similar. Enough for a mansion in the UK, another in Hawaii and one in the South of France. Maybe a few yachts and a private jet plane to get around easily.

However, is the Billionaire's wealth really so bad? Some people are Communists because they are dreamers and idealists, as evinced by the socialist mantras: "The brotherhood of man" and "To each according to his need; from each according to his ability", and so on. Many I suspect, are simply full of envious rage; they simply hate the rich and want to destroy them. However, there is only so much money a person can spend. No matter how rich, a person can only be in one place and do one thing at a time. In the spending of the wealth, jobs for other people are created; for the people who build the mansions, the people who build the yachts and the private jet plane. What happens to the rest of the billionaire's money? The worst thing he could do is to convert it into gold and bury it somewhere, then it would do nothing. Fortunately, wealthy people don't usually do that; they invest it. The money ends up in businesses or in Banks or in Financial Institutions or it is invested directly. "Making more money!" some people would sneer. They are right, but it is also invested in factories, and the machines in the factories, that enable the businesses to produce goods; to produce, in other words, jobs. It doesn't really matter whether the money comes from a Billionaire or the Government – as long as the money works – creates jobs and makes the wheels of the Nation turn. Occasionally, people get 'hooked' on making money. They think about nothing else, and cannot sleep, or maybe develop ulcers. Some are born to it and they enjoy it; to them it is just a great game; as War used to be to some people.

Rich people are not all grasping misers. Bill Gates – who has made more money than anyone else on Earth – set up a philanthropic

Foundation which sponsors development in the Third World. Warren Buffet, another Billionaire – a wizard with stocks and shares – decided this was a good idea and has transferred all his billions into the Foundation (bar a few million to live on of course). George Soros, another investment genius, is another philanthropist. He rose from being a railway porter at one time and became a multi billionaire. (He made a billion from just one operation, I remember). When the USSR collapsed he realised – if things were not sorted out quickly – there might be chaos, as there was in Germany after 1918, and another maniac dictator might arise. (In 1945 the United States, remembering what happened after 1918, helped Germany recover. They invested Billions of dollars, and today Germany is a healthy democracy). After the collapse of the USSR, nobody moved to help the millions of people experiencing economic misery in the ex-USSR countries. George Soros saw the danger! He invested billions in Soros Foundations – in nearly every ex-USSR state – to help them set up businesses and Capitalism; to show them how to do it; to become prosperous and to prevent them starving. He practically never gets any credit for it. Have you ever heard of a Soros Foundation?

As long as Billionaires pay their taxes – the same as everybody else – I don't think their wealth matters too much. Wait a moment! What did I say? As long as they pay their taxes the same as everybody else! The question is – do they? I know that any income I may receive over and above £35,000 a year is taxed at 40%. I am willing to accept this. I remember when I first started a business, the top rate of Income Tax was 97½% and, if you think that was only for millionaires, think again! By the time my income was up to £10,000 a year I was already losing 50% of the total in tax. After £20,000 I would have been in the 97½% bracket. No sane person anywhere on Earth is going to be willing to pay tax at the rate of 97½%. Think of it! Out of a thousand pounds of your earnings the taxman took £975, and left you the last twenty five pounds for yourself. I don't know who introduced that level of income tax or when, but he must have been totally out of his mind. The inevitable result was, everybody cheated and fiddled. People who had businesses or were executives used to fiddle on a grand scale. Fantastically expensive things were paid for by the firm and booked to expenses.

I remember the famous case of Lord and Lady Docker. Lord Docker used to drive about in a gold-plated Daimler car. His wife was often seen wearing her £30,000 (in those days) fur coat. They used to go to Monte Carlo and entertain friends in their fabulous yacht (heaven knows how many millions that cost). Of course, on the books, Lord Docker didn't actually own the Daimler, or the yacht, or the mansion he lived in, and Lady Docker did not legally own the fur coat; they belonged to the Company. They were just loaned (permanently) to the Dockers. This sort of thing went on all the time. Anybody who was actually paid a large salary – Film Stars for instance – fled to Switzerland and set up home there and thus paid no tax into the UK coffers at all. It took a practical person like Mrs Thatcher to sort this madness out. She brought in a sensible top rate of tax, and created rules that charged people like the Dockers for 'Benefits in Kind'. Result – most people pay their taxes and most of the fiddling has stopped.

Let us repeat the question! Do the really wealthy pay their taxes like the rest of us? I'm not so sure! I read of all these tax havens, such as the Isle of Man, the Channel Islands and the Cayman Islands, and I wonder what is going on. I always thought the Channel Islands and the Isle of Man were classed as parts of the UK – they are listed as Direct Dependencies and the Cayman Islands are a British Colony. Why then are they treated differently for tax? Why should someone who lives in the Isle of Man be taxed at a different rate to someone on the mainland? Now – I am an Engineer – not a financial expert, but I do know that Britain, and particularly London, is the financial centre of the World. I know that a fantastic amount of money is handled in International transactions, enormous profits are made, vast amounts of taxes go to the Exchequer and tens of thousands of people are employed. I note that successive UK Governments, no matter what their politics are, do nothing to change the situation. I can only conclude that the arguments for keeping the tax havens, which must be linked to the Financial Services success of the UK, are so strong that no one thinks it is sensible to rock the boat. To somebody outside the system, such as myself, it seems an anomaly that ought to be corrected. Logically, everybody should pay their taxes. There should not be a legal way of avoiding them available to the few – which is what tax havens look like to the many.

There is another crazy anomaly, the madness of the Duty Free. If I go to a shop just outside Heathrow Airport (or even in it) I pay tax on a bottle of whisky, or whatever. As soon as I step over an imaginary line on the floor of the airport I can buy 'tax free'; the same applies on a ship. This seems to me to be wrong. Either a thing should be taxed or it should not. Everybody should pay the same tax; the people who fly all the time and the people who stay at home and never fly. (Even today – there are a few). I fly all the time, sometimes I buy Duty Free, but I am not going to pretend I think it is right.

The Chancellor has to amass a certain amount of money every year, through taxation, one way or the other (Gordon Brown was a genius in 'the other'!). However, if you think about it, if he loses billions of pounds a year because of 'escapees', such as the Cayman Island boys or the Duty Free enthusiasts, (I used to know a man who – every time he travelled – homed in on the Duty Free booze like a moth to a candle flame) then the rest of the people have to make it up; it is as simple as that. If someone in the Channel Islands makes an extra million because he doesn't pay tax it is, in my mind, little different to stealing it from the rest of us. Certainly, his one million will not amount to much, for 30 million tax payers, (or whatever the number is) but there are a lot of tax dodgers. I wonder how much the Chancellor could cut our taxes by if they all paid up. However – the Chancellor probably wouldn't cut our taxes if he could, anyway! He would just spend more. On second thoughts, he would also probably say, "If it wasn't for this windfall I would have had to raise the taxes", and most of us – not all I assure you – would be thinking how lucky we were. (I hope I am not going to be sarcastic in my old age. Fortunately that's a fair way off yet. I am only 78!). Nevertheless, the question is still in my mind. Would somebody please tell me why successive Governments continue to allow Tax Havens and Duty Free Shops? There must be a reason, surely!

They used to say, "Money makes the World go around" and "The love of money is the root of all evil". What they should have said is "The love of money makes the World go around". Capitalism works! I have had experience myself. When I decided I was going to start a small manufacturing business, if at all possible, I worked like a maniac to achieve it. I worked in the day, at the Production Engineering Research Association and in the evenings, until 11 p.m., in a little workshop in a back street of Melton Mowbray. I also had a girl friend – I am human! Sometimes I tumbled into bed at 2 a.m. or later. Insomnia – what's that? I slogged for seven years to achieve 'lift off'. Fortunately, I had a very understanding boss. He was incredibly tolerant and a great friend and remains so to this day. Can you imagine anyone working like that without the incentive of money? It is possible! If you are really patriotic you may work yourself to death, (As R J Mitchell did designing his 'Spitfire'. He was convinced Britain desperately needed his plane – to stand a chance against Hitler's Messerschmidts). No doubt a lot of Russians did the same during World War Two and during the Cold War. However, the great bulk of the population will not work so hard. Ideals or no ideals!

After the Second World War, in 1945, Germany was divided. Roughly half came under Communist control and the other half under the control of the West and were, therefore, Capitalist. I remember, as a student, studying Engineering at night classes and sometimes, during breaks, discussing world matters. I remember a friend of mine saying Communism would appear to have many advantages over Capitalism, when one considered business enterprises. Consider the production of

Television sets. In the West, there would be six or more different companies all competing for the market. Six factories with six separate production lines, producing six different TV sets or probably far more. All these companies would be spending fortunes on advertising – competing against each other; inherently inefficient. Under Communism, you could have one enormous state television factory, producing a better quality product for half the price of a TV in the West, because of better efficiency and without wasting money on advertising. You must admit it sounds a convincing argument!

In the Army, I spent some time in Berlin. At that time, East Germany, or to give it its proper name – the German Democratic Republic, ('Democratic' – the Communists must have a sense of humour!) was haemorrhaging its best talent, and most able people, to West Germany; about one thousand five hundred people a day were defecting to the West through Berlin. I remember thinking – if Communism is so good why aren't they going the other way? The answer was, of course, people had a far higher standard of living in West Germany. To stop the loss of people to the West, the GDR was eventually forced to use barbed wire, watch towers, armed guards, mines and the Berlin Wall, and even then people risked their lives to come over to the West.

In East Germany, people worked under the Communist System. No private enterprise was allowed. People were paid the same whether they worked hard or not. Managers would employ far more people than they needed, because a factory is easier to run that way. If the factory ran OK and produced goods, which were sold without difficulty since customers had no alternative, why bother to improve production methods or the quality of the product. (The reason the rockets, the planes, the tanks and the guns were some of the best in the World was because, in those industries there <u>was</u> competition – with the West, and the Government was breathing down the necks of the designers, engineers and factory managers). Other than this, there was no competition to force improvement; without incentives people became casual, lazy and apathetic.

When the USSR collapsed and the Berlin Wall came down, Germans on both sides of the divide could not believe their luck. Suddenly there was a chance Germany could be reunited again and they grabbed the opportunity. The Government of West Germany was so anxious to complete the re-unification quickly – before, as they thought, the USSR might sort itself out and clamp down again – that they offered the GDR monetary unification, and offered to replace each East German Mark with one West German Mark. The GDR was in such a parlous state, they would probably have been happy with 1 West Mark for 4 GDR

Marks. Re-unification was rapidly completed; the politicians ignored the cost.

Everything in East Germany was dilapidated; the houses, the roads, the railways, the infrastructure, everything. I went there and saw it myself. There was no comparison with the prosperous West. The West poured cash into East Germany to build new infrastructure, new roads, and improve everything; to get East Germany up to the living standard of the West as quickly as possible. There was, however, one big snag. West Germans were used to working hard. They had created the West German Economic Miracle which, in the 1950's and 60's, impressed the World. When unification took place, the East Germans were delighted and poured west in their ghastly Trabant cars (those few that could afford them). They wanted the good life – the standards of the West, but they did not want the hard work. Years of Communism had destroyed the work ethic; they had become lazy. German economic growth slowed and almost stalled. Only now, after more than a decade of stagnation, is the German economy beginning to expand again.

In the USSR it was the same. Despite the May Day Parades, and the fact (so they were told) that the USA was just waiting for the opportunity to attack Russia, the people were apathetic; "Stop worrying Ivan – and pass the Vodka". In general, productivity was low. In the 1970's, the nationalised collective farms in the USSR failed to produce enough to feed the population. Millions of tons of grain had to be imported from the USA every year. As an experiment, the Government decided to relax the rules slightly and allow peasants to own a few acres of land, cultivate the land themselves, and permitted them to market the produce. It soon became apparent that the productivity of the peasant-owned land was three or four times greater than the productivity of the big collective farms.

For years there was a 'Cold War' between the West and the USSR. Most people thought it was just a turn of phrase, but it really was a war; an economic war as much as anything. In the end, the USSR collapsed; the first war in history to be won and lost without a shot (or a missile) being fired. The USSR simply could not match the economic vitality of the USA. The USSR, economically speaking, bled to death. It was made worse by the Communist mind set. We must have more of everything (Military) than anyone else. More guns, tanks, planes, A bombs, H bombs, missiles, and nuclear submarines. This, paradoxically, led to the expenditures that crippled them.

The evidence shows Capitalism works. It works because of incentives; the desire for personal betterment, wealth, more spending money and more consumer goods; a higher standard of living.

Fortunately, Capitalism has evolved. We no longer have the extreme Capitalism, where people would be thrown out on the streets and where they might be allowed to starve. We have a sort of hybrid Socialism/Capitalism; nobody is allowed to starve or go homeless; nobody is denied medical treatment; nobody is allowed to die of cold or is denied care in old age. All this is commendable, but there is a fine line to tread. Capitalism must be allowed to work! There must remain incentives, both for the individual and business. Make too much available too easily and many people will not bother to work. Millions will become 'disabled' or prefer to stay unemployed.

A few years ago, after I retired, I fished a local lake regularly during the summer. Every time I went, in the middle of the week, a young man of 20 or so was happily fishing. Eventually, I asked him what his job was. He was an honest young man. He said he had calculated that, if he worked a forty hour week and paid his taxes, he would be only £12 pounds a week better off than he was on the 'dole'. He waved his hand at the beautiful lake, on a summer's day, and said "It is worth more than £12 a week to be here, fishing, instead of working, don't you think?!" I was forced to admit to myself that, in his position, I would have almost certainly felt the same. The Government has tightened up a little now – I believe the unemployed at least have to pretend they are looking for work. I have enormous sympathy for anyone who is genuinely disabled but I think a high percentage of the millions that now claim to be disabled are simply playing the 'old game'.

Businesses must be allowed to get on with their work, and not be bedevilled with too many rules and regulations; with costs not perpetually escalated by people being allowed paternity leave, and similar concessions. Companies have to compete in world markets. Destroy their competitiveness and the firms will go and the jobs disappear with them.

THE DOTCOM/TECHNO FINANCIAL CRASH

I have mentioned the DOTCOM crash of the year 2000 under the Chapter entitled MONEY, but I have decided it justifies a chapter on its own. Every so often, from the time money was first invented, human beings with money have been carried away with a form of illogical madness, based on greed.

A classic example was the 'Tulip Mania' that occurred in Holland in the 1630's. Tulips, which had just come to the attention of the Middle and Upper Classes, as a new and exotic flower that they must have in their gardens, in order to be in fashion, had begun to be imported from Turkey and the Middle East. The demand for this flower and, particularly its bulbs grew. People began to trade in tulip bulbs, as they might in jewels or gold. The price of bulbs began to escalate, so people decided they were a good investment; buy some today and sell them tomorrow at double the price. The market took off and exploded into a classic investment bubble. Just before the 'crash' in 1637, the price of one single bulb went as high as £100,000 in today's money. Total madness! After the crash the price of bulbs fell by over 95%, never to rise to such insane heights again.

In the early 1700's, there was the 'Mississippi Scheme' in France and the 'South Sea Bubble' in England. The start of the South Sea Bubble was a company that was set up, and granted a monopoly to trade with islands in the South Seas. It seemed it might be such a profitable venture that the price of shares took off. Surprisingly this triggered a boom, not only in the original company but a general boom across the entire stock market, almost like a similar boom in 1929. The South Sea Bubble eventually collapsed leaving ruin and financial devastation in its wake.

In 1929 a similar situation developed. People became fascinated by the endless rise in stock prices; common sense went out of the window. Nobody bothered to calculate if the performance or the assets of a company justified the share price. People said, "Jump on the bandwagon! Buy today! Next week the shares will be worth double." Everybody was carried away by euphoria. Then came the Crash, and a number of financiers who lost all, or nearly all, jumped from the high buildings. The financial shock waves affected the entire world, causing a collapse of trade and world Depression. Factories closed, and millions were put out of work. The big problem, after such a financial disaster, is how to get the wheels of industry and commerce moving again. Recovery can take many years. The desperate Depression conditions in the USA in the 1930's were tackled by President Franklin D Roosevelt, who famously said, "All it needs is to prime the pump". He was right, but it is much easier said than done. It is the collapse of confidence that is, perhaps, the most damaging.

In the late 1990's, with the rapid development of the Electronics industry and, to a lesser extent, other 'Techno' businesses, Vaccines, Genetic Engineering and so on, investing in companies specialising in these fields became popular. Shares began to climb far faster than those of the general 'run of the mill', old, well established firms. More people began to invest in companies involved in the electronic revolution. The shares climbed higher – as they always will if there are more buyers than sellers. People began to notice. Almost any firm that had a name that ended 'dotcom' seemed to have its shares climbing. The rush started. Everyone wanted to be in on the bonanza. 'Dotcom' shares rocketed; greed took over. No one stopped to consider the firms – the actual businesses they represented. Buy 'dotcom' and double your money in a week, and again the following week.

An astute businessman in the USA, who had been running a small business successfully for years, but whose shares were in the doldrums because his business, although successful, did not expand, had an idea. He had noticed the 'dotcom' companies usually had fancy modern names, sometimes bordering on the ridiculous but, of course, they always finished with the letters '.com'. So he renamed his company (I cannot remember the new name but it ended dotcom). This simple trick resulted in the price of his firms shares doubling in no time. If he was clever enough to do that little manoeuvre, I feel sure he was sharp enough to sell off his shares, or the entire firm, and make a fortune.

Because of the boom in 'dotcom' companies, enthusiasm for shares in general grew. The Dow Jones and the British F.T.S.E. and every other Bourse in the world climbed, though at a lesser pace. I watched what was happening with interest, and then foreboding. This was beginning to look dangerous. The more I read about the 'dotcom' companies the more obvious it was that a classic financial bubble was developing.

As I have stated elsewhere in this book, I cannot make money in these situations. When prices are crazy, and bear no relation to the real value of a business, I cannot buy. I expect the shares to fall back or collapse every day – but they do not; they still climb. My brother mentioned the boom to me; I warned him off. I told him that, when the crash came, it would come fast; he would not be able to get out. No one would answer his telephone calls or his Emails. He would not be able to sell and would just watch the price fall into the ground. He agreed and left 'dotcoms' alone. In late 1999 I started to keep a file with newspaper cuttings. The file was headed – "Run Up to the DotCom/Techno Crash."

Let us, for a moment, consider the ownership of shares. You pay money and what do you own? A few pieces of paper which say you own so many shares in such and such a company. The shares entitle you to a part of the company's profit – which is paid to you, usually annually, as a dividend. Originally, when a company is founded, the money you pay goes into setting up the firm, and getting it to run as a viable profit-making business. After that, any share transactions are a buying/selling transfer of the shares from one person to another, or one Institution to another. This is a bargaining transaction and depends entirely on what the buyer thinks, or calculates, the shares are worth.

As a simple guide to the value of a share in say, an old established company, ask yourself what is the return on the investment. If you had £10,000 to invest, you might place it in a secure deposit – in a bank for instance – at 5% return. The money you place in the bank is actually loaned to the bank and they will lend it to somebody else. Many people do not seem to realise this. If a bank went bankrupt you could lose your money, the same as if you loaned it to any other business. (To give confidence the banks have a guarantee system – but only up to a certain level). Alternatively, you might invest your £10,000 in a Brewery or an Armaments Manufacturer by buying their shares. However, many businesses are far less secure and safe than a Bank (I once invested in Rolls Royce and lost my money – Rolls Royce went bust). So, logically, when a firm pays a dividend on your shares, the income should be better than the return you would expect from a bank, say 1% or 2%, or more, than a bank would pay, depending on the degree of risk. Why risk your money otherwise? In fact, of course, a number of other things might affect the value of the shares – for example – the value of the firm's assets; what is its potential for the future? – and so on. Maybe the firm will take off and its profits skyrocket. So you might decide to gamble on the future of the firm.

If you invest your £10,000 in shares of a firm, along with a thousand other investors, and the shares double in price – you will feel rich, and may say, "Great! I have made £10,000." All the other investors tell themselves the same thing, but it is an illusion. Where do you think all the extra millions came from? Nowhere! The answer is, of course, there is no extra money at all. You just think there is. Everybody feels rich. However, the only way you can get your hands on real money is to sell your shares. To do that, you must find somebody willing to buy. Until you do, all you have are the same pieces of paper – the shares – that you had before the price went up. While there are a lot of people wanting

287

to buy the shares and only a few willing to sell – the price will go up; but as soon as there are a lot of people wanting to sell, and only a few interested in buying, the price will fall. So as soon as you sell – and maybe a few others do too – the price is likely to fall. A few more sell – the price drops further. To the majority of the people who haven't sold their shares their magical gains have suddenly melted away. They no longer feel rich. The illusion is destroyed! The only way you make money when shares go up, is to sell to someone who is willing to buy them while they are high. The very act of selling usually drops the price. The greater the number of shares sold the greater the fall.

Some professional investors are very good at share dealing. They watch the shares day and night; they watch the progress and assets of the businesses behind the shares; above all – they know investor psychology and they move in and out of shares fast – much faster than you and I can do it; they trade sometimes during the night (out of hours trading) and even make profits when shares fall. If they decide that a firms shares are likely to fall, they sell shares they don't even possess ('selling short'). When the shares have fallen – then they buy them cheaply – to fulfil their obligations. There are many other similar manoeuvres. Many professional investors, these days, work with computers, which are programmed to indicate 'buy' or 'sell' when they pick up indications – trends or fluctuations in the market. The danger of this, of course, is that a host of computers will all be signalling 'buy' or 'sell' at the same time leading to extreme and excessive fluctuations in share price values.

I kept my eye on the 'dotcom' situation and, as it became more and more precarious, I made sure neither I nor my brother could be affected by a crash. That meant not only did we not invest in 'dotcom' shares ourselves but that nothing connected with us – Pension Funds, etc – were invested in shares, of any kind, either. Pension Funds were transferred to Bank Deposits – despite some people suggesting this was a mistake – "shares were doing so well!"

In my file I have many newspaper cuttings; some with my scribbled comments. Somebody launched a travel agency – 'Last Minute 'DotCom'. I could not see that it was anything more than a travel agency, and travel agents don't usually make too many millions, there is too much competition. Incredibly the shares raced away. In no time the shares of the business were valued at £500 million, and more. Somebody launched an 'on-line' bookshop 'Amazon DotCom'. The shares rocketed until they were worth over £1 billion. The amazing thing is they did this despite the fact the bookshop actually ran at a loss at the time.

I spoke to an American who had a fortune invested in DotCom companies. He was so rich it was untrue – at least he thought he was! In the event he did not get out – did not sell before the crash. He lost 97% of his capital. The people who had invested directly into DotCom shares were affected most, of course, and made the biggest losses but, unfortunately, a collapse of this nature frightens everybody and stocks and shares, in general, take a pounding. Shares in perfectly good old established firms also fell – to a lesser degree. The losses were not as great as the DotCom Companies but a fall of 30% to 50% can still be very painful.

The real tragedy of course, is that millions of ordinary people, who really had no idea what was going on, lost immense amounts in the Crash – mainly in the value of their Pension Funds but also in other, managed, funds. Imagine yourself a financial manager – a funds manager – one of those people who looks after Pension Funds. They handle billions of pounds and dollars in funds, and are supposed to invest them, using all their skill and knowledge, to get the best return and boost the funds that, one day, will provide the investor with his well earned pension. As a funds manager you are faced with a decision – whether to invest your client's money (all those thousands of 'would be pensioners' money) in steadily performing, everyday, stocks, and shares, or in this new DotCom boom. If you invest cautiously, and other managers go into DotComs and double their client's money, you will be castigated. Nobody will think of the risk. Better to 'go with the herd'; you then cannot lose; if they win you win. More importantly, if you lose they lose – and you can say to your clients, "Terrible this DotCom crash. I'm afraid you have lost half your money – of course so has everybody else. We all suffer!" And you would keep your job. Naturally, this is what happens.

In America, Warren Buffet, acknowledged one of the worlds greatest investment 'gurus', told his many clients he would not invest their money in crazy DotCom Stocks. Many of his clients deserted him – their friends were making fortunes with somebody else – or so they thought. When the crash finally came, the total losses are said to have been in trillions – about 5 trillion dollars – worldwide. (A trillion is a thousand billion or a million, million – whichever you prefer). I was greatly afraid a crash of this magnitude would trigger a world recession or a full scale Depression; I am still amazed that it did not. However, it caused enormous damage nevertheless. Millions of people found their pension funds drastically reduced. People, who had calculated on retiring with a decent pension, suddenly found the pension they would really get would only be a fraction of what they expected. This, not to beat about the bush, is totally wrong. The DotCom crash should never have been allowed to happen. If an ordinary Engineer like myself can see what is coming then the experts who advise Governments should. I blame Governments fair and square.

In this day and age financial bubbles like the DotCom bust, simply should not be allowed to happen. Governments are supposed to Govern! There should be rules and regulations and regulatory bodies that could step in and stop share trading, when such trading is obviously ridiculous and totally out of touch with business reality. Governments have a responsibility to their people. You could argue that it does not matter too much if a few billionaires get their fingers burned, but what about the millions of ordinary people – who have worked, and saved, and paid their contributions into Pension Funds. People who have worked hard all their lives, and deserve to be able to relax and be happy and have a reasonable income in retirement. They should have been protected. Governments must and should, in the future, ensure that such a financial debacle can never happen again.

At the time of writing, stock markets, in general, have recovered to the levels they were before the 'Dotcom' crash. (They are still 20% down if you allow for inflation). The Dotcoms, of course, have not but they have improved a little above the extreme lows reached after the crash (those 'Dotcoms' that survived that is). So Pension funds seem to have recovered most of the losses incurred in the crash. Obviously, because of the damage caused by the Dotcom debacle, the funds would have been higher had the crash not occurred. The worst hit pensioners were those who took retirement and their pensions immediately or shortly after the crash.

At the present time several factors have combined to create a situation where pensions taken today are far lower than they were a few years ago. (For example a person retiring at age 65 in 1990 with a pension 'pot' of £200,000 would have been able to purchase an annuity of around £26,000 a year whereas a person today (2006) would only get an annuity of £13,000 for the same £200,000 which, incidentally, allowing for inflation, is only worth £8,000 in 1990 prices). One of the reasons is that pension providers i.e. Insurance Companies, woke up to the fact that people are living far longer than they used to do and will, therefore, be taking a pension for a longer period of time. Another factor is that Bank of England interest rates are lower and so are yields on Government Bonds. Finally, of course, the Chancellor – Gordon Brown – has guaranteed that pensioners of the future will be worse off by raiding the funds and extracting 5 to 6 billion pounds from the funds each and every year. It is more important than ever, therefore, that pension funds are invested efficiently and grow to the highest possible figure to compensate for these effects and provide a decent annuity in retirement. The last thing we need are Dotcom calamities and such like which affect the final value of pension funds.

THE GREATEST SHUTTLE DISASTER

The greatest disaster to befall the space program is the failure of the Space Shuttle. I do not mean the destruction of the Challenger and Columbia space shuttles. They were awful disasters, to be sure, but they did not threaten the whole future of space development and exploration. The failure of the shuttle concept does!

When the shuttle program was first announced and I saw details of the proposals, I knew this was the great step forward, the quantum leap that would enable the exploitation of space to take off. I recognised that the old method of using an enormous machine, all of which was scrapped in the process, to deliver a few tons of payload into orbit, would always be hopelessly expensive and limited. The sheer cost per ton into orbit would always be so great as to curtail development and limit space activities. So, when I saw the drawings and details of the shuttle, I knew – this is it – the "Key to Space". A shuttle vehicle that would slash the cost of payload into orbit to one twentieth of the cost incurred by using a Soyuz or Saturn type of launcher. This was the way ahead. NASA had really pulled out the ace!

Let us consider the economics. The Saturn 5 and Soyuz used an enormous and expensive booster, with very costly liquid fuel engines, turbo pumps, control systems, navigation gear, and so on; all of which are jettisoned – scrapped – during the flight. The second stage is a smaller repeat of the main booster. High efficiency liquid hydrogen-oxygen engines, turbo pumps, control systems – all again jettisoned before the final payload is delivered into orbit. The entire enormous cost of building the launch vehicle is lost – simply to place a few tons in orbit. The turbo pumps alone are expensive miracles of engineering. On the Saturn 5 each massive engine on the main booster (there were 5 of these) produced 750 tons thrust. Each engine burned 1½ tons of fuel per second. This fuel had to be pumped through small holes into the combustion chamber, against a backpressure of over 1000lbs/sq inch. The power required to force the fuel into the chamber was immense. The pumps had to be small – as compact as possible to minimise the weight. The turbo pumps on the Saturn 5 developed around 100,000 horsepower from a volume no bigger than a 4ft (1.2m) cube. Engines, gimbals, fuel pumps, control systems – all incredibly expensive and repeated stage upon stage – all thrown away to deliver a small payload into orbit. A hopelessly expensive way to get into space. How far do you think commercial aviation would have developed if, after every flight to America from London, you had to scrap the plane and build another? There would be no commercial aviation.

The only flights would be government-sponsored novelties. That was the situation, and was recognised as such, when the shuttle concept was proposed.

The space shuttle would be a space plane in the true sense of the word. All the expensive gear – the oxy/hydrogen engines, the turbo pumps, the control systems, the computers – every expensive item would be in the plane and would be reused time and time again – as on a Boeing 747 jumbo jet. The main boosters would be simple, giant, November the fifth style, rockets with a casing full of solid fuel. Even with these, the casings would be reused. When the fuel was expended, they would fall into the sea on parachutes for recovery and reuse. Only one item would truly be lost on each launch and that was simply a fuel tank. Large, it is true, but still a simple fuel tank. The shuttle would be used over and over again – like a commercial aircraft. Bring it down, place the next payload aboard, hoist it back up on another fuel tank and booster assembly and, off you go. With four of these space planes you could launch once a week – twice a week maybe. I knew – when I saw the design – this was the breakthrough. This was the future! This was the design that would change the whole future of space exploitation – both commercial and exploration. This first space shuttle would drastically slash the cost of placing payload in orbit.

I am not a rocket engineer but I understand the basic principles and was surprised when I discovered the shuttle vehicle (orbiter) main engines would be fired up on the launch pad, just before the solid boosters were ignited, and would continue firing all through the boost phase. The shuttle engines are high performance oxygen/hydrogen engines whereas the big solid fuel main boosters are high thrust but relatively low efficiency rockets. It is generally considered that it is better to use the big, low efficiency boosters to get the assembly off the ground and on its way before firing the high efficiency oxy/hydrogen engines for the final push to Orbit. The old Saturn 5 used this principle to send the astronauts to the Moon. The Saturn was lifted off the ground using 5 enormous, 750 ton thrust, low efficiency, paraffin/oxygen engines giving 3750 tons total thrust. Only when these engines stopped firing and the lower booster stage fell away was the oxy/hydrogen engine of the second stage fired up to propel the upper stages to orbit. In the case of the shuttle the three oxy/hydrogen engines produce a total of 530 tons thrust whereas the two solid fuel boosters produce, between them, 2500 tons thrust at lift-off giving a grand total of 3030 tons thrust. The orbiter engines, therefore, only produce 17½% of the total thrust at lift off. The boosters burn for 2 minutes before falling away and the orbiter engines continue to fire for a further 6 minutes to accelerate the craft to the 17,300 mph (27,843km) needed for orbit. It follows therefore that 25% of the oxygen and hydrogen in the big fuel tank is consumed before the boosters fall away.

If the solid boosters could be designed to produce 17½% more thrust at lift-off and the orbiter engines were only ignited when the boosters had fallen away then, at this point, the big fuel tank would be 100% full. This, I estimate, would roughly double the weight of payload which could be taken to orbit, thereby reducing the cost of payload to orbit still further. The big boosters are constructed from a number of segments (7), containing the solid fuel, to form a stack with a shaped hole down the centre from top to bottom. In other words, all seven segments are burning together to produce the hot gas which issues from the rocket nozzle to produce the thrust. If two more fuel segments were added to the booster then thrust would be increased by over 28% for the same burning time. It would be necessary, of course, to increase the size of the rocket nozzle, by 28% on the cross sectional area to allow for the extra flow of gas. The diameter of the boosters would stay the same. Since the orbiter engines would not fire on lift-off it would be necessary to shift the attachment points of the boosters on the big fuel tank a short distance towards the orbiter to correct the imbalance that would otherwise occur. Steering of such a modified design should be no problem during the boost phase since the rocket nozzles on the boosters are already designed to be moveable for guidance purposes. Since the space shuttle represents a masterpiece of engineering there must, I assume, be a very good reason why this enhanced performance design was not adopted. Safety (for the Astronauts) perhaps? I do not know but the Saturn 5 worked perfectly well to place men on the Moon. The Ariane and Russian satellite launchers also fire up the oxy/hydrogen engines after the main booster falls away.

Nevertheless, this apparent discrepancy didn't bother me. I knew that, sooner or later, the problem, whatever it was, would be solved and they would go to a maximum efficiency design – or someone else would – in another country. The key thing was for the shuttle to work. I carefully considered the shuttle potential. I estimated that a cargo shuttle just 35% larger than the existing design, but with no crew compartment and, instead, an enlarged cargo bay, and using the more efficient system I have described, whereby the shuttle's oxy/hydrogen engines are only started after the solid fuel boosters have fallen away, could deliver a payload of maybe as much as 100 tons into low Earth orbit. This is as much as the mighty Saturn 5 Apollo moon rocket achieved, but would be done at maybe as little as one thirtieth of the cost. This could be done automatically – no crew would be needed. I knew this was possible but, later, the Russians proved it by launching an unmanned BURAN shuttle 'copy' into orbit and bringing it safely back to land on a runway – totally automatically.

I imagined that, in the near future, freight shuttles would roar into the sky, deliver 100 tons to orbit and return for another load. I also knew that, with a little ingenuity – the business of astronauts space walking with spanners and screwdrivers could be dispensed with. You could design an automatically self-assembling space station or spacecraft – the pieces being located, clamped and welded together, with no more than two or three robotic devices to do the job. A massive space station, like Arthur C Clarke's "Wheel", could be assembled without human intervention and the astronauts, when they arrived, would find that all they needed to do was sort out the interior and furnish it to their satisfaction. Massive spacecraft – to go to the moon or Mars or anywhere else in the solar system would, likewise, be assembled in orbit. My own suggestion, the interstellar spacecraft 'GENESIS', (See Chapter – COLONISING THE STARS AND THE 'GENESIS' SPACECRAFT) could have been built with just a few shuttle freighter loads. The new shuttle design promised to be the breakthrough to a new era of space activity.

I find it hard to believe that all these dreams have come to nothing. NASA have announced the whole 'Shuttle Program' is being scrapped. I have thought about it carefully and have come to the conclusion that it can only be because the heat protection problem cannot be solved. The hellish friction and searing heat caused by re-entering the Earth's atmosphere at 17,000 miles per hour (27,360km) must be the unbeatable problem. Nobody, neither the public nor the politicians, seems to grasp the immense loss the shuttle failure and cancellation represents. NASA must know – but they are keeping quiet. I know, and I have decided to spell it out. If the shuttle had worked, any nation wishing to have a presence in space would have had to adopt a similar approach (the Russians immediately saw the potential and produced their 'BURAN' – a shuttle look alike). I visualised a future where Europe, Russia, Japan, China and India would all be operating shuttles – large and small; the NASA shuttle was simply the first. Shuttles would roar off their launch pads – somewhere – every week or, more likely, every day. Space development would boom. British Engineers began to realise the potential of a reusable shuttle, and produced proposals for a new space plane design – 'HOTOL' – which is an acronym for Horizontal Take Off and Landing. The idea was to have a space shuttle that took off and landed on a conventional runway, like a passenger jet liner. The machine would be entirely self-contained. It would take off and accelerate to high speed using a special type of air breathing engine (a kind of super jet engine) and only use pure rocket motors for the final boost into orbit.

Like the American 'Shuttle' it would, of course, have to withstand the searing heat of re-entering the atmosphere at 17,000 mph (27,360km).

After seeing the first drawings and details of the shuttle design, I was convinced, and thought we really might yet see a space station like Arthur C Clarke's great "Wheel" in the film "2001". We really might see a permanent manned base on the moon. Later I went to see an IMAX film in Bradford called 'The Dream is Alive' and I thought, Yes! The shuttle could make it so. What I have described would have happened. Everybody would have been designing shuttles – bigger, better, more efficient. The cost of delivering payload to orbit might, eventually, have been reduced to as little as one fortieth or less of the cost of the old way. Sadly, this dream has failed!

The 'Challenger' disaster was a disaster that should never have happened. It was a relatively simple failure of a rubber-sealing ring on one of the big solid fuel boosters; a problem that could undoubtedly be solved by a new seal design. You could consider the 'Challenger' disaster as like the crashing of a prototype airliner. A disaster, but it would not stop the development of airliners. The second shuttle disaster, the 'Columbia' – was a similar, avoidable disaster, curable by redesign. Again, not in itself anything to stop the overall development of space shuttles. The real disaster – the one that has finally sounded the death knell of the whole American shuttle program – and everyone else's as well, is far deeper and totally overwhelming. It is the insuperable problem of adequately protecting the shuttle against the friction and searing heat of re-entry from space.

To deliver payload into low Earth Orbit, any shuttle or rocket must reach a speed of 17,300 miles (27,843km) per hour. Below that speed the vehicle and its payload will fall back to Earth. There is no way around this. It is 17,300 mph (27,843km), or higher, if the payload is to stay in orbit for any length of time. So the shuttle, having delivered its payload, must slow down a little and re-enter the Earth's atmosphere at around 17,000 mph (27,360km).

Richard Branson's 'spaceship' is merely a novelty. A number of fare paying passengers will climb aboard, be boosted vertically for 150 miles (241.40 kilometres) or so, spend a couple of minutes in free fall after the engines have stopped and the craft coasts up to the top of its climb and starts to fall back. 100,000 dollars plus sounds a lot of money to me for a few minutes free fall and a quick look at the Earth from 150 miles (241.40 kilometres) high. Some people have been fooled into thinking this is a new breakthrough into cheap space travel which it most certainly is not. It is far simpler to zoom vertically upwards and fall back than it is to go up 200 miles (322 kilometres) and at the same time accelerate up to the 17,300 miles (27,840 kilometres) per hour needed to stay in orbit.

Friction with the air generates enormous temperatures. The leading edges of the wings, and the nose and belly of the shuttle, will be heated white hot on re-entry. Back on Earth even the Concorde supersonic airliner, made of aluminium, could not have flown much faster than it did, (1,200 miles (1,931 kilometres) per hour) because frictional heating would have weakened the aluminium. To fly faster the plane would need to be made of more heat resistant materials. America's fantastic futuristic supersonic bomber – the Valkyrie – which flew at 2,000 miles (3,219 kilometres) per hour at 80,000 feet (24,384 metres) altitude had to be built of titanium and stainless steel to withstand the 600° F friction temperatures generated in flight. (Note – only two prototypes were ever built and flown).

I am of the opinion that protecting the shuttle, against the friction and terrific heat generated by re-entry, must be the insurmountable problem that has wrecked the shuttle program. NASA is only too well aware of the situation, and so are the Russians. Whoever cracks this problem, cracks the primary problem of space travel. Both NASA and the Russians (Chinese and Japanese too, for all I know) must have worked and tried every possible, imaginable, heat resisting coating. And they appear to have failed! The best that NASA could come up with was a foamed silica tile. In all fairness, this was a remarkable achievement. The foam tile can withstand terrific heat and, very importantly, it does not transmit the heat to the thermally sensitive aluminium underneath. It looked as though NASA had solved the problem. However, it was not so! The foam silica tiles are hopelessly fragile. When the shuttle returned to Earth, after delivering it's payload into orbit, it could not simply be reloaded, mated with a new tank and boosters and launched back into orbit, as originally intended. It has to be refurbished – every time. We have seen that this process, instead of taking a week for refurbishing, reloading and mounting on the next tank/booster assembly, as originally envisaged, actually takes months. No one has ever said why it takes such an interminable time. My guess is, it must be the tiles. I can see no other explanation. The tiles must be eroded on re-entry and many of them must need replacing. I read somewhere that the shuttle was fitted with over 30,000 refractory tiles – every one individually shaped to fit precisely into position and perfectly resin bonded to the aluminium skin. (No wonder an astronaut jokingly referred to the shuttle as "the flying brickyard"). If this is the case and if, say, 20% of the tiles needed renewing after every flight, we begin to grasp what would be involved. Damaged or eroded tiles would have to be carefully removed. The used resin bonding agent –

which cannot be removed with a solvent – would have to be laboriously and very carefully abraded off, right down to the metal skin, but without damaging or reducing the thickness of the underlying aluminium. Then, new tiles – every one individually shaped – would have to be made and carefully, precisely, bonded into position.

Now we begin to understand the magnitude of the problem. Now we begin to understand why it takes 6 months, or more, to refurbish just one shuttle, and why each shuttle flies just once a year instead of once a fortnight. Now we begin to understand why they are scrapping a space vehicle that held such tremendous promise. Instead of a launch every week – what has been the real experience? A launch every six months – and this is despite having four launch vehicles. The inevitable result is – instead of reducing the cost of payload to orbit to one twentieth of the old rocket costs – it is actually even more expensive. So expensive, in fact, that it is cheaper to use the old style Ariane or Russian Soyuz. The Russians abandoned their shuttle copy – the Buran – after just one flight. (No doubt they had also copied NASA's silica tiles). NASA now says it is going to scrap the whole shuttle program, and go back to the old, crude, non re-useable, one shot, totally wasteful and inherently expensive way, to place payload in orbit. That is the measure of the failure of the shuttle program.

NASA must be utterly convinced the shuttle is non-viable. The problems really must be insurmountable. The shuttle was of such enormous importance and had such tremendous potential. The scrapping of the whole shuttle program is such a momentous failure, I am stunned! The whole future of space exploration and exploitation is changed. Unless someone produces a viable, cheap way to place payload in orbit, in some manner like the original shuttle idea, then the whole future of the space industry will be drastically curtailed. If there is no better way to place payload in orbit than a Russian Soyuz, or a Saturn 5 type multi-stage booster, then we can say goodbye to Arthur C Clarke's great "Wheel" of a space station; goodbye to Professor O'Neill's fancy 'Space Colonies'; goodbye to long term space colonies on the Moon or Mars. That is the meaning of the greatest space disaster ever – the failure of the space shuttle as a cheap means of placing payload in orbit.

I had hoped that, even if NASA did not come up with the answer to the thermal protection problem, someone else would – some spray-on ablative coating perhaps or a combination of thinner tiles and a spray-on outer coating. Every space organisation on Earth must be aware of how important the shuttle concept was. If the Russians, French, Japanese or Chinese solved the problem of re-entry protection, they would lead the world and open up a new era of space technology, exploration and industry. No one, so far, has been able to do it. From now on all space operations will be constrained – strangled – by the sheer cost of placing payload in orbit. (At the present time it costs around ten thousand dollars just to take a half litre container of drinking water to the Space Station or twenty million dollars to deliver a ton of supplies).

It is, as we know, possible to produce an ablation shield that will protect a returning spacecraft once, even at much higher re-entry speeds. (The Apollo spacecraft came back from the moon and re-entered Earth's atmosphere at nearly 25,000 mph (40,232km)). It is only a question of how thick you make the shield – which burns away during re-entry. To produce a shield that will do the job, not once but many times, without burning away at all, seems not to be possible – or I would have expected it to have been done by now. If it was at all possible, the shuttle project would not have been abandoned. Certainly, awful though they were, the two shuttle disasters would never have been allowed to prevent further development, any more than aircraft disasters do, although they involve much greater numbers of people.

NASA is quietly getting on with its work. Obviously they are not going to proclaim failure from the rooftops. President Bush has asked them to undertake to create a base on the moon and send men to Mars. If the original shuttle idea had worked, these projects would have been relatively easy and not too costly. Shuttles would have simply ferried parts and fuel up into orbit, where the components would be assembled and fuelled, and – away you go to the Moon or Mars. Now, components and fuel tanks will have to be ferried up into orbit, and assembled to make the Mars spacecraft, using multiple launches of old type expensive boosters, otherwise they would need a rocket which would make the Saturn 5 look small. The same 'assembly in orbit' technique will have to be carried out for the Moon Base Project. Without the shuttle, the costs of both the Moon and Mars projects will be horrendous. At least the Mars trip will be a one off!

The Moon Base could end up being an endless, colossal, burden and drain on NASA's resources (funded by US taxpayers) as the Space Station already is. At maybe 100 billion dollars cost or more, it seems to me it will be merely another very expensive novelty. Maybe the next US President will cancel the Moon/Mars projects when he realises the costs, but there is a problem; so many people now work at NASA and the myriad of supply companies. Those people must be kept in work – even if the product is basically useless. The Mars trip seems to me to be merely a rerun of the Moon landing – with a US flag on Mars instead of the Moon – but at far greater cost and a far greater risk of disaster. The Moon Base would mean immense expenditure just to keep people alive there, with spacecraft regularly ferrying supplies and replacement crew. Has anybody worked out the cost, per ton, of delivering payload to the Moon?

I feel very sad about the shuttle's demise. I would have liked to have seen far more exploratory vehicles going out to the different planets and moons. I mean robot type vehicles of course; ones you can forget when they have done their job. More space telescopes; maybe an array of space telescopes, 100 miles or more apart, that could work together and give us the resolution to actually see Earth sized planets around other stars, and perhaps detect water or oxygen. I would have liked to have seen some project like my suggested interstellar spacecraft 'GENESIS'. We could have done all these things, and more, if the shuttle had been successful in the manner for which it was designed. Now we will be restricted to what can be expensively boosted into orbit the old way.

Doing things the old way means we will never see a giant space station or massive Moon Base – as per the film "2001". The same applies to Professor O'Neill's grandiose schemes of space colonies, with tens of thousands of people in space, and any idea we might have had of sending massive spacecraft to the stars. (The latter were a 'No-No' even with space shuttle economics). All these things are now relegated to the realms of Science Fiction. If they never crack the re-entry problem for shuttle type vehicles I foresee that, in a hundred years time, all ideas of human colonies on the Moon or Mars or anywhere else in the Solar System will have been abandoned. The main space effort will be restricted to communication satellites and more practical, lightweight, robotic probes and devices to explore the planets. I think all dreams of large groups of humans living indefinitely in space or on other planets will remain unfulfilled; the practicalities being too expensive and inefficient.

PRESIDENT BUSH'S MOON BASE AND MANNED TRIP TO MARS

President George W Bush has instructed NASA to prepare plans and work on two new projects. The first proposal is for a permanently manned base on the Moon. The second is for a manned trip to Mars.

It must be admitted that the successful completion of these two projects would represent the most remarkable and impressive Scientific and Engineering achievements of all time. However, before we applaud these ventures, let us pause and carefully consider the problems, the cost and the implications.

I was surprised when I read a few more details of the proposals. Apparently the idea is to set up a manned base on the Moon and then use this base as a 'stepping stone', firstly for a manned trip to Mars and then to other places. President Bush has said "We are going to the Cosmos". I translate this as meaning we are going to the stars.

If we were, indeed, going to build a massive spacecraft to take human beings to colonise a planet around another star, the Moon base would make good sense. If equipment could be set up on the Moon to make rocket fuel for the journey, it would be much easier, energy wise, to lift it into orbit around the Moon, i.e. into space, ready to go, than it would be to do the same thing working from the Earth. The Moon has only one sixth Earth's gravity and no air.

What amazes me is how many people seem to think the human race is going to go to the stars. Even Professor Hawking – one of our great Mathematicians and Cosmologists has suggested "We must colonise the stars as an insurance policy against disaster here on Earth". All this when a simple rational analysis – such as I have done in the Chapter – 'COLONISING THE STARS AND THE GENESIS SPACECRAFT' demonstrates that it is an utterly impractical idea. The conclusion of the Chapter is that it is unrealistic to the point of being impossible for human beings to travel to, and colonise planets around, other stars. We are simply not going to be able to do it! So, if we are not going to the stars then to go to all the expense and trouble to set a rocket fuel factory on the Moon, purely to fuel a trip to Mars makes no sense. It would be far simpler and cheaper to go to Mars directly from the Earth – a sort of scaled up Apollo mission, but to Mars instead of the Moon. On this basis I have assumed that, if the Mars trip is undertaken, it will be done working from Earth orbit rather than from a Moon Base. I intend, therefore, to analyse the requirements as being for two independent projects – the Moon Base and Trip to Mars. If both projects were undertaken, the only connection would be the use of similar boosters and, perhaps, some spacecraft modules for the two projects.

Firstly – let us consider The Mars trip. In effect, the Mars proposal would be a repeat of President Kennedy's manned Moon landing project of the late 1960's, but with human beings travelling to and landing on Mars instead of the Moon. Although, superficially, the Mars trip would follow a similar pattern to the Moon project there would be substantial differences. Instead of a trip of a few days the Mars expedition would take probably eighteen months or more to complete. (The absolute minimum is seventeen months). Also Mars is bigger than the Moon with a greater gravity pull. (At the surface, Mars gravity is 2.3 times greater than the Moon). It also has an atmosphere (thin though it is) where the Moon has none. The Mars trip is, therefore, going to be far more difficult and complicated.

I would expect the spacecraft which leaves the Earth to go to Mars to be based on the successful system which took men to the Moon and back. It will probably consist of an assembly of four modules. There will be a Command Module – with crew accommodation and living quarters, complete with shower, toilet and exercising equipment. Attached to this will be the Mars Lander – the section that will actually descend to the Martian surface. Attached to the lander, and which will go to the Martian surface with it, will be the Ascent Vehicle – to take the Astronauts back to the orbiting Command Module when the ground phase of the expedition is finished. Finally there will be an Earth re-entry Module, similar to the Apollo capsule, for the crew to enter the atmosphere and plunge back to Earth at the end of the mission – probably to be picked up from the sea in the Apollo fashion but possibly coming down on land, with the landing cushioned by retro-rockets, Russian style. With the exception of the Earth re-entry Module the assemblies will need to be considerably larger and heavier than for the Apollo project.

In the Command Module, everything will have to be scaled up. The living quarters of the crew, for their several months trip to Mars, and, later, their several months trip back to Earth, will have to be big enough to let them move about, exercise, have showers and use toilets. They will have to take large quantities of food although water can be recycled. There will have to be oxygen regenerating equipment and maybe even laundry facilities. Then there will be another module – the Mars Lander which will need to be far larger, more complicated and heavier than the Moon lander. It will need to carry far more fuel to get down and, since the Astronauts are likely to be on Mars surface for months, not days, it will need to incorporate living space, showers, toilet facilities and considerable supplies of food. Ideally, if the Astronauts are really going to have scope to explore Mars, they will need a 'Moon Buggy' type vehicle, drilling equipment, etc.

I am not sure how they will handle the initial descent problem because of the atmosphere. One way would be to use rockets to slow the lander down, while it was at orbital height, to near ground speed and then drop almost straight down. This would reduce atmospheric effects to a minimum but use an excessive amount of fuel. On the other hand, to minimise the amount of fuel required, the craft could use aero-braking to slow down, only using rockets for the final landing phase. However, this would need special design of the lander to handle aerodynamic forces and frictional heating. Entry speeds on Mars would be considerably lower than the Shuttle entry speed on Earth, because of Mars' lower gravitational field, but, nevertheless, even with Mars thin air, high aerodynamic pressures and frictional heating would occur. The Lander would enter Mars' outer atmosphere at a speed of over 7,000 miles (11,265 kilometres) per hour.

Attached to the lander, in a similar manner to Apollo, would be the Ascent Module, to take the Astronauts back up into orbit when the ground mission is finished. This module, whilst similar to the Apollo ascent module would, nevertheless, have to be bigger and heavier. It would have to carry far more fuel to leave the surface and reach the Command Module in Mars' orbit and be designed to handle some degree of aerodynamic forces during acceleration.

The Apollo had a crew of three. Two descended to the Moon surface and the third man stayed in orbit in the Command Module. If this was done on the Mars trip, the third man would be on his own, in orbit, for months. It would seem sensible, therefore, to limit the crew of the Mars expedition to just two, who would go down to Mars surface and leave the Command Module in orbit under automatic control. This would reduce fuel and food requirements and make the whole project simpler.

Assuming all goes well and the Astronauts complete their mission, return to the Command Module and return to Earth, a fourth Module will be required which could simply be a copy of the Apollo lunar Earth re-entry Capsule in which case they will plunge down into the sea as before. NASA might decide, however, to be more sophisticated this time and have the capsule descend on land, cushioned by retro-rockets, as the Russians do.

The spacecraft assembly which leaves Earth for Mars will, therefore, be far larger and heavier than the Apollo assembly. To launch such a spacecraft as a one off shot, like Apollo II, would need a gigantic rocket that would dwarf the Saturn V. Logically, therefore, the various components will be placed in Earth orbit by a number of separate rocket launches and the components assembled in orbit. A side effect of this approach is that all the components and modules will have to be duplicated, when they are made, on the ground, otherwise the failure of just one rocket, and the loss of its cargo, would jeopardise the whole mission. Some form of back-up with spare components is, therefore, essential.

I have analysed the Mars Project in some detail to demonstrate that it is an enormous, complicated, extremely difficult and of course, a very expensive project, on its own, with out undertaking the Moon Base Project. If the Mars project was successful it would, without a doubt, be a remarkable achievement. Since the Astronauts would be on Mars for months, not days, and assuming they have suitable equipment, it is probable they would make some interesting discoveries and produce a lot of scientific data. Most importantly it would prove the USA was still top, technologically, and America would go down in the history books as the first nation to land their people on another planet. There is, of course, only ever one first time. Another important factor is that it would keep NASA, its suppliers and probably 100,000 or more people in work and preserve a winning team. If you once break up an organisation like NASA, it would be almost impossible to rebuild it, if you ever needed to. The big question is – "Is it all worth the hundred billion dollars plus, that it will probably cost"? I know, of course, that if they go ahead and do it I will be glued to the TV screen as I was in 1969.

However, because of the time factors – the long trip out, the long stay on the ground (the expedition will have to wait until Mars is in the right place in its orbit before they can launch to come back to Earth), the long trip back home, the hazards of descent through Mars atmosphere to the surface and so on, there will be a far higher risk of disaster than there was on the moon trip. What if the Mars project fails and the Astronauts die? Is America going to write it off or refuse to admit failure and do it all again? If a robot mission fails you can write it off, but could you do that with a manned mission? Think of the loss of prestige, which would be made worse if some other Nation, later, managed to do it successfully.

Instead of the Mars project, some people would argue that, with the same amount of money, we could place scientific robots on nearly every planet and moon in the Solar System and probably on asteroids and comets too. Others would argue that the money could be used building nuclear power stations, hydro-electric dams and generating stations, building shale oil and tar sands projects and so on, all to mitigate the effects of oil and gas shortages which will hit in the next few years. Rationally I am inclined to think the latter makes more sense but the problem of keeping NASA busy will probably be the prime factor affecting decisions.

Now let us consider the Moon Base Project. If NASA does go ahead on the Mars Mission and also the Moon Base project then they will probably use the same booster rockets to get components and Moon Base modules into Earth orbit. These modules will then need to be ferried to the Moon and taken down to the Moon surface where they will be assembled to form the Moon Base. The most economic and efficient way to do this would be to do it automatically i.e. under computer control. Each module delivery mission would be similar to a mission to land a robot space station or vehicle on the Moon. The only difference would be the precision that would be required since all the modules must be landed in precisely the same place to within a few metres. I expect the first module would incorporate a radio beacon and later modules would home in on it. Only when all the modules and substantial quantities of supplies and equipment have been accurately delivered would Astronauts go to the Moon and start assembly.

In many ways the creation of the Moon Base would be like assembling and creating a copy of the International Space Station but on the Moon. However, whilst delivering modules, stores and equipment would all be done with one-way trips, the whole project becomes far more complicated when human beings are involved. We would then need a Moon Orbiting Station and some form of shuttle to take Astronauts down to the Moon Base and return them to the Orbiting Station.

Then we have the problem of getting Astronauts from the Earth to the Moon Orbiter and also back from Moon Orbiter to the Earth. This could be done using a large rocket which would lift off from Earth and deliver the Astronauts directly to the Moon Orbiter, Apollo style. This large rocket would also need to incorporate a module, complete with fuel, for a return journey from the Moon Orbiter back to Earth. However, the most efficient way to transfer Astronauts from the Earth to the Moon and back would be to use an Earth Orbiting Station as a transfer point. Astronauts would be ferried up from the ground to the Earth Orbiter and then transferred to a Shuttle which would travel regularly between the Earth Orbiter and Moon Orbiter Stations. Maybe the International Space Station could be used as the Earth Orbiter for the shuttle transfer system.

Gradually we begin to realise what a colossal undertaking the manned Moon Base would be. It would incur enormous expense just to establish the Moon Base and, when that was accomplished, there would be further enormous on-going expenses involved in operating it. Transfer flights from Earth to the Earth Orbiter for Astronauts and also supplies and equipment. Shuttle flights from Earth Orbiter to Moon Orbiter and back. Shuttle flights from Moon Orbiter to Moon Base and back and finally facilities for transferring, returning Astronauts from Earth Orbiter back to the ground.

The next question is "What will all this effort to create and run a manned Moon Base achieve?" The Moon Base would not create the same psychological impact on the world that the Apollo Moon Landings did and as the Mars Landing might. The Moon Base, therefore, would represent an enormous initial financial outlay and continuing massive financial drain on US resources for no really valid purpose. It would be likely to become a colossal 'White Elephant' – a massive and endless financial burden as, it must be said, the International Space Station now is.

At its inception the I.S.S. was envisaged as a great scientific co-operative venture especially with regard to friendship and co-operation between the new Russia and the West. Unfortunately, at the present time, president Putin seems bent on turning the clock back, producing renewed tension and there are even hints of a new Cold War. The I.S.S. is in danger now of becoming an embarrassment and a very expensive one at that. If you think about it – have you ever heard of any useful experiment or valuable research being carried out on the I.S.S? It seems to me that it is not much more than a very expensive 'Space Hotel' where a few Astronauts can enjoy the view. The Russians have certainly used it as such, on a few occasions, ferrying up a few, fare paying, millionaire passengers. I think it would be very unlikely that zero G experiments could be carried out on the I.S.S. because of the vibration from Astronauts exercising all the time. (This is necessary to keep their bones, muscles and hearts in trim during extended periods of weightlessness). The astronauts on the I.S.S. are doing nothing scientifically that cannot be done quite easily on an unmanned and far smaller satellite – other, that is, than experiments to do with the effects of prolonged weightlessness on the human body – which I thought the Russians had already done anyway. To give you an idea of how expensive everything to do with the I.S.S. is – it costs roughly ten thousand dollars just to deliver a half litre bottle of drinking water. How much, one wonders, would it cost to deliver to the Moon? Astronauts on the Moon could, of course, carry out exploration of the Moon, analysis of rocks and so on but this could be done at a minute fraction of the cost using robots.

We come to the conclusion, therefore, that both the Mars Landing and the Moon Base are simply very expensive novelties. To explore Mars it would be far, far cheaper and simpler using robots. Small, mobile, long life, robots armed with many sensors and cameras can be lofted into Earth orbit on medium sized boosters. Since there need be no tight time schedule, the Mars craft can be placed in a low, elliptical orbit, and the slingshot effect used, over and over again, to finally throw the spacecraft away from Earth and into a Mars trajectory. This can be done using very little fuel. The only thing required is time. It may take several years to get to Mars instead of months, but robots care nothing for time and need no food or oxygen; four years or ten makes no difference to a robot. When the craft reaches Mars it can also take its time and use aero braking, in pass after pass, to slowly reduce its speed into a low Mars orbit. Finally the robot is sent down to the surface on a one way trip, with the minimal heat shielding and parachutes. When the robot has roamed the Martian surface and done its job, it will simply be switched off and abandoned. It is all so cheap and easy compared with a manned mission. If a robot mission fails, at any stage, it can just be written off and forgotten.

At the time of writing NASA has already done exactly what I have described, and there are two robot surveyors happily trundling over the Martian surface, taking pictures and sampling everything in sight. These little machines – about the size of a coffee table – have been doing this now for two years. Two years, mind you instead of the few weeks or months the astronauts would be on Mars. These rovers, called, "Spirit" and "Opportunity", were sent to Mars using a booster only a fraction of the size of the Saturn 5. The way things are being miniaturised, such small rovers will soon be able to analyse and study the rocks of Mars as well as a scientist back home could do with a chunk of Martian rock in a modern laboratory.

When the Apollo astronauts went to the Moon, it was to rescue American pride, which had been badly dented by the early Russian successes – the first satellite in orbit and the first man in space. The Apollo mission was primarily to show the Russians "Anything you can do we can do better." OK! The point was made. It was the height of the cold war, remember! Also the Russian Premier – Nikita Kruschev – had taken his shoe off in the United Nations Assembly and battered his desk with it, and insolently told America – "We will bury you." So – it is easy to understand the motive behind the 'Apollo' Moon landing project.

Some people have suggested the Mars landing would be a forerunner to a Space Colony on Mars. Just think of people living in a plastic bubble in the middle of an endless desert with no air (the air on Mars is as thin as Earth's air at 100,000 ft (30,769km) altitude and not breathable anyway, even if it was compressed). Imagine people desperately trying to stay alive on Mars. I would sooner try it in the middle of the Sahara desert. At least I could breathe as I fried or starved to death! Living on Mars is fine for Science Fiction, but let us pause and think carefully. For less than half the cost of the proposed Moon Base and

Mars Landing we could explore the entire solar system. We could place a robot explorer on every planet and every moon. We could send probes to comets and asteroids. We could afford to launch a multi spacecraft telescope array, with eight telescopes spaced a hundred miles apart, that would give us fantastically greater resolving power than the Hubble Space Telescope. We could even consider designing and building a star ship (see chapter on COLONISING THE STARS). Just think what could be done back here on Earth with the rest of the money.

Considered rationally and logically the Moon Base and Mars Landing are an economic nonsense. It is interesting to learn all about Mars and I look forward to more robot explorations. As for the idea of a human colony on Mars! Forget it! The brutal truth is, there is nowhere in the solar system for human beings to live, in anything like reasonable conditions, except Earth. The stars are ruled out because of the impossibly unrealistic distances to get to them. The idea of an Ark floating through space for thousands of years may make for a good Science Fiction film, but in reality – utterly impractical. The Earth is and always will be – our one and only home, whether we like it or not, and no matter how much of a mess we make of it.

It will be interesting to see what happens in the next Presidency. Maybe the next US Government will scrap both schemes. Maybe they will keep the Mars project for the prestige but, I will be amazed if they go ahead with the Moon proposal.

COLONISING THE STARS AND THE 'GENESIS' SPACECRAFT

In the 1960's, after the first satellites were placed in orbit and then men walked on the moon, the idea of space travel was in everybody's mind. People began to talk about 'going into Space' and even 'Colonising the Stars' – by which they meant, of course, human beings colonising planets around other stars. The big question is – would it really be possible?

Astronomers have now reached the point where they can detect planets around stars other than our Sun; so we have proof other stars also have planets. Indeed it would have been very surprising if they had not, as it would seem a natural consequence of the condensation and accretion of a mass of gas and dust to form a solar system.

The astronomers actually deduce and calculate the mass of these extra-solar planets and their orbits, from slight wobbles they can detect in the parent star, caused by the gravitational pull of the planet on the star. So far, only large planets, Jupiter size and above, have been detected in this way. As I write, scientists are preparing to launch a new spacecraft intended to detect other smaller planets down to a size only slightly larger than the Earth. This will be done by detecting the reduction in starlight caused when a planet passes across the face of the star – as Venus sometimes passes between us and the face of the Sun. Remarkable – but astronomers think this is possible!

I have little doubt in my mind that it will not be long, maybe fifty years or so, before astronomers can actually see Earth sized planets around nearby stars. They will then be able to know the size of a planet and whether it is in an orbit suitable for life to exist – if conditions on the planet also permitted it. In other words, they will be able to see Earth-like planets or with potential to become Earth-like. Obviously there will be many complications. For the planet really to be Earth-like, the star would need to be similar to our own; one which would be stable for billions of years. The planet should have plenty of water and be at the critical distance from its star to permit the existence of liquid water. Not many will fill these criteria but I would expect some will do so. The next big question will be "How can we possibly get there?". To be realistic, we cannot expect the perfect world to exist in orbit around our nearest neighbour stars – Alpha Centauri and Proxima Centauri which are 4.37 and 4.2 light years away respectively.

First, let us consider what sort of a planet would be required. The early Earth, although it was the right size, the right distance from the sun and had plenty of water probably had an atmosphere of CO_2 nitrogen, methane and probably ammonia. It certainly did not have an oxygen containing atmosphere. Not very suitable conditions for human colonising. The ideal world for colonising would be a planet already supporting primitive life up to the level of photosynthetic bacteria, and with an oxygen atmosphere and a reasonable atmospheric pressure level – close to Earths. If life had advanced to a point where there were multi-cellular plants and animals there would also be predators, parasites and pathogens. The most important would be the pathogens. The Science Fiction writer H. G. Wells was bright enough to think this out in 1910. His all conquering Martians in the 'War of the Worlds' were beaten and destroyed, not by humans but by Earth's deadly bacteria. It has been suggested it might be possible to colonise a planet with a primitive, pre-oxygen, atmosphere and 'terra form' the planet using Earth type bacteria. Sci-Fi stories have been written where colonists live in 'bubble' type enclosures and 'terra form' a planet in a couple of generations. In reality it would take many millions of years for photosynthetic bacteria to create an oxygen containing atmosphere, as it did on Earth. It must, therefore, be totally unrealistic to consider colonising a 'non oxygen' planet and terra forming it to be fit for human habitation. The planet we need then is going to be very rare.

The scale of the Universe being what it is we find, when we study the stars nearest the sun, there are only about 100 stellar systems within a radius of 20 light years. The planet we are looking for is likely to be found only once in a 1000 stellar systems or more (which implies one suitable planet in a volume of space roughly 43 light years radius). Let us be very optimistic and assume we find a suitable planet only 10 light years distance. I calculate ten light years is fifty eight trillion seven hundred billion miles (to the nearest few billion miles). To give you a better grasp of what that means, it is one million eight hundred and ninety thousand times as far as it is from Earth to Mars at Mars nearest distance from Earth. (Remember – at ten light years – that is a nearby star in cosmological terms). For us it would be quite a journey.

Now, let us consider the problems of space travel. The fundamental problem of space travel is propulsion, not power. We could generate enormous amounts of power using nuclear reactors but it does not solve the problem of propulsion. People have talked about matter/anti-matter reactions but again that would only produce power not propulsion. In space there is nothing to help us. Nothing to get a grip on to push ourselves forward. On Earth we zoom around in our cars with a two hundred horse-power engine, but the engine, on its own, would not get you anywhere. If you were presented with a perfectly working engine on a stand it would be useless to you.

To get from A to B we have to add transmission and wheels that can grip the road and force the car forward. We also need brakes, which again work through the wheels to grip the road, to slow us down. Just imagine the car was placed on a frozen lake, with a surface of ice that was perfectly slippery, so there was no grip at all. You would not be going anywhere. This would be similar to the situation in space. There is nothing to get a grip on. The only way to propel a vehicle forward is to throw something in the opposite direction. This is called reaction thrust and is the principle behind a rocket motor. In deep space – in other words away from planets and stars – the only known way to propel a spacecraft is by reaction thrust. It is also the only known way to slow down again. I would also emphasise it is almost certain to remain the only way.

Terminal Velocity of a rocket propelled vehicle is proportional to the amount of fuel used and the speed of the rocket exhaust. That means, if you can double the exhaust velocity you can double the speed it is possible to reach with your spacecraft for a given amount of fuel. The Saturn Five rocket that lifted the astronauts from Cape Canaveral to go to the Moon used paraffin and oxygen for the first stage engines. Paraffin and oxygen will only produce a certain maximum exhaust velocity, no matter how well you design the engines. However, since paraffin and oxygen are easy to handle, and relatively dense, it was chosen for the booster stage. When the booster has fallen away and only the upper stages are left, then high efficiency engines are needed for the rest of the flight. Oxygen/hydrogen engines are then used, because this gives the highest exhaust velocity possible with chemical combustion and so reduces the amount of fuel that has to be carried into space and to the Moon or Mars or anywhere else.

Just to place two men on the Moon and return them needed a rocket weighing about 3000 tons of which over 90% was simply fuel. The bulk of the fuel was required merely to lift off the Earth's surface and place the spacecraft in Earth orbit. There is no easy way to do this and massive chemically fuelled boosters are likely to remain the only way (See Chapter on 'SPACE ELEVATOR'). The best way, therefore, to build a spacecraft to go to the stars would be to build it in orbit around the Earth, or possibly near the Moon. Once a spacecraft is built in orbit it is possible to place it in an eccentric orbit, using a small amount of fuel, and use the Earth's gravity, to gradually (over several orbits) slingshot the spacecraft away from Earth. Ideally the spacecraft, as it left the Earth, could be placed on a trajectory which would take it to Jupiter and, again using the slingshot technique, Jupiter's massive gravity field could be used to speed up the spacecraft to around 80,000 mph, which would be enough to ensure the craft would escape the Sun's gravitational attraction and start it on the way to the stars. Eighty thousand miles an hour is, of course, hopelessly slow if you wish to reach the stars in anything like a reasonable time. The Pioneer probes, were propelled from the solar system in this way. They will not reach the distance to Alpha Centauri for another 100,000 years or so. Fortunately the slingshot manoeuvre can be used to propel any size of spacecraft up to the 80,000 mph required to leave the solar system – whether it is the few hundred pounds of the Pioneer probes or a monster of half a million tons.

Once the craft is away from the solar system the problem remains of how to accelerate the craft to a high speed in interstellar space. One of the suggestions put forward to accelerate a spacecraft without the use of fuel is Solar Sails. This would only be useful within the solar system because, as soon as the spacecraft is out past Neptune, the radiation pressure would be negligible. So we can forget Solar Sails. We can also forget Warp Drives and such things as Hyper-Spatial Tubes. They are purely Science Fiction and no more likely to become reality than a magic wand. I am an Engineer. Engineers have to work with reality and this is a book concerned with rational thinking. If we ever reach the stars it will be done using sound scientific and engineering principles.

So, imagine we have our spacecraft out past Neptune in deep space. What can we realistically use for propulsion? Chemical rockets are out. They are hopelessly inefficient for the task. The best hope is an Ion Drive. Experiments have been carried out for the last 50 years to create an ion rocket motor. Briefly, the idea is to take a gas and ionise it (electrically charge the atoms). The charged atoms can then be electrostatically accelerated to high speeds and allowed to escape into space. The jet of high-speed atoms is, in effect, a form of rocket motor. The thrust is very small but the key thing is the fact that the jet exhausts at a speed far higher than that possible with chemical fuel rocket engines.

At the present time the fuel of choice for ion engines is Xenon and the maximum thrust reached so far is about equal to the pressure of a postcard balanced on your finger. The ion engine producing this thrust is small and the power used is in kilowatts. There were problems developing a practical engine, for instance it is necessary to neutralise the charge on the ion jet before it leaves the spacecraft, otherwise a charge builds up on the spacecraft and attracts the ejected particles back again which would, of course, cancel out the thrust. This problem has been solved and, as I write, a spacecraft is accelerating on a mission between the planets being driven by an ion engine. The ion engine has been proven to work.

Using Xenon, which has relatively heavy atoms and only the power obtainable from a few solar panels boosted to a few thousand volts, a working ion engine with a thrust of 0.07 Newton is slowly accelerating the spacecraft to higher speeds. Knowing scientists and engineers, I am sure they will continue to work on and develop the ion drive. At the present time the ion drive is only 10 times more efficient than a chemical rocket motor. However, if a lighter gas was used, say hydrogen, or helium, then much higher exhaust velocities could be reached – especially if you used a nuclear reactor for power and millions of volts for the accelerating field. Also the engine may be scaled up in size and/or multiple engines could be used. I know the reason the engineers used the heavier gas Xenon was to get a useful thrust out of the small engine. Hydrogen or helium would have given them negligible thrust with such a small motor but it would be far more efficient.

To conclude – I think it is quite possible that, in the next 50 to 100 years, ion drives of useful thrust, and with an efficiency maybe 200 times that of chemical rockets will be constructed. With such a drive some form of travel to the stars is just about feasible. I will point out, however, that even with ion drives, 95% or more of the total mass of a starship leaving the solar system would need to be fuel. Even the ion drive has to use fuel in the form of propellant gas to produce thrust. Because of its low thrust the ion drive would have to work for years to build up the spacecraft's speed. Probably three quarters of the total fuel load would be used propelling the spacecraft up to its maximum speed. The craft would then drift though space towards its destination for thousands of years. At a certain point the craft would be reversed and the ion drive again used for years, to slow the craft down. This description applies to the smallest or the largest spacecraft humanity might decide to despatch to another extra-solar planet.

Let us now consider what would be involved in setting up a human space colony on a new planet. A colony that was intended to survive indefinitely. No going back to Earth – ever! The target is to completely colonise a new planet; make it a new and permanent home for the human race. The intent would be to create another "Earth" as far as possible – with millions of people happily existing with a decent standard of living. To go to another planet and set up a small colony of people desperately struggling to survive and dying out after a few years/decades is surely not worth doing. All you would be doing is adding to the sum total of human misery. The idea of a colony on a new planet would be as an 'Insurance Policy' – to ensure the survival of the human race if a catastrophe wiped out human beings on Earth. Why bother otherwise? On this basis let us consider what would be required on a new planet.

How many people would we need for a start? A Geneticist would probably say 500. An Engineer would probably ask for 1000 at least. Let us assume a figure as low as 100 is the final choice. A dozen or so could never, reasonably, be expected to succeed and, apart from themselves, what would these pioneers want to take with them?

Recently, I visited New Zealand and was amazed to find how many UK plants, trees and animals were there. One evening, on the hotel lawns, I saw hedgehogs (who would bother to take hedgehogs all the way to New Zealand – but they did!). I found that parts of New Zealand were so close to conditions in the UK that if I had been anaesthetised and shipped, unknowing, to New Zealand and woken up, I would have totally believed I was still in the UK. The trees were UK trees, the sheep, the grass, the plants; even the weeds were ex UK! The settlers imported rabbits, foxes, hedgehogs, sparrows, stoats. You name it! They wanted to make New Zealand a new UK. You can rest assured that if a group of colonists are going to go to a New World – on a one way trip – forever, they are not going to be willing to go alone. In addition to the essential food plants and food animals they are going to want to take a veritable Noah's Ark or they won't be willing to go at all.

The spacecraft would have to be truly enormous – dwarfing even the massive spacecraft Arthur C Clarke thought up for the film "2001". The maximum speed it is possible to reach with a rocket propelled spacecraft is governed by the amount of fuel, compared to the payload, and the exhaust velocity. If 95% by weight of the spacecraft, leaving the vicinity of Jupiter, was fuel and the exhaust velocity of the propellant leaving the motors was 200 times as fast as the exhaust velocity of a chemical rocket such as was used on the Saturn 5 or the Shuttle, then we could expect to boost the spacecraft up to a maximum speed of around six million miles per hour (9.6 million kilometres per hour). This is slightly less than one hundredth of the speed of light. That means, to reach a star 10 light years away would take over 1000 years.

A spacecraft carrying humans and animals would need artificial gravity, created by a rotating section, again as per Arthur C Clarke's spacecraft, for people to function and remain healthy – and have families with children. Scientists might eventually make it possible for people to hibernate – as bears do, but bears can still only hibernate for six months or so at a time. Suspended animation for a thousand years is a dream – like Teleportation and Hyper-Spatial Tubes. A lot of Sci-Fi is no more likely to become real than children's fairy tales. In this book I am trying to write of something that could be within the bounds of reality. So, to colonise a new planet and create a new home for human beings, a place really fit for people to live, and have children and enjoy life – you would need at least a hundred people to start with; a Noah's Ark of animals, plants, fish, bacteria and so on. You would need facilities to supply food to the people and animals. This would mean massive Hydroponics rooms to grow plants and create food and oxygen. There would need to be radiation shields, (to shield against cosmic rays as well as reactor radiation) medical and veterinary facilities, repair workshops, gymnasiums, educational departments, sewage treatment and recycling systems. To supply power there would need to be nuclear reactors and generators with all the necessary radiation screening. All this, you could say, is part of the payload.

Initially the pioneers, their families and all the animals and plants, would have to be shipped up from the Earth in Shuttlecraft, a group at a time, and transferred to the space craft. What is going to happen when they arrive at the new planet – which would have to be roughly Earth sized or larger? (Any smaller and it would lose its atmosphere to space as Mars has done). When the enormous spacecraft reaches the new planet it would not be able to land. It would be slowed down and go into a near-planet orbit. There would then be the tremendous problem of getting people, animals, plants, equipment and stores down to the planets surface. Some form of shuttle craft would be needed. It is pointed out that a craft like the existing 'space shuttle' would not work. It is true the shuttle can bring large objects weighing several tons back to Earth but, having dissipated its orbital energy by frictional drag in the atmosphere, it still has to land (at 200 mph) on a very long concrete runway. On the new world the shuttle would have to land vertically, using a lot of precious fuel. To produce rocket fuel on the new world would require a lot of equipment and a small nuclear power station to power it. If we assume the total weight to be transferred from the orbiting spacecraft to the planets surface is likely to be – say – 5000 tons (I consider this to be a very low estimate) then, if a shuttle delivered 20 tons per trip there would need to be 250 shuttle trips. Since a shuttle disaster might maroon the remaining people and cargo in orbit there would need to be at least 3 shuttles (all adding to the original payload weight). To power the shuttle up to rendezvous with the mother ship and come back down again would probably need at least 3000 tons of fuel per trip which, for 250 trips, works out at a total of 750,000 tons of fuel. All this, bar the fuel for the first descent, would have to be manufactured on the planet's surface.

So, what are we talking about? Imagine the payload module with the people, animals, plants, facilities, nuclear power stations, shuttles etc. We are talking about something at least ocean liner size, say 80,000 tons, and that is just the payload. To this must be added the drive system and, most importantly, the fuel for the ion engines. A reasonable ratio of fuel/payload for such a trip would be 20 to 1. In other words, to accelerate the payload to a reasonable speed for the journey, and then decelerate at the end of the voyage, you would need one million six hundred thousand tons of fuel. Add the mass of the structure, engines, and so on, and you have a total spacecraft weight of around one and three quarter million tons. I very much doubt if any reasonable engineer would disagree with these figures. He would probably say they were too optimistic.

What can we conclude from all this? The answer must be that the idea of a spacecraft taking people to colonise the stars is unrealistic. In fact – it is totally absurd. For instance – at present costs of delivering cargo into orbit – it would cost about forty thousand billion dollars to simply transport the space craft components, fuel, people, plants and animals from the ground up to low Earth orbit, and we would have to burn about forty five million tons of rocket fuel to do it. There is, therefore, no chance whatsoever, of the Noah's Ark space ship to the stars ever becoming reality. Such a space journey is utterly and absolutely in the realms of fantasy. The human race, as such, is simply not going to get away from this planet and go to the stars. However, if you really use your imagination – and think more deeply and profoundly – there just might be a way we could colonise the stars. A far easier way. A far better way. It just might – only just might, mind you – become possible. First – read the Chapter on EVOLUTION.

As I have stated we are, genetically speaking, related to everything on this Earth large enough to see with the naked eye, as well as to a good many life forms too small to see – such as yeast cells for instance. Just imagine, instead of trying to send human beings in a gigantic spacecraft to the stars we consider a different approach. We look carefully for a dozen or more Earth sized planets with liquid water and with their solar systems in the early stages of development. In other words, look for planets that have only just cooled off and are ready for life to begin or, say, in the first 500 million years after life might have started. We then decide we are going to try to colonise these planets. If you think about it carefully you will realise we could actually do this by sending each planet one thimbleful of Earth bacteria (advanced bacteria, preferably with DNA) and seed the oceans of the new worlds. When scientists study the more advanced bacteria the degree of complexity is incredible, (NOTE – I am writing of bacteria – not viruses. Viruses are a very crude form of life – not capable of reproducing themselves – they have to parasitise some other life form). Advanced bacteria have evolved biological mechanisms to enable the bacteria to extract and absorb nutrients and metabolise them, the ability to reproduce and so on. The bacteria, in reality, are a very advanced form of life – although they are so small and still single independent cells. After all, it took roughly three billion years of evolution to bring them to their present level of development.

When primitive cells learned the trick of cooperating and banding together for mutual benefit – and thus created the first animals, it only took a further six hundred million additional years to create us – and all the other animals and plants on Earth.

One thimbleful of bacteria to seed the sea of one of the new planets and, in only a billion years or less (roughly one quarter of the time it took on Earth), through the magic of Evolution, you could have a complete new Earth – with all the wonderful variety with which Mother Earth is endowed. It could be done with a few far smaller spacecraft, each craft weighing perhaps only 500 tons or so. It would not matter if it needed several years to initially slingshot the spacecraft to the speed needed to escape the sun's gravitational influence. The propulsion system would then accelerate the small craft far more rapidly than the monster required for human colonisation. Some of the bacteria in the capsule might be in the form of spores. To shield a few grams of bacteria against the radiation of space should not be too difficult. Interstellar space is extremely cold at around - 270°C. It might well be the bacteria and spores would remain viable for a far longer time if frozen to these temperatures than they would at Earth normal. Experiments could be carried out to see if this was likely to be the case. (The Norwegians have set up a World Seed Bank on Spitzbergen island where seeds will be stored indefinitely at – 18°C. Grains such as wheat and barley are expected to remain viable for 1,500 to 2,000 years and seeds such as sorghum up to 15,000 years. A few years ago, samples of algae, over a million years old, were taken from a salt mine in Siberia, taken to a lab, cultured, and found to be viable). Once the capsule of bacteria was delivered to the new planet, then, if conditions were suitable, the bacteria would convert the entire sea into a bacterial soup in a very short time. If primitive life forms had already developed, the Earth bacteria – being billions of years ahead in evolutionary terms – would simply use the existing primitive life forms as nutrients. The more primitive cells would not be able to compete. The stage would be set and competitive evolution would commence.

Eventually you would have an Earth type planet, with all the variety and magic of the original Mother Earth, not a parody of the Earth with a handful of human beings desperately trying to survive in a hostile environment. We would have to consider, very carefully, the conditions that would be likely to prevail on the target planet. Such a planet as I describe would not be an oxygen planet. That would come later. It would probably have an atmosphere of methane, CO_2 and even ammonia – similar to our early Earth conditions. (Life converted it to what it is today). Suitable bacteria would have to be carefully selected and a dozen different varieties or more might be needed. Alternatively, we might genetically engineer them to do the job. We would need bacteria that can thrive in a methane environment – there are many such bacteria on this Earth. Ideally the bacteria should form spores, which can be very resistant and long-lived. For example there is evidence to suggest anthrax spores can survive at least for centuries. Many bacteria have amazing capabilities and some have been found that can withstand a thousand times more hard radiation than humans can. Each bacterial payload could be tailored to the target planet. I would point out that if only one, out of the billion or so bacteria contained in the tiny capsule, survived to grow and multiply, the mission to seed the planet would have been successful.

The spacecraft would probably be controlled by computers no bigger than a walnut. There would probably be a dozen of them, connected together and arranged to 'vote' on the various manoeuvres, to allow for computer failure. (The Space Shuttle already uses this technique. I believe it uses five. If one computer produces the same answer as any other computer – both with the same program – that answer must be correct. Any computer that is faulty and gives an answer that does not agree with the consensus is disconnected).

In the small spacecraft, many systems could be duplicated and even triplicated for reliability. We could probably launch a hundred or more of these small spacecraft for far less than the cost of one monstrous human carrying spacecraft. The freezing conditions of interplanetary space, instead of being a problem, may well act to prolong the viability of the spores and would be ideal for preserving the liquid hydrogen or helium fuel during the journey. The longer the time the spores could survive, the longer the journey that would be feasible. Maybe we could opt for slower accelerations and speeds or perhaps target planets further away.

The capsule of spores would be capable of withstanding far more shock and stress than a human cargo – possibly an impact shock of 1000Gs or more – which would vastly simplify the problem of delivery to the target planet. The spacecraft would simply slow to near orbital speed on approach then eject the re entry capsule so that it plunged, at a shallow angle, into the atmosphere. When the capsule had been slowed down enough by atmospheric friction it would fall directly into the sea. No parachute would be needed; the capsule would be designed to take the final impact.

If only twenty percent of the small 'Genesis' spacecraft actually made it, and successfully seeded a planet – what an achievement that would be. The assuring of the survival of the original Mother Earth – Tree of Life. If it was achieved it would be the most amazing and the most noble thing the human race had ever done. You might even say it could, in part at least, compensate for the damage we have already done – and the far more damage we are yet to do – to this planet. On Earth we are very anxious to ensure the survival of our race so we have children and plan for the future. We feel sure it is worth our while – though we will never see anything beyond our own lives. We know – instinctively – it is worth it. Instead of worrying over the survival of the human species (the Earth can support us for the next billion years if we use a little sense – providing an asteroid doesn't intervene), why not ensure the survival of the basic Tree of Life? I also point out, if the seeding project succeeded, it just might be the beginning of a chain reaction that could, one day, in the far future, see the whole Galaxy seeded with Earth life. Who knows!

Let us take a deep breath – and not be so parochial. Let us do something really magnificent and leave a legacy to be proud of. I wonder what a re-run of Earth's evolution would produce – next time – and the time after that. Because of the relative simplicity, and the small size of the spacecraft, it might be possible to launch such a craft in as little as fifty years from now. The engineers and scientists who sent the spacecraft would never know if they had been successful or not, but their descendents might – if they checked the target planets and, one day, found traces of oxygen.

DESIGN OF PROJECT GENESIS SPACECRAFT

The spacecraft to carry the tiny capsule of life to another planet could be a very flimsy affair. Power would be supplied by a compact nuclear reactor/electricity generator placed out in front of the main assembly on a long boom. The reactor need not be shielded, so reducing weight, and would not be started until the craft was on its way, out past Jupiter. On launch from the ground there would be no nuclear danger. The components of a nuclear reactor are almost inert until the reactor is started so, if an accident occurred on launch, the reactor fragments reaching the ground would present no hazard.

The main bulk of the assembled spacecraft would be the fuel tanks carrying liquid hydrogen or helium for the ion engines. The tanks would simply be attached to the fragile spine of the spacecraft and jettisoned as soon as each tank became empty. Far to the rear, behind the tanks, would be the payload module consisting of an ablative sphere 12 inches (30.5 cm) in diameter containing, in its centre, the precious capsule of bacterial spores. Attached to the sphere would be a control module with small fuel tank, computer and thrusters – to control the sphere's final approach and descent into the atmosphere of the new planet. Further back on the spacecraft would be the propulsion module with a cluster of ion engines.

The structure of the spacecraft would be extremely fragile, almost gossamer like with ultra thin tubes of carbon fibre. It would be assembled in Earth orbit. Propulsion to eject it from its initial circular orbit would be by a gentle thrust of an ion engine or a very small chemical rocket. As soon as an elliptical orbit was induced, the slingshot effect would be used so that, gradually, after several orbits, the craft would break free of the Earth's gravitational pull and head for Jupiter. Upon reaching Jupiter the slingshot effect would be used again, to eject the spacecraft away and out of the solar system at around 80,000 mph. No stresses would be incurred in the spacecraft as it is accelerated by Jupiter, since the gravitational forces act equally on every part of the craft. As the spacecraft left the solar system it would still have its full load of fuel; all the acceleration since leaving low Earth orbit having been achieved by exploitation of the slingshot effect. To help keep the fuel at cryogenic temperatures a sunshade might be necessary initially, but this would be jettisoned after the craft left Jupiter. After leaving Jupiter the nuclear reactor would be activated and the craft slowly accelerated by the high efficiency ion engines. These engines would continue to operate until, perhaps, three quarters or more of the fuel had been consumed. At this point, when maximum speed had been reached, the nuclear reactor would be shut down. The craft would then coast through space until it reached the point, later in the trip, when it would be reversed, the reactor restarted and the ion engines operated, to commence the long braking period to reduce speed to a point where it would approach the target planet at a speed, preferably no more than the planet's escape velocity. During the long flight, residual heat from the nuclear reactor would provide enough electricity to power signals to keep in touch with Earth.

During the voyage the cold of interstellar space, – minus 270°C – would mean there would be no problem of keeping the liquid hydrogen or helium cool, and the spores in the capsule would be cryogenically preserved almost indefinitely. The intensity of radiation from the nuclear reactor would be reduced by the distance from the spore capsule, and both the capsule and the computer electronics could be shielded from the reactor radiation by a cylinder of lead, about 3cms (1¼ins) diameter by 1 foot (30cm) long, along the axis of the spacecraft. This would produce a radiation free shadow 3cms (1¼ins) diameter.

The design of the GENESIS SPACECRAFT would be relatively simple and all we need to be able to build it, is high efficiency ion engines and compact nuclear reactor/electric generator units. (Compact high power nuclear reactors already exist for submarine propulsion). Maybe, if President Bush was to decide to scrap the manned Mars project and pour a similar amount of money into the GENESIS project, the necessary ion engines could be produced in twenty years, instead of the fifty I estimated earlier. The seeding of a new planet would be a fantastically greater achievement than planting the US flag on Mars.

On approach to the new planet, the whole spine and nuclear reactor/generator assembly at the front and also the ion drive system at the rear would be jettisoned. Only the small remaining spacecraft would be manoeuvred into the approach trajectory. Just before contact with the atmosphere the ablation sphere, not much larger than a football, would be ejected. Ideally the sphere would enter the atmosphere at a shallow angle, so as to extend the time in the upper atmosphere and prevent the temperatures building too high. A shallow trajectory, would mean the sphere would lose nearly all its speed in the atmosphere before finally plunging into the sea at just a few hundred miles an hour. The shock of impact in the sea would be no problem. As long as the capsule plunges into a liquid water sea, anywhere on the planet, the seeding should be successful.

Let us pause for a moment and imagine the final scene. The re-entry vehicle blazes across the sky like a shooting star, as it makes the final plunge through the atmosphere of the new world, its four inch thick ablative shield protecting the metal capsule inside. When all its energy is dissipated in the atmosphere it simply drops into the sea at a relatively slow speed. The ablative shield falls away – and a metal capsule, no bigger than a tennis ball, is released. The sphere, covered in micro sensors, sinks slowly in the sea. When the sensors register conditions suitable for life – not necessarily at the surface of the sea – the metal egg breaks open and releases the spoonful of bacterial spores to the sea. Mission accomplished. The planet is seeded.

THE ION DRIVE

In my opinion the ion drive is in its infancy. Scientists have been experimenting for 50 years, but there has been no massive effort to develop such an engine. Effort has mainly been concentrated on chemical rocket motors because of the much greater thrust they provide. They are also fundamentally simpler and, for most purposes, the ion rocket has far too small a thrust. Most projected spacecraft missions within the solar system can be accomplished perfectly well with chemical rockets. However, when we discuss travelling interstellar distances, the efficiency of the engines becomes of paramount importance. Chemical rocket engine exhausts have a definite limit to the achievable exhaust velocity, which is linked to the energy in the fuel and the density of the exhaust gas. The great advantage of the ion engine is that, technically, there is practically no limit to the exhaust velocity. It is, in effect, a small particle accelerator – projecting ionised atoms out into space. The great thing about particle accelerators is that the only limit to the speed to which charged particles can be accelerated is the speed of light. The exhaust velocity is only dependent on the amount of energy that is imparted to the ionised atoms.

In the design of ion engine that is actually being used on an existing spacecraft, the engine is very small. Xenon gas is fed into a small chamber, ionised, and electrically accelerated over a short distance (just a few centimetres). Remarkably enough this is sufficient to produce an exhaust velocity of 60,000 mph (16.7 miles per second), ten times faster than the exhaust from the shuttles engines. At full power the ion engine uses 2½ kilowatts of electrical power which is supplied by solar panels.

This first practical ion engine, is a very small device – a 'proof of concept' gadget accelerating atoms of xenon over distances measured in centimetres. It is impossible, at this stage, to predict accurately how far the development of this device can go but I visualize ion engines of the future using megawatts of power, accelerating atoms over many metres distance instead of centimetres and each 'thruster' incorporating maybe a dozen accelerating chambers in parallel. The amount of gas ejected from each chamber might be many times more than in the existing small engine. My thinking on this matter is influenced by remembering the past. Who would have thought that the Wright brothers first flimsy plane would start a progression culminating, today, in a plane (The Airbus A380) weighing 600 tons capable of carrying 800 people, at nearly 600 miles per hour, halfway around the planet, or that the first novelty rockets produced by the Chinese would lead, one day, to the giant Saturn 5 and see men walk on the Moon. I have assumed, therefore, before writing this chapter, that practical, long life, high efficiency ion engines producing reasonable thrust may, in the future, be developed.

As a professional Engineer, I think it is quite likely that, in 40 or 50 years there could be ion engines in existence, using power from a nuclear reactor and generator, producing exhaust velocities of 300 miles (483 kilometres) per second or more together with greater thrust. It is an interesting fact that, in nature, ionised or charged particles are sometimes accelerated, by a star's magnetic field, to velocities approaching the speed of light. The ion engine appears to be the only engine which has the potential to power a spacecraft to speeds which would make interstellar journeys at all possible. Even the minimum design of craft such as the proposed GENESIS spacecraft would probably be on the absolute limit of what could actually be achieved. Ideas of vastly larger interstellar spacecraft carrying people to the stars are simply dreams.

I have produced a sketch showing a proposed design for the GENESIS spacecraft, which is shown overleaf, together with an artist's impression of what such a craft would look like in flight.

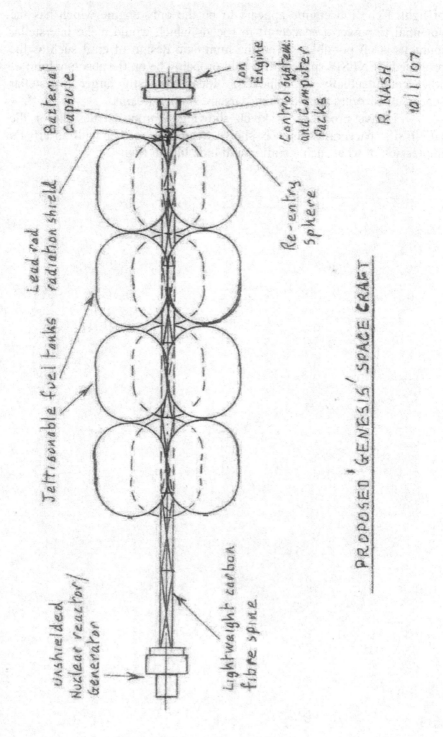

Bacterial Capsule

Lead rod radiation shield

Jettisonable fuel tanks

Unshielded Nuclear reactor/ Generator

Lightweight carbon fibre spine

Ion Engine

Control System and Computer Packs

Re-entry Sphere

PROPOSED 'GENESIS' SPACE CRAFT

R. NASH
10.11.07

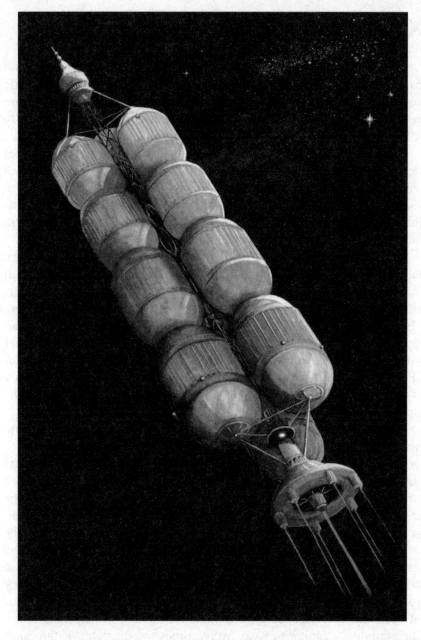

An artist's impression of a GENESIS spacecraft on its way to seed an
extra-solar planet with Earth-life.

EXTRA-TERRESTRIAL LIFE

We are all familiar with the depictions of extra-terrestrials on films and TV ranging from horrendous monsters to cuddly little humanoids. However, what is the likelihood of a real, intelligent, advanced E.T. existing somewhere in the Universe, what would he really look like, how far away is he likely to be and will he ever come here?

In an earlier chapter, it was pointed out that the geological evidence on this Earth shows that, apart from the right conditions, an immense amount of time was required, after life first started – some three thousand four hundred million years – just to get to the point where multi-cellular life, the first animals and plants, commenced. Then a further 600 million years to reach the level we are today.

The key thing about this is that the Earth has been in a condition suitable for life, and the continued development of life, for all of the full four thousand million years. That, in itself, is nothing less than a miracle. There have been a number of close shaves. Many times, over this period, the Earth has suffered massive disasters – whether by meteorite impact such as wiped out the dinosaurs, comet strikes, volcanism or other disasters; for instance, it has been pointed out that it would be possible for the Earth to be sterilised by radiation from a supernova explosion many light years away. The Sun too has varied over this time according to the geological record.

Some of the disasters have destroyed up to 90% of all life on Earth. The asteroid that wiped out the dinosaurs, and a vast amount of other life as well, is reckoned to have been about 7 miles (11 kilometres) in diameter. If the asteroid had been twice as big, i.e. 14 miles (22 kilometres) in diameter (by no means an impossibility) the energy released, at the same speed of impact, would have been 8 times as great. That would probably have done the trick and practically sterilised the planet, at least down to the level of bacteria. I am reminded that, a few years ago, astronomers detected a comet (Shoemaker-Levy) that had passed near Jupiter and broken up into about 20 fragments. Then they realised the fragments would strike Jupiter in the near future. There was great excitement; telescopes were trained. A number of scientists said – "Wait a minute – Jupiter is vast; twelve times the diameter of the Earth (1700 times the volume) and with an enormously thick atmosphere. The comet pieces are so small compared to Jupiter they will just vanish into the atmosphere. You will see nothing"! When the first strike occurred, which was just a reasonable sized chunk of the original comet, everybody was stunned. There was a tremendous flash and an explosion so great that it left a mark on Jupiter as far across as the Earth. The other pieces did the same as they went in and the great marks made were visible on the surface of Jupiter for 6 months.

When the comet Halley returned in 1997, spacecraft were sent to pass close and take a look. It turned out that the nucleus, the solid centre of the comet, was 10 miles (16 kilometres) long and 5 miles (8 kilometres) wide. Impressive! So the chance of the Earth being struck by an object much more massive than the one that destroyed the dinosaurs is by no means impossible. That it hasn't happened in 4000 million years is amazing.

So the real miracle of this Earth and life is that the fine balance of just the right conditions for life have been maintained unbroken – but with a few close shaves – for all the 4000 million years it has taken to produce advanced life such as Homo Sapiens. How is this relevant to extra-terrestrial life?

There are vast numbers of stars in the Universe – it is estimated there are at least one hundred billion stars in our Galaxy alone and at least a hundred billion galaxies in the visible Universe (giving a grand total of around ten thousand million, million, million stars). Since it is now apparent that our Sun is a very ordinary run-of-the-mill star, as stars go, and that it was formed by condensation from a local concentration of dust and gas, of which there are immense quantities floating about the cosmos, it is reasonable to expect that the whole solar system, complete with planets, is also the norm. If there was only one planet in orbit around our Sun we might think it could be a rarity – but with nine? Obviously commonplace!

With this in mind, I concluded, when I was 20, that the number of planets in the Universe was likely to be as great as, or greater than, the number of stars, and since the stars were in their trillions, then, if only one planet in 1000 was suitable for life, there must be a vast number of suitable planets. Assuming, as I think is reasonable, that life will start, sooner or later, on any planet that has the right conditions then Extra-terrestrial life must be common. I still hold that view! However – what are we talking about? Primitive life or the ET of science fiction? The ET the astronomers are looking for, as they search the skies with their impressive arrays, hoping to find signals, would have to be highly developed beings, at least as advanced as we are. That implies a planet that has sustained the precise conditions suitable for life, continuously, for thousands of millions of years. In my mind, that completely changes the picture; such a planet is likely to be very rare indeed.

We have a clue here in our solar system. Explorations of Mars so far have indicated that there was flowing water on Mars at one stage; that means conditions for life did exist on Mars. We already know that, on Earth, life can exist in water at temperatures up to boiling point. So – for a time – conditions for life existed on Mars. It would not surprise me if evidence for a very primitive life form on Mars was discovered in the next 30 years.

Another planet – Venus – in our solar system, was once considered a possibility for life and there was a time when Science Fiction writers delighted in describing Venusians. However, what the space probes found was a hellish planet, where greenhouse conditions had run away, and the whole planetary surface was at a temperature hot enough to melt lead. Was it always that way – or did conditions exist, for a short time, for life to start on Venus. Nobody knows!

Bearing in mind that, after the first 3,000 million years of evolution of life on this Earth, we had reached a level no more advanced than that represented by the black gunge that sometimes grows on a lavatory bowl, if it is not cleaned often enough, I have reached the conclusion that extra-terrestrial life is probably common, but very primitive. Primitive life forms probably abound. There may be trillions of planets with life in the Universe, but how many have maintained the knife edge balance for thousands of millions of years, for evolution to work its magic and produce beings at our level or beyond. I think it is likely to be very few. Even planets which have supported life, unbroken, for 4,000 million years or more may still not have made the breakthrough to multi-cellular life let alone reached our level or beyond. It may well be that we still have no real grasp of how rare our planet is and how much of a marvel the advanced life on it is.

It is extremely difficult to grasp the incredible organisation and complexity that a human body represents. It is an almost unbelievable construct of vast numbers of living cells. Biologist's have estimated the average human body consists of at least ten trillion cells. Ten trillion rolls off the tongue easily enough but, in reality, it is an enormous number. (A trillion is a million, million). To try to give you a grasp of what that means imagine, if you can, a six foot man enlarged until he was half a mile high (over 17 times the height of the Statue of Liberty or 2½ times the height of the Eifel Tower). At this size every individual cell would have been enlarged up to about the size of your little finger nail. If a machine was set up, somehow, to count the individual cells, one by one, at a rate of one a second, continuously, day and night until the job was done, it would take the machine roughly three hundred thousand years to complete the task. To keep you alive, all this enormous agglomeration of cells has to be continuously fed nutrients and oxygen, and all the waste products have to be removed. This is done with a system so remarkable and so efficient that if something enters the bloodstream, be it nutrients, oxygen or drugs, it will reach all the immense numbers of cells (over 1500 times more than the total number of people on the planet) in less than thirty seconds. Bear in mind that each individual cell is, itself, a living miracle of biological complexity that needed 3 billion years of evolution to create. Life originated in the sea, so the natural habitat of cells is water or brine. For a group of cells to venture on to dry land, the habitat has to be taken with them. To the cells, the body must be like some gigantic space colony. The liquid environment is enclosed within a special wall (the skin itself is a layer of dead cells, continuously being repaired and replenished by living cells within). The whole environment is very carefully controlled; temperature, pressure, oxygen levels, nutrient levels and a finely controlled chemical balance. The colony is continuously being damaged, infiltrated and invaded by foreign bacteria, viruses and parasites. To maintain integrity there is a complex repair and maintenance system and a multi-component task force, armed with various weapons, to repel and destroy invaders. An elaborate policing system exists to monitor every part of the colony and even detect dissident cells who would prefer to ignore orders and go their own way (cancer cells). An endless war is being fought to keep the colony intact and alive. To enable the colony to exist, survive and function there are over 200 different types of cells, all of which are carefully organised and controlled. In charge and co-ordinating all this are over a hundred billion specialised cells co-operating and working together to form a self assembling, self wiring, self organising computer system which is the most complex organic construct known. That this living, walking, talking, colossal colony of co-operating cells, which is you, can be created from one set of instructions encapsulated within just one precursor cell (the egg cell) is almost beyond belief. Yet because we have the evidence of ourselves and all the other plants and animals, we do believe it and, because we have proof it happened, we not only believe it but take it for granted. We take it for granted to such a degree we consider there is nothing special about it and think there must be plenty of other planets in the Universe which could have similar life. The miracle of advanced multi-cellular life on this Earth does not necessarily mean such life is commonplace or even that it has occurred anywhere else at all.

I am not in the least surprised that the search for ET signals has so far produced nothing, despite the fact that the search has now been going on for over 30 years. I shall be amazed if they do find evidence in my lifetime. There is a remote possibility, but real none the-less, that we may just be the highest form of life in this Galaxy. I doubt it – but it is not totally impossible that we may even be the highest in the whole Universe.

Somebody has to be first, and the Universe is very young. A friend of mine laughed when I said that, but it is true – cosmologically speaking.

The Universe has existed about 14 thousand million years – which is a fantastically long time by our standards. Cosmologically speaking it is not.

After the Big Bang the Universe consisted of nothing but hydrogen, a little helium and a few traces of other light elements. After a few hundred million years, clumps of this gas condensed under local gravitation to produce the first stars – many of which were very massive – many times larger than our own Sun. These massive stars blazed for a few million years and, as they did so, nuclear reactions in their interiors produced heavier elements including oxygen, carbon, silicon and a whole gamut of others. Eventually these massive stars exploded in supernovae, scattering these new elements into space. The really heavy elements beyond iron such as gold, platinum and uranium are only actually produced in the explosion.

As more and more of these massive stars burned out and exploded, they seeded space with the new heavier elements. The scene was now set for stage two. There were now great clumps of the original hydrogen and helium mixed, polluted you might say, with the new heavy elements and these began to collapse under local gravity to produce the next batch of stars. Stars such as our own, the Sun, where some of the material in the outer part of the accretion disc coalesced to form planets. Without the first supernovae there would be no solid planets (only gas planets would exist). No Earth! No Water! No Oxygen! No you! It is interesting to look at my finger, as I write, and reflect that the material of which it is made was created in the furnace interior of a star and spread into space by the incredible blast of a supernova.

Our Sun is around 5 thousand million years old. In other words it is about a third of the age of the Universe. It must have taken billions of years before the first generation of massive stars had formed, run their lives, exploded and seeded the cosmos, ready for the next generation of stars to form, and probably an additional few billion years for the new suns and solar systems, like ours, to form. There may indeed be solar systems that could support life, older than ours; but how many? We could at least be in the first wave of intelligent life in this Universe, if not leading it. However it would seem, therefore, that there really is a good chance of a highly developed Extra-Terrestrial being existing somewhere in the Universe. On our doorstep? Not so likely!

Some would say, there must be other intelligent life in our Galaxy. Our Galaxy – mind you – out of billions! Perhaps they are right, but our Galaxy is a staggering 100 thousand light years across, so if there was an intelligent civilisation, say a thousand light years away, it is hardly nearby. If we should, incidentally, pick up signals from someone 1000 light years away it will prove that they are at least 900 years development ahead of us, and also that they could not learn of us for another 900 years, as our signals have only been going out for the last 100 years. The really stunning thought, though, is, what if they really got going early and are a billion years ahead of us?

I have said that I think the Universe is young. Since evidence indicates the Universe is around fourteen thousand million years old, some people might find this statement ridiculous. However, if you pause to think carefully, on a cosmological scale, this is, in fact, quite reasonable. Our Sun alone will last another 5 billion years or so before it finally becomes a red giant and then a white dwarf and there is plenty of gas and dust around to provide more stars. In any case, there is now plenty of astronomical evidence to confirm the Universe is not going to collapse back into a reverse Big Bang. On the contrary, latest evidence points to the expansion of the Universe speeding up – not slowing down.

Maybe when the Universe is 14 trillion years old (1000 times older than it is now) it could be said to be ageing a little! It is bound to reach 14,000 trillion years old, (a thousand times older still) and eventually, in the far far future, there will come a time when the whole Universe has burned out, the very last star has ceased to shine and all is darkness. From this perspective, there is obviously plenty of time for the Universe to produce intelligent advanced life in the future. Not so much time, however, in the past.

Let us now speculate on the nature of an Extra Terrestrial intelligent being. All we know so far is that life is possible under the conditions found on Earth. However, even if we assume life is only possible with liquid water (as is quite likely) there could be considerable variation in planetary conditions. A planet could be far larger than ours, spin faster or slower, or be tilted differently. The planet is unlikely to be much smaller than ours, because a reasonable size is needed for the planet to hold onto its atmosphere. Mars is a good example. Mars simply did not have enough gravity to hold on to its atmosphere for long periods of time. Most of its atmosphere has escaped into space. On a larger, heavier planet, let us say 5 times the gravitational pull of the Earth, land animals would be unlikely to be walking around on two legs. More likely 10 or 20 legs I would guess! However, in the sea, the extra gravity would make little difference. Buoyancy would stay the same. The extra weight of the animal would be cancelled by the extra weight of the water. However, with increasing depth, the pressure would increase five times as fast as it would on Earth.

The one thing we can reasonably say about ET though, is the fact that, if he is highly intelligent, he will be the result of a multi-billion year evolutionary war – the same as with us. Intelligence is a survival thing. Brains are the ultimate weapon. Brains help you to survive predation and to be a predator. (It amuses me to think people actually make films about monsters such as Godzilla and King Kong. In reality, we would just call up an anti tank gun and Godzilla would be 50 or 100 tons of dead meat before you could shout 'stop firing'). ET would have brains; he would be the result of billions of years of brutal competition. He must be dangerous to have come out on top. He must also be cooperative. Only a cooperative group could create machines and technological devices such as radios. ET might be tolerant of course, as we are tolerant, in supreme confidence that we are 'top of the pile' and could clobber anything if we had a mind to! I think it might be better if we did not meet!

In Science Fiction – Star Trek being a classic example – it is common to show ET's as being humanoid. Parallel evolution is quoted as the reason. Not so fast! That is a very simplistic view. Let us consider the requirements.

ET will need to be mobile – probably some form of legs, since legs are a tried and proven system here on Earth, although his home planet gravity will determine how many and how strong, long or short they will be. ET will be a land animal. You can't build furnaces, electrical gadgets and such-like, under water. It is probable that ET would live on a planet with an oxygen rich atmosphere. An active ET would need lots of energy and an oxygen burning metabolism is the most efficient, so he would need some form of lungs. He will need efficient arms or appendages for manipulators for handling tools. He will need sensors to get around; sense of touch, sense of hearing; sight, which is very useful, but his eyes may work on a different frequency to ours, depending on his surroundings and the type of star that is his local sun. ET's eyes may look very different to human eyes. On this planet of ours there are two forms of eyes; our own, with the single lens and camera like system, and compound eyes which are favourite with insects.

For some reason people think compound eyes are inferior. They think of short sighted spiders and blue bottle flies. However, I have watched dragonflies catching and eating mosquitoes in the dusk of a summer evening. There is no chance I can see a mosquito twenty feet (6 metres) away in those conditions. For the dragonfly it appears to be no problem. He just zips up and grabs the mosquito out of the air. Some scientists like to show us mosaic pictures on TV, and say "This is what a dragonfly sees. " Are they joking? The dragonfly can see better than I can. The dragonfly's brain, small though it is, will integrate the inputs from all those little lenses to see a clear picture; in a similar way, I have two eyes but I don't see double – not normally anyway. The dragonfly's performance proves compound eyes can work very well indeed. So there is no reason ET would not have compound eyes. I think human beings would have great difficulty in coming to terms with that. It becomes apparent that ET might look like an oversized wasp without wings, or a king sized ant or a centipede (if he lives on a high G planet) or even a land crab. By king sized I mean a minimum of 3 or 4 feet (0.9 or 1.2 metres), possibly much larger. It is difficult to imagine anything smaller building a giant telescope or a Saturn 5 type rocket. An octopus might just fulfil the requirement – but he would need to be drastically toughened up, and develop some sort of skeleton for support on land, as well as lungs, but he would have the necessary mobility plus manipulators. So, if we ever find out about the nearest real ET, we might be in for an unpleasant surprise. No friendly little humanoid with pointy ears! No Klingon or Mr Spock!. He might be tolerant; he might even be friendly; but it would take a massive adjustment to our thinking to really feel friendly to some ghastly, mechanical looking, animal with compound eyes. He might not think too much of us either! Despite all the Sci-Fi films I think it would be a massive shock to realise that this particular bug-eyed alien was real and not just the fanciful dreams of some film producer.

It would not surprise me if ET was telepathic – by which I mean simple, biological radio communication. After all, our brains work using electrical signals. Some fish can generate pulses of electricity up to 600 volts. There are also fish in turbid waters, such as are found in parts of the Amazon river, that use electrical signals to detect their surroundings. Some sharks can detect the electrical signals emanating from prey fish buried in the sand on the sea floor. It would only be a slightly further evolutionary step to have some form of electrical communication, and then on to radio communication – which, to us, would be indistinguishable from telepathy, unless we had a radio we could use to tune in, of course. ET is also likely to be sexual in some way. I say this because sex is almost universal in advanced plants and animals on this Earth, because it allows efficient shuffling of the genes to produce the best solutions for competition and survival. Cloning is an efficient means of reproduction, but it slows down the evolutionary process drastically.

Remarkably, it has been shown that, on this Earth, even bacteria often join together (mate) to swap genes. This is one of the reasons bacteria often evolve fast to beat the latest antibiotics.

So ET will be intelligent, capable, sexual and lethal, and may not look much like a human at all. Even if we only discovered his radio waves – and perhaps deciphered his TV code, (I'm sure ET would soon crack ours) we might be in for a shock. If we could see what ET was like, and what he could do, we might not like it. For instance, ET might be a lot more clever than we are. Just imagine if he could learn more in a week than we could in a year, and had a memory like a super computer; he just might also have the attitude that everything in the Universe was put there for his benefit. I think maybe the gulf between the stars could be a good thing. Remember what happened to the Native Americans when Europeans arrived – and we were close relatives. Incidentally, I sometimes think that if ET picks up our TV and radio signals and deciphers them he will be convinced we are out of our minds.

This brings us to the subject of Flying Saucers and Alien Visits. Ignoring the enormous distances which have to be covered (of which I will write later) then if alien craft have visited the Earth it raises a few questions. Firstly – if they are friendly – why don't they simply land on the White House lawn, or in front of Buckingham Palace, or near the Eiffel Tower and say "Hello"! Why not? Secondly – if they are hostile – what are they messing about for? Having abducted a few of us for samples for study – surely by now they would have developed some murderous disease to eliminate us. (If we can do it – surely they can). There does remain, I admit, a disturbing third possibility. What if they are more advanced than we are (far, far more advanced) and they are decent and considerate. They might be afraid to contact us directly, because we might realise just how far we are behind, and develop an inferiority complex. A friend to whom I mentioned this, years ago, laughed and said "No problem, we will simply learn from them and copy what they had done". Not wishing to offend him I walked away. I realised this was a classic example of the supreme confidence that Homo Sapiens is the highest form of life. What I really meant by the idea of their being superior to us was – superior in every way. Say – 200 or 500 million years of evolution superior. What if they could crack problems in a day that would take us a year of brain racking. What if they had a perfect memory; one hundred percent; never forgot anything. Everything they had ever read, seen or experienced, immediately available for instant, accurate recall and, on top of that, an IQ of 200 plus. We could never compete; never catch up; ever!

Let us consider chimpanzees. They are a very close relative (I detest the animals). They are intelligent, and I think they are on the brink of making the breakthrough (to using weapons) we made 5 million years ago; they hunt, they plan ahead, trap and kill monkeys. They use tools – simple sticks for digging grubs out of tree trunks. The most thought provoking thing about chimpanzees I ever saw on television was an experiment carried out by a group of researchers in Africa. They located a resting group of chimpanzees in a bush area. To see what would happen they had obtained a stuffed lion from somewhere. The stuffed lion was brought close to the chimps, without them noticing, and then slightly exposed to view. The chimps went mad. A number ran around shrieking, but others immediately started looking for rocks, picked them up and threw them at the stuffed lion. I was amazed; I didn't realise chimpanzees would do that. It occurred to me that one of these days, a chimpanzee is going to pick up a thick stick and really realise what a murderous weapon it represents; very much like the classic scene in the film "2001". In fact – I'm surprised it hasn't happened already – from chimpanzees watching what humans do. The point I am trying to make is – the chimpanzees have missed the boat. They are 5 million years too late. They are never going to catch up with us. If, by some miracle, we left them alone to develop, as we did, for 5 million years, then, after that time, we will have advanced further. We will still be 5 million years ahead. So – if ET was 200 million years of evolution ahead of us – we are never going to catch up. The realisation might destroy us. It doesn't destroy the chimps because they are not quite bright enough to understand and know how inferior they are.

I remember, years ago, discussing with my brother the possibility of extra-terrestrial life and the question of evidence on flying saucers. I said the big problem was the ease with which photographs, and even films, could be faked. "Why," I said, "It would even be fairly easy for us to make a fake flying saucer." Instantly his eyes lit up, "How do you think we could do that". So we talked about it and I came up with the suggestion of a simple flying saucer, made of a thin balsa-wood frame and black polythene film. This was way back in the days before the UK had natural gas. At that time we did have a domestic gas supply but it was made from coal. Coal gas, in those days, incorporated a considerable percentage of hydrogen which meant it was buoyant. (If you are interested I have explained how and why in the chapter THE WINDSCALE ACCIDENT). I happened to know the density and could work out how much buoyancy a certain volume would have. In other words, I was able to work out the weight of balsa wood and polythene we could use to create a flying saucer of a given volume. When I said this was possible my brother said "lets do it" and that was that. The result was that a week later we had a nine foot (3 metres) diameter, black, flying saucer on the back lawn. It couldn't be any smaller because, with the low buoyancy of the coal gas, it wouldn't have lifted off. I had designed it carefully. The residual lift – over and above the weight of the balsa and polythene – was such that the contraption would only rise to about 3000/4000 feet (923/1230 metres) altitude. (No point in having it go straight up and disappear). It was stabilised to fly in the correct horizontal posture by a small weight slung underneath on a triangle of fine fishing line. A simple non-return valve was fitted so spare gas would vent as the saucer rose (otherwise the saucer might have burst as it gained height). We then ran a hose back to the gas cooker in mothers kitchen, connected it to the saucer and turned the gas on. There was a steady breeze in a direction which should waft it right over the Midlands. Perfect! After what seemed an interminable time, the saucer lifted off and was restrained by us as the buoyancy built up. When we deemed it was at maximum we let go and the saucer rose steadily off the lawn and away. We climbed into an old banger of a car we had then and followed the saucer. At 500 feet (154 metres) it was very impressive and, as we travelled (we followed it for about15 miles I remember), we saw quite a number of people staring at it and talking to one another. Very gratifying! We then drove back home, leaving the saucer to cruise impressively over the Midland counties and waited for all the fuss to break. We confidently expected it to be on the news and in the papers. We were very disappointed. Nothing! Not a word! Not a report! What was wrong with these people?

I admit to being worried when there was a news item about a plane approaching Birmingham airport reporting a near miss with a balloon. However, our contraption was a flying saucer and looked nothing like a common balloon. It later turned out that what the pilot had reported was indeed a weather balloon, but it gave me qualms. I didn't fancy being responsible for a plane going in to land with a mass of black polythene wrapped around the cockpit window. My brother was disgusted, and suggested we repeat the performance using metallised plastic so the saucer would show up on the radar. I put him off, saying if the RAF sent up a plane in pursuit, and then somehow traced the saucer to us, they might just send us the bill.

I remember we weren't the only ones with imagination. A silver flying saucer shaped object was found near a road over the Yorkshire moors. The thing was only about 4 feet (1.2 metres) in diameter, but very heavy and with no sign of any means of entry. This was reported and taken off to a laboratory for study. After some time the boffins finally decided to drill their way in. When the drill broke through, and was extracted, the tip was covered in a horrible slimy goo that looked a bit like porridge. Awful! After being treated with considerable caution, a sample of the goo was extracted and taken away for analysis. The results came back; it really was porridge! Some students had carefully constructed a fibreglass flying saucer, filled it with porridge (I can't guess how many gallons) and sealed the hole. Magic!

The real problem with aliens visiting us or we ever visiting them someday, is the immense distances involved. We hear glib comments about outer space and space travel, and "we are going to the stars". We then see Star Trek where they are happily cruising through space at 'Warp 6' with the stars sailing past. Reality is very different.

So far, the only way we know how to get into space at all, is to use the same basic principle of the rocket the Chinese discovered a thousand years ago. The Saturn 5 was a fantastic engineering achievement and to place men on the moon and bring them back an almost incredible operation. Probably the greatest engineering achievement of all time. (I say engineering achievement because that is what it was, Scientists discover the science and the principles and engineers take the knowledge and build something that works). In that remarkable journey, the men involved reached, on the return, the highest speed ever reached by man; just under 25,000 miles (40,232 kilometres) per hour. At the present time scientists are experimenting with a new form of rocket; an ion rocket that uses electricity to produce a far more efficient propulsion system for space use. This device is very low thrust but the rocket jet exhausts at a very much higher velocity. By this means you could accelerate a spacecraft to a far higher speed (but taking a long time to do it) than is possible with a simple, chemical fuel, rocket. However, the ion drive still uses fuel for reaction mass, and you still have to use the usual massive booster to get into space in the first place. It is reasonable to expect the ion drive to enable us to reach speeds far greater than the speed the moon astronauts reached. Let us be optimistic and suggest they could reach speeds 100 times as fast. The nearest star to us is Proxima Centauri, which is approximately four light years away. In cosmic terms – on our doorstep. (With our telescopes we can see objects ten thousand million light years away). In human terms four light years is (wait for it) 23.5 million, million miles. At the 2,500,000 miles per hour we are talking about, it would take just over a thousand years to reach Proxima Centauri.

The idea of somehow creating a spacecraft that can reach, say, 90% of the speed of light, is thrown into perspective when you realise that the speed of light is six hundred and seventy million miles an hour. Lets face it – human beings aren't going anywhere except our own solar system. Neither, I suspect is ET, which is probably just as well!

So, we might as well accept that this Earth is home, and the only one we'll ever have, and look after it as best we can. We can also forget about ET and flying saucers. Nobody is going to be abducted. There has to be another explanation for UFO phenomena. Abduction scenarios are a trick of the mind.

As a final note on travel, Einstein theorised that it was impossible for a physical object to travel faster than light, and hundreds of experiments have confirmed the theory. In the most powerful accelerators on Earth they have managed to get to 99.999999% of the speed of light; and that's it! "Warp Drive" is strictly for Star Trek fans. Such things as teleportation, and the hyperspatial tubes of the 'Stargate' series, are no more likely to become reality than a sorcerer's magic wand. Incidentally – ET will have exactly the same problems getting into space as we have. One of the basic tenets of Einstein's Theory of Relativity is that the Laws of Nature are exactly the same wherever you are in the Universe. There is plenty of evidence to confirm that this is true. ET will also have to face the fact that you cannot travel faster than light, just the same as we have to.

I used to enjoy reading science fiction stories of other worlds, so I had to accept the authors must write of some sort of super light-speed travel to get us there. Imagination is one thing. Reality is reality and we have to live with it and so does ET

SPACE ELEVATOR

Quite a long time ago, when scientists first realised it might be possible to place an object – a small satellite – in orbit around the Earth, they first calculated how fast a satellite would have to travel to stay in orbit, just out of the atmosphere, at an altitude of 200 miles (322km). The speed they calculated, around 17,300 miles (27,850km) per hour, meant that such an object would travel around the world, so that it completed one orbit in about 1½ hours. Since the moon, at 240,000 miles (386,232km) distance, did one circuit in 28 days, it became apparent that, in between, there would be a distance from the Earth, where a satellite would orbit once in 24 hours. If you placed such a satellite in an orbit in line with, and over, the equator and travelling in the right direction then, to an observer on the ground, the satellite would appear to be fixed in the sky. We now call these satellites geo-synchronous or geo-stationary satellites.

It then occurred to someone that, if you built a space station in such an orbit, and connected it to the ground at the equator with a cable, you might be able to travel, from earth to the space station in a lift which would run up and down the cable. It was realised, because the cable below the space station would not have sufficient orbital speed, it would, in fact, hang from the space station and act to pull it down. However, if you then extended another cable outwards from the space station, and attached a counterweight (such as a small asteroid) to the end of the second cable, the counterweight, going around the earth once in 24 hours, would be travelling too fast for orbit at that distance, and would tend to be flung outwards. If the counterweight was massive enough and at a suitable distance, the outward pull could counteract the weight of the cable, and the system could continue to rotate indefinitely. It all sounded very ingenious! If such a system were set up, some people said, you would be able to travel up to the orbiting space station using an electric motor powered lift. No massive rocket needed at all. Better still, the lift could be used to carry payload into orbit also. Arthur C Clarke, the science fiction writer, wrote a book "The Fountains of Paradise" based on exactly this proposition. In the story, the cable was made of diamond fibre (this does not yet exist) which, according to the story, might be strong enough to do the job.

A very entertaining tale, but some people have wondered if such a thing could be done in reality. The short answer is NO! First – consider the dimensions. The distance to a geo-stationary position is a little over 22,000 miles (35,405km). To be effective, a counterweight, depending on its mass, would have to be at least 10,000 to 20,000 miles (16,093 to

32,186 kilometres) or more further out. I have calculated that the material required to make the cable would have to have a 'Strength to Weight' Ratio of at least 200 times better than our finest steel. (There is speculation that carbon 'Buckytubes' – single molecule wide ultra-fine filaments of pure carbon – might approach this strength). Even with this strength the weight of the cable from ground to space station would probably be around 40,000 tons or more, the mass of the asteroid counterweight would need to be of the order of ¼ million tons or more, depending on the distance from the Space Station. Even if it were ever possible to assemble such a system, with such immensely long cables, there are factors that would make the operation of such a system impractical. For instance, one of the big problems would be the Coriolis Force acting on a lift as it travelled up the cable to the space station. When a satellite is launched from Cape Canaveral, (or anywhere else) only a fraction of the fuel is used to lift the payload to orbital altitude. A large amount of the fuel is used to accelerate the payload towards the East to orbital velocity. Without orbital speed, the payload would simply fall back to Earth. Any satellite must be accelerated sideways until it reaches orbital velocity, no matter what that orbital velocity might be. (Orbital speeds vary and depend on the altitude). A satellite in geo-stationary orbit has an orbital velocity of around 5,840 miles (9,398km) per hour. Consider how the Space Elevator would work. A lift on the ground, waiting to go up to the space station would have a speed, to the East, of 1,040 miles (1,674km) per hour, due to the earth's rotation. When the lift reaches the space station it will have a sideways velocity, towards the East, of 5,840 mph (9,398km), so the difference of 4,800 mph (7,725km) must be made up somehow. It would be made up by a Coriolis Force acting on the lift as it ascends.

Imagine a railway running North/South on the surface of the earth. Imagine it ran all the way from the North Pole to the equator. If the train started at the North Pole it would have a speed of 0 miles per hour to the East. When it reached the equator it would have a sideways speed of 1,040 mph (1,674km), due to the earth's rotation. In order to accelerate the train sideways, to 1,040 mph (1,674km), the rails would have to supply the 'push' as the train travels. In effect, the rails would feel a slight sideways pressure to the West as the train travelled. Remarkably, this effect is actually detectable on rivers running North/South or vice versa. A North/South river erodes its banks slightly more on one side due to the Coriolis Force.

So, if we consider the Space Elevator, as soon as the lift starts to rise up the cable there will be a Coriolis Force pushing sideways against the cable, increasing to maximum when the lift reaches maximum speed.

There will be a Coriolis Force exerted on the cable all the way to the space station. When the lift stops the Coriolis Force will stop. Imagine the effect of the Coriolis Force when the lift is half way to the space station. The cable will be pushed to the west. An enormous snaking ripple would run up the cable, inducing extra tension, which would act to pull the space station and the counterweight slightly downwards and to the west. When the lift reaches the space station, and the Coriolis Force ceases, the counterweight would act to straighten the cable, and the cable would whip slowly backwards and forwards like an enormous violin string. In addition, the space station and counterweight, which would have been pulled slightly West as the lift ascended, would tend to swing back when the lift had arrived – like a giant pendulum. If one considers two lifts, one going up and one going down at the same time, the Coriolis Forces will not cancel out. It is true the Coriolis Force on the lift going down would act in the opposite direction to the force on the lift going up, but they would only cancel perfectly at the moment the lifts passed each other – and only if the lifts were exactly the same weight i.e. not with one loaded and one empty. With the lifts at the quarter points i.e. with the lift coming down reaching a point a quarter of the way to Earth and the lift going up reaching a point a quarter of the way to the Space Station, the Coriolis Forces would tend to bow the cable into a gigantic S shape and the ripples would become more and more complicated with harmonics being introduced.

There is another problem. It might be thought, at first, that a space station in geo-stationary orbit over a point on the ground, at the equator, would sit in the sky precisely over the ground base. This would not, in fact, be the case. The space station, cable system and counterweight, despite being precisely balanced against Earth's gravity would, nevertheless, be subject to the gravitational pull of both the Moon and the Sun. These forces would act to pull the space station, first one way and then the other, as the Earth rotated, away from its position over ground base. (On Earth we see the effect as these forces pull on the sea and create the tides). The space station (and counterbalance asteroid) would oscillate (wobble) around the perfect geo-stationary position. We would, therefore, have a situation where the cable, under tension, was attached to a fixed position at one end and a wobbling, unstable, position at the other. Even the wobble would not be regular and would vary, depending on the relative positions of the Sun and the Moon. Obviously the motion of the space station and counterweight would, again, induce snaking ripples to run up and down the immensely long cable. These ripples, added to the ripples induced by the Coriolis Forces caused by the moving lifts, would induce additional forces and stress waves. The ripples in the cable would reverberate, back and forth, almost indefinitely since there is nothing, in space, to damp them out as there would be in air (only the final 20 miles (32km) to Earth would be in air). Sooner or later the ripples caused by the movement of the elevators and the ripples caused by the wobble of the asteroid and space station would interact – as waves on the sea occasionally conjoin to create a super wave. The space station would be likely to be 'cracked off' by a sudden force – such as occurs at the end of a whip when it is 'cracked'.

If the cable snapped at its point of maximum load, which would be where it was attached to the space station, the entire 22,000 mile (35,405 kilometres) long cable would fall to the Earth, accelerating faster and faster. Initially, at the ground end, it would appear to start to fall to Earth quite slowly and then the speed would build up, until, by the time the top end of the 40,000 ton cable struck the Earth it would impact at something like 20,000 miles (32,186 kilometres) per hour. To say the least, it would be spectacular. Meanwhile the space station would have been yanked out of its orbit by the asteroid counterweight and would have gone sailing off in a new elliptical orbit. It is possible that the new elliptical orbit would keep the space station and asteroid clear of the Earth but, as would be far more likely, if the elliptical orbit was elongated enough, some unfortunate place on Earth might be hammered by an impacting asteroid and space station, again with an impact speed of around 20,000 miles (32,186 kilometres) per hour.

So far we have not even considered the risk which would be posed by satellites and space 'junk' in low earth orbit. There are thousands of communication, surveillance and scientific satellites (including the Hubble telescope) in orbit at heights of between 200 to 600 miles (322 to 966 kilometres). Additionally there are scores of thousands of bits of space 'junk' such as empty boosters and bits and pieces, down to screw and bolt size. (The Chinese recently added to the mess by blowing up one of their satellites in orbit). All of these items are in inclined orbits. In other words their orbits take them over the Northern and Southern hemispheres of the globe – which means they all pass over the Equator regularly – every three quarters of an hour or so. They are all travelling at around 17,000 miles (27,358km) per hour whereas the Space Elevator cable would be stationary, relative to the ground. It would be like having a stationary vertical post in the middle of a race track. Sooner or later the cable would be struck by an orbiting object. At 17,000 miles (27,358km) per hour the impact of something as light as a sheet of paper would be enough to shatter the cable.

The only possible rational conclusion from all this is that the idea of a Space Elevator is non viable. It is, and will remain, purely in the realms of Science Fiction with no possibility of ever becoming reality. There is no, and never will be, any easy way to get into space.

WAR AND NUCLEAR WEAPONS

When I was fifteen years of age, in 1944 – the middle of World War Two, when the public, in general, had no idea of nuclear energy and all atomic weapon research was top secret – I already knew about Uranium fission and the possibility of making an atomic bomb. I even knew how an atomic bomb might be designed. Twelve months later a bomb of this design wiped out Hiroshima. If this sounds extremely unlikely it is, nevertheless, true.

The reason for this remarkable knowledge in one so young is simple; I read Science Fiction stories. As a child I was very curious and, fortunately, had an Uncle who was a Sci-Fi enthusiast. In those days very few people ever bothered to read science fiction. The people who did were usually Scientists or Engineers. (My uncle was an electrical engineer working at Siemens of Stafford). Once, when I met him, he realised how curious I was and gave me a copy of 'The Time Machine' by H. G. Wells. I read this and was fascinated. He then let me have other books – 'The War of the Worlds' again by H. G. Wells and Jules Verne's 'Twenty Thousand Leagues Under the Sea'. I found these books fascinating. Incidentally, as a testament to the imaginative and inventive powers of Jules Verne it was found, when Governments and Engineers finally got around to designing and building submarines for War, there was literally nothing they could patent. Jules Verne had already invented it. Periscopes, ballast tanks, hydroplanes and so on. Verne also imagined and described in his book, how the submarine, called 'Nautilus' had a remarkable power source which enabled the submarine to cruise almost endlessly beneath the sea, without having to refuel all the time. Naturally, when the USA finally produced the World's first nuclear powered submarine that could do just that – there was really only one suitable name to call it – 'Nautilus'. Other Science Fiction writers, over the years, have thought up, years in advance, many of the things we see today.

The remarkable H. G. Wells, back in 1914, upon learning about Einstein's 'Relativity' and the implications of $E=MC^2$ (that matter, and hence atoms, are simply another form of energy) promptly wrote a science fiction novel – 'The World Set Free' predicting atomic bombs, nuclear war, the destruction of all major cities by atomic weapons and the creation of World Government in the aftermath.

Having found I was interested in Science Fiction, my uncle gave me a whole stack of Science Fiction magazines and books. This was in the early 1940's. Some of the magazines, in addition to fascinating stories, also contained scientific articles. As I waded through all these books I read stories which included descriptions of rocket ships, guided missiles, flying bombs and even lasers, long before any of these were really developed. In some of these magazines there were stories referring to Atomic Power Stations. In others, a reference to Atomic Bombs and the immense power they would produce. I even read a story which described a proposed design of an atomic bomb. According to the story Uranium was naturally radioactive, which means a few of its atoms spontaneously fission (disintegrate) and, as part of the process, neutrons are released. In a very small piece of uranium these neutrons would pass through the metal and escape, but if one of them happened to strike the nucleus of another uranium atom, it would trigger the fission of the second atom which would again produce neutrons. Therefore, if you had a large enough piece of uranium – termed 'The Critical Mass' – a chain reaction could build up, very rapidly, and result in an explosion.

To design an atomic bomb, all that would be necessary would be to have two pieces of uranium – both of sub-critical mass - and bring the pieces together at high speed to produce a mass above critical size and you would produce a nuclear explosion. The proposed design of an atomic bomb incorporated a tube of metal, like a gun barrel with a collar of uranium at one end and, at the other, a solid shell made of uranium. Behind the uranium shell was an explosive charge just like in a gun. Apparently, if you fired the charge, the uranium shell would travel down the barrel at high speed, pass through the collar, create a critical mass and the bomb would detonate. Everything I read about Atomic Bombs in these Science Fiction stories insisted that an Atomic Bomb would be vastly more powerful than ordinary high explosive bombs. They would make war impossible. I was about 15 years old when I read this. The bomb design described was published in March 1944. It was proposed by a science fiction writer – Cleve Cartmill. I read, a year or two ago, an article about the reaction it caused.

When the Sci Fi was published, the writer had the FBI on his doorstep very quickly, demanding to know where he had obtained this information, and making threats. He told them he hadn't obtained information about the bomb from anywhere, he had just 'thought it up' after reading that the physicist – Otto Hahn, in Germany, had experimented with Uranium and found that it would fission under neutron bombardment. (Hahn published details of his research and results). The Science Fiction writer thought about it and devised his own idea of how to make an atomic bomb. The FBI need not have bothered. It didn't matter. It didn't matter at all! The German scientists were no fools. They could have sketched the Bomb just as easily themselves – and probably already had. The following will give a clue to their capabilities. In the war the

British invented a revolutionary new short wavelength radar, capable of showing the ground in detail – even on a hopelessly cloudy night. It used a device called a Resonant Cavity Magnetron (a version of which is used in your Microwave today). They only fitted this radar in special planes called "Pathfinders", and wondered what would happen if one crashed, as was certain to happen sooner or later, probably sooner. They decided to include an explosive device – to blow the magnetron to smithereens if the plane came down in enemy territory. Eventually a plane crashed, the explosive worked and the magnetron was blown to the four winds. The Germans had realised the British must have something new, the bombing was too good – and on cloudy nights too! They searched, found the pieces, put them together, worked out how the device operated and made a working copy – in six weeks.

So in 1945 I already knew of the possibility of atomic bombs. I was in the house when Mum and Dad were sitting listening to the radio, waiting to hear the news. In those days everything was precise. The news was at nine o'clock; on the dot – to the second – the announcer came on. His words were something like this. "Good evening. Here is the news, and this is Alvar Liddell reading it. The Allies have dropped an Atomic Bomb on Japan." I didn't hear anymore. I turned to my father and said "The war is over! That must mean the end of the war!" I remember he smiled and said, "We'll see!"

The bomb that destroyed Hiroshima was almost exactly like the suggested design in the Sci Fi magazine. The bomb seemed so simple it was untrue. In practice, of course, building the bomb wasn't anything like as easy as it sounds. There is a problem, a very big problem. When you extract Uranium metal from the ore – which can be found all over the planet – the metal consists of a mixture of two isotopes of uranium, U235 and U238. The bomb can only be made with U235 and it is the devil's own job to separate the two. Cutting a long story short, (there are plenty of books to read on the subject if you are interested) the separation of uranium to make the bomb involved America in the biggest industrial effort ever made on this planet up to that time. They felt they had to do it. Had to work like maniacs to do it. After all – uranium fission was discovered in Germany and Germany had some of the best scientists in the World. The thought of Adolf Hitler getting the atomic bomb was too horrendous to contemplate.

In the event it turned out, because German industrial capacity and their economy was already stretched to the absolute limit, they simply didn't have the industrial capacity available to do it. At least – not to produce an atomic bomb using uranium. The German scientists, of course, knew as much about uranium as the Allies did, and they did set up a nuclear reactor device in the mountains of Bavaria. It was a fairly crude effort, with uranium blocks suspended on chains in a large tank intended to be filled with heavy water. The thing might well have worked – a sort of cheap and nasty nuclear reactor. Fortunately, heavy water is hard to come by. The main source for the Germans was a heavy water extraction plant created and run by a firm called 'Norsk Hydro' in Norway. The British, working with Norwegian colleagues, sent a team to Norway and sabotaged the heavy water plant. They also succeeded in sinking a ship, loaded with the only tanks of heavy water already extracted, starting on the trip to Germany. After this, the British bombed the Norsk Hydro installation to try and prevent rebuilding. The Allies were panicking. And rightly so! In Germany, a brilliant engineer by the name of Werner von Braun had managed to design, and build, the biggest and most remarkable rocket the World had ever seen – the V2.

This rocket was the first modern style, liquid fuelled rocket. To make it work, the Germans solved enormous problems and invented all of the devices and systems that make a space rocket work today. This rocket was capable of reaching London from France, and did. It carried a ton of explosive. Many fell on London in the latter stages of the war and one dropped on a Woolworths store, killing 300 people. In 1945, having cracked all the problems, von Braun was working on a much more massive rocket, capable of striking the United States. The Germans were also planning one that would go around the World – the Sanger Bomber. It doesn't take much imagination to realise that, with an atomic bomb on the nose of these things, Hitler's dream of conquering the World might not be such a crazy dream after all. The Allies were right to panic – more than they actually knew.

When they started out – the only imaginable way to make an Atomic Bomb was to use Uranium 235 and, to make the first bomb, they spent billions of dollars. When Uranium metal is produced from the ore it is, in fact, a mixture of two uranium isotopes – U235 and U238. Less than 1% is U235 and over 99% is U238. An Atomic Bomb can only be constructed using U235. To separate U235 from U238 was a gargantuan task. U235 cannot be separated from U238 chemically, so they built enormous industrial complexes to do the separation electrically. They built other enormous installations to do the job by diffusion. The financial outlay was immense. Today it is possible to separate U235 from U238 using ultra high speed centrifuges, as the Iranians are doing at the present time. If you would like to know more about the colossal industrial effort needed to produce the first uranium fuelled atomic bomb there is plenty of information –dig it out! The remarkable thing, which nobody knew at the time, is that all this work and expenditure on separating uranium was unnecessary.

It is possible to build a working nuclear reactor – not a bomb – using U238. In other words – the common U238/U235 mix that was first produced from the ore. Such a reactor is a great cumbersome thing – bigger than a house – but you can do it. The Americans built one in Chicago under the leadership of a great scientist – Enrico Fermi. When this reactor was operated (it was achieved before the first bomb was made) they made a remarkable discovery. The neutron radiation created, when the reactor was operating, converted some of the uranium into a new, previously unknown, metal – Plutonium. This substance proved to be even better for making atomic bombs than uranium and, most importantly, it could be separated chemically. So we realise that, if Germanys crude reactor had worked, as it probably would have, the Germans would have made Plutonium – which could be extracted relatively easily by chemical means. It was a good thing the Allies did panic and that the Americans committed unbelievable efforts and money to get the A Bomb first.

At this point it might interest the reader to know something that has never been properly emphasised. The staggering thing is that, all along, Hitler had a weapon almost as dangerous as the Atomic Bomb. He had a weapon that could have killed millions of people in the U.K. in a few nights; could have devastated the Russian armies; could have wrecked and destroyed the Allied D Day landings in Normandy and probably set back the liberation of Europe for years. I refer to the nerve gases Tabun and Sarin which were invented by German scientists just before the war. These gases are absolutely lethal. The gas masks of the time would have been useless. It is not even necessary to breathe any into the lungs, just one speck on the skin can kill, and these gases are odourless and invisible. They were produced as a result of research carried out on the effects of insecticides. The modern nerve gases – which the armies of today are so scared of – are only very slightly more effective than the German originals. At any time during the war, fifty Heinkel bombers, carefully placing their nerve gas bombs upwind of London, could probably have killed 200,000 or more people in one night.

To me – as a 15 year old boy in 1944 – it never made sense for Germany to build the V2 ballistic missile rockets. They were committing an enormous amount of their war effort to build elaborate, and expensive, machines, which would be used only once and simply dumped one ton of high explosive somewhere on London (the V2 was not very accurate). A British Lancaster bomber would carry 8 tons of bombs (ten tons at a pinch) and drop them just where you wanted. It would then fly home for another load and repeat the performance again and again. The average survival time of a Lancaster (and crew) was about 20 trips. So, to me it made more sense to make Lancasters – or the German equivalent thereof. Why waste time with these V2s? However, if you were to load a ton of Sarin on the nose of the V2, what then? The incredible thing is – Hitler refused to use the nerve gas even at critical stages of the war; even during the last days in the bunker in Berlin he would not give the order. It is true he was gassed himself in the First World War, but that cannot have been the reason. The reason is far simpler. He was convinced, since making Sarin and Tabun was so easy, the Allies must have it too. He thought that if he used the nerve gases the Allies would retaliate in kind and Germany, a relatively small country – every part of which was accessible to Allied bombers, would be just about exterminated. He might be able to do that to Britain – but not to America or Russia. They were too vast and he didn't have the means to deliver.

That this possibility was real – of Hitler having the power to order mass slaughter using nerve gas weapons – was proved when the War ended in 1945. When the Allies occupied Germany they found stock piles of nerve gas weapons – more than half a million artillery shells and a hundred thousand aircraft bombs, all filled with the deadly nerve gases, ready to be used if Hitler gave the order. Most of these weapons were disposed of, by the Allies, by being dumped in the sea. The nerve gas production facility, in Poland, was found by the advancing Russians who dismantled the entire facility, together with all the manufacturing equipment, and took everything back to Russia.

Just imagine! The day after D Day; vast numbers of Allied troops crowded on the beach heads in Normandy; tremendous concentrations of ships and men; and he had the means to practically wipe them out with a massive night attack – bombers and fighters loaded with bombs full of Tabun, then follow this up with an artillery bombardment of nerve gas shells. If, in reality, he had done this – it would probably have prolonged the war for years with heaven knows what consequences. It wouldn't have been long, though, before the Allies had copied the Sarin, once the chemists managed to get their hands on a sample. It makes you think doesn't it?

One conclusion is – Hitler was not mad; whatever he was, he was not mad. A madman would have used it and, in the end, Germany would have been nearly exterminated in one gigantic Gotterdammerung. Hitler knew this and he was right. Churchill was already considering saturating Germany with Anthrax. It was the same thinking that made Nikita Khrushchev back down during the Cuban Missile Crisis. He had to! Khrushchev was not mad. He simply had to back down – otherwise the

Soviet Union would have been practically wiped from the face of the Earth.

If one considers the design of the Atomic weapons, the early "gun barrel" device was a basically dangerous design. If it is to be delivered by an aircraft such as the 'Enola Gay' (the B29 bomber that dropped the Hiroshima bomb), then the explosive charge could be inserted behind the uranium shell, just before the weapon was due to be dropped. However, if the bomb is to be delivered by a hundred foot (30.7 metre) rocket missile which, in a crisis, might be standing on the pad, ready to go, with sirens blaring, what then? Or, if the explosive was in position, and the missile caught fire on the pad or, after launch, veered off course and fell on one of your own cities? What then? It would be possible for the explosive to detonate and set off the nuclear bomb if it was simply heated and not deliberately detonated at all.

Time for more rational thinking! It is a fact that, in the height of the Cold War, a great many people were very scared that we, or the Russians, might have a silo fire and a missile would blow up in its silo, producing a nuclear explosion and the usual mushroom cloud. Somebody might panic, assume it was an enemy attack, push the red button and start World War Three. I was very pleased to learn how a modern Atomic Bomb worked and that it was impossible for it to explode accidentally, fire or no fire!

The first Atom Bomb dropped on Japan was the crude gun barrel type, which worked as planned and devastated Hiroshima. The second bomb was far more sophisticated. It was made using Plutonium, instead of Uranium, and was detonated by a process known as implosion. If one has a slightly sub-critical mass of Plutonium and you then compress it into a smaller volume, the mass will become critical and explode. This will work if a hollow ball is used or even a solid one. (A solid ball can be compressed if sufficient force is applied; there is no such thing as an incompressible material).

A simplified description of the working of a Plutonium bomb is as follows. A spherical plutonium core of a bomb is surrounded by a complete shell of explosive – as the stone in a cherry is surrounded by flesh. There are a dozen detonators or more arranged evenly over the outside surface of the shell of explosive. To make the bomb work – it is essential that all the detonators fire together; by together I mean together to a millionth of a second or less. If this doesn't happen – if just one of these detonators fails to work - the bomb will fail. When all these detonators fire together, a spherical detonation wave is produced in the explosive. A spherical shock wave, of tremendous power, blasts inwards and strikes the plutonium core with an even blow – perfectly symmetrically, with a pressure of millions of pounds per square inch. The plutonium core is pounded inwards, compressed by the colossal force, to create a critical mass.

Originally the early designs incorporated a hollow sphere of plutonium, but now it is usual to use a solid sphere. The solid ball of plutonium is momentarily crushed. It reaches criticality, a chain reaction is initiated, resulting in an enormous release of energy, which creates a massive fireball and, finally, the mushroom cloud.

I referred to the plutonium ball being crushed momentarily. If you used a solid ball of – say – iron. (Yes! Iron would be crushed – just the same;) the ball would be momentarily crushed but then, as the shock wave subsided, the ball would 'bounce back' to normal size, in fact, it would bounce back so violently it would, itself, explode into fragments. In practice the plutonium ball becomes critical and the nuclear explosion is created in the micro-second it is compressed. (You can read all about neutron induced chain reactions and critical mass if you wish to. Just dig out the info!). It was necessary to invent special detonators to make the plutonium bomb work. These are exploding wire devices that are fired electrically – by a pulse from a capacitor - so you have a dozen pulses going down a dozen wires simultaneously, to a millionth of a second or less. All you then need is some type of switch, to connect the wires, so that you can arm the bomb just before it drops on an enemy city, and you have an inherently safe atomic bomb. If the missile you launch explodes on the pad, or drops on one of your own cities, the bomb will not go off; not as a nuclear bomb. There will be a fire. The explosive will detonate but it will not explode perfectly enough to crush the plutonium sphere. It will splatter it around and contaminate a small area, but there will not be a Nagasaki explosion – or far worse. Believe it or not, but the B52 bombers cruising around the skies during the Cold War were bombed up; armed with multi-megaton Hydrogen bombs – not low yield little fission bombs, like the one that destroyed Nagasaki.

The Hydrogen Bomb uses a plutonium bomb as a trigger. It works on a principle called Thermonuclear Fusion. Briefly, if you compress a form of hydrogen (Deuterium) and heat it to millions of degrees centigrade (or Celsius if you prefer) the hydrogen undergoes a nuclear reaction and produces far, far, more energy than the A bomb did. A plutonium bomb can do the trick and set off the thermonuclear detonation. We are now talking explosive power to the equivalent of millions of tons of TNT; bombs a thousand times more powerful than the bomb that destroyed Nagasaki. They need to be safe!

During the cold war a number of B52 bombers – fully armed with hydrogen bombs - were in the air twenty four hours a day 365 days a year, so that the U.S.A. could not be caught out with the bombers on the ground, should the Russians start World War Three. Accidents, however, will happen! On January 17th, 1966 over Spain, a B52 collided with the tanker aircraft refuelling it in the sky, near the town of Palomares. There was an enormous fireball of blazing fuel. Out of the fireball dropped four hydrogen bombs. Twenty two million tons of TNT equivalent each. The plane was carrying bombs with explosive power equivalent to 88 million tons of TNT! Three of the bombs fell on land. There were dynamite explosions; plutonium was scattered around but Palomares and a big chunk of Spain were not wiped off the map. The Americans paid for the clean-up operation and drums of contaminated ground were shipped back to the United States. The fourth bomb fell in the sea – which is very deep just there. Even just off the coast the bomb went down to 8000 feet (2461 metres). It cost a fortune to get it back. I saw a photograph of the rescued bomb lying on the deck of a ship. It was less than twelve feet (3.7 metres) long and two and a half feet (76 centimetres) in diameter. Twenty two megatons. Unbelievable!

Two years later the 'fail safe' design of Thermonuclear bombs was again demonstrated when another B52 carrying its four H Bombs caught fire as it flew over Baffin Bay near the west coast of Greenland. The fire was in the main fuselage and the crew made valiant attempts to extinguish it while trying to reach the U.S. air base at Thule, on the north west Greenland coast. On the approach to the base the fire became intense, the plane began to disintegrate and it became obvious a landing was impossible. Despite the fire affecting the controls, the pilot managed to keep the plane in the air long enough to pass over the air base at a low altitude which, fortunately, was enough to allow the crew to bale out (except for one man who was killed). The blazing plane, complete with bombs, plunged on to the ice only 5 miles (8.047 kilometres) away. The explosive in the bombs detonated on impact; the resulting shock wave jolting the entire air base. However, there was no nuclear detonation or Thule would have disappeared from the map. No doubt there were a lot of white faces and sweaty palms. Another massive clean-up was required.

By July 1945 the Americans had managed to make just three atomic bombs. They were confident the uranium bomb would work. The plutonium weapon was a different thing all together, far more complicated and difficult. With the plutonium bomb, the explosive surrounding the plutonium core had to detonate perfectly. All the detonators had to work at the same time – to within a millionth of a second. The explosive was not homogeneous, (the same all through) it varied. Some parts had to propagate the shock wave of the detonation faster than other parts, so that a perfect imploding spherical shock wave was produced. When this perfect shock wave struck the plutonium sphere at the centre, crushing it evenly on all sides, it would only be in the perfect compressed state for a millionth of a second or less. In the uranium bomb – the gun barrel type – there would be far more time, and the natural radioactivity of the uranium would be enough to initiate the chain reaction. Not so the plutonium bomb! Not enough time! The chain reaction must start and propagate instantly the compressed plutonium ball reaches criticality. To ensure this happened they had to use an initiator – a little spherical ball – less than the size of a hazelnut, made up of polonium and beryllium, nested in the centre of the plutonium sphere. Upon detonation, the shock wave strikes the sphere of plutonium, compressing it, and passing right through it, until it strikes the little initiator ball in the centre. Here the designers did not want perfect compression. The initiator was arranged so the shock wave mixes the polonium and beryllium. Without going into too much detail, the mixing of the polonium and beryllium creates a blast of neutron radiation, instantly; enough to start the chain reaction in the plutonium sphere. Nuclear reactions are so fast that the plutonium sphere reacted, and produced 90% of the 10 or 15 kilotons (TNT equivalent) energy of the bomb in a millionth of a second, before the condition of the plutonium sphere could change. After that, the explosion is a question of vaporisation and expansion. An Atomic Bomb does not produce any blast to speak of, itself. It produces energy which is released in the form of radiation. The radiation is absorbed by the material of its surroundings and by the air, which then heats up to produce the fireball.

The Americans could risk dropping the uranium bomb on Japan. They were confident it would work. Not so the plutonium bomb! If it did not work, the Japanese would be handed a free sample of plutonium; not in a nice neat ball, but as radioactive residue left when the surrounding explosive detonated, but without the essential precision. Nevertheless that would be a disaster. They had 3 bombs. One uranium and two plutonium. Because of the extreme complexity of the plutonium bombs, it was decided that a final, actual, test of a working bomb must be carried out. Only in that way could they really be sure of efficient detonation. A number of scientists did not believe it would work. Others were afraid that, if it did, there was a risk of starting a fusion reaction in the very atmosphere itself and converting the planet into a small star. Before they went ahead, this latter idea was carefully considered, before it was dismissed as extremely unlikely.

When the bomb finally detonated on top of the tower, that morning at Alamagordo, with a flash that was seen hundreds of miles away, the World changed forever. Robert Oppenheimer – when he saw the blast - realised the implications and muttered a line from an Indian religious text, "Now I am become Death, The Destroyer of Worlds" It is said that Enrico Fermi, who was also there, dropped small pieces of paper and watched how far the pieces were displaced by the shock wave – when that arrived. He knew the distance to the explosion and saw how far the paper kicked – which gave him an indication of the power of the shock wave. They say that he worked out the power of the bomb, accurate to within 10%, right then and there. A clever man that – as all were who worked on the bomb. Soon afterwards, the Enola Gay (a B29 bomber) lifted off to deliver her deadly cargo to Japan.

I am of the opinion that President Truman must have been a good poker player. After the first nuclear bomb detonated over Hiroshima and reduced it to ashes and rubble, in one single enormous explosion, the Japanese were stunned. However, they did nothing and said nothing. It must be remembered that General Curtis-Le-May's firebombing of Tokyo actually killed more people, in one night, than were killed by the atomic bomb over Hiroshima. It was the fact that one single bomb dropped by one plane had created so much devastation that was so staggering. President Truman dispatched a message to the Japanese, stating that, if they did not surrender, then the whole of Japan would rapidly be reduced to ashes. After twenty four hours there was no reply, at which point President Truman ordered the dropping of the second bomb (the plutonium bomb) on Nagasaki. With a second city destroyed by a single weapon, the Japanese were convinced, and offered to surrender – but with one condition, that they be permitted to keep their Emperor. Not quite the unconditional surrender that had been demanded for so long, but it would be the end of a war that threatened to degenerate into a nightmare of slaughter. The Americans decided to accept the Japanese surrender on these terms. After all, they had no more nuclear bombs immediately available. If the Japanese had known the truth – that there were only the two bombs – and it would take months to produce any more, they might well have decided to hang on and maybe fight it out.

A great deal has been written about the rights and wrongs of the destruction of the two Japanese cities by the atomic bomb. For myself – I have no doubt whatsoever that it was the right thing to do. The Japanese were already being slaughtered in their hundreds of thousands by the US Air force under General Curtis-Le-May, a dedicated ruthless slayer of enemies if ever there was one.

During the European war, it had been demonstrated that, if bombers could cause enough fires in a given area of a city, the whole area – no matter how large – would heat up to the point where everything would burst into flames. Hamburg was the first city where this actually occurred. Thus was created the first example of a situation called a 'Fire

Storm'. The words 'Fire Storm' have been used incorrectly on a number of occasions – to describe large fires; but the true meaning of Fire Storm is terrible indeed. All the buildings and all the combustibles in the Fire Storm area catch fire. The very air can reach temperatures of up to a thousand degrees. Any person out in the open in that area will be roasted. The firestorm at Hamburg is believed to have killed forty thousand people in one night. When the news gradually leaked out, and finally reached London, they wondered if it was true, but the reports were convincing. It was decided to find out if it could be done again. World War Two was a savage, murderous war. No holds barred! At one stage, the German Propaganda minister, Goebbels, had screamed, "Do you want total war?" to a great crowd at a gathering. Consumed by patriotism, the crowds roared their reply. "YES!" They got it! The British decided to try to destroy Dresden. When the bombers went in they knew exactly what to do. Firebombs and explosives in the first loads, to stop the fire brigades and let the first fires develop; then saturate the entire city with incendiaries. Every Lancaster bomber could carry eight tons. The fires caught, they multiplied and extended, and finally became a true Fire Storm.

The buildings burned. Everything burned. Even the tarmacadam on the pavements and roads caught fire. The city became a furnace. People on the streets were reduced to cinders and even ashes, others, deep down in cellars, where you would think they would be safe, died. They were suffocated because the fires used up all the oxygen in the air. Dreadful beyond belief! No one knows how many people died – many had just disappeared. It is estimated the figure might have been as high as 100,000 dead or more. It was terrible! It was dreadful! It was not really necessary. Germany was beaten; everybody knew it! Germany was on the brink of collapse. Dresden was famous for its bone china; there weren't any important factories there, which was why it had mainly been left alone up to that date. Before this bombing, Dresden was, to all intents and purposes, intact. Many, indeed most, German cities were in ruins. (In 1952, 7 years after the end of the war, I went to Berlin. Rebuilding was going on, but I went to Charlottenburg – an area where rebuilding had not yet started, I was utterly appalled. There was not a single intact building as far as the eye could see, just endless acres of rubble, with the remains of half destroyed chimneys sticking up like the fingers of a gigantic corpse. It took my breath away). Dresden was the perfect city for an experiment and that is what I believe it was. An experiment! In my mind, Dresden was an atrocity committed by my own country. What else can you call it? It has been said that some RAF pilots, knowing a little about Dresden, refused to drop their bombs there. I am a little sceptical. Not many people on our side, or theirs, would disobey orders in World War Two. The news the next day in Britain was quite normal. "Here is the news. Last night British Bombers attacked Berlin and Dresden." That was all!

General Curtis-Le-May was told about Dresden and Hamburg. He then knew what to do, and he did it with his usual utterly ruthless efficiency. He had every B29 (Superfortress) bomber that could fly, filled with firebombs. He ordered the crews to strip out every single defensive machine gun – every round of ammunition – so that they could load a few more firebombs in the bomb bays. He sent out pathfinders to mark the targets with coloured flares and lights (a technique developed by the British). Curtis-Le-May sent the bombers to Tokyo. The pathfinders had their orders, and sub-divided Tokyo into areas with different coloured markers. The bomber pilots were told – "You bomb the green! You bomb the yellow! You bomb the red!" – and so on.

The bombers went in low to make sure they were accurate – to spread the firebombs as evenly as possible (the bombers normally operated at over thirty thousand feet). Tokyo burned – from end to end. The whole of Tokyo was razed to the ground. The dead were reckoned to be well over one hundred thousand and possibly might have been twice that many. People who haven't lived through World War Two, have little idea of how savage the war was. I was only ten years old at the start; sixteen at the end; but I knew! The RAF used to suffer losses of up to one hundred bombers a night (700 men). A loss of up to 50 bombers a night was considered normal. This was an acceptable loss for the damage achieved. Three hundred and fifty men a night – just written off; 'Expendable' they called it. Bomber crews could expect to last roughly 20 Operations (flights over enemy territory). Bomber crews who actually lasted for 30 trips and were allowed a rest (only a short one mind you - they were expendable) were very lucky. You really cannot compare any recent war with World War Two. It was utter, total, brutal savagery – on both sides.

Curtis-Le-May set out to burn every single city in Japan, from end to end. Make no mistake – he would have done it; but when the atomic bomb was dropped it was an even greater shock. One bomb! One plane! Seventy or eighty thousand dead! Can it be possible? The fact that they were already killing as many, and more, in one day's normal operations was lost. (Up to one thousand bombers were used to do that). Everybody was staggered. The Japanese were stunned, (they had no idea how many of these bombs the Americans might have) and they were given a reasonable excuse to end the war. No country – no matter how brave – no matter how resolute – could stand against atomic bombs. So the Japanese capitulated, unconditionally, or so it was said by everybody in the West.

Since 1943 the Allies had repeatedly stated, "This time there will be no deals, no negotiations, no quibbling, no arguing. We will not stop war against Germany and Japan until there is Total and Unconditional Surrender." They said it over and over again, "Unconditional Surrender!" In the event, the Japanese surrendered – on one condition – that they could keep their Emperor; even when threatened with the atomic bomb! The Allies agreed.

If there had been no atomic bomb the Japanese would have fought on. Curtis-Le-May would have burned every single Japanese city to cinders. The Allies – mainly the Americans – would have had to invade Japan; a direct 'D Day' style landing on Japanese homeland beaches. The slaughter would have been unbelievable. The Japanese were keeping back thousands of planes for the final desperate suicide attacks. They are reputed to have built five thousand suicide power boats, loaded with explosives, to attack ships and landing craft.

The Allies had already had a demonstration of what the Japanese were like if you touched their home islands. Okinawa, an island to the south of the main Japanese islands, was attacked by a massive American combined assault. The Japanese considered Okinawa a part of Japan. There were 100 thousand Japanese troops on the island. The Americans landed, despite murderous attacks by Kamikaze planes on ships and transports. The battle raged on, until the whole one hundred thousand Japanese were killed or committed suicide. The Americans shot them, bombed them, shelled them and burned them. They had to! They would not give in! I stated the whole of the 100,000 Japanese soldiers were killed; not quite! But less than one man in a hundred surrendered.

Even the civilians refused to accept defeat! Rather than live under the Americans they jumped off cliffs in droves, including some women carrying babies. Some of this is on film. Harrowing – almost beyond belief! It would have been the same if we had invaded the mainland. (It couldn't be worse could it? Not possible!) The slaughter would have been beyond comprehension. The Allies had vowed to defeat them – and they had already showed they meant it. There was no way the Allies would give up – and there was no way the Japanese would give in – not while there was one live Japanese soldier standing; there were still millions of them. And what of the civilians? Remember Okinawa!

The scene was set for the greatest human slaughter the World had ever seen. It would have reduced any previous slaughter into insignificance. The only way I can imagine anything exceeding the slaughter in the Battle of Japan, would be in a full scale nuclear war. If you can set aside the emotion – and look at it as efficiently as an accountant and simply consider the figures - with the bomb or without the bomb - I have no doubt whatsoever in my mind, Truman was right. To use the bomb was the correct decision. If you look at it unemotionally, the atomic bomb saved millions of lives, both Allied and Japanese. Hiroshima and Nagasaki would have gone anyway. Curtis-Le-May would have seen to that! I lived at that time. The attitude of the people was absolute resolve. The Japanese will be beaten; the Japanese must be beaten and it will be done come what may – no matter what – no matter the cost.

The savagery of war is shown in attitudes. The Japanese were 'animals'. The kamikaze pilots were 'mindless fanatics'. In Europe, after D Day, a small town in Normandy was defended by German troops. The Allies attacked again and again. The Germans would not budge. "OK!" they said "Bring in the bombers!" So they called up six hundred bombers – six hundred! – on a small town. The town was literally bombed flat. Nothing but rubble! Piles of bricks! When the Allies advanced, the remaining Germans came up out of the rubble (those few that were left) and fought. An American commander is reported to have written home, "These Nazi's are like rats. They still come up out of the rubble."

In my mind we are all Homo Sapiens. Courage is courage, bravery is bravery. I take my hat off to them. I bow my head; no matter to what nation they belonged. If the Germans in Normandy had been Allied troops they would have been Brave Soldiers, Men of Courage and Resolve, Men of Steel! And they were!

Those people who have argued against the use of the atomic bomb have made much of the fact that, before Hiroshima, the Japanese had put out the first 'peace feelers'. In other words they had hinted they might be prepared to negotiate. This is not too surprising because it became obvious to them, as it was obvious to everybody else, that they could no longer hope to win the war. Therefore it made sense to back off, if they could, and do some sort of deal whereby Japan would be able to get out of the war with minimum inconvenience. There were two key tenets to the proposals. One was that they keep their Emperor and the other – that Japan would be left alone and not occupied. The idea that the enemy would occupy the Japanese main islands and flaunt the fact that they had beaten the Japanese into submission was too painful to bear. Better to die than to suffer the loss of face and humiliation.

The possibility of Japan negotiating its way out of the war was exactly the situation the Allies had vowed would not happen; not with Germany; not with Japan. Unconditional Surrender it must be. The Allies vowed to pursue the war to the bitter end so that they and they alone would dictate the terms. They and they alone would say what form of Government would be allowed in the defeated nations and would control every detail of the organisation and running of the countries. The attitude was that the Armistice of 1918, tough though it had been had, nevertheless, given Germany chance to recuperate, re-arm and 'have another go'. No way were they going to make the same mistake again. This time it was going to be Unconditional Surrender. No ifs, no buts, no maybes. It can be seen, therefore, that, in the circumstances that existed at the time, there was no real possibility of the war being brought to an end by negotiation at that stage. There was no possibility the Japanese would countenance unconditional surrender. Better to keep their honour and die to the last man.

In the event, the Japanese accepted surrender and occupation of the Japanese Mainlands only because the Emperor himself stepped in (after Hiroshima and Nagasaki), spoke to them personally, on the radio, for the very first time in history and ordered them to accept. He stated that, for the survival of Japan, they must tolerate the intolerable and endure the unendurable. If he had said, instead, that they must fight on, for the honour of the Emperor and the honour of Japan – A bomb or no A bomb, I feel sure they would have done so. I have little doubt the Allies realised this and decided maybe it might be wise to let them keep their Emperor.

When World War Two ended in 1945 everybody took a deep breath. No more war! However, Joseph Stalin in the Kremlin was not of the same mind. Stalin had a Hitler complex. The Communists would rule the World! The Allied leaders, late in the war, Roosevelt, Stalin and Churchill, had met at Yalta – and had made a deal. The Russians could take Eastern Europe, all the way to Germany, and half of Germany as well. (Better to split them up – they were too dangerous). At the end of the war the Russians moved as agreed; all Eastern Europe became Communist; America and Britain disarmed; thousands of unwanted planes, tanks, guns and ships were scrapped. Stalin did not disarm; the only thing stopping him from advancing his troops to the Atlantic was the atomic bomb.

Russia were the spy masters of the World. In the midst of World War Two, when Russia was on the brink of defeat, Stalin never wavered. Capitalists were his sworn enemies. He would cooperate with them, only while it was necessary, to beat Hitler.

When Hitler invaded the USSR they were heavily outnumbered (No! Not the Russians – the Germans!) Russia had more than ten times as many planes as Germany; far, far more tanks, guns and men. Stalin was warned of the impending German attack on Russia by his spies, and even the British, but he was paranoid; he distrusted everything and everyone. It was just a ruse to get Russia to attack Germany – to relieve the pressure on the beleaguered capitalist British. In his own time, he would attack. (Germany and Russia had earlier signed a Non Aggression pact; a peace agreement; neither intended to keep it. Stalin thought he had fooled Hitler but Hitler struck first. Despite Russia's overwhelming superiority (so they thought) the result was devastating. Hitler's planes were superior, his tanks and guns were superior, and his men were better trained. They massacred the Russians. They cut through the Russian forward battle formations like a knife. The Luftwaffe slaughtered the Russian Air Force. German tanks charged forward – unstoppable! The 88mm anti-tank gun blew up the Russian tanks like so many tin cans.

With regard to the air fighting – it is an almost incredible fact that, in the course of the war, just three hundred top German fighter pilots (who had practiced in the Spanish Civil War) shot down, between them, over forty thousand Russian planes. The top German fighter ace – Erich Hartmann – shot down no less than 360 Russian planes. That gives you a clue as to what can happen when you pit obsolete planes, with poorly trained pilots, against the cream of the Luftwaffe; it also gives you an idea of the enormous numbers of planes the Russians had at the start of the war. As well as in the air, they also lost thousands of planes on the ground, caught by the strafing fighters and the screaming Stuka dive bombers.

The Germans captured over a million Russian soldiers in the first few weeks. They were a massive encumbrance. Where to put them? How to feed them? The Germans charged on, unstoppable, to within fourteen miles of Moscow – a town called Tula. At that point the attack ground to a halt. The German offensive was not stopped by the Russians; the Russian winter arrived – early.

Hitler was unlucky, it was the worst winter for a hundred years. It gave the Russians breathing space; time to dismantle the factories and ship them back beyond the Urals; time to reorganise; time to start building a new superb tank (the T34) and for the Allies, America and Britain, to help the battered Russians. The British frantically organised dozens of convoys to Russia – carrying tanks, guns and planes – a lot of which came from America. The convoys had to go north – right around the top of Finland to Murmansk, in freezing arctic conditions, and run the gauntlet of German bombers and submarines based in Norway. Convoys lost anything up to half their number; the sailors freezing to death in the arctic seas; but the convoys went on. The price had to be paid. Hitler had to be stopped! Hitler's Blitzkrieg (lightning war) worked! Only the winter saved the Russians!

The Germans advanced again next spring – which was late. They advanced south almost to the Black Sea – to grab the oil that Hitler needed; but the pause in the winter had allowed the Russians to reorganise and regroup. The German army was finally stopped, at Stalingrad. Slowly the tide turned – and Hitler lost his gamble! When it looked as though the Russians might be beaten, the Allies, America and Britain, worked frantically to help them. If Russia fell, Hitler would take the Middle East next – with all its oil; then he would take Britain (he came very close to doing that in 1940). Fortress Europe ("Festung Europa," in Hitler's words) would have been impregnable. To have invaded Europe from America would have been impossible. Hitler would have filled the Atlantic with his new high speed submarines. The ships would have been sunk with the new guided torpedoes.

America realised that this scenario might well happen. They started to design and build a new super, long range, ten engine bomber – the Convair B36. This gigantic bomber was designed to be able to fly to Europe, deliver its bomb load and then fly back to the USA. (It was actually produced and became an intercontinental atom bomber). However, it only cruised at 300 to 350 miles (483 to 563 kilometres) per hour and, in my opinion, wouldn't have stood a chance against Germany's new weapon systems. It would have been blown out of the sky before it got anywhere near Europe; tracked by the new Radar; attacked by new long range jet fighters; blasted by the new air to air guided missiles. (In 1945 Germany was developing all these new devices). Hitler might have conquered half the World, if not all of it. Also German scientists and engineers were working on an intercontinental missile, the A4, (which the Allies hadn't even started to think of building). This missile could have delivered a bomb on New York. The Germans already had a crude cruise missile (the V1). It was, of course, the German rocket designer, Werner Von Braun, who was later responsible for the mighty Saturn 5 rocket that took the first men to the moon. The only thing Hitler lacked, to make his dream of World conquest come true, was – the atomic bomb.

The Germans were so confident in 1942, they even started planning how they were going to beat the Japanese. (When I was in Germany, in 1952, I met a woman who spoke seven languages, and had been a secretary to one of the German Generals. She told me they had already started planning how to conquer Japan, "This was no war game!" she said, "They were deadly serious!") It could be that if it wasn't for one hellish Russian winter, (it even froze the oil in the engines of the German tanks, fighters and bombers) the World would be a very different place today. The atomic bomb – Hitler would have got that too, given time. He only needed a simple nuclear reactor, which worked, and he would have

had plutonium. Ask yourself, – if you were the American President –
would you have risked dropping an atomic bomb on Germany? When
you knew they were working on it (what else would they need heavy
water for?) and they might soon have a gigantic missile to deliver it on
New York – and elsewhere (they already had the V2) – and your country
didn't have missiles – only bombers. The Germans were considering an
orbital bomber – The Sanger Bomber – that would be able to drop a bomb
anywhere on Earth. President Truman knew the Japanese couldn't have
an atomic bomb – which left him free to use it. Would he have dared use
it on "Fortress Europe"? I doubt it!

In 1945, the United States of America was the only nation on
Earth that had an atomic bomb but, back in the USSR, Joseph Stalin still
nurtured dreams of World domination. During the war, when Russia had
its back to the wall and was fighting desperately to stem the German
invasion, America and Britain did their best to aid Russia. Convoys of
tanks, guns and planes forced their way through Arctic ice, U. Boat wolf
packs and murderous attacks by NAZI planes based in Norway, to the
Russian ports of Murmansk and Archangel.

As part of the aid, America allowed Russia to send aircraft
directly to America, to pick up urgently needed items. Despite the
situation, the Russians thought and planned for the future. Communist
World Domination was still on the agenda. So – after an aircraft shuttle
service, from the USSR to the USA and back, had been set up, to get
much needed spares and components to Russia, quickly, the Russian
planes did not arrive empty. Incredibly, they came loaded with spies. An
American serviceman, who saw what was going on, could hardly believe
his eyes. When a Russian plane landed, a number of people simply
stepped off the plane, walked to the perimeter fence and – disappeared.
He went to the police and reported the matter, but was told they couldn't
do anything as they had been ordered to "Leave the Russians alone!" The
planes flew back to Russia (I don't know the route – probably Kamchatka,
Aleutian Islands, Alaska and so on) loaded with various items, of war
material along with crates of files and papers. Joseph Stalin was looking
ahead!

Working on the atomic bomb project was one Klaus Fuchs, a
German who had fled to Britain and then to America. Fuchs was a
brilliant mathematician. They needed him at Los Alamos. He learned
everything there was to know about the construction of atomic bombs,
particularly the complicated plutonium bomb. In addition to being a
brilliant mathematician, Klaus Fuchs was also a dreamer. An idealist! A
secret Communist! He thought, quite honestly, the World would, perhaps,
be a better place if his friends in Russia also had the bomb. He provided

the Russians with all the atomic bomb secrets for nothing. Not one dollar! They never even offered money to Fuchs; it might have offended him. Fuchs gave everything to the Russians; he saved them countless billions of Roubles in research, and ten years or more of time. They now knew how to build a reactor and create plutonium, and they also knew exactly what to do to make a plutonium bomb.

Russia stunned America, and the rest of the World, by exploding a test atomic bomb in 1949. (They were working on it even before the bomb was dropped on Hiroshima). At the Yalta conference Churchill hinted to Stalin that they now had a new and devastating weapon. "Oh!" said Stalin "How interesting! I hope you use it!"; keeping a straight face – which wasn't difficult. (Joseph Stalin had a face that looked as if it was carved out of stone). The Americans knew the only way the Russians could possibly have produced a working atomic bomb, in particular a plutonium bomb, in such a short time was if they had obtained the information by espionage. There must be a spy amongst the scientists who had worked on the plutonium bomb; no other explanation was possible. Finally it was narrowed down and the spy – Klaus Fuchs – was apprehended. Originally he came from Germany, but later had British citizenship; because of this he was flown to Britain and placed on trial. The judge must have been very lenient. In his summing up he stated Fuchs was misguided, and when Fuchs was found guilty he was given ten years jail. Ten years! People get more than that for robbing banks, let alone placing the entire Western World in jeopardy. He gave away information it had cost billions of dollars to discover; information that could have started World War Three, and almost did, in the Cuba Crisis. At this point I get mad! If it had been left to me, Fuchs would have been standing in front of a firing squad. Dreamer or no dreamer!

So, Klaus Fuchs gave Stalin the information to build his nuclear bomb and the arms race started. I stated earlier that, when the American test bomb exploded at Alamagordo, a few scientists were slightly nervous – fingers crossed maybe! Somebody had said that they were scared; what about fusion reactions? If hydrogen is heated to a high enough temperature – ten million degrees or so - it is possible to start a fusion reaction. The heated hydrogen atoms fuse together to form a heavier substance, helium, releasing an enormous amount of energy in the process (as in the hydrogen bomb). In actual fact it is possible, with higher temperatures, to do this with any element, all the way up the periodic table, to iron. (Not further – any element heavier than iron is only produced in a supernova explosion). Fusion is only a question of temperature and pressure. The question, therefore, arose "What about the nitrogen and oxygen in the air? How hot does an atomic explosion get?" Millions of degrees for sure!

If it so happened the temperatures and pressures were enough to cause nitrogen to fuse then, soon after they pressed the button at Alamagordo, the whole World might light up and shine for a while on Venus and Mars. So – cross your fingers!

Incidentally, even Nuclear Physicists are not infallible. They are good – but not infallible. (They were caught out at Eniwetok, with the first test of a lithium hydride fuelled H. Bomb and they hopelessly underestimated the electro-magnetic pulse created by the detonation of an atomic bomb in space as I will describe later). The test firing of the first plutonium bomb went ahead at Alamagordo. Fortunately, the World did not catch fire. As was demonstrated, the plutonium type atomic bomb worked. Even while they were perfecting the fission bomb, Edward Teller was arguing for work to be done on his idea of the 'Super', by which he meant a hydrogen fusion bomb – which would be of vastly greater explosive power. Most scientists thought the plutonium fission bomb was quite powerful enough. Did anyone really need anything far more powerful than that?

Then, in 1949, the Russians detonated their own plutonium fission bomb; suddenly people started to listen to Edward Teller. After all – what if the Russians worked on it and succeeded first? No doubt Klaus Fuchs would have mentioned the possibility to them. America decided it simply could not afford to take the risk, and orders were given for work to commence, with the intention of creating a hydrogen bomb – if such a thing were indeed possible.

The first hydrogen device the Americans produced was a monstrous affair – as big as a fair sized house – constructed on an island in the Pacific (Eniwetok – a coral atoll). The device incorporated a large tank of liquid deuterium (heavy hydrogen). Knowing a little more about hydrogen bombs now, I admit I would not have expected it to work – but in the event – it did. The explosion produced a blast equivalent to eight million tons of TNT, and left a crater almost 2 miles (3.2 kilometres) across. I saw a cine film of the explosion, taken by a camera positioned about 70 miles (113 kilometres) away. The film was unedited – not clipped in any way. I have never seen any film since to compare with it. All the films, or scenes of nuclear explosions, I have seen since have been drastically clipped, and many that portray thermonuclear bombs have, in reality, been films of much less powerful fission bombs. I walked away after seeing the film utterly, totally, stunned.

I will describe it to you – as I saw it. When the atomic bomb exploded over Hiroshima, there was a tremendous flash lasting about two seconds. This was the visible part of the radiation resulting from the detonation, and was so intense that anyone within 1½ miles (2.4 kilometres), who was looking in that direction, would be permanently blinded, and any exposed skin burned. Curtains, clothing and paper would flash into flame. This visible part of the radiation was, of course, only a small part of the total radiation released. Most would be hard radiation, gamma rays and x rays, which is absorbed by the surrounding air and creates the fireball and blast wave. At a distance of two miles from ground zero, all the hard radiation would have been absorbed and an observer would receive only visible light, u.v. and infra-red radiation. The intensity of the momentary flash was so great that, in some instances, silhouettes of people were burned on to walls and pavements.

I was aware of all this when I witnessed the film of the first hydrogen bomb test, at Eniwetok atoll in the South Pacific. At first, the film showed a few islands in the distance, a fine day with a few clouds, and then the scientists commencing the usual countdown. As the clock reached zero, the screen flashed white. I waited, expecting the flash to subside after a few seconds and the explosion to become visible. But no! The flash went on and on for what seemed an interminable time but, in reality, was probably 30 seconds. This, incredibly, was just the duration of the initial flash. Then, slowly, a picture came out of the white. There was the sun, just rising; a half sun as you might see at the break of day. This half sun slowly expanded and grew, until the top of the half sun was breaking through the clouds, at heaven knows what thousands of feet altitude. Very slowly, this colossal fireball rose off the ground and became a true ball. Very slowly, it began to cool and turn into an immense mushroom cloud. The cloud rose higher and higher but, as it reached maximum altitude, (it can only rise as far as the top of the atmosphere) it began to spread. Eventually, the mushroom cloud spread out like an enormous flat "pancake" one hundred miles across. I could hardly believe what I was watching. It was incredible that human beings could create – this!

After that, I knew what the words 'H Bomb' really meant. Later, Nikita Khrushchev watched, as the USSR detonated the biggest Hydrogen bomb explosion ever seen on this Earth. Fifty six megatons! (I find it hard to visualise a mass of 56 million tons of TNT!) It is reported that, after the blast, he walked away slowly and said, "We can't ever use these things!" Even Khrushchev! Maybe it was good that he saw it; he backed down during the Cuban Missile Crisis. Khrushchev understood!

Obviously, you cannot transport a bomb as big as a house and drop it on Moscow; so the scientists pondered the problem and the engineers went back to their drawing boards. Imagine, if you will, a bottle into which hydrogen gas is pumped, up to the maximum pressure the bottle can withstand; you now have a certain amount of hydrogen in the bottle. Imagine emptying the bottle and instead fill it with water. There will now be far more hydrogen in the bottle. It is combined with oxygen to be sure but there is, nevertheless, far more hydrogen in the container.

In a similar way, scientists found they could pack far more heavy hydrogen (Deuterium) in a given space by combining it with lithium in a compound – lithium hydride. This is perfectly stable at normal temperatures; no necessity to liquefy the hydrogen and keep it refrigerated, as at Eniwetok. The question is, if you incorporate lithium hydride in your H bomb, will the lithium interfere with the fusion reaction? The scientific calculations indicated it would not; so an H bomb was designed and built, using lithium hydride, and taken to Eniwetok for testing. According to calculations, it might be possible to achieve a 5 megaton blast from this much smaller device. If it worked, they were well on the way to a deliverable bomb. Bunkers and detector gear were set up, at what was calculated to be a safe distance away from the detonation point.

When everything was ready, the new bomb was fired. There was an enormous fireball. The blast was so great it practically wrecked the equipment, and the people in the bunkers emerged – very shaken. The explosion had actually produced fifteen megatons – three times greater than calculated. It was later realised that the heat of the detonation had been sufficient to trigger a reaction in the lithium, as well as in the heavy hydrogen. It tripled the power. Now they were on the way to practical, deliverable, hydrogen bombs; on the way to B52 bombers, during the 'Cold War', cruising around the sky, each carrying four, twenty two megaton, bombs.

A twenty two megaton bomb is capable of converting Moscow or New York for that matter, into a very large hole in the ground! People in houses thirty or forty miles (48 or 64 kilometres) away are likely to have their houses collapse around their ears from the impact of the shock wave. It also became possible to place quite a small H bomb on the top of a rocket, only a few times larger than Von Braun's V2. Quite a small H bomb – only one megaton. I think it is reasonable to say, that, if one of these bombs detonated over London or New York, that city would totally cease to exist. Gradually the scientists perfected their techniques and started making H bombs of all sizes, and smaller and smaller plutonium bombs. Just how little high explosive is really needed to detonate an atomic bomb? (You cannot alter the plutonium core. That size is fixed and is about the size of a small orange. Too small – and it will not detonate; too large – and you wouldn't be assembling anything any more).

Suffice to say, they could soon make a fission bomb small enough to be fired through the barrel of a large field gun – even in the 1950s. I wonder just how small they can make them today; small suitcase size? Briefcase size? Perhaps I'd rather not know. The H bombs came down in size too; the H bomb has to be larger, after all it uses an A bomb as trigger.

Those little Cruise Missiles – the ones they pounded Baghdad with a few years ago, carried a few hundred pounds of high explosive on board. In a real war, World War Three style, they would unbolt the TNT warhead and attach a quite small nuclear bomb. Result – no Baghdad! That little Nuke on the cruise missile would be quite low yield – only one hundred and fifty kilotons – about ten times more powerful than the bomb that destroyed Nagasaki.

The Russians did not waste time either. Knowing the Russians you can guess what happened. If the West is going to build a smallish rocket, carrying a one megaton bomb, why not build a bigger rocket and place a five megaton bomb on the top, or perhaps a ten!

This thinking led the Russians to produce a rocket large enough to launch Yuri Gagarin into orbit around the Earth. Make no mistake – that rocket was originally designed to deliver H bombs to the United States. How many megatons? Beyond my imagination! The trick with Yuri Gagarin was an afterthought – but it also let the Americans know what they could expect, if there was a war. The competition that resulted, between the two Super Powers, led to man going to the moon. What is not often mentioned, is the fact that a Saturn Five rocket could place one hundred tons in orbit. I am unaware of any technical reason why one cannot build an H bomb weighing one hundred tons (probably of something like 1,000 megatons power). If you did, and launched a Saturn Five loaded with such a bomb, (tell them it was Apollo 23 or something) it would be possible to simply let it sail over the USSR in orbit and, when it was in the right place, push the button. It would probably wipe out half of Russia with just the one bomb. Two bombs, and it would probably be possible to flatten Russia from the Baltic to Vladivostok. The same could apply, of course, to the USA or Europe. At this point, the Russians and the Americans got their heads together and agreed, "No Nukes in Space!" The first sign of a hint of sanity!

Somebody pointed out (Bright lad!) that you could possibly build a thousand ton H bomb; not a thousand megatons power, but an H bomb weighing a thousand tons. Then, somebody suggested a similar bomb laced with cobalt; if exposed to neutron radiation cobalt becomes hellishly radioactive, and can last for thousands of years. The suggestion was – you build this gigantic Hydrogen/Cobalt bomb in your own backyard and, if you are attacked, push the button and it ensures the whole planet is sterilised! It would certainly make sure the enemy did not win! How insane can you get? However, despite these lunatic suggestions, the madness did go on. How many H bombs do you need to ruin a nation? It was calculated in the 1960s – about six – to put Britain out of any war. However it is not as simple as that. The six might just allow Britain to fire a few missiles back, so maybe it might be better to launch a few more just to make sure! Shall we say 50 targeted on Britain or 100? OK – lets settle for 200. (Do you think I joke?)

In the early 1960s, President Nikita Khrushchev, of the Soviet Union, and President John Fitzgerald Kennedy, of the United States of America, met and talked, face to face. President Kennedy looked very young and boyish, almost like a young man fresh out of high school; nothing like his predecessor President Eisenhower. This led Khrushchev to underestimate him. For a number of years NATO (North Atlantic Treaty Organisation) had installed nuclear missiles in the UK, in Europe and even in Turkey, constituting a massive threat to the western part of the Soviet Union. America had far more, and better, strategic bombers than the Russians, and they were building a super bomber – the Valkyrie. This was an enormous, long range, 300 ton, futuristic monster, capable of flying at 80,000 feet (24,616 metres) and 2,000 mph (3,219 km). (When the prototype first flew, the Russians had nothing that could stop such a bomber and they worked frantically to produce a new super fighter, the 'Foxbat', capable of reaching similar heights and speeds).

Khrushchev was most unhappy about the situation and, after meeting Kennedy, decided to take a gamble. Cuba was Communist, under a leader, Fidel Castro, who hated America. Khrushchev talked to Castro, and decided to install medium range nuclear missiles in Cuba, which could threaten most of North America and so, in Khrushchev's mind, even the balance. The program went ahead. Russian technicians arrived in Cuba. Ground installations were prepared and missiles shipped to Cuba. At this point, American reconnaissance flights – U2 aircraft – photographed the work-in-progress, and experts correctly deduced what was going on. The resulting confrontation, between the United States and the USSR, is known as the Cuba Missile Crisis. A deadly battle of wills ensued.

When Khrushchev went eyeball to eyeball with Kennedy, in 1962, during the Cuba Missile Crisis, the Soviet Union was badly outgunned and Khrushchev knew it. The USSR only possessed five thousand H bombs and fission bombs, against the Americans twenty seven thousand. (They used to call this situation 'overkill'. How many times can you kill a person or destroy a nation?)

I recently saw a documentary film on TV about the Cuba Crisis. After describing the build up to the crisis, the commentators described how Britain's Vulcan V bombers were bombed up and ready to go, and the Polaris armed nuclear submarines were on station and on standby, but there was not a mention of Britain's ballistic missiles. Not a mention of the fact that Britain had purchased, from the United States, sixty "Thor" intermediate range ballistic missiles, each carrying a one megaton hydrogen bomb. There were enough missiles in Britain to wipe out every major Russian city to the west of the Ural Mountains. I was very much aware of this fact, because there were three of these missiles sited within one mile of the flat in which I lived. At the time of the crisis I lived in the little market town of Melton Mowbray in Leicestershire. On the outskirts of the town was a small airfield on which three Thors were installed. By coincidence, I actually knew one of the RAF personnel in charge of these missiles. I used to chat with my RAF friend and, being curious, couldn't resist asking a few questions. He was reasonably forthcoming (he probably shouldn't have been but knew I could keep my mouth shut). I asked him what would happen if, after the missiles had just been launched, Khrushchev phoned up and said "Wait minute! Let's talk it over," would it be possible to stop them? "Sorry !" my friend said "No! Once the umbilical disconnects they are on their way. You could shoot at them, I suppose, as they climbed the first thousand feet, if you had a machine gun or AA gun. There is no self destruct button as they have at Canaveral because, in war, there is the risk that enemy agents might learn the code or signal and blow them up in flight." I then asked how the missiles were targeted. "Oh!" he said, "Simple! Just take out the tape for Moscow and shove in the tape for Leningrad" (now St. Petersburg). For a moment, an insane picture floated through my mind; somebody rummaging through a great pile of tapes, "Now where did I put that tape for Murmansk. Damn it – I know I put it somewhere." (I must have a peculiar sense of humour).

So, as the crisis escalated I pondered the situation. There were three 'Thor' nuclear tipped missiles a mile away, Cottesmore air base about seven miles away and, not far, in a northerly direction, Vulcan V bomber bases. I was sure the Russians had a map showing the lot, Thors and all, and some Russian missile technician had just shoved in a tape marked Melton Mowbray. The TV stated that reconnaissance planes had spotted Russian ships, with large missiles on the decks, heading for Cuba, and President Kennedy had ordered the U S Navy to intercept and stop the convoy. Films showed the ships with massive missiles on the decks – easily big enough for a Cuba/New York trip. It was reported that Khrushchev was ranting on about the ships being in International Waters and interception would be an "act of Piracy". I had a vision of Khrushchev in a rage, battering his desk with his shoe, as he had done at the United Nations. At this time, I worked at a Research Association in Melton Mowbray, which had a large multi-storey building, so I went to the top of the block and looked out of a window. The three Thors were out of their bunkers and standing vertically on their launch pads; the white plumes of liquid oxygen boiling off. They were fuelled, loaded and ready to go; a one megaton bomb on the top of each and, no doubt, the necessary tape in place. I wondered what the targets were, Leningrad? Kiev? Stalingrad?

After work I went back to my flat. If the Russians dropped a five megaton bomb on Melton Mowbray I would be likely to be in the crater. If they dropped one on Cottesmore it would be just as bad, but I would not be in the crater. The V bomber base at Waddington? An H bomb on that would only flatten the house with the shock wave. Logically, the Russians would target all three , and every other base that was a threat as well. I could, I suppose, jump in my old car and head for the Welsh coast and not stop until I reached the sea. Rational thought told me that would be the best place; no air bases and upwind of the fall-out. I clicked on the TV. An announcer said the U S Navy would make contact with the Russian ships during the night. I decided, if they were going to throw H bombs around, I didn't really want to live in the aftermath. Who would want to survive in a World of radioactive ruins? So I went to bed! I remember thinking, before I went to sleep, what if I hear the thunder of the Thors taking off in the night, or, if the Russians struck first, would I live long enough to see the flash. Remarkably, when I awoke in the morning, I was still alive. I never asked my RAF friend what the targets were. He is still around, but I never asked him and he never told me – I decided I didn't want to know. It all sounds like some crazy sci-fi story; the sort you watch on TV for twenty minutes and switch off because it's too far-fetched; or some sort of nightmare. But it wasn't. Those Thors were so convincingly real.

Only recently has it been discovered the situation during the Cuba Crisis was even more dangerous than was realised at the time. The Russians already had nuclear weapons on Cuba – and short range missiles. The Russian Commander in Cuba was authorised to use nuclear weapons 'at his own discretion'. The only time in history a military commander could, on his own, start a nuclear war. If President Kennedy had listened to the people who exhorted him to conduct a pre-emptive strike on Cuba it would almost certainly have led to World War Three, and probable disaster for the entire planet.

Incidentally, at the time of the Cuban Missile Crisis, the man in charge of America's Strategic Air Command was General Curtis-Le-May. Earlier, I described how General-Le-May's bombers devastated Japan – before the atomic bombs were dropped. Le-May was probably the most efficient, and ruthless, Air Force commander the USA ever had. If he considered it necessary to wipe out cities and massacre millions – to win the war – he was prepared to do it. "The enemy would do it to us if they could" he said. In this he was almost certainly right; World War Two was a murderous war.

In 1945 the dropping of the two atomic bombs on Japan, and its subsequent surrender, pre-empted Joseph Stalin's plans to enter the war against Japan in the Far East, and extend the Soviet Union's influence in that area. In the few days after the dropping of the atomic bomb, before Japan formally surrendered, the Russians declared war on Japan, and attacked Japanese troops in Manchuria and the North Korean area. When hostilities ceased negotiations were begun and, as a result, some countries were divided, mainly according to the political influence that could be brought to bear. The country of Vietnam was divided. North Vietnam was Communist controlled. South Vietnam became Capitalist. In a similar fashion, Korea was split into two sections. North Korea was a Communist nation under Kim il Sung; South Korea was Capitalist, under its leader Syngman Rhee, and was sponsored by the West. The border between the two states was the 38th Parallel (Latitude). Joseph Stalin was never happy with this arrangement and intended to extend Communism, wherever he could, anywhere in the World, conditions permitting. Kim il Sung was a dedicated communist who hated the idea of a divided Korea. He approached Stalin with a plan to invade South Korea; a "Blitzkrieg" type attack to conquer, and take over, South Korea before the rest of the World could react. Stalin gave Kim il Sung his approval.

The North Korean attack commenced as planned, and South Korean forces were overwhelmed. There were a few US troops in South Korea at this time, but nothing that could hold the North Korean onslaught. The United Nations Organisation called an emergency meeting, at which North Korea was condemned for an act of naked aggression and ordered to withdraw. The USA, Britain, Australia and other member states of the United Nations decided to send troops to assist South Korea and enforce the UN orders. In the event, the North Koreans bulldozed south, until they had pushed what remained of the resisting forces into a small area around the southern port of Pusan. The North Koreans very nearly completed their conquest of the South, but America poured in troops by air and sea and the line was finally held, although the situation was very precarious. The battle raged.

At about this point General Le-May, who was still in charge of the U S Air Force, was called in and instructed to bomb North Korea. Remembering how the Japanese cities had been devastated, he was instructed to bomb North Korea, but concentrate on factories. Curtis-Le-May did not believe in 'pussy footing' about. Either you were in a war or you were not! If you were in a war – hammer the enemy! He ordered his bombers into North Korea and they started to systematically flatten the North Korean cities. I have read somewhere that over a million North Korean citizens were killed. When General Le-May was questioned about this, years later, he said, "Well! There were factories there – weren't there?"

The reason I am quoting all this – is so that you will get it firmly in your mind that General Le-May believed unquestionably that, if you were in a war, and you had bombers and weapons, you used them, ruthlessly and as efficiently as possible. The tide turned in Korea and the North Koreans were driven back to the Thirty Eighth Parallel – the border between North and South Korea.

The man in charge of the army was General Douglas MacArthur; the same man who was in charge of ground forces in the fighting against Japan and, finally, accepted the Japanese surrender on a battleship in Tokyo bay.

MacArthur was of like mind to General Le-May, so he pursued the North Koreans and continued to attack beyond the original border, with the intention of finally forcing the North Koreans to capitulate. Joseph Stalin was not happy – and neither were the Chinese communists under Mao Tze Tung. MacArthur's forces pushed northwards until they were close to the Chinese border. At this point, Mao Tze Tung decided he was not going to sit back and watch his communist brethren in North Korea be forced into a humiliating surrender. He gave the order, and an enormous army of Chinese troops surged into North Korea and joined battle with UN forces (mainly American) under General MacArthur. The UN forces were overwhelmed by the immense assault and fell back, fighting desperate rearguard actions. This was the time when the British battalion, "Glorious Gloucesters" put up a heroic defence against the advancing Chinese.

MacArthur considered the situation. If there was anything the Chinese did have, it was almost unlimited supplies of men. He made up his mind and sent orders back to the States for ten atomic bombs to be delivered to Guam, for use against the Chinese. General Curtis Le-May would see to it those bombs would be delivered where requested. No problem! I have read that a plane carrying one of the bombs crashed at some stage of its journey to Guam and, as a result, only nine bombs were actually delivered. At this point the American President, Truman, became aware of what was going on, and realised the World might be on the brink of World War Three. China didn't have atomic bombs – unless Russia gave them some. However, Russia had already supplied North Korea with fighter planes to oppose the UN Air Forces; they even supplied pilots to fly them too; so Russian planes flown by Russian pilots were shooting at American planes flown by American pilots, and vice versa. Things were getting very dangerous! Fortunately Truman was as tough as MacArthur, if not Le-May. He sacked MacArthur, installed a new General and gave orders; no atomic bombs are to be used in Korea or China. Eventually, even the Chinese were fought to a standstill and an armistice, a ceasefire, was negotiated with both sides, North and South Korea, back on the Thirty Eighth Parallel. No 'End of the War' was ever declared and the Korean War has been in a cease fire state only, to this day.

You would think, of course, that President Truman would be the only person who could authorise the use of atomic weapons, as he did when they were used on Japan. Today, only the leaders of nations can authorise their use; the President of the USA, the Prime Minister of Britain and the Presidents of France and Russia; but it wasn't always that way. As has been mentioned earlier, on Cuba, the Russian Military Commander there, had nuclear bombs at his disposal and authorisation to use them at his discretion; that is, bombs other than those earmarked for the inter-continental missiles. If Kennedy had invaded Cuba – as he was urged to do – the Russian Commander might have decided to use tactical nuclear weapons on US Troops, to stop them overrunning his long range missiles. If he had done that – it would, almost certainly, have triggered World War Three right then and there.

Who do you think was in charge of America's 'Strategic Air Command' and all the nuclear bombers during the time of the Cuba Missile Crisis? General Curtis-Le-May, of course! Before the Cuba Crisis, some Americans had begun to worry, with the development of intercontinental missiles, whether there was a risk of the bombers being knocked out on the ground, before they could get aloft with their nuclear weapons. The solution decided upon, was to have a number of the big intercontinental B52 eight-jet bombers loaded with four, twenty two megaton, H bombs each and fly them towards their targets in Russia; twenty four hours a day, three hundred and sixty five days a year. The bombers flew to a predetermined point outside Russia, received a signal and turned back for home. The next shift did the same; which sounded a rather dodgy game to me – as it did to quite a few people.

General Le-May also made absolutely sure his bombers were not going to be caught on the ground. To back up the twenty four hour, airborne bomber, manoeuvre he ordered planes to overfly Russia and keep an eye on things. Some were reconnaissance planes, but some were bombers. He is reputed to have sent a flight of three bombers to within sight of Moscow. Provocative! You wouldn't believe it! Le-May decided to do this because he could keep an eye on developments on Russian airfields and missile sites and, also, he knew that if the Russians didn't shoot his planes down it was simply because they couldn't. Their radar and fighters weren't good enough, and they didn't have missiles with the capability. He knew his bombers could get through, if required. The amazing thing is that President Eisenhower was completely unaware of what was going on. He was later informed of the U2 flights – but not the bombers.

I have written this, at length, to indicate how independent and self controlling General Curtis-Le-May was. Curtis-Le-May believed – as most of us did – that a war between the USA and Russia was inevitable. He thought, if we are going to have a nuclear war with the Russians, let's have it now, while we have overwhelming superiority in nuclear weapons. Why wait for the Russians to catch up? He could very easily have been perfectly right in his thinking! It is simply a miracle that World War Three, with the horror of nuclear weapons, never happened. So Curtis-Le-May had enough bombers, and thermonuclear bombs, to reduce the USSR to cinders. He openly stated that the war would only last eight hours and it was his avowed intention to drop every single bomb he had – in that eight hours. His 'Sunday Punch' he called it. His bombers, he said, would bomb Russia "back to the stone age." For several years, he overflew Russia with his reconnaissance planes and bombers. He almost certainly wanted to get the war going – while he could win it.

When the Cuba Missile Crisis arose, the young President Kennedy was in charge. The Russian President Nikita Khrushchev was a bullet headed little man. He looked about twice as mean as Al Capone. Russia had the biggest missiles; they proved it when they used their enormous rocket, Vostok, to launch Yuri Gagarin into orbit around the Earth. If they could do that – they could drop a ten megaton bomb on New York or anywhere else in the USA. Khrushchev became more and more arrogant and bombastic. At the United Nations he shouted and screamed, and bashed his desk with his shoe, to make a point. He told Kennedy, to his face, that Russia would 'bury' the USA. I wonder what Curtis-Le-May was thinking at this time.

During the Cuba Crisis, I read that Le-May tried to provoke Kennedy into giving the 'strike' order, practically calling him a coward to his face but, fortunately, Kennedy refused to be provoked. If a nuclear war had been triggered, at that time, the World might be a very different place today. We now know, if Curtis Le-May had unleashed his bombers and, additionally, there would have been the land based missiles and those from the nuclear submarines, then, not only would Russia have been bombed 'back to the stone age' but civilisation over the entire World would probably have been destroyed.

Earlier, I described how the H bomb test at Eniwetok produced a colossal mushroom cloud of dust, smoke and radioactive debris a hundred miles (161 kilometres) across. (Some Japanese fishermen about a hundred miles away, downwind, were very badly irradiated by the fallout). A group of top scientists began to wonder, if there was a nuclear war, what the effects of so many nuclear bombs exploding at the same time might be so they fed data and information into computers. For the first time, the realisation came how such a conflict would devastate the entire World. They coined the term 'Nuclear Winter'. After the destruction from the actual blasts, the flash, the heat, the radiation, the shock waves and the fallout, the whole planet would be covered in an immense shroud of radioactive dust and smoke, from the explosions and billions of fires. The computers indicated the smoke cloud would spread from the Northern hemisphere, to cover the whole World. (Remarkably, at a later date, a sandstorm was observed on Mars, which developed in a similar manner to cover the entire planet). The sun would be totally blocked out. Temperatures over the entire planet would plummet. In the UK we would experience darkness at noon, for months with vicious frosts, even in July – the middle of summer. The pall of smoke, up in the stratosphere where it would not be washed out by the rain, would probably last at least a year, so photosynthesis would stop, in the sea and on land. The food chain would collapse and the survivors would starve. If you wish to read the whole nightmarish scenario, obtain a copy of 'The Cold and the Dark' by Paul Ehrlich, Carl Sagan, Donald Kennedy and Walter Orr Roberts. It is interesting to wonder what would have happened if Curtis-Le-May, or Douglas MacArthur, had become President of the United States. After all, Eisenhower did, and he was Supreme Commander-Allied Forces in Europe, in the war against Hitler, and Douglas MacArthur was a national hero.

When the Cuba Crisis was resolved everyone took a deep breath. However the arms race continued. The Russians were unhappy with the American superiority in nuclear weapons and delivery systems, so they continued to build their nuclear arsenal as fast as possible. The Americans did likewise so that they would not be overtaken. At this stage – in the 1960s – missiles were primarily targeted at cities, since intercontinental missiles were only accurate to within a mile or two. Polaris submarines carried sixteen missiles with one bomb on each missile. Land based missiles were now housed vertically, in underground concrete silos, to ensure some would survive if the enemy made a 'first strike'. So a 'stand off' situation was created that became aptly named, Mutually Assured Destruction (MAD), not a bad acronym.

Scientists and engineers continued to improve weapons, missiles and, above all, navigation systems. The physical size of nuclear bombs was reduced. Guidance systems became more precise and the idea of MIRVs, (Multiple Independently targeted Re-entry Vehicles) came into being. Gradually, accuracy improved until it was possible to deliver a nuclear bomb so close to an enemy missile silo as to ensure its destruction. Missile submarines began to carry Polaris missiles, each armed with three MIRVs, tripling the number of bombs each submarine could deliver. Land based missiles were also updated. Both the United States and Russia placed surveillance satellites in orbit to watch for signs of missile launches. The time from the launch of an intercontinental missile to its detonation was, and remains, around twenty five to thirty minutes; very little time to check whether a warning is valid or not.

After the Cuba Crisis, a group of despairing top scientists set up a large clock face – the 'Doomsday Clock'; where twelve o'clock would indicate the end of the civilised World. They set the hands at twenty minutes to twelve, but by the 1970s they had advanced it to 15 minutes to 12. By the 1980s, the accuracy of the MIRVs had been improved further. The missiles could also carry decoys to make it impossible for defensive radar to identify the real warheads until they actually re-entered the atmosphere, with only seconds to detonation.

Both America and Russia worked on anti missile, missile systems. America tested one called 'Sprint' which accelerated off its pad at about 30Gs. Incredibly fast! The idea was to carry a small nuclear bomb, and detonate it near the enemy warhead, moments before the enemy thermonuclear bomb exploded. Better a small nuclear detonation over your city than a multi megaton blast! The radiation from the small bomb would wreck the electronics of the enemy weapon and prevent detonation. In the same way, if two or more missiles were launched at the same city, and they arrived at the same time, the first detonation might destroy the other nearby bombs. (Did it matter? One would totally incinerate the city). This effect was called 'fratricide'.

For some reason, the Americans and Russians brokered a deal to limit the deployment of anti missile, missiles. By the 1980s, the new large American missile (the MX – known as 'Peacekeeper') carried no less than ten, highly accurate, MIRVs. Nuclear missile submarines became larger, carrying larger missiles, with up to eight MIRVs on each missile. The scientists advanced their clock to five minutes to twelve.

You must remember that missile making is big business; hundreds of billions of dollars. People need jobs! Engineers will continue to work at their jobs – designing, innovating, and improving. Having made fortunes designing and building one type of missile, manufacturers will be pleased to make more money designing and building a better one – ad infinitum. People have raved about big business making money out of weapons – right back to Bernard Shaw's play, 'Major Barbara' – with a leading character – the arms manufacturer, 'Undershaft,' who is prepared to make anything, to kill any number of people, in order to make money. However, I point out, this attitude (peoples hostility to armaments manufacturers) is wrong! Businesses exist basically to make money. It is the Government who makes the decision to pay the businesses to build the weapons and to allow them to sell weapons to other countries. The manufacturers will advertise, and lobby, and issue propaganda under the guise of Public Relations, but that is part of normal business procedure. Sell your goods – or go bust. The Government makes the decisions. The Government holds the purse strings. If the Government says, "No! We don't want your weapons!" or, "You cannot sell your weapons abroad." that is it. The Government is the Government! They have control! If the Government can be pushed, cajoled, coerced or bribed, you have a bad Government. Change it! As soon as possible!

In the 1950s the United States carried out a series of atomic tests at Bikini and Eniwetok in the Pacific. A Nagasaki type plutonium bomb was detonated over a fleet of obsolete warships and the results observed. This was an air burst and animals, mainly pigs, were placed on some of the ships, in various degrees of protective clothing, to study the effects of flash and radiation at various distances from ground (sea) zero. Then a similar test was carried out but with the nuclear bomb suspended 10 metres (32.5 feet) below the surface of the sea. Nearly everyone is familiar with the sight of the staggering water column, towering over the ships, that resulted. A third test, planned to be carried out with detonation of a bomb 1000 feet (308 metres) down in the sea, was abandoned.

Far less well known is that there was another, later, test to find out what effects would be produced by the detonation of an atomic bomb in space. An Atlas missile, complete with bomb, was assembled and launched but, unfortunately, the missile failed in flight and dropped into the Pacific where it remains, 10,000 feet (3,077 metres) down, to this day. Undeterred, the scientists obtained, assembled and launched another Atlas which was successful. The missile climbed through the atmosphere and into space where the bomb was then detonated. On the ground or in the atmosphere, most of the energy of the bomb is dissipated heating and vaporising its surroundings. A lesser known effect of the detonation of an atomic bomb is the generation of an electro-magnetic pulse. In space there is nothing – other than the material of the bomb itself – for the energy to work on. The result was, as expected, an enormous blast of radiation but, remarkably, a high percentage of the total energy was converted into a tremendous electro-magnetic pulse, far higher in intensity than anyone had imagined.

Cast your mind back to the days when radio operators – on ships like the Titanic – used Morse code transmitters. Every time the operator tapped his key an electro-magnetic pulse was generated which radiated out from the ship. This pulse travelled out until it struck a metal conductor – the detector antenna – on another ship or even to another antenna a thousand miles away on land. When the pulse struck the antenna, the energy of the pulse was converted into an electric current. This was detected, amplified and created a signal for the receiving operator. The power of the ships transmitter is relatively low so the electro-magnetic pulse was very weak but, nevertheless, detectable. In the case of the bomb, the electro-magnetic pulse created was immense. Scientists were staggered by its power. To give you an idea – if an enemy fired a missile over the United States and detonated an atomic bomb in space just above the atmosphere – it is likely the electro-magnetic pulse would wreck all unprotected electronic devices within 500 miles (805 kilometres) radius of the point of detonation. That includes computers, mobile phones, electronic controllers and so on, including the electronic 'black box' ignition systems in cars and other vehicles. In addition, the overhead power transmission lines, suspended from pylons, forming a spider web network across the country would act as an enormous antenna. The immense electro-magnetic pulse, striking this antenna would generate enormous voltages and currents. Power transmission and generating systems would almost certainly be knocked out for a considerable time. By 'considerable time' I do not mean a temporary 'black out' of two or three days. Probably the worst effect on the power transmission system would be the fact that most of the massive transformers would be burned out. These would have to be totally replaced. Very few spare units would exist so new ones would have to be manufactured. It would probably be months before the 'grid' system was fully functional again. With no mains electrical supply there would be no mains water and no sewage system working – at least until local emergency systems could be installed and operated. One wonders what would happen to civil aircraft with their modern electronic and 'fly by wire' systems. (Military aircraft and vehicles have their electronics specially protected and shielded).

A nuclear bomb, specially designed to enhance the electro-magnetic pulse- as the Russians are certain to have – detonated over the right place at the right height would knock out the entire American electrical power supply system from the Atlantic to the Pacific and probably Canada's as well. In addition it would wreck landline telephone networks and create havoc with electronic systems, knocking out communication satellites in orbit, devastating television and radio communication systems and probably bringing all civil transport to a halt by damaging electronic ignition and control systems. The whole scenario reminds me of the film 'The Day the Earth Stood Still' when an Alien operates a device causing all electrical equipment to fail.

The Americans were so stunned by the results of the 'bomb in space' test. (An electro-magnetic pulse had been predicted but the actual pulse generated was thousands of times greater than expected) that they decided to carry out a series of high altitude and space tests in the Pacific, with bombs of various sizes. The Russians rapidly followed suit. It was found that a high powered uranium fission bomb – not an H Bomb – would produce the most devastating E.M.P. (Electro Magnetic Pulse) and it is probably because of this – and the fear that Iran might be crazy enough to launch such a bomb against the U.S.A. – that the anti-missile missile system has been proposed to be installed in Poland. (Poland would be under the flight path of an intercontinental missile travelling from Iran to the U.S.A.). Obviously, in the case of a nuclear war between Russia and the U.S.A. or maybe, at a later date, between China and the U.S.A., the first bomb to detonate over the U.S.A. would almost certainly be an E.M.P. weapon launched from a submarine, or even a seemingly innocuous commercial ship, close to the American coast so as to give the absolute minimum warning. This would be followed up a few minutes later by in-falling I.C.B.M.s

In his Sci-Fi story – 'The War of The Worlds' written by H.G. Wells, around 1910, he describes a 'heat ray' weapon the invading Martians use. He also describes how it might work. He describes a fantastically refractory container within which is an extremely powerful heat source. The heat builds up and up in the container and then a small aperture is opened. The heat has no way to escape from the chamber except through the small aperture from which it blasts in a tight beam which constitutes the heat ray. Very imaginative! During the period when President Reagan's 'Star Wars' missile defence proposals were being debated, Edward Teller (The H Bomb man) came up with a suggestion. (Maybe he had read H. G. Wells' story but, more likely, he simply thought it up himself). He proposed a weapon, in space, that would be able to destroy enemy intercontinental missiles while they were still a long way away (maybe 1000 miles or more). The idea was to have a thick walled container (a satellite) in orbit around the Earth. The container would be pierced by a number of tubes, like gun barrels. These tubes could be moved and aimed like guns but would be open ended, front and rear, i.e. no breeches. There might be as many as a dozen tubes that could all be aimed separately but in a similar direction. In the centre of the container was an atomic bomb. If an enemy power launched intercontinental missiles aimed at America, the missiles would be detected and tracked as they climbed into space. Once in space the tubes of the defence satellite would be targeted on the missiles, one tube to each missile and the atomic bomb at the centre of the container detonated. The blast of radiation created by the exploding atomic bomb is produced so rapidly the outside container does not have time to vaporise. A great deal of radiation is therefore trapped, for an instant of time, and, during that time, the only way the radiation can escape is through the aimed tubes. A tremendous bolt of radiation will project from each tube, pass unhindered through space and wreck the enemy missiles before the satellite and its tubes vaporises in the nuclear fireball. An up to date version of H. G. Wells' idea. The idea was tested underground with A bomb, container and tube. The tube was aimed down a long tunnel at recording equipment. When the bomb was detonated the idea worked, an enormous blast of energy was directed down the tunnel and the recording equipment destroyed. No attempt to deploy such a device in space was ever made and it is obvious the answer to such defensive weapons would simply be to launch far more missiles than the satellites could handle. With H Bombs, if only one missile in twenty gets through, the nation is destroyed.

Incidentally, the idea of trapping the radiation from an atomic bomb explosion, for a brief instant of time inside a thick walled container, in a similar manner to that described above, is used to achieve the necessary conditions of temperature and pressure required to induce thermonuclear fusion in a hydrogen bomb. In the H bomb casing there are, of course, no tubes or apertures for escape of the radiation. Therefore, in the sub-microsecond before the bomb casing vaporises, a part of the energy of the A bomb blast is trapped and builds up enormous pressures and temperatures. Whereas, in the plutonium fuelled A bomb, high explosive is used to implode the plutonium core, the radiation from the A bomb explosion is used to implode the lithium hydride fuel of the thermonuclear bomb.

By the 1980s, it was said that the Russians had about twenty thousand nuclear bombs and America about thirty thousand. Both sides had enough nuclear weapons to destroy the enemy a hundred times over (and the rest of the World with them!) Even then, some military genius suggested there now existed the possibility of winning a nuclear war. The idea was – if America launched 10% of its weapons, armed with MIRVs, in a pre-emptive strike targeted on the Russian missile silos, it might be possible to destroy ninety percent of their missiles before they could be launched. Do a Pearl Harbour; catch the Russians celebrating 'May Day' or the 'October Uprising' or something! Then you would tell them that – if they were stupid enough to start launching their few remaining missiles in retaliation, you would then launch the entire remaining 90% of yours against them. As if anyone would be thinking rationally after a thermonuclear attack!

In the 1950s I was in favour of nuclear weapons. I was sure the only thing stopping Joseph Stalin taking over Europe was his fear of nuclear weapons.

In the 1960s I had similar views but I thought things were getting a little extreme. In the 1970s the 'overkill' situation was on the brink of madness. By the early 1980s I was convinced I was living on a planet populated by stark raving lunatics. However, during all those years, I did not sit around worrying and chewing my nails. I did what everyone else did – got on with my life and enjoyed it. Occasionally I would think about the situation and say – "But we can't do anything about it can we?" Shake my head, and think of something else. What was the point of worrying?

In 1981 Ronald Reagan was elected President in America. He called the USSR – 'The Evil Empire'. It didn't seem that there was going to be much of a change in attitudes. Business as usual! The Russian President, when Reagan came to power, was an ailing old man named Yuri Andropov – an ex KGB boss who was one of the old school – paranoid, hostile to the West and who was convinced the USA would attack Russia with nuclear weapons as soon as it could find a suitable excuse. The Politbureau was also an Institution of Geriatrics – full of old, war embittered, neurotics who held similar views to Andropov. In late 1983, NATO which, of course, includes America decided to hold Military Exercises. The basis of these exercises was to practise NATO responses to a theoretical attack by the Warsaw Pact Nations (which included Russia) where, in addition to a main attack by conventional forces, the Russians used chemical and biological weapons. All through the period 1950s to 1980s NATO, because of its inferior conventional forces had specifically stated it would rely on and, if necessary, use nuclear weapons to stop an attack from the East. It was intended that, should such an attack occur, the West would use tactical i.e. battlefield nuclear weapons to stem the initial assault. It was also realised that, in this situation, the Russians might use similar weapons and then there might be escalation to all out nuclear war. Accordingly the full scale NATO exercise would be a practise scenario including all the necessary military activity and also a simulated nuclear response even up to the point of having President Reagan practise his part in authorising use of nuclear weapons. Unfortunately, the paranoid Andropov and the Politbureau members remembered, only too well, that Adolf Hitler had used the pretext of military exercises to mass his forces on the Russian border just before, and as part of, the 1941 invasion. Russian planners had already decided that the most likely scenario for them, when the USA mounted the expected nuclear attack on Russia, was that the USA would use the cover of NATO military exercises to catch Russia off guard again as Hitler had done. Accordingly they ordered all Russian nuclear forces to come to total launch readiness for the moment when NATO would simulate the launch of nuclear weapons. As NATO Commanders approached the point where they would practise ordering the launch of nuclear weapons, all Russian nuclear bombers were on the runways, fuelled up, bombed up, the crews standing by. All the Intercontinental Missiles with their multi-megaton warheads were fuelled up, the silo covers drawn back, and ready for the push of a button. All the intermediate range missiles, hidden in the forests, were standing vertically, fuelled up, ready for instant launch. All the available missile submarines were on station and prepared, ready to launch at a moments notice. All it needed, in the last tense minutes, while NATO completed the final phase of their Exercise, was for one of the Russian Surveillance Satellites to give a false alarm (as they had done many times before) of an American Intercontinental Missile launch and it might have been all over. Fortunately there were no false alarms, the Russian commanders kept their nerve, NATO completed their simulations, declared the Exercises/War Games a success, congratulated everybody and declared the Exercises over. Gradually the Russians relaxed and took their forces off imminent attack status. The NATO Military Exercises had produced a situation almost as dangerous as the Cuba Crisis. One of these times our luck would run out.

In early 1984, Andropov died. He was succeeded by Konstantin Chernenko – another stone face. However, Chernenko only lasted thirteen months and then he too died. Following Chernenko the Russians elected another new, younger, President – Mikhail Gorbachev. Gorbachev was unusual – he smiled! All the Russian Presidents previously, all the way back to Joe Stalin and Lenin, had faces carved out of granite!

The arms race continued; more missiles, more and bigger submarines. The Russian's latest submarine was a monster, the Typhoon class, at thirty thousand tons carrying no less than twenty ballistic missiles, each carrying nine MIRV's. One ship capable of destroying 180 towns and cities or other targets. There was a rumour that the Americans were developing a new super-fast nuclear submarine, so the Russians built the fastest in the World. The Americans could go deep, so the Russians built a titanium hulled submarine that could go deeper still. There were accidents and there were losses. The American nuclear submarine 'Thresher' dived too deep, collapsed, and the wreckage now lies on the bottom of the Atlantic at 8 to 10 thousand feet (2 to 3 thousand metres) deep. Both the Russians and the Americans adopted the policy of 'tailing' (closely following) any enemy submarine they detected. One tactic to discourage tailing was to turn the 'tailed' submarine around and 'charge' the following submarine, forcing it to break away or risk collision. Perhaps it is not surprising there are at least half a dozen wrecked nuclear submarines on the seabed in various parts of the World.

You have, no doubt, heard of Howard Hughes; the eccentric American billionaire. When he was young he was a keen aviator, but had one plane crash too many. He survived, but with brain injuries. He gradually became totally neurotic and developed a terrible phobia, from which there could be no escape. He became obsessed with, and terrified of, germs. This Earth is, of course, saturated with bacteria. We live in a total soup of them all the time – in water – in the air – everywhere. Sometimes he would leave his business and his friends and disappear, dressed like a tramp. A lorry driver, in the middle of nowhere, once gave a tramp a lift, and they chatted in a friendly fashion. Later, the driver received a cheque for a million dollars; the tramp had been Howard Hughes. However, despite his phobias, Hughes still had brains. The United States Government contacted Hughes. There was a wrecked Russian nuclear submarine on the bottom of the Pacific Ocean, ten thousand feet down. It would be of immense value to the United States if they could recover the submarine; bring it to the surface and study everything; the sub, the missiles, the torpedoes, the nukes, the sonar, the nuclear reactor and all the systems. The submarine weighed 7 to 10 thousand tons. The Russians would never dream it might be salvaged, from that depth. Was it possible?

Hughes thought about it carefully. One of his companies was a firm named Global Marine Inc. A few years earlier scientists had found that, on the floor of the Pacific Ocean, there were areas carpeted with metal nodules, roughly the size of a potato; very valuable if they could be dredged up. Hughes built a ship, the Glomar Explorer, and announced it was being built to dredge manganese nodules from the seabed, at 10,000 feet (3,000 metres) depth. Nobody was surprised. Hughes was half crazy anyway! However, in reality, the ship had a very different purpose. It was a large ship with massive derricks fore and aft. It also had enormous doors, in the bottom of the ship, and a cavity big enough to accommodate a Russian nuclear submarine. Within the cavity was a gigantic lifting frame.   They took the Glomar Explorer to the Pacific, located the submarine, lowered the frame and, incredibly, clamped it on the nuclear submarine and lifted it – all seven or ten thousand tons of it, from nearly two miles deep, to the surface and into the colossal cavity in the belly of the ship. No one outside of the ships crew, and a few others, had any idea of what was going on. Having learned everything there was to know about a Russian nuclear submarine, they decided, in order to demoralise the Russians, to tell them what they had done and as proof of a technological and intelligence gathering 'tour de force', offered to return the bodies of the lost sailors for burial.

In the late 1980s, there was a new development. The United States had improved Cruise Missiles (Cruise Missiles were, of course, invented by Hitler's Germany in World War Two; the V1, or Flying Bomb. They were crude and not very accurate, but dangerous all the same, with a ton of high explosive in the nose. London was pounded by the things, and Londoners called them 'Doodle Bugs' or 'Buzz Bombs'). The new Cruise Missiles were far more sophisticated. A map of enemy territory was reduced to pixels – the same as in a digital camera - a computer in the missile was programmed, so that the missile could deliver its load on one particular pixel, which might be as small as 15 yards (14 metres) square. They could practically drop one in your lounge from six hundred miles (966 kilometres) away. Not only that, but it could be programmed to fly up valleys, close to the ground, follow the terrain and go willy nilly all over the place, before it arrived at its final target pixel. It was impossible for the enemy to predict where it was going when it came over their territory, and it could carry a one hundred and fifty kiloton nuclear bomb on the nose. As an engineer, I was impressed and thought the system very clever and ingenious, but not something to worry about particularly. No one would start World War Three with Cruise Missiles. They were far too slow.

When these missiles were installed at Greenham Common, in the UK, there were wild demonstrations. A group of women camped out near the perimeter fence for months. Placards were displayed everywhere. "No Cruise Missiles!" Yet, at the same time as the Greenham Common anti cruise missile demonstrations were at their height, a far more sinister development was taking place. There were rumours that the Americans had discovered the location of the Russian Missile Command Centre, near Moscow, and a special missile, the Pershing 2, was being created with the express purpose of destroying the Command Centre. Whether this was true, or not, I am unsure but the really disturbing fact was that the missile was capable of reaching the Command Centre, or Moscow itself, in only 8 minutes from launch in Germany. I find it difficult to believe the

Russians would build their Missile Command Centre as far west as Moscow; surely the logical thing to do would be to build not one but several, hidden in the depths of Siberia, in mines 1,000 feet below the surface, and have a flying Command Centre as back up, as the Americans did. Whatever the situation was, the Russians reacted very strongly to the news of the Pershing 2 and stated, quite bluntly, that if the Americans installed the Pershing 2 missiles they, the Russians, would have no alternative but to go to a policy of 'Launch on Warning'. In other words, eight minutes would simply not be enough time, if sensors or satellites gave warning of an American missile launch, to check if the warning was false or not, and the Russians would launch their intercontinental missiles purely on an indication from one of their sensors that an American launch had taken place. The Russians clearly stated they would definitely go to a policy of Launch on Warning if the Pershing 2 missiles were deployed in Germany. The American response was to state that they too would go to a policy of Launch on Warning if they considered it necessary. It is worth reflecting here that, in the years since surveillance satellites were placed in orbit to monitor various parameters, including the burst of heat which was the signature of a rocket launch, the Americans had experienced at least one thousand five hundred false alarms. Some of these had taken the American response all the way up to DEFCON 2 (Defence Condition 2 – when nuclear missiles are being prepared for launch) before it was found they had a false alarm; machines are fallible – as well as humans. The Russians probably had more – their detectors weren't as reliable.

There was a classic case when Russian satellites detected a mass American missile launch, early one morning on a fine summer's day. There was near panic in Russia and frantic communications to missile stations to ready the missiles for launch. The Russian satellites had been fooled by the sudden appearance of puffs of cloud at the tops of thermals, developing as the sun warmed the prairies – an effect that is sometimes seen in the UK and is merely the result of atmospheric conditions. It was not until minutes later, when the radar failed to pick up the incoming missiles, that the Russians realised it might be a false alarm.

Incredibly, the Americans went ahead and installed the Pershing 2s in Germany. In America an alarmed citizen went to Court and sued the US Government, on the principle that it would be a breach of the Constitution to place the future of the United States under the control of a machine (a computer). The scientists advanced the hands on their 'Doomsday Clock' to read three minutes to twelve. Amazingly, the women at Greenham Common continued to rant against Cruise Missiles. Not a word against the Pershing 2. There were, however, demonstrations in Germany against the Pershing 2. At this point I knew we were on the

Final Countdown to Hell; what else could you call it?! However, as everyone says in this kind of situation, "I can't do anything can I?" Then, one night, I had a few minutes to spare, so I thought, "Is it true that there is absolutely nothing I can do?" and decided to take time out to do some serious thinking.

At that time, I ran a small mail order business and had a number of contacts on newspapers and magazines. There were also a number of other firms who sold goods by mail order – some considerably larger than we were. I sat down and thought carefully and long. What about a petition? But there had been demonstrations and petitions for years. Nobody took any notice of them. These people were usually labelled 'Political Wierdos' or 'Dreamers'.

I decided – maybe we could run large adverts in newspapers and magazines; if I could drum up support from other firms. (I knew my brother would agree as we think similarly). We couldn't finance a campaign entirely on our own. The idea I came up with was to offer people the chance to vote, on the future of the human race, and send the votes to the American and Russian Embassies, calling on the President of the United States and the President of the USSR to have a rethink, and do something sensible about the Arms Race. Recently, I was rummaging in the attic and found my original draft of the proposed advertisement. A copy of the wording and layout is reproduced here. You just might be interested. See page 388 and 389.

NUCLEAR WEAPONS

A CHANCE FOR EVERY MAN, WOMAN AND CHILD TO VOTE FOR THE SURVIVAL OF THE HUMAN RACE

PEOPLE ALL OVER THE WORLD ARE BECOMING MORE AND MORE ANXIOUS AND AWARE OF THE DANGERS OF NUCLEAR WAR. IF SUCH A WAR EVER STARTS IT WILL NOT MATTER WHO STARTED IT. IT WILL NOT MATTER WHAT POLITICS WERE INVOLVED. IT WILL BE UNUTTERABLE DISASTER FOR THE HUMAN RACE.

NO ONE CAN PREDICT ACCURATELY WHAT THE RESULTS OF SUCH A WAR WOULD BE.

NO ONE CAN PREDICT FOR CERTAIN WHETHER THE HUMAN RACE WOULD SURVIVE OR NOT.

THE ONLY THING THAT IS CERTAIN IS THAT IT WOULD BE A DISASTER UNPARALLELED IN HUMAN HISTORY.

MANY PEOPLE WILL SAY, "I KNOW ALL THIS BUT I CAN'T DO ANYTHING ABOUT IT – AS AN INDIVIDUAL." PEOPLE KNOW THAT PROTEST GROUPS OR FACTIONS OF ANY KIND ARE ALWAYS TAGGED WITH A POLITICAL LABEL AND ARE THEN IGNORED BY POLITICIANS IN POWER.

WHAT IS REQUIRED IS A TOTALLY NON POLITICAL WAY FOR PEOPLE TO INDICATE THEIR ANXIETY AND COMMUNICATE IT TO THE LEADERS OF THE WORLD. NOW YOU HAVE A CHANCE TO DO THIS. YOU CAN DO IT BY RECORDING YOUR VOTE – YOUR CALL TO THE LEADERS OF THE WORLD – ON THE FORMS AT THE BOTTOM OF THIS PAGE AND POSTING THEM TO THE EMBASSIES OF THE USA AND USSR IN LONDON. THERE ARE TWO FORMS ADDRESSED TO THE PRESIDENT OF THE UNITED STATES OF AMERICA AND THE PRESIDENT OF THE UNION OF SOCIALIST SOVIET REPUBLICS. THE FORMS ARE TOTALLY NON-POLITICAL WHICH IS WHY THE WORDING IS STRAIGHT FORWARD AND IDENTICAL.

IT IS IMPORTANT THAT YOU ADDRESS AN ENVELOPE AND POST THE DOCUMENTS DIRECT TO THE EMBASSIES. IN THIS WAY THEY WILL KNOW YOU HAVE MADE UP YOUR OWN MIND AND POSTED YOUR VOTE COMPLETELY INDEPENDENTLY AND WITHOUT BEING DIRECTLY ORGANISED OR PRESSURED INTO DOING SO.

THE IDEA AND PURPOSE OF THIS ARTICLE AND THE FORMS IS TO BRING TO THE NOTICE OF PEOPLE IN POWER THAT A GREAT NUMBER OF ORDINARY PEOPLE ARE ANXIOUS ABOUT THE DANGERS OF NUCLEAR WAR AND WISH THE LEADERS OF THE WORLD TO TAKE ACTION TO REDUCE AND FINALLY ELIMINATE THAT DANGER.

IF ENOUGH PEOPLE GO TO THE TROUBLE AND ENOUGH LETTERS REACH THE EMBASSIES OF THE USSR AND THE USA THEN SOMEONE WILL TAKE NOTICE. THE IDEA MAY THEN BE TAKEN UP IN OTHER COUNTRIES AND IF ENOUGH PEOPLE RECORD THEIR DESIRE FOR ACTION TO BE TAKEN THEN IT MAY BE YOUR 5 MINUTES AND 33p WILL REALLY HAVE CONTRIBUTED TO THE FUTURE SAFETY AND SURVIVAL OF MANKIND.

SIGN, CUT OUT AND POST THIS TO:
THE PRESIDENT OF THE UNITED STATES OF AMERICA
C/O AMERICAN EMBASSY
LONDON

TO THE PRESIDENT OF THE UNITED STATES OF AMERICA

As a member of the same human race as yourself, your people and all peoples on this planet, I hereby state my view that no possible disagreement, be it political or otherwise, can be so great as to justify the manufacture and deployment of nuclear weapons which, if used would seriously threaten the future, or even survival, of the human race. I therefore call upon you, as a fellow human being, and a major representative of the human race, to do everything in your power to:

1) Reduce the risk of nuclear weapons   Signed........
2) Devise and arrange agreements   Signed........
   leading to reduction in numbers
   of nuclear weapons   Signed........
3) Work toward a final goal of abolition   Signed........
   of all nuclear weapons

NOTE This is in no way a political document. I have dispatched an identical document to the President of the Union of Socialist Soviet Republics

---

SIGN, CUT OUT AND POST THIS TO:
THE PRESIDENT OF THE UNION OF SOCIALIST SOVIET REPUBLICS
C/O RUSSIAN EMBASSY
LONDON

TO THE PRESIDENT OF THE UNION OF SOCIALIST SOVIET REPUBLICS

As a member of the same human race as yourself, your people and all peoples on this planet, I hereby state my view that no possible disagreement, be it political or otherwise, can be so great as to justify the manufacture and deployment of nuclear weapons which, if used would seriously threaten the future, or even survival, of the human race. I therefore call upon you, as a fellow human being, and a major representative of the human race, to do everything in your power to:

1) Reduce the risk of nuclear weapons   Signed........
2) Devise and arrange agreements   Signed........
   leading to reduction in numbers
   of nuclear weapons   Signed........
3) Work toward a final goal of abolition   Signed........
   of all nuclear weapons

NOTE This is in no way a political document. I have dispatched an identical document to the President of the United States

I was almost ready to put this scheme into operation, when I read about a little girl in America who had written a letter directly to President Gorbachev in Russia. Remarkably, the letter was received and read by him. I understand the letter said, in effect, that she was simply a little girl who did not want to die; she just wanted to live and for all the World to live happily and she wouldn't want to hurt anybody. Would Mr Gorbachev please do something. Shortly afterwards, President Gorbachev travelled to Reykjavik and met President Reagan. They had discussions and a historic Arms Reduction Programme was signed. Following this, President Gorbachev travelled with his wife, Raisa, to the United States, and walked on the streets. He was met with delight and open arms. Sanity was at last appearing! I decided I did not need to proceed with my advert. By a miracle the Russians appeared to have produced a sane and decent man as President. (In practice – he must be a little tougher than he looks – otherwise he could never have reached the top in Russia). I honestly think President Gorbachev is the man who should get the accolade for reducing the arms race and reducing the risk of thermonuclear war. We were, after all, on the very brink of total disaster.

I have a feeling that many young people today do not have a proper comprehension of what a multi-megaton H bomb can do. They see films of A bomb and H bomb tests but they all look similar. They then see a film like Terminator 2 where there is a flash, a rising fireball and then the shock wave, racing through the city, destroying the skyscrapers. This is utterly misleading. That would be the effect of a quite small fission bomb. If a ten megaton H Bomb detonated over Manhattan, New York, the skyscrapers would not be knocked down by the shock wave; they would, in fact, be inside the initial colossal fireball. If you visited New York afterwards you would not find ruins. You would simply find an enormous shallow crater. Instead of flattening New York the shock wave would have flattened skyscrapers and buildings 30 to 40 miles (48 to 64 kilometres) away.

The Cold War was as much an economic war as anything. The USSR impoverished itself to the point of collapse trying to compete with the West and, most of all, America. When economic collapse finally came there was great danger from missiles and nuclear weapons, inadequately guarded, all over the place. Fortunately, one of the features of nuclear weapons is that they rapidly deteriorate. In normal conditions, these weapons are regularly stripped down and refurbished to keep them in efficient working order. Stored missiles also deteriorate with time.

A couple of years ago President Putin was on a ship in Arctic waters. observing part of the Russian Northern Fleet manoeuvres. To impress President Putin it was decided to launch a large missile. The missile failed, either on launch, or shortly afterwards. They tried another; that also failed. The idea was abandoned to avoid further embarrassment.

Modern nuclear bombs deteriorate fairly rapidly and would not detonate properly, or not at all, if they were stored without attention for long. There are various reasons, but I will quote one example. In the centre of a plutonium bomb there is a small initiator, which must work correctly if the bomb is to achieve nuclear detonation. Included in this initiator is a substance named Polonium 210. (The same substance that was used to poison Alexander Litvinenko recently). Polonium 210 is extremely radioactive, although it only produces alpha rays instead of the more penetrating gamma rays. The half-life of Polonium is short; something like six months or so. If you stored a plutonium bomb for five years, at the end of this time there would not remain enough polonium to efficiently trigger the chain reaction. This applies to fission bombs and also to thermonuclear bombs (in these a plutonium bomb is used as a detonator for the thermonuclear explosion). So, fortunately, if someone gave Osama Bin Laden a modern, plutonium based, nuclear bomb – and he stored it in a cave somewhere for a few years, it would not explode properly anyway if he tried to use it later. The same thing applies to nuclear bombs in sunken submarines, for instance. Fortunately, they do not become more dangerous with time – as conventional high explosive bombs often do.

We therefore have the situation that if, in the future, terrorists explode a plutonium type nuclear bomb in a capital city somewhere, we will know that, either they have been given a recently constructed bomb, or a bomb that has been refurbished recently by experts, using materials that could only be supplied by a nuclear power. It is also very likely that the source of the bomb could be traced by analysis of the radioactive fallout. However, the reason the atomic energy experts and Western Governments are so concerned about Iran is they have set up facilities to produce highly enriched uranium instead of a reactor to produce plutonium. With their 3000 ultra-high speed centrifuges, operating in series, they will, before long, be able to produce weapons grade uranium. This is ideal for providing terrorists with the means to devastate a western city. It is far less suitable for producing nuclear tipped missiles. (All Iran's protestations that their nuclear developments are for peaceful purposes constitutes merely a verbal smoke screen). I have described the dangers of weapons grade uranium in the Chapter 9/11 AND THE BUSH/BLAIR RESPONSE. Nevertheless, I feel that a devastating attack by terrorists, using something like Anthrax, is much more likely. Even Anthrax might be traced back to the laboratory that created it.

Although the threat of terrorists using nuclear weapons is nowhere near as great as many people think, it is obviously not zero; somebody might be foolish enough to give them a nuclear bomb or the material to create one. Although the World is now at far less risk of nuclear disaster than it was just twenty years ago, it is a fact that a number of nations still possess an alarming number of up-to-date thermonuclear weapons, in perfect working order, attached to fully functional short range and intercontinental missiles, ready to be fired at very short notice.

It is surprising to realise that the policy of 'Launch on Warning' was never fully resolved. Neither America nor Russia has categorically stated that the policy has been abolished. One wonders – what exactly is the situation at the present time? Many nuclear submarines, missile carriers and attack submarines, still prowl the oceans of the World. Just one missile submarine is capable of almost totally destroying a nation; just how much power does the captain of a missile carrying submarine have? In the event of a dangerous international situation a missile submarine must remain submerged, only approaching the surface to release missiles. It is possible, with ultra-low frequency radio, to signal to a submerged submarine, but the rate of information transmission is very low. On receipt of a radio signal, the submarine, through its captain and crew, must have the power and ability to launch the missiles that could destroy a nation.

As I write, there are still perfectly functional intercontinental missiles sitting in their silos, with multi megaton thermonuclear warheads fitted, ready to go. I have no doubt the B52, B1 and Stealth bombers could lift off with their 22 megaton bombs, if required, and the Cruise Missiles could have their 150 kiloton weapons attached. In my mind, the human race has enough problems on the horizon to think about. It really is time the people of the World faced the fact that we are all on a finite planet and must work together. The major powers should now take a deep breath and agree that, henceforth, nuclear weapons should form no part of the armoury of any civilized nation. At the very least, it should be agreed that no nation should have more than ten thermonuclear bombs that could be delivered on cities and possess no other nuclear weapons. Ten H bombs would be enough to deter anyone. All other nuclear weapons should be dismantled and scrapped. The best answer to conflict between nations is trade. When the people at the village near Murmansk in Russia, see their standard of living improving because of trade with the West, the red flag I saw still flying recently will come down. The Communist Chinese are no longer so great a menace; trade with the West is too good. North Korea will come in out of the cold in the next ten years. Only Iran remains a problem. I recently read that the President of Iran, no less, stated that nuclear bombs could destroy Israel, but would only damage Iran. He should be shown the same film of the Eniwetok H bomb test that I saw, but perhaps he is so foolish he still wouldn't change his mind. The Israelis are sure to have thermonuclear weapons by now. To threaten Israel with nuclear weapons is a very dangerous thing to do. The Israelis are paranoid (and with good reason) and are quite likely to go for a pre-emptive strike if they ever think such a threat is serious. Maybe Iran will be the place where the human race sees the last city destroyed by atomic weapons before they are finally banned forever.

I remember on one of my salmon fishing trips to Russia, during an evening meal one night I was sitting at a long table opposite some Americans. Somehow, the conversation worked round to atomic bombs. Heaven knows how! The conversation usually is, as you would expect, about the one that got away – or even the one that didn't get away. We were, at the time, fishing a river on the Kola Peninsula, in Northern Russia, which is, or was, studded with atomic bombs, (Hydrogen bombs, to be exact. Multi megaton ones, sitting on enormous rockets in underground silos). Maybe that is how the topic arose. One of the Americans said to me "Does the UK have atom bombs?" "Yes!" I replied. "Oh!" he said, "I suppose the US gave them some." Normally I would have smiled and kept my mouth shut, or said, "Actually – we built our own," in a carefully modulated English voice. (Some chance – I have an awful Midlands accent). But I got mad! Must have been too much real Russian Vodka (terrible stuff) and I said, "We built our own – later – but during the war we couldn't afford it so we gave the info to the Americans. As I understand it, the atom bomb was created by a lot of international scientists working together, financed by American money." I then reeled off the names of half a dozen scientists; Enrico Fermi – Italian. Stanislas Ulam – Polish, Edward Teller – Hungarian, William Penny – English, Hans Bethe – German, Neils Bohr – Danish, etc. There was an awkward silence. I was lucky. The Americans were gentlemen. It's a wonder I didn't get a punch in the teeth. It just goes to show. Leave the vodka alone – or the other strong stuff – when talking to people who are not your immediate compatriots (come to think of it I have come very close to having my teeth knocked in by some who were, on occasions). It also goes to show what emotions – and Vodka – can do. Rational thinking can go out of the window. However, I always think, no matter how good you think your country is, give other nations credit too. There was, of course, some truth in what I said but it was only – as usual in arguments – a biased half truth. There were a good number of American scientists involved, for instance Lawrence, Oppenheimer, Wheeler, and so on, and we are forever indebted to the Americans. The truth is, we owe them our freedom. In World War Two, without America, we could not possibly have beaten Hitler on our own. Even when we supposedly "Stood on our own," in 1940, we were supported, massively, by the Americans; food, supplies, ships and so on. America is a great nation. Most, if not all, of the people in the free and democratic nations of the World today, owe their freedom to them. Make no mistake about it! It always galls me to see the hostility in France towards the USA. Without the USA they might be part of the 'Greater German Empire' or, failing that, part of the 'Greater Russian Empire'. There must be plenty of intelligent Frenchmen who are perfectly well aware, but many of their politicians seem to be hostile to the USA. Not much Rational Thinking there!

Remarkably, the first Patents to do with the construction of an Atomic Bomb were taken out in Britain. Even more remarkably, they were taken out before Otto Hahn discovered Uranium Fission. They were not, I might add, taken out by an Englishman – but by a Hungarian. The first discovery, that atoms could be split, was made by Ernest Rutherford – a New Zealander, working in Britain. It was a fascinating scientific discovery, but that was all. This was followed up by Chadwick's discovery of the neutron. At this point one or two people began to talk of the possibility that, in the future, it might be possible to release vast amounts of atomic energy. Most scientists were sceptical and even the great Rutherford stated that, in his opinion, such people were talking 'Moonshine!'

However, working in Britain at that time (in the early 1930's) was a brilliant Hungarian physicist – Leo Szilard. Szilard thought very carefully about the recent discoveries and concluded there might be a real possibility that a substance might exist that would fission under neutron bombardment and, in the process, produce more neutrons – raising the possibility that a chain reaction might be created. He continued to think about the implications and, in 1934, (nearly five years before Otto Hahn discovered Uranium Fission) applied for patents on the basic construction of an atomic bomb. Remarkably, he had worked out the principle of 'critical mass' and how the rapid assembly of a supercritical mass would cause a nuclear explosion. Fortunately these patents were brought to the attention of the British Admiralty and were classified as 'top secret'. Szilard did, of course, end up in America working on the atom bomb project.

Another brilliant scientist – Stanislas Ulam, who was Polish, also worked on the Manhattan Project. At a later date, in the 1950's, when nuclear scientists were having great difficulty in designing a functional hydrogen bomb it was Ulam who came up with the answer. Edward Teller, who was another brilliant Hungarian, is called 'The Father of the

Hydrogen Bomb' but I think it should be Stanislas Ulam who was the real 'Father of the H bomb'. It was he who recognised the key to thermonuclear fusion was radiation pressure.

At the present time there is friction between the USA and Russia, over American proposals to place an Anti-Missile system in Eastern Europe. The purpose, we are told, is for defence against any possible future attack by nuclear tipped missiles launched by Iran against the United States. To me, that is an extremely unlikely scenario. The Iranians would have to be totally insane to try such a thing. It would be akin to someone armed with an old fashioned, single shot pistol, firing a shot against someone armed with a Kalashnikov. A deliberate, overt, nuclear attack on America might, possibly, provoke a response that would probably wipe most, if not all, of Iran off the map. I think the possibility of Iran undertaking such an attack is so utterly unlikely, it can be dismissed out of hand. If some Americans are still worried, all they need do is state that any nuclear attack on America, whether directly or indirectly, i.e. through terrorists, would trigger massive response against the nation responsible. That threat should be enough to stop any nation on Earth even considering the idea. The conclusion, therefore, is that the anti-missile installation in Eastern Europe is totally unnecessary. The Iranians must be thrilled that they are frightening someone; all they are doing is playing psychological games. Nuclear bombs for second rank nations are only acquired to boost public morale and allow their politicians to strut and bluff and bluster. Even if Iran gets the Bomb, they couldn't do anything with it, any more than India and Pakistan can. There is a very slight possibility they might give a nuclear weapon to terrorists, or the materials to build one but it would still be a crazy thing to do. It is highly likely that, if such a bomb did devastate an American city, it would soon be traced back to the country of origin, and the massive wave of rage and hatred generated in Americans would be such that some degree of nuclear retaliation would be extremely likely. My personal view is, the chance of a nuclear attack on Europe or America by a relatively weak nation such as Iran or North Korea, whether by direct attack or in a clandestine manner via terrorists, is extremely low.

I consider the idea of placing Anti-Missile Missiles in Eastern Europe is a political mistake. It is totally unnecessary. I am a little surprised however, at the reaction of the USSR and, I confess, I am disappointed in President Putin. I thought he was an enlightened, intelligent, man but he is beginning to behave and talk like one of the old paranoid communists we used to have before Gorbachev. If he doesn't like the idea of Anti- Missile Missiles in Eastern Europe – let him say so. I cannot quite see how such missiles would constitute a threat to the

USSR, but here he is threatening to target Europe with massive thermonuclear tipped missiles. He has also made other blunders, such as shutting off European gas supplies, because he had a disagreement with his neighbours – the Ukrainians. He is also carefully sabotaging all the gas and oil deals that were done with Western businesses to develop oil and gas fields in various parts of Russia. All these things destroy confidence. Russia could have joined China and India in massive economic expansion and prosperity by trading with the West. Now the West is having second thoughts. If President Putin is not very careful he will create an inferior, smaller version of the old paranoid USSR. The bulk of manufacturing trade, in the future, will go to China and India. Russia will be able to sell her natural resources – but what is he going to do with the cash? Build nuclear submarines and missiles again! What an outdated, negative attitude! Forget the Anti-Missile, Missiles, Mr. Putin. They will probably never be installed and, if they are, they will simply be a waste of time and money.

My message to President Bush is also – Forget the Anti-Missile, Missiles, in Eastern Europe. As a defence against Iran they are totally unnecessary and you are frightening President Putin. The old Russian paranoia has not yet totally evaporated and Mr. Putin thinks you are proposing these missiles, not as a defence against Iran, but as a defence against Russian missiles which, in Mr. Putin's mind, means you are thinking of a war between the USA and Russia. For heavens sake scrap the idea of an East European Anti-Missile Missile system and let President Putin sleep at night. The Iranians must be delighted that their nuclear games are causing trouble between Russia and the West.

I admit I am puzzled by the actions of the Iranians. Obviously they do not need nuclear power for energy (they are sitting on top of one of the World's largest deposits of oil) but their antics with uranium separation centrifuges are surprising and worrying. If they really want a nuclear bomb, for deterrent missiles, plutonium is the way to go. Centrifuges are usually used to create enriched uranium for power station reactors or compact nuclear submarine power units. As stated earlier it is possible to make an atomic bomb using enriched uranium but the degree of enrichment would have to be very high and the quantity of uranium quite large (over 100 kilograms (220.5lbs). Far easier to obtain and use plutonium. Maybe this whole uranium enrichment game is simply an elaborate, psychological, way to worry the West and particularly the USA. Let us, for our sake – and theirs, hope it is no more than that.

THE WINDSCALE ACCIDENT

One morning in 1957, the British public heard, on their radios and TV sets, that there had been a minor fire at one of the two Windscale nuclear reactors. They were told the fire was extinguished but there had been, however, a slight release of radioactivity. It was nothing to be alarmed about but, as a precaution, a small quantity of milk from nearby farms was being disposed of. Hidden behind this bland statement was the fact that we had come terrifyingly close to a disaster that could have devastated Britain and contaminated half of Europe.

In 1939 Professor Otto Hahn, in Germany, working on the effects of radiation, made the discovery that neutron emission would trigger fission in Uranium atoms. Not only that, but the fission process released a substantial amount of energy and additional neutrons as well. It was obvious to any physicist that the possibility of creating a nuclear chain reaction existed. Hahn, as an internationally famous scientist, did not keep his discovery secret and published his data, with the result that, in 1939, the entire scientific world knew of uranium fission.

Uranium – a very heavy metal – is found, in a type of ore, in various locations all over the planet. It is uncommon but not rare. The metal, if analysed carefully, is found to be a mixture of two isotopes. (All atoms are made up of a nucleus, consisting of a number of protons and neutrons, and an outer 'shell' of electrons. It is possible to have two or more forms of the same element, in which the number of neutrons in the nucleus differs slightly. For instance, uranium consists mainly of atoms containing 238 protons and neutrons, but with a small percentage consisting of atoms with only 235 protons and neutrons. The different atoms are said to be isotopes). Although the two isotopes behave in a chemically identical manner, they are, on an atomic level, slightly different. U238, having more protons and neutrons is slightly heavier than U235. In addition, it was found, from experiment that the two behaved differently when exposed to neutron radiation. U235 would fission when subjected to bombardment by neutrons, whether the neutrons were travelling at a high or at a low speed. U238, in contrast, would fission only when bombarded by low velocity neutrons. The neutrons produced by the actual uranium fission process are high velocity or 'fast' neutrons. When these facts were discovered, it was immediately obvious to scientists all over the world that, although it would not be possible to make a bomb using U238 material, it might well be possible if one could obtain a sufficient quantity of U235. However, only a very small percentage of a sample of natural uranium is U235 and it is impossible to separate the two isotopes chemically, as they behave, chemically, in an identical manner.

So in 1939, physicists knew there was a possibility of making an atomic bomb, if someone could find a way of separating U235 from U238. It was because of the fear that somehow, German scientists, known to be some of the best in the world, might find a way to separate uranium 235, and give Hitler the Atomic Bomb, that America decided to invest billions of dollars in the Manhattan Project! To separate U235 from U238 was immensely difficult. The only possible way imaginable was to try to exploit the extremely small difference in the weight of the two isotopes. That was how it was attempted in the Manhattan Project and remains the basis of methods used today. Physicists calculated there could be two types of chain reaction. One was the bomb reaction in U235, the other was to create a sufficient mass of U238 or 238/235 mix (including natural uranium) and intersperse the uranium with a second substance (moderator) that would act to capture fast neutrons, slow them down and reintroduce them to the uranium. Natural uranium is slightly radioactive – in other words some of the atoms undergo spontaneous fission and, in the process, produce a few fast neutrons. If, therefore, a sufficient quantity of uranium, interspersed with a moderator, could be assembled then it might be possible to start a chain reaction. This approach is, of course, the basis of the design of nuclear power station reactors today.

The Americans, therefore, decided to experiment to see if a natural uranium reactor was possible and, also, to see if U235 could be extracted from natural uranium in order to make a bomb. Accordingly, to work on the Manhattan Project, as it was called, was brought together the greatest assembly of the world's top scientists ever known. A group, under the Italian Physicist Enrico Fermi, worked to design and produce a slow neutron, natural uranium, reactor using graphite as a moderator. It was realised, of course, that if such a reactor did achieve a chain reaction, it would destroy itself in a burst of heat and explode (though not on atomic bomb scale) or melt down if it was not carefully controlled. Control rods of a substance that absorbed neutrons were, therefore, placed in the assembly. Finally, when the reactor (in Chicago) was completed the control rods were withdrawn, step by step, until the assembly became critical and the neutron flux began to surge. The world's first man-made nuclear chain reaction had been achieved. A coded message was sent to the President of the United States. It read – "The Italian Navigator has Entered the New World".

Meanwhile, other scientists, at Los Alamos, were considering the problems of creating an atomic bomb and, in particular, the problem of separating U235 from U238. Two main approaches were considered.

The first proposal was to gasify uranium (in the form of Uranium Hexafluoride) and pass the gas through porous membranes (the diffusion process). The very slightly lighter gas (U235 Hexafluoride) would diffuse through the membrane slightly faster than the U238 material. Repeat the process thousands of times and, eventually, the bulk of the diffused material would be U235. To actually do this was far more difficult than it sounds. Uranium Hexafluoride is a hellishly corrosive and difficult gas to work with. An enormous diffusion facility was set up, at Oak Ridge, and a clue as to the immensity of the undertaking, can be gained from the fact that the total area of membranes in the diffusers could be quoted in acres.

As an alternative to the diffusion method an electro static/electro magnetic approach was devised. This involved creating an electrified beam of uranium atoms projected through a vacuum tube to a target. To assist in understanding the idea let me describe something similar. In an old fashioned, cathode ray tube type of television set, a device at the back of the set (an electron gun) creates a beam of electrons that travel forward, through a vacuum, to strike a phosphor coating on the inside of the television screen. When the beam strikes the coating the phosphor glows, producing a white spot on the screen. High voltage plates arranged on either side of the electron beam act to focus, or defocus, the beam and also to move it up and down and from side to side. The movement of the beam and, also, the focussing/defocussing act to produce the picture.

In the uranium separation device, a beam of uranium atoms (the natural mixture of U235 and U238) is projected, and deflected electromagnetically, in a similar fashion to the TV arrangement, except that the beam is simply projected on to a screen and deflected to one side without being moved around. Uranium atoms will strike the screen, and accumulate over time, until there is a collectible deposit. However, instead of there being only one deposit, there will be two. One deposit will be U238 and the other will be U235. Since the U235 atoms are lighter, they will be deflected more by the electromagnetic plates. In effect, the atoms in the uranium beam are being sorted, atom by atom. A single very powerful machine of this type would have to operate continuously for months to produce milligram amounts of U235. To produce the necessary kilogram quantities for a bomb, thousands of machines were built, and a completely new power station built to power them. It will be appreciated that the gaseous diffusion and electro separator systems could be run sequentially, to improve efficiency. In addition to the dedicated power station, the US Government authorised the use of 14,000 tons of silver 'borrowed' from the US Treasury to provide the electrical windings of the separator machines (silver is an even better conductor than copper). After all this immense effort and expenditure, the total amount of U235 produced by June 1945 was enough to make just one bomb, and that was the bomb that destroyed Hiroshima.

Let us now return to the large natural uranium 'slow reactor' that had been built, and successfully operated, at Chicago. As the reactor operated, it produced an immense flux of neutrons and it was discovered that this neutron bombardment could, and did, transmute elements, as well as affect the atoms of everything it touched, making them highly radioactive. Remarkably enough, it even transmuted some of the uranium itself, as well as promoting fission, and it was found the reactor produced a whole range of new elements, some of which only lasted a fraction of a second before they disintegrated into lighter substances. One of the new elements was called Plutonium and was relatively stable. Scientists experimented with samples of the new transmuted materials, and found that plutonium would fission with fast neutrons, in the process produced more neutrons, had a remarkably small critical mass and would be better for making atomic bombs than U235. Additionally, and most importantly, plutonium could be extracted fairly easily from its mix in the reactor fuel rods, by a chemical process. All the enormous effort to build the gaseous diffusion and electro separation plants had not really been necessary in order to produce atomic weapons. However, nobody could possibly have foreseen the creation, in a nuclear reactor, of a material such as plutonium. I sometimes think it might have been better for the human race if plutonium had never existed. It made possible the immense proliferation of all kinds and sizes of nuclear bombs and, in particular, it made the fusion (thermonuclear) bomb a reality. Fortunately, the creation of a nuclear bomb using plutonium is, due to a technicality, tricky and needs a far more sophisticated device than is needed to create a bomb using uranium. Nevertheless, the fact remains that to produce plutonium, and hence the material for an atomic bomb, all that is really needed is a nuclear reactor, such as exists in a power station, and an extraction facility to remove the plutonium from the reactor fuel rods.

Through its spies, the USSR learned all the details, built a reactor, extracted the plutonium and stunned the world by detonating its first atomic bomb in 1949, at least ten years earlier than anyone expected. Because most of the nuclear secrets were given to the USSR by spies of British Nationality, relations with the USA became strained, to say the least, and the British Government decided it needed an independent nuclear deterrent. This is where we come to the matter of Windscale. The British, of course, knew all about making atomic weapons. All they lacked was a supply of plutonium, so the Government authorised the building of two nuclear reactors at Windscale, Cumbria, with no other purpose than to produce plutonium for weapons. No doubt the Russians had done exactly the same thing. For this purpose the reactors could be very simple, far more so than if the reactors were intended to be part of an electrical generating station. All that was needed was several hundred tons of uranium, several thousand tons of graphite as a moderator and an arrangement of cooling channels through which air could be blown to remove the heat. The hot air would exhaust through two large, tall chimneys. The reactors would operate at high level (to produce the maximum amount of plutonium in the minimum time) so enormous blowers were installed to force through the necessary cooling air. The intention was to run the two reactors at a high level for as long as possible, let quantities of plutonium build up, then extract the fuel rods, dissolve them in acid and chemically process to remove the plutonium.

Natural uranium can be found, in the form of ore, all over the world; in Australia, Africa, Canada, Europe, Siberia. When it is extracted from the ore, and becomes uranium metal, it is a relatively innocuous material and is only very slightly radioactive. It is safe enough to be handled. However, when uranium is placed in a nuclear reactor, which is then started up, a massive flux of neutron radiation is created, by fission of some of the uranium atoms. The radiation creates heat, transmutes some of the uranium into plutonium and other waste products, and also makes all the uranium in the reactor extremely radioactive. By extremely radioactive, I mean absolutely lethal!

In the 1960s I worked on the design of a machine at Harwell (Britain's Atomic Energy Research Establishment) that was required to cut samples of 'hot' (highly radioactive) uranium taken from a nuclear reactor. Under the effect of neutron radiation the uranium fuel rods deteriorate. The metal slowly changes, from a condition similar to steel, into a more brittle and fragile state akin to crude cast-iron. It also expands due to the accumulation of waste products. Whilst it would be preferable to run the reactor as long as possible before removing the rods for processing, in order to maximise the quantity of plutonium in each rod, care must be taken to ensure the rods do not degenerate, and swell so much they cannot be removed. It was in order to understand, and control, this danger that it was decided samples must be taken, and tested, at various levels of exposure and activity. This necessitated the design and construction of a remotely controlled machine, to cut carefully designed test pieces from samples of irradiated uranium. The machine had to be operated by remote control, with the operator working and observing through a special window, which was, in fact, a glass walled tank of a clear, very dense, liquid. The tank was about 2 metres (6 feet, 6 inches) from front to back. I was looking through this tank at a small piece of 'hot' uranium, about 5 centimetres (2 inches) long and 7 millimetres (¼ of an inch) diameter and said to a physicist "Just how dangerous is that small piece"? "If you drained this tank," he said, "you would receive a lethal dose of radiation in about twenty seconds". "And how far would I have to be away from it in the open – in a field, say, to be safe"? "About one thousand yards (923 metres)" was his answer. That gives you a measure of how dangerous this stuff is. Think of hundreds of tons of it!

The Windscale reactors, having top priority for the Government's Nuclear Weapons programme, were rapidly designed, and work commenced. Most of the basic construction work was completed and the cooling chimneys were under construction, when a top engineer or physicist began to worry. What would happen if anything went wrong? With the reactors in operation, there would be hundreds of tons of hot, murderously radioactive uranium there, and the whole lot simply air-cooled. (Uranium is pyrophoric when hot. In other words it is likely to burst into flames on contact with air. To prevent this, the uranium fuel rods were enclosed in aluminium canisters. Unfortunately, aluminium has a relatively low melting point). He proposed that, to be on the safe side, filter systems should be installed. The filters would have to be enormous, of course, because of the huge volume of cooling air from the blowers. At first it was pointed out it was far too late in the process of construction, but he persisted and, as a last resort, massive filter boxes were incorporated into the top of the chimneys. Any photograph of the Windscale reactors was unmistakeable. Two enormous chimneys, with great rectangular filter boxes on the top of each chimney – the only chimneys like it in the world. The reactors were finally finished, started up and operated. Britain obtained plutonium and it's nuclear weapons; but there came a day when something went wrong.

In the course of the development of nuclear reactors and weapons, there have been a few surprises and discoveries. Not many, because the scientists involved were the world's best and, from their deep understanding of nuclear physics, could, and did, predict with remarkable accuracy, the outcome of many experiments and situations. Nevertheless, there has never been 100% certainty, which is why so many nuclear weapon tests were carried out. An interesting example is the test of the first hydrogen (thermonuclear) bomb using lithium hydride as the fuel. The very first hydrogen bomb, detonated at Eniwetok Atoll in 1952, incorporated a large tank of heavy hydrogen as the thermonuclear fuel. The whole contraption was as large as a small house so, although it detonated with an incredible 8 megatons power, it was hardly suitable for modification to be a deliverable military weapon. To produce a smaller, more compact device that could be carried by aircraft, a new design was produced using lithium hydride as the fuel. Lithium hydride would contain far more heavy hydrogen in a given volume than could be contained in gaseous, or even liquid gas, form and would also be far easier to handle. In a similar way, a bucket of water contains a large volume of hydrogen (chemically combined with oxygen) in an easily handled form. For technical reasons the compound of lithium (a light metal) and heavy hydrogen was chosen as being a promising fuel for a thermonuclear bomb. All the calculations of the energy output of a bomb using lithium hydride, were based on the quantity of heavy hydrogen in the bomb. Lithium would simply be the 'carrier'. When the new design was taken to Eniwetok Atoll for test it was calculated the yield would be around 5 megatons. Upon detonation, the blast was staggeringly larger than expected and it was later calculated the yield was around 15 megatons. Three times greater than anticipated. It was later determined that, in addition to the energy released by the heavy hydrogen (deuterium), the lithium 'carrier' had also reacted and contributed to the total yield. (You may remember – the creation of plutonium in a functioning nuclear reactor was also an unanticipated discovery). Another unanticipated effect that occurs in the operation of nuclear reactors is the creation of 'Wigner' energy.

Wigner energy is a form of latent energy that builds up in a functioning nuclear reactor over a period of time. Chemists and metallurgists are familiar with latent energy. It is usually manifested in the form of heat release during a phase change. There is no indication of the presence of the energy until there is a phase change, when the heat is then released. It must be borne in mind that the Windscale reactors were some of the earliest nuclear reactors built and, so far as I am aware, very little was known about Wigner energy at the time. When a nuclear reactor is shut down, after operating for a length of time, the Wigner energy can be released and, if the reactor is shut down quickly, can result in a sudden, short lived, rise in temperature in the reactor before the normal cooling takes place that would be expected from the reduction of nuclear activity. Therefore, if a reactor is shut down too rapidly it is possible for the reactor temperature, already at a high level, to jump to a sudden high peak, before falling away as the nuclear reactions are reduced. It is believed this is what happened at Windscale, and also at Chernobyl.

Whatever happened at Windscale, it remains a fact that, in 1957, one of the reactors overheated and caught fire. The aluminium cladding on some of the fuel rods burst or melted, exposing the hot uranium to the cooling air, with the result that some of the uranium caught fire. In addition, the reactor contained more than a thousand tons of graphite (the moderator) which is pure carbon, some of which also caught fire. All the conditions existed, therefore, for the creation of an immense furnace; a thousand tons of carbon, the combustible uranium and a forced blast of air. Initially, only a small part of the reactor actually caught fire, but the indications were there and the horrendous potential was obvious. If the main bulk of the reactor caught fire, a considerable amount of the uranium could burn (out of the hundreds of tons total) and the rest would probably melt down. A desperate situation indeed. When a nuclear reactor is shut down it is not a simple situation like switching off an electric fire. There is still an enormous amount of residual activity – a lot of heat is still being generated. A shut down reactor will still produce some heat for a long time and must continue to be cooled to some degree.

So the engineers at Windscale were in a classic 'no win' situation. If they switched the cooling fans off, the reactor was likely to overheat and cause a melt down. If they did not switch off the fans, the reactor would be gradually converted into a gigantic blast furnace. Fortunately, thanks to the foresight of the man who insisted on the filters, the enormous box on top of the Windscale chimney did it's job and trapped 99% of the radioactive dust that was created in the early stages of the fire. That could not last however; if the fire developed, the filter system would be overwhelmed.

When the sensors first indicated an increase in the temperature of the reactor, the engineers were unsure of what was happening. Then, later, when radiation monitors at the top of the chimney showed a release of radioactive dust, there was alarm. One of the engineers volunteered to actually look into the reactor to see what was happening. The roof and sides of a reactor are of course, many feet thick to contain the radiation but there are many holes in the sides for insertion of fuel rods, etc and inspection holes in the roof. These are normally plugged when not in use. A roof plug was removed, but it is impossible to look directly down the hole into the reactor. The beam of radiation, emanating from the hole, would be lethal from mere seconds exposure. So the engineer used a mirror so that he could peer down to see if there was any indication of a fire. The worst fears were confirmed. The reactor was on the way to becoming a furnace.

It may be thought that it was safe to use a mirror to look down into the reactor but, in fact, it was an extremely dangerous manoeuvre. The engineer was risking his life – and knew it. When he placed the mirror so that he could peer into the reactor, the light from the fire was reflected off the mirror as one would expect. The immensely powerful, invisible, beam of nuclear radiation would pass through the mirror, through the roof of the building and on through thousands of feet of air before it would be absorbed. However, as the beam of neutron and gamma radiation passed through the mirror it would cause the mirror itself to produce secondary radiation. That is why, at a later date, the engineer was awarded the George Cross for bravery and dedication to duty.

With the worst fears confirmed, engineers frantically worked to try to remove fuel rods from the reactor but many were already jammed because of the excess heat. In desperation it was finally decided to send for the Fire Brigade, flood the reactor with water and simply put out the fire the old fashioned way. The Fire Brigade duly arrived and, with their normal efficiency, connected up the hoses, flooded the reactor, and, in next to no time, the fire was out and the blowers shut down. The reactor was, of course, ruined and remained shut down forever, but the emergency was over. The Government announced to the people of Great Britain that there had been a minor fire at one of the reactors at Windscale, resulting in a slight leak of radioactive material. There was absolutely nothing to worry about but, as a precaution, a certain amount of milk produced by some of the local cows would be disposed of. Television and Cinema News Reels showed a few churns of milk being poured down a drain. The public forgot about the incident and everything was normal. To this day, most people believe there has never been a serious nuclear accident in the UK.

When I read that there had been a fire in one of the nuclear reactors at Windscale and realised the fire had actually been in the fuel rods and the graphite moderator – and that the fire had been extinguished by simply calling the Fire Brigade and injecting water into the burning reactor I was stunned. I would have thought there was a great risk of explosion as I will explain. Engineering is a very wide field and engineers have to specialise. There are Aeronautical Engineers, Marine Engineers, Civil Engineers, Structural Engineers, Hydraulic Engineers and a whole host of specialists the public has never heard of, including, at one time, Gas Engineers. In my younger days I worked for a firm of Structural and Gas Engineers and, believe it or not, I once won a prize for the Most Promising Student in Gas Engineering. (I got out of Gas Engineering believing it was too limited a field, and was proved right when North Sea Gas was discovered).

In those days, before natural gas, the gas that was burned in the stoves and cookers of the average British home was produced from coal. To do this, coal was first roasted in enormous ovens and the volatiles (gas and liquids) driven off, leaving a hard residue of nearly pure carbon (coke). The coal gas was purified but, additionally, the engineers and chemists managed to make gas from the coke itself, which was a good thing, otherwise we would have had mountains of the stuff. To do this they reheated the coke red hot in special ovens and blew water, in the form of steam, over the coke. There was then a chemical reaction. The red-hot carbon (coke) had such an affinity for oxygen that it actually pulled the oxygen out of the water to form carbon monoxide (which is combustible) and, at the same time, creating hydrogen, which was again combustible. The purified coal gas and the 'water gas' (as it was called) were mixed and eventually sold to the consumer.

It was the hydrogen in the coal gas that allowed my brother and myself to construct and fly the fake flying saucer referred to in another chapter. Another feature of coal gas was the percentage of lethal carbon monoxide, that led to a number of accidents (not too common because coal gas had a strong smell) and many suicides. The water gas plant could be dangerous and much care was required when starting the reaction. An engineer friend of mine was seriously injured by an explosion that occurred during a water gas equipment start up.

The carbon/water reaction is endothermic – which means the reaction absorbs heat, rather than releasing it. In the case of the water gas plant, oil fired heaters were used to supply heat to sustain the reaction, but, in a nuclear reactor, there will be plenty of spare heat – at least to sustain the reaction long enough to cause an explosion. So – at Windscale – we had a situation with hundreds of tons of uranium and red hot carbon, (graphite is a particular form of pure carbon – as is the coke), a blazing fire, plenty of heat from the reactor and someone proposing to pump water into this cauldron. (If the reader has ever seen what happens if you throw water on a blazing oil fire or a kitchen chip pan fire he or she will know the result is usually disastrous. The water/blazing oil reaction can be considered similar to the water/red hot carbon reaction).

If there had been an explosion – even a relatively mild one that did not wreck the reactor – it would, almost certainly, have wrecked the filters at the top of the chimney and radioactive dust would have spread far and wide across the countryside. If I had been an engineer at Windscale when the suggestion of calling the Fire Brigade had been mooted I would have screamed "NO! NO! What about the water gas reaction"? And then where would we have been? Heaven knows! It is highly probable that the engineers in charge at Windscale had never heard about the water gas reaction, (they were Engineers, not Chemists), which was just as well, because the introduction of the water worked and the fire was quenched. We do, however, know perfectly well what the worst-case scenario could have been, because we had a classic demonstration at Chernobyl. The Chernobyl Nuclear Power Station Reactor was a water-cooled reactor, with hundreds of tons of uranium, plus a thousand tons of graphite, as moderator. For some reason, inexperienced operatives decided to shut down the reactor, and must have done it too quickly.

There was a release of Wigner energy and the reactor overheated. The hot graphite reacted with the water, exactly as I have described, created carbon monoxide and hydrogen, and the resulting blast was enough to blow the reactor apart, wreck the building and cause the rest of the uranium in the reactor to melt down. The explosion was so powerful that the entire concrete top of the reactor, weighing over 100 tons, was completely blown off. The resulting escape of radioactive material contaminated a large area of Russia and half of Europe including parts of Britain.

Will somebody please tell me how we managed to get away with it at Windscale?

NUCLEAR AND FUSION POWER

When, during the Second World War, Enrico Fermi and his fellow scientists in Chicago delicately, and very slowly, extracted the control rods from the first experimental nuclear reactor and finally saw the instruments register a surge in neutron radiation that signalled the worlds first man made, self sustaining, nuclear chain reaction had been achieved, it was the first step to producing an atomic powered electricity generating station.

Remarkably, it was not the first nuclear reactor to go 'critical' on this Earth. Deep in the mantle of the planet, various metals are dissolved in the molten rock and superheated water that exist at those depths. Occasionally, the lava breaks through the surface to form volcanoes and often, around the volcanic area, cracks and fissures allow the ancient water, loaded with dissolved minerals and metals, to rise to the surface. As the enormous pressures and temperatures are released, the metals precipitate, and it is in this way that surface deposits of gold and other rare metals including uranium, are produced. It so happened, millions of years ago, in Gabon, West Africa, that volcanic fissures released steam from a supply of deep, archaic, water containing uranium and, gradually, over many years, built up deposits of uranium. There is nothing particularly unusual about the process – it happened, and is still happening, all over the world – but in this particular case something very remarkable occurred. The deposit of uranium built up into such a mass, and of such a configuration and the surrounding rocks must have acted as a moderator so that, eventually, the mass became 'critical' and a natural nuclear reactor was formed. Because the mass of uranium was built up very slowly, until it just became critical, it is probable that the amount of radiation given off was never very great but, over a long period of time, a quantity of uranium reacted and produced the tell-tale fission products that, many years later, allowed scientists to deduce that once, a natural nuclear reactor had existed.

Nuclear reactors produce radiation, which converts into heat. All that is necessary to create a nuclear power station is to build a reactor, typically containing hundreds of tons of uranium, to generate heat at a sufficient temperature to boil water. Boiling water produces steam which, in turn, can be used to drive turbines and electrical generators. In practice, of course, it is not as simple as it sounds. In a large power station the uranium is usually in the form of fuel rods, contained in metal canisters, interspersed with graphite blocks, which act to modify the neutron radiation and enhance the reaction. Cooling, and hence heat transfer, is usually done with water but some have been built which are gas cooled. However, many different designs are possible and, with very compact, high power reactors, such as those used to drive nuclear submarines or aircraft carriers, even liquid metal (sodium) has been used for efficient heat transfer. The problem with all nuclear reactors is radiation. The fission process generates large amounts of neutron radiation, and gamma rays lethal to every living thing. (Remarkably some bacteria have been found to be capable of surviving doses of up to 1,000 times greater than would kill a human being). To stop this penetrating radiation needs roughly a foot thick of solid lead, or nearly two feet of solid steel, or six feet of concrete. Nevertheless, it is feasible to create reactors with this kind of shielding.

The real curse of nuclear reactors is residual radiation and radioactive waste. If a nuclear reactor or power station could be assembled, switched on, operated for its working life and then switched off, and the radiation stopped when it was shut down, everything would be fine. Nuclear power would be the primary answer to man's energy needs. Unfortunately, that is not the case. Neutron radiation disrupts atoms, transmutes elements, and creates isotopes. A perfectly innocuous substance can be placed in a nuclear reactor and, when it is removed, it has been converted into something absolutely lethal – a highly radioactive version of the original. The uranium fuel, before it is inserted in the reactor, is safe enough to be handled. In the reactor some of it disintegrates, produces radiation and heat and, in the process, creates various fission products lighter than the original uranium (such as lead, barium, etc). Conversely some uranium atoms are transmuted into even heavier materials such as plutonium. Most importantly of all, the neutron radiation makes atoms unstable, which means some of the atoms spontaneously disintegrate – again producing radiation. This applies to everything the neutron radiation penetrates. The uranium itself, the canisters, the moderator, the structure of the reactor, steel work, everything. Various materials have different levels of radioactivity and the intensity of the radiation falls with time. Some intensely radioactive materials may have a half-life (time to reduce radiation intensity by 50%) of weeks or months. Some, however, can be 1,000 years or more, meaning the materials could still be dangerous to humans (and animals and plants) in 10,000 years time. Radioactive waste is the hellish legacy of Nuclear Power.

To construct a nuclear power station is relatively easy. To dismantle one and get rid of the waste (hide it somewhere) and dispose of the radio-active structure is a nightmare. It is possible to build a new nuclear power station in a few years, but to dismantle one may take 30 to

50 years and cost as much as the original construction. I suspect, when the original calculations were done regarding the relative cost of electricity produced by nuclear power, nobody took into account the true cost of decommissioning. There was probably a hopelessly low 'guesstimate' of the cost of closing down the nuclear power stations. Britain led the way, in the 1950's and 60's, in the building of nuclear power stations, but limited the number built. The French became the enthusiasts and built far, far more nuclear installations. Many of these will now be approaching the end of their working lives. What a colossal burden on the French economy decommissioning will be. With oil and gas supplies in the world beginning to tail off, there will be great pressure to build more nuclear powered electricity generating stations. After all, there is plenty of uranium, and it is possible, with a special kind of reactor, to create more fuel than is used (fast breeder reactor) but what of the legacy for the future. In order to create power for the billions in the short term, the people of 500 and 1,000 years in the future may be saddled with the incubus of nuclear waste, and derelict nuclear power stations. It may well be, when the population has reached maximum, and the world economy reached the point where no further growth is possible, nations will not be able to afford the immense costs of decommissioning.

At some point, either by deliberate birth control and planning or, more likely, natural disasters, the population of the Earth is going to be reduced. It is very unlikely there will be 20 to 30 billion people on the Earth in 1,000 years time. More probably the figure will be one billion or 500 million or even less. These people will have to live on a hot, impoverished planet with no oil, no natural gas, possibly no coal, and a great many of the species of fish, plants and animals we know now, disappeared. They will have problems enough, without having an endless legacy of nuclear waste and defunct nuclear power stations to contend with. In the nearer future, a proliferation of nuclear plants will bring about an increased risk of accidents. Experts will tell you the chance of an accident with a nuclear power station is almost zero. (That's what they said before Windscale, Three Mile Island and Chernobyl!). In all three cases, it was not a defect in the plant that caused the accident, but human error. Nobody seems to mention the possibility of deliberate sabotage, or someone crashing a plane into a reactor (very unlikely after 9/11), but what about the possibility of an armed, SAS style, attack by a group of terrorists or even just one deranged man, on the staff, who knows which buttons to push, and which valves to close, to wreck a reactor. Chernobyl was wrecked accidentally. It could easily be done deliberately. (I hope the Authorities are fully aware of this and have taken the necessary precautions). The brutal truth is that nuclear power stations mortgage the future for thousands of years, in return for a brief period of nuclear generated electricity today. A power station will operate for fifty years, but the nuclear waste, and the radioactive remains of the reactor, will persist, to some degree, for 20,000 years. We could, and should, do without uranium generated nuclear power but, short termism and expediency being the watch-words of most Governments and administrations, expect a 'blizzard' of pro-nuclear power propaganda and a rapid proliferation of atomic power stations. Forget about the people who will be alive a thousand years from now! As long as we can make our toast, and run our computers, today, why worry?

Atomic power stations run on the principle of nuclear fission, where heavy atoms (uranium or plutonium) disintegrate and produce lighter elements such as lead bismuth and radon. Remarkably, the fusion of lighter elements to create heavier atoms can also produce power. The key thing in both processes, fission and fusion, is that the resulting mass should be less than the mass of the original material. In other words, if a ton of uranium fissioned it would produce slightly less than a ton of fission products and, if a ton of hydrogen fused to form the heavier substance, helium, it would produce slightly less than a ton of helium. The difference is matter that has been destroyed in the process – converted into energy in accordance with Einstein's formula $E=MC^2$. Fusion power is what keeps the sun shining and provides the energy of a hydrogen bomb. All that is needed to cause atoms of hydrogen to fuse, to create helium, is to slam them together violently enough. All atoms at a temperature above absolute zero vibrate – which is a form of local movement. The higher the temperature the more violent the movement. If atoms are brought very close together they will repel each other – in a similar manner to the way two magnets of the same polarity repel each other, as you can confirm yourself. If two magnets are brought together, slowly, they will push each other away but, if you bring them together fast enough, you can beat the repulsion and make the magnets strike each other. If there are sufficient hydrogen atoms in a confined space, and the temperature is raised high enough, some of the atoms will, because of their vibration, collide violently enough to overcome their natural repulsion and fuse together to form helium. This process goes on at a steady pace in the sun and at a very fast pace in a hydrogen bomb. A fusion power reactor is a device intended to operate somewhere between the two.

To cause fusion of hydrogen atoms requires violent collisions. Below a certain temperature the collisions will never be violent enough but, above the critical temperature, a second factor will influence the frequency of the fusion reactions, and that is density. The more hydrogen atoms that are crammed together in a given space, the more fusion reactions will occur at a given temperature. In a hydrogen bomb a high density is achieved by having the hydrogen combined with lithium in a solid form. A plutonium fuelled atomic bomb explosion is then used to crush the Lithium Hydride to even higher density and create the highest possible temperatures, in order to fuse the maximum number of hydrogen atoms in the shortest possible time. Once hydrogen 'ignition' has occurred, the extra heat produced by the fusion reaction extends the 'burning' time and consumes more of the hydrogen available.

There are two different approaches to producing fusion power to generate electricity. The first is to create a large doughnut shaped tube or torus and, having first evacuated all other gases, insert a quantity of heavy hydrogen in gaseous form. The gas is then heated electrically whilst, at the same time, it is electromagnetically squeezed into a thin band at the centre of the torus. The squeezing causes compression, but a secondary effect of the electromagnetic confinement is to prevent the intensely hot gas from touching the material of the structure of the torus. In this way, the heavy hydrogen (deuterium and tritium) can be heated to millions of degrees without destroying the containment vessel. At a certain point, the critical parameters of temperature and pressure are met and fusion occurs. (For a practical sustained power generating fusion reactor an ideal temperature would be around a hundred million degrees C). When fusion occurs, radiation is produced, which escapes from the created nuclear furnace and reaches and heats the containment vessel. To generate electrical power it will be necessary to remove the heat by a coolant system, use the heat to boil water or other working fluid and use the steam produced to drive turbines and generators. Although the system described sounds relatively simple it is, in fact, extremely difficult and it has taken over 50 years of experiment to reach the point where a fusion reactor capable of producing power station levels of energy has become feasible. An experimental, power station type, fusion reactor – ITER (International Thermonuclear Experimental Reactor) is now under construction at a place called Cadarache in the South of France. This is an international effort and will cost at least ten billion pounds (around 20 billion dollars) to construct. The reactor will be considered a success if it can produce power station levels of energy (around 500 megawatts) for a period of five minutes. This, obviously, whilst it would be a remarkable achievement, is very far from being close to a practical high power fusion reactor capable of operating for many years.

Great problems of stability – holding the compressed gas in a tight ring and keeping it away from the walls of the containment vessel – have dogged the design and creation of a toroidal fusion reactor from the beginning. In all the early fusion reactor designs, a major problem was the difficulty of holding the compressed, immensely hot, gas steady at the centre of the toroidal tube. The compressed ionised gas began to pulse and flutter in the magnetic field, and this instability not only made it difficult to reach the desired temperatures of millions of degrees, but also caused erosion of the inner surface of the containment vessel. The first real signs of success came with a modified Russian design named 'Tokamak' but, obviously, there is a vast difference between creating a design that produces fusion for a brief time, and a working electricity generating station.

The fusion process produces vast amounts of very high energy neutrons. It is the interaction of these neutrons with the containment vessel that creates the heat that can be used to operate the turbines and generators to produce electricity. Unfortunately, in the process, the neutrons will act to damage and degrade the structure of the containment vessel and also the vital superconducting magnets which act to hold and control the reacting plasma. My own guess, as a professional engineer, is that it will probably take another 50 or even 100 years or more to reach commercial viability, if it proves to be possible at all, which means fusion power is unlikely to make much of a contribution to world energy supplies before the oil and gas runs out.

Another approach to creating a fusion reactor is laser-powered fusion. In this device a continuous series of miniature hydrogen fusion explosions is envisaged, almost like a series of sub-miniature hydrogen bomb detonations. In the Chapter WAR AND NUCLEAR WEAPONS, I have described how a spherical shock wave, produced by high explosive, can implode and compress a solid sphere of plutonium, to trigger a fission bomb detonation. It is also possible to trigger a fusion reaction by simultaneously compressing, and heating, a small pellet of heavy hydrogen (deuterium plus tritium). To achieve the necessary conditions of heat and pressure, a number of very powerful lasers are used. A small spherical fuel pellet is projected into a vacuum chamber and, at the exact moment the pellet is in the correct position, the lasers are fired. The impulse lasers release an enormous amount of energy, in a blast of light lasting less than a millionth of a second, and are so arranged that the entire surface of the pellet is equally illuminated. The result is, the surface of the pellet is instantly vapourised at tremendous pressures and temperatures. The expanding shell of vapourised material creates an immensely powerful spherical shock wave, that compresses the inner part of the pellet down to a small fraction of its initial volume. So great is the compression and heating – millions of degrees and millions of pounds per square inch – that fusion conditions are created and the small pellet becomes, to all intents and purposes, a miniature hydrogen bomb creating heat and radiation.

To produce continuous, extractable power for an electrical generating station a steady series of pellet injection and detonating cycles would have to be created, heating the containment vessel and allowing useable heat to be extracted. At the present time limited information is available on laser fusion. This is not surprising, since the experimental set up I have described would, with suitable instrumentation, provide an enormous amount of information relative to the design of military hydrogen bombs. To a great extent, this would eliminate the need for full scale nuclear testing of such weapons (such full scale nuclear weapon testing is internationally banned). Whilst the laser thermonuclear ignition of a single fuel pellet is undoubtedly feasible, a reactor where a continuous stream of pellets was detonated, at frequent intervals, to produce continuous power in a generating station continuing, day and night, for years is far less likely to be practical.

It has been said that fusion power would be clean power, in that it would not create radioactive waste as a by-product as a fission reactor does. This is correct, but what is not mentioned is the fact that the fusion process still produces nuclear radiation that would make the containment vessel, and structure, highly radioactive, so there would still be decommissioning problems. So great are the difficulties, that I feel thermonuclear fusion may never, ever, be a practical proposition for producing large amounts of cheap electrical power. In my mind the creation of large numbers of uranium/plutonium fuelled nuclear power stations is likely to bring relatively short term (a few hundred years) benefits to the human race and create a terrible, long term (thousands of years) menace for the future.

We are continuously reminded that fusion power would mean endless and unlimited power from the 'heavy water' in the sea as though this was a miraculous and unique feature of fusion power. I would point out that we already have endless, almost unlimited and clean sources of power on this Earth which are far easier to exploit. I refer, of course, to hydro-electric power and, to a lesser extent wind, wave and solar power. If there were just a reasonable number of us we could have all the clean power we needed without resorting to coal and gas fired power stations or nuclear reactors.

RADIOACTIVE WASTE DISPOSAL AND REACTOR DECOMMISSIONING

When a nuclear reactor is initially assembled, all the components are relatively inert. Even the uranium is only slightly radioactive. However, as soon as the reactor is started, an immense flux of neutron radiation floods the reactor, and penetrates deeply into the internal and external structure. The radiation will penetrate over a foot thick of solid steel, or 5 feet (1.5 metres) of concrete. Moreover, the neutron radiation destabilises atoms of the material it penetrates and, thereby, makes those previously inert materials highly radioactive. In the reactor itself, the uranium undergoes fission, producing the intense radiation which, through interactions, is converted into heat and, through heat exchangers, boilers and turbines, drives generators to produce the electricity we need.

In the process of fission, uranium atoms are destroyed and converted into various lighter elements (fission products) which are themselves highly radioactive. However, the fission products, which slowly accumulate over time, produce a number of detrimental effects, one of which is to cause the uranium fuel rods to distort and expand. If a reactor incorporating fuel rods (there are other designs such as fluidised bed reactors) were run for an excessive length of time, it might become very difficult or even impossible, to remove the rods from the reactor for processing. A second effect of some of the reactor by-products is to poison the reactor, i.e. to absorb a proportion of the neutron flux and make the reactor less efficient. In practice, a reactor is run for a certain length of time, and then fuel rods are removed for processing and replacement. Fuel rods are dissolved in acid, the radioactive waste products removed and new fuel rods fabricated from the purified uranium.

Here, we come to the crux of the radioactive waste disposal problem. The waste products extracted from the fuel rods are extremely radioactive. There are a number of different waste products, with varying half lives (half life is the time it takes for the level of radioactivity to fall 50%). Some materials have half lives measured in weeks, some years and some – thousands of years. Disposal becomes a major problem. Residual radioactivity also produces heat. In America, there is a massive storage tank facility, containing liquid radioactive waste, which produces so much heat the tanks have to be continually cooled, with a powerful system incorporating electrically driven fans. This, in itself, may not sound so bad until you realise that, if the waste continues to be stored in this way, the fans will need to be run for thousands of years. If, somehow, the tanks were destroyed, and the radioactive material escaped, it would be a major disaster.

It is believed that, in Russia in the 1950's, quantities of highly radioactive waste were simply dumped in a disused mine and the mine sealed. The heat from the waste gradually built up and, eventually, there was an explosion and a massive escape of radioactive material. At the time, this was hushed up, but details were later leaked out to the West. Disposal of high level radioactive waste is not, therefore, an easy matter. I remember, on a trip to the nuclear facility at Sellafield, a few years ago, I saw details of a new process which was expected to solve the problem once and for all. The idea was to vitrify the waste, in other words to incorporate it in glass, to enable it to be safely buried, (taking due account of the heat which would be produced) so that there would be no risk of radioactive material getting into ground water at any time. However, I recently read that even the vitrifying technique has been found to be inadequate. The reason being that the radiation from the incorporated waste slowly damages the molecular structure of the glass and, over a long period of time, it would probably disintegrate.

Other solutions to the problem of disposal have been suggested over the years. One was the idea of disposing of the waste in space. Whilst this would undoubtedly get rid of it, the risk of a transporting rocket failing, either on launch, or before a minimal orbital or escape speed has been reached, must rule out such a proposal. Another proposition was to dump the waste in the sea, in a deep subduction trench. As everybody now knows, the surface of the earth consists of a number of enormous rocky masses or plates, floating on the semi-liquid, hot, mantle material below. The plates are constantly moving, very slowly, often of the order of millimetres or centimetres a year. In some places the plates are moving apart – as in the Mid Atlantic Ridge – and, in other places, the plates are colliding and being forced together. In some cases where this occurs, the rock buckles and mountain chains are forced upwards. However, in a few places, one of the colliding plates is forced down into the supporting mantle and slides under the other plate. Over time, usually millions of years, the material of the lower plate may slowly melt and, mainly because of the trapped water, eventually form a more liquid molten rock, which may rise to the surface and create volcanoes. The process is, however, fantastically slow, and takes many millions of years before the subducted material is eventually brought to the surface again by volcanic activity.

It seems to me, therefore, that the most practical way to dispose of the high level nuclear waste is to vitrify it, as in the earlier proposal, and then to ship out the vitrified blocks, or spheres, and spread them over a wide area at the bottom of a suitable subduction trench. The glass would probably last long enough for the spheres to be covered in sediment, which would gradually be subducted and, since it would be fifty million years or so before the material resurfaced again, in a volcanic eruption, the radioactivity would have reduced by then to little more than the normal background radiation. If there was considered to be any risk of the glass disintegrating before subduction, and contaminating the sea water, then I suggest slugs of vitrified waste could be incorporated into the noses of heavy steel penetrator bombs, which could be released from a surface ship in sequence – like a 'stick' of bombs from an aeroplane. Each 'bomb' would be a 2 metre (6ft 6in) long solid steel rod, maybe 130mm (5in) diameter, with a point at one end and fins at the rear or alternatively – made from reinforced concrete, say, 300mm (12in) diameter by 3 metres (9ft 9ins) long. The radioactive slugs would be incorporated in the nose of the 'bomb'. The terminal velocity of such a bomb, falling through 5,000 metres (16,250 feet) of water, or more, would be high, and its momentum, when it reached the sea bed, would be enough to drive it metres deep into the ooze, ensuring that the radioactive slugs were safely buried out of harms way. Obviously, tests would be carried out to check the efficiency of such a penetrator. Dropped, as described, the penetrators should impact the sea floor at distances 10 or 20 metres (32 or 65 feet) apart, so making sure too much radioactive waste could not accumulate in one place. Sat/Nav location of the ships would make sure each load of penetrator bombs was dropped clear of previous waste disposal areas. This approach would probably, in the long run, be safer and cheaper than other alternatives. This method is, of course, only proposed for disposal of the really high level radioactive waste, such as that in the American storage tanks described earlier. (In the case of high level liquid waste the radioactive material would be taken out of solution and concentrated before being incorporated in vitrified slugs for ocean disposal). Lower level waste could be stored in bulk in deep depositories, such as mines, in geologically safe areas. This latter approach is well known and already under examination, but is not suitable for the high level waste, as was demonstrated by the Russian disaster.

Finally, of course, we have the problem of decommissioning old nuclear power stations. When a nuclear power station reaches the end of its working life, and is finally shut down for the last time, all the fuel rods are removed. However, the internal structure and containment vessel material is extremely radioactive. No attempt to start to dismantle the reactor is likely to be considered for 20 years or so, while the residual radioactivity falls to a lower level. Then begins the extremely slow, laborious and expensive business of decommissioning, getting rid of radioactive materials and so on. To decommission and dismantle a nuclear power station, and return the site to approximately the condition it was before the power station was built, can cost billions of pounds. Maybe as much as or more than, the cost of building the power station in the first place.

It seems to me there could possibly be a far simpler solution. Before a nuclear power station is built, construct a cavity, twelve feet (3.7 metres) or more, deeper than the maximum height of the nuclear reactor structure. Imagine a deep, circular, flat bottomed, hole in the ground. Build the nuclear reactor and its containment structure inside the hole. Everything else – the cooling towers, the turbine and generator hall, the control room, etc, can be built as usual above ground level. When the power station eventually reaches the end of its working life, the reactor is finally shut down and all the fuel rods removed. All the power station facilities above ground level would be dismantled, and removed in the normal way, and then the reactor and its containment vessel left, for twenty or thirty years or so, to allow the residual radiation to reduce to lower levels. If the dome of the containment vessel projects above ground, that too, could now be removed, down to a level six feet (1.8 metres) above the top of the reactor. A flat layer of reinforced concrete, six feet (1.8 metres) thick, would then be formed on top of the reactor. There will, of course, still be a considerable level of residual radioactivity in the reactor 20 or 30 years after it has been shut down, and it may be necessary to have some sort of simple cooling system installed, to prevent heat building up. This final cooling system could be built-in when the power station is originally designed. After the concrete slab on top of the reactor is finished, the entire hole containing the reactor and the remains of the containment vessel would be filled in, earth placed on top of the concrete slab and the whole area levelled off. The only thing left above ground would be the small cooling installation.

If enough heat was still created at this stage, by residual radioactivity, then even this could be used to generate a small amount of power. The important point is that all the radioactive components of the reactor would be sealed away underground, and could be left indefinitely. In the system used at the present time, when the reactor and all its structure is dismantled, the radioactive material still remains and must be disposed of somewhere, somehow. Burying the entire reactor structure in situ, would be the easiest, simplest and by far the most economic, method of disposal.

If the Chernobyl reactor had been designed and built in the fashion I have described, how very much easier it would have been to bury the damaged reactor. As it is, they have had to build a gigantic concrete mausoleum and, in effect, bury the thing above ground. Eventually, the concrete structure at Chernobyl will, like an enormous house, weather and crack and finally fail. Since the remains of the reactor will be dangerously radioactive for thousands of years, let us hope that people in the future will be capable of rebuilding the sarcophagus. If the reactor had been in a hole in the ground, as described, then a simple covering of earth, topped off by a layer of concrete, to prevent rain water penetration, would have made the site safe, indefinitely, and in a far more, simple manner. Were this reactor burying proposal to be adopted, each site could be topped off by a distinctive, solid, reinforced concrete marker, such as a 40 foot (12 metres) high truncated pyramid. The people of the future would learn to leave such marked sites alone – just as we, for thousands of years, have left alone the ancient mound type burial sites, or Tumuli, which are common throughout Britain.

9/11 AND THE BUSH/BLAIR RESPONSE

As time passes and the shock and horror of the terrorist attack on the Twin Towers becomes a thing of the past, people are changing their views. The 9/11 happening was years ago and, here we are today with troops in Iraq and Afghanistan fighting what appears to be an unending war. People are saying "What are we fighting for? Pull the troops out!"

Osama Bin Laden and Al Qa'eda had been in existence, and active, long before the attack on the Twin Towers. Years before, when Colonel Oliver North testified before the Senate Committee – to do with illegal funding for the fight against Communists, in South America – he referred to "The most dangerous man in the world. His name is Osama Bin Laden". Nobody had ever heard the name before, or of the organisation – Al Qa'eda – other than a few like Colonel North. A number of bomb attacks on US troops and Institutions were carried out over a period of years; hundreds were killed. Al Qa'eda set up training camps in Afghanistan and recruited thousands to the cause which is, basically, a 'Holy War' against the West.

As Al Qa'eda grew stronger, they grew more ambitious. They plotted to explode a massive bomb at the base of one of the Twin Towers, in such a position as to cause the tower to topple and, in falling, bring down the second tower. If this had succeeded, it could have resulted in up to twenty thousand deaths. The truck load of explosive was placed in the car park, under the tower, and exploded as planned. Fortunately, there were floor levels below the level of the car park. The floor collapsed and a large part of the blast was channelled into the basement. The Twin Towers survived. After the earlier attacks, and even after the first Twin Towers attempt, there was no serious response – no serious action to bother, or threaten, the Al-Qa'eda organisation was mounted in any way. So Al-Qa'eda grew stronger and more bold.

We have been through this sort of game before – for example with Germany's Adolf Hitler. Before World War Two no one in the USA, or the UK or France wanted to be involved in another war. Hitler knew it! First he took over the Rhineland, in the face of French occupation and the 1918 Agreements, and got away with it; as a result he grew more bold. Then he took over Austria. Again he was successful; no one wanted war. So Hitler pushed further and began to demand Czechoslovakia. Although the British Prime Minister – Chamberlain – travelled to Munich to meet Hitler, again the Dictator was allowed to have his way. No one was prepared to take decisive action. Hitler began to think, in the face of this

420

weakness, he could get away with anything. When he invaded Poland, people finally woke up and faced the facts. Hitler was not going to stop. He was, people finally admitted, going to have to be stopped by force.

It was the same with Osama Bin Laden and Al Qa'eda. They had planned and carried out a number of terrorist attacks, even the first attack on the Twin Towers, in the heart of America – with no real response. So they planned the greatest and most audacious terrorist attack of all time. Let us consider the full extent of that planned assault on the USA, using hi-jacked aircraft.

Firstly – to attack and destroy the Twin Towers, with the aim of destroying the economic heart of America and, possibly, killing up to 20,000 people in the process.

Secondly – to attack and, if possible, destroy the Pentagon – the heart of the US Military Command.

Thirdly – to attack and destroy the White House and also kill the President if possible.

Fourthly – to attack and destroy the Capitol Building and eliminate the Senate and the House of Representatives as well, if possible.

In the event, one of the five airliners scheduled to be hi-jacked was delayed, to such an extent that the hi-jacking was abandoned and the hi-jack team fled and escaped. The attacks on the Twin Towers were horrifically successful. The Towers collapsed and were totally destroyed – but not before most of the people working in the Towers had been evacuated. Nearly three thousand died but, if the Towers had collapsed quickly and not withstood the flames for an hour, a far greater number of people would have been killed. All eyes were fixed on the Twin Towers. Meanwhile, hi-jacked plane No.3 flew on, and dived as planned into the Pentagon, causing massive fires and killing many people. In plane No.4 the hi-jackers made a mistake; they allowed people to keep their mobile phones. Passengers learned of the attack on the Twin Towers and realised the purpose of the hi-jackers on their plane. With enormous courage, they organised and mounted an attack on the hi-jackers, beat them down and, finally, forced their way into the cockpit, where the Al Qa'eda terrorist who had killed the pilot and taken his place, finally flew the plane into the ground in a last savage display of determination and religious fervour. This act of courage and bravery by the passengers of the fourth hi-jacked plane saved either the White House or the Capitol.

Consider again the true extent of the Master Plan. To destroy the economic centre of America and tens of thousands of people; to destroy the Pentagon; to destroy the White House and the President; to destroy the Capitol and the Senate. If that was not a Declaration and Act of War what on Earth was it? President Bush's declaration of War against Terrorism no more started the war than President Roosevelt did when he declared War on Japan after the murderous Pearl Harbour attack; the war had already been started!

After the 9/11 attack, US and British forces went into Afghanistan, and destroyed the Al Qa'eda training bases, and ousted the Taliban – the extreme religious government who were supporting them. For the first time, a positive, definite, reaction to Al Qa'eda terrorism occurred.

It came out, after 9/11, that Al Qa'eda people had been making enquiries about hiring, or getting hold of, crop spraying planes; obviously for a planned chemical or biological attack, probably against a major American city. I am relieved we didn't find out what that plan was, the hard way! Following the action in Afghanistan, Bush and Blair decided to go into Iraq and oust Saddam Hussein, with the blessing, they hoped, of the United Nations. Saddam Hussein obviously hated the West. They had previously thwarted his plans to take over and dominate the Middle East Oil States – starting with his invasion of Kuwait. If this had succeeded, Saudi Arabia would probably have been next. Why would anyone think he would have stopped at Kuwait if he had not been opposed? I would point out that, under Saddam Hussein, Iraq had built up the third most powerful army in the world. What did people think he had bothered to do that for? We also know, as proven fact, that Saddam Hussein had previously used chemical weapons against the Kurds. We know he had 'Scud' missiles because he fired a number against Israel during the Kuwait conflict. He had chemical and biological research laboratories and would, obviously, be keen to get revenge for the humiliation of Kuwait. How better than to give Al Qa'eda half a ton of Sarin or, better still, Anthrax.

People now say the invasion of Iraq was unjustified. The fact that Inspectors found no evidence of weapons of mass destruction doesn't impress me. It would be the easiest thing in the world, today, to hide almost anything in a desert area like Iraq, whether it was something large, like a 'Scud' missile or a smaller container of Anthrax. You could simply go out into the middle of nowhere – the middle of the desert, one dark night, at a time when the Satellites are not overhead to see you – dig a hole and bury your Scuds and Anthrax in the sand, then, punch the buttons on your Sat Nav, record the co-ordinates and only you – of all the people on the Earth – could find it again. Within 24 hours the wind will have erased all trace of disturbance. Somewhere in Egypt lies the tomb of Alexander the Great. Nobody has ever been able to find it. When they do find it, the people who do so could completely hide it again if they wished – and only they could re-find it using Sat Nav coordinates. It is the same with the 'Titanic'; it took years to find. Now they can go out into the middle of nowhere, with nothing but sea from horizon to horizon – and say, with absolute certainty, the Titanic is directly below us – Now!

The real mistake in Iraq, in my opinion, was not to complete the job and depose Saddam Hussein when America and its allies intervened, during the first Iraq war, and threw the Iraqis out of Kuwait. Although the first Iraq war was a sobering demonstration, to the rest of the world, of the power of American military might, it still left Saddam Hussein (no doubt seething with rage and a desire for revenge) in power and in control of Iraq. It would have been better to have continued after Kuwait, conquered Iraq and deposed Saddam Hussein then, rather then go in later. However, hindsight is a wonderful thing. After George. W. Bush and Tony Blair made up their minds and finally did depose Hussein, we do, at least, know for sure – Saddam Hussein is not going to give Al Qa'eda half a ton of Anthrax.

There has also been an indirect benefit from the action in Afghanistan and Iraq. Libya used to sponsor terrorism. When Colonel Ghaddafi saw how easily the mighty Iraq army was defeated by modern weapons, he decided it might be wiser to stop supporting terrorism and be friendly to the West; a policy he has adopted with enthusiasm. So the only rogue states remaining today, if you ignore South America, are Iran and North Korea.

North Korea can be discounted. It is a Communist, atheist, state in a desperate economic and political situation. Whether they get an effective atomic bomb or not does not matter that much. (Their recent test was a dud – as atomic bombs go). They can't do anything with it except bluster. Any serious threat and the United States would give South Korea and Japan more than enough atomic weapons and missiles to defend themselves.

The Chinese will not want North Korea to start anything and upset the economic 'apple cart'. The Chinese will gradually convince Kim-Jong-iL to come in out of the cold. The real and very dangerous problem is Iran. They are in a key strategic position, have a large chunk of the world's reserves of oil, are religious and hate the West.

The deposed Shah of Persia was an enlightened man (some would disagree, because of his secret police who killed hundreds – they forget the many thousands killed when the present regime came to power). He tried to modernise Iraq, and wanted to spend the oil money to transform Iran into a modern industrial country. (Apart from a few million for his pension fund of course). People from PERA, (The Industrial Research Association where I once worked), travelled to Iran to organise and set up new factories, but this work stopped when the Shah was ousted, and Iran went back to extreme religion. At the present time it is they who are supporting terrorism; they who sponsor unrest in Iraq; they who are supplying the sophisticated roadside bombs which are killing American and British soldiers in Iraq and Afghanistan. If they could annexe Iraq they would have a powerful hold on world oil supplies. What next – Kuwait? Saudi Arabia? They hate the West; America Is openly called 'The Great Satan'! They say they only want nuclear power for peaceful purposes. How can they possibly want nuclear power stations for energy, when the country is, literally, floating on a sea of oil? The only possible reason is for development of nuclear weapons – no matter what they say. They either want nuclear weapons so that they can bluster and threaten, and frighten a lot of people in the West or for a more devious purpose.

There is the possibility, which I consider remote, that Iran is planning to create and launch an intercontinental missile, equipped with an E.M.P).Electro-Magnetic Pulse) nuclear weapon, to devastate the U.S.A. (I have described the effect of an E.M.P. nuclear explosion in the Chapter WAR AND NUCLEAR WEAPONS). This, no doubt, is the reason America wishes to install an Anti-Missile Missile System in Poland which would be under the flight path of a missile launched by Iran against the U.S.A.

The really disturbing thing about the Iranian determination to pursue the uranium enrichment program is the relevance to terrorism. If Iran wishes to simply have an atomic bomb in its arsenal the best way to go is plutonium as the USSR, Britain and other countries did. As described elsewhere in this book it is, however, difficult to make a plutonium bomb; requiring very sophisticated explosives, detonators, a special initiator and a lot of precision engineering. However, with a little help from people like A.Q. Khan (the Pakistani nuclear physicist) I think they could do it. However, if there was then the idea of supplying a terrorist organisation with a nuclear bomb for use against America or Europe the terrorists would have to be supplied with a complete working nuclear bomb or all the components to assemble such a bomb. To smuggle such a device into the USA or Europe would not be impossible but the plutonium core would give off radiation which might trigger alarms at airports or shipping centres. Also, and more importantly, it would be obvious that a plutonium bomb, because of its sophistication, must have been designed and built by a Nation capable of such things and deliberately given to a terrorist organisation for use against the target country. This would be seen, correctly, as an overt act of war. The only difference between a terrorist detonated bomb and an attack by a nuclear armed intercontinental missile being the method of delivery.

The production of enriched uranium is far more devious and sinister. It can be claimed that enriched uranium is being produced as nuclear reactor fuel (as the Iranians continue to insist). However, with 3000 centrifuges or more, operating in series, as the Iranians have constructed, the process of enrichment can be continued until weapons grade material is produced. Having produced enough material, the actual creation of a nuclear bomb is then extremely, frighteningly, simple.

If Iran uses natural uranium as the basic material to produce the uranium hexafluoride to put through its centrifuges, the weapons grade uranium they finally produce will have a very low level of radioactivity; so low that it would be extremely easy to smuggle it into any European or American city. The level of radioactivity would make even Kilogram quantities virtually undetectable to radiation monitors and there would be no radiation risk to the smugglers. It would be easy to gradually accumulate enough to make a bomb. Enriched uranium also has the feature that it could be hidden away and stored indefinitely without deterioration.

Under normal conditions military weapons are designed for efficiency – to produce the largest explosion possible using the smallest amount of fissile material and the lightest deliverable weapon. However, if the bomb maker didn't care much about efficiency (as a terrorist wouldn't) and he was supplied with enough material to make two slightly sub-critical masses of uranium 235 it would be very simple – so simple almost anyone could do it if they were told how – to make a low yield nuclear bomb. By low yield I mean one to several Kilotons TNT equivalent. All that is needed is to slam the two sub-critical masses of uranium together quickly to make a super-critical mass and a bomb reaction will occur. In the Hiroshima bomb this was done with an explosive charge but something so simple as dropping one piece on to the other could still create an explosion of perhaps 500 tons TNT equivalent along with the usual radioactive fall-out. To produce a one Kiloton blast would be almost as easy and it would not need much ingenuity to increase the yield to, maybe, two to three kilotons. Whilst a one Kiloton explosion is less than a tenth of the power of the Hiroshima bomb it would still devastate a city.

One of the worst features would be the fact that, if the bomb was detonated at or near ground level, as it almost certainly would be, then it would produce even more radioactive fall-out than was experienced from either of the two bombs detonated over Japan. In this situation it would be far more difficult to prove the detonation of the bomb was an act of war committed by a particular country. It would be difficult to prove where the enriched uranium originated. It could be argued the terrorists had stolen the material. Responsibility could be denied. No nation would have actually created and given the terrorists a weapon. The terrorists would have created the weapon themselves. However, we are still left with the question of what happens when, after an American city is devastated, bomb materials are eventually traced back to Iran? I leave the answer to that question to your imagination. Better to try to convince Iran to give up its nuclear ambitions now, before things get out of hand.

It is easy to criticise Bush and Blair – when nothing drastic has happened since 9/11 and our soldiers are being killed by bullets and bombs in Afghanistan and Iraq. However, you cannot see the other possibilities that may have been avoided. There might have been something far worse than 9/11 if there had been no intervention. In the 12 months following the Twin Tower attack, I was expecting a major biological or chemical attack at the least. Such as, a light plane, flying over London or Chicago, spreading three hundred pounds or more of Anthrax spores. Anthrax spores can survive almost indefinitely. (I read of an ancient burial ground in Russia being opened up after hundreds of years. The people and animals of the original settlement had died of Anthrax. Very quickly, one of the excavating team developed Anthrax). During the Cold War, the Russians (the West also) created not hundreds of pounds, but thousands of tons, of various lethal bacterial weapons. The Russians are said to have created enough Yersinia Pestis, (the Black Death) to saturate Europe from end to end. Be aware that Al Qa'eda and the religious extremists are not simply going to give up. If they could get hold of biological weapons they would be likely to use them. They would never really be satisfied until the whole world was of their Faith – and every woman wearing a Burka. You know, and I know, it is a hopeless dream that will never come about, but a lot of people may die before that is proved.

A considerable number of people in the Free World are critical and resentful of American 'interference' in International Affairs. They don't like the way Americans 'throw their weight about'. I have met a number of Americans. Most are wonderfully friendly, likeable, people; a few are arrogant and exasperating. However, I never let the arrogant and exasperating people make me lose sight of the fundamental fact, that everybody who is free today, throughout the world, owes that freedom to America. I think it was very doubtful whether, in 1940, Britain could have stood against Hitler without American help. There is not a chance we could have successfully invaded, and freed Europe, on our own. Later, in the 1950's, only American power stopped Communism from taking over the world. America has now become the 'Policeman of the World' – and, like most policemen, is berated and detested for doing his job.

426

Let us hope that the Iranians will recognise that they cannot possibly expect to convert the rest of the world to Islam, and settle for living in their own way, in their own country and let the peoples of the rest of the world also live as they wish. We must all live together, somehow, and be tolerant. The alternative is disaster.

CORPORAL PUNISHMENT

From the very beginning, when human beings first came down from the trees and began to co-operate, so that they could survive in caves, and in the open Savannah, it has been necessary to have rules of behaviour. Total freedom ceased when we moved into the caves and formed small bands and, later, tribes. A co-operating group must have rules!

Co-operating animals, like wild dogs and wolves, have a hierarchy, with the leader of the pack and his mate at the top and all others in a subservient role. Any member of the group that breaks the rules is punished with a savage bite. Even errant pups are painfully nipped until they acknowledge the authority of the adults. Once all the members of the pack conform to the rules there is harmony, an efficient, cooperating and generally happy group. So it was, with the first human beings to co-operate, and so it remains to this day. Freedom – total freedom – which many people seem to long for, is an illusion. If, in reality, these people were somehow transferred into a place where everyone had total freedom, they would be horrified. No one would be safe. Violence, murder and rape would be everywhere. It would not be possible to create anything, build anything or own anything. Life would be just a vicious, primitive struggle for survival. The strongest and most brutal would fight over and take whatever they liked. There could be no civilisation. The law of the jungle would prevail – and the law of the jungle is Darwinian survival – raw and brutal – the survival of the fittest.

For billions of years, from the earliest stages of life on this planet, total freedom reigned. Endless strife! Endless competition! Endless slaughter! Kill and be killed! Gradually, from the maelstrom, intelligent life emerged, and with that intelligence, an understanding that co-operation could be beneficial. A group, working together, could be better fed, more secure and generally, more successful. However, there had to be rules. The food had to be shared; the weak must have their share along with the strong. Hunting must be co-ordinated so some members of the hunting group must be leaders and organisers and some must be subservient – and obey their instructions. Rules of behaviour were created. Selfishness and discord could destroy the benefits enjoyed by a co-operating, co-ordinating group. Punishment was invented. In the most intelligent species on the planet – Homo Sapiens – communication skills developed and the co-operating groups became larger and larger with commensurately greater potential benefits for members of the group. Unfortunately, the brutal Darwinian law of the jungle, although restricted within the groups, still remained. Tribe attacked tribe, nation attacked nation and, with no rules, slaughter, rape and pillage prevailed.

Gradually, tribes and nations became larger; alliances were created and mutual defence pacts signed. The beginnings of agreement on world wide rules began to be reached and the first International Laws were framed. Eventually, as the end of a natural progression, in the far future, a unified set of rules will apply to every single person and nation on this planet. However, we have a long way to go to reach that final condition. No matter how small, or how large the group of people, the vital thing, for the maintenance of civilisation, is that the rules must work. If the rules that underpin any society cease to be effective, sooner or later anarchy will prevail. It follows, therefore, that if a society, or a civilisation, is to be maintained, rules of behaviour must be devised and must be made to work, otherwise eventually, chaos will ensue.

Throughout the last five thousand years, civilisations have waxed and waned. Many different systems of rules, and methods of enforcing them, have been devised, with varying levels of success. There is little doubt Draconian methods do, indeed, work, as evinced by the fact that the Roman Empire lasted a thousand years. The Romans had harsh rules for control of the population, harsh rules for control of any subjugated states, and the will and determination to apply these rules ruthlessly and efficiently. In general, the Romans get a bad press but the truth is that, in the Roman Empire, providing people obeyed the rules, life was, in general, far better in the Empire than out of it. In pre-Roman Britain, the natives were divided into tribes and continually fought vicious battles with each other. Britain, to this day, is dotted with the remains of ancient hill forts. Originally, these were small settlements enclosed within earthen ramparts, with massive gates and palisades to help stop other marauding tribes from gaining entry. When the Romans came, the ancient Britons fought savagely. Gradually, after the conquest, the hill forts were abandoned. Peace reigned! As excavations of Roman Villas and buildings of the time have revealed, it was possible to build a habitation anywhere in the conquered country – without fortifications. People could sleep in their beds secure in the knowledge that, under the Romans, they would not be attacked in the night by marauding bands. Naturally, most of the films made about the Roman Empire are about wars, battles and strife. Peace is boring! Not enough is said about 'Pax Romana' (Roman Peace). As long as you obeyed the rules (including paying your taxes) you would be left alone to live your life in peace, and relative tranquillity. You might, if it suited your temperament, get a decent job in the Roman Army (supported by the taxes the rest of the Britons paid), well fed and well housed in one of the barracks along Hadrian's wall, and doing a good job keeping the barbarian Picts from endlessly raiding.

That life, under the Romans, was generally peaceful and reasonable, was demonstrated, (after a few hundred years of occupation) when the Britons, upon learning that the Romans were finally going to pack their bags and leave, begged the Romans to stay. Their fears were well justified. Following the disappearance of the Romans, Britain was mercilessly ravaged, for hundreds of years, by repeated invasions of murderous Anglo Saxons and endless Viking raids. The Vikings are a good example of what can happen when laws and rules of behaviour are abandoned. Back home the Vikings had to obey tribal laws, practice self control and behave in a civilised manner to each other. However, when they were raiding, as soon as they attacked a British village, they were released from control and had total freedom. They used this freedom to indulge their base desires. They slaughtered, burned houses, pillaged and raped mercilessly.

When the Romans were in control there was peace but there is no doubt how ruthlessly brutal the Romans could be if anyone was foolish enough – or brave enough – to break their rules. The epic of the 'Slave Uprising' under Spartacus is a good example. A Greek slave, who became a gladiator, escaped and led a general uprising of slaves in southern Italy. Eventually, Spartacus was leading an army of 40,000 slaves. Obviously this was not good for Roman morale, the economy or, more importantly, the Roman reputation. A decision was made; Spartacus must go; the slaves must be taught a lesson and the rest of the world shown an example. After some time, and more than one battle, Spartacus was defeated. To hammer home the message that rebellion would not be tolerated, and to impress the outside world, the entire slave army was slaughtered. As the victorious General and his army marched back to Rome, along the Appian Way, to impress the people and to impress Rome, they left a crucified man on a post every one hundred yards (92 metres) for a total distance of eighty miles (129 kilometres).

Another demonstration of Roman ruthlessness and efficiency was in Israel at the fortress of Masada. At one time a large group of Jewish Zealots rebelled and, later, when they knew a Roman Army was coming to crush them, retreated to Masada, a remarkable fortification, built on top of an enormous rock outcrop two hundred or more feet (61.5 metres) high, with near vertical walls on all sides. Special cisterns to hold rain water had been cut into the rock, and food supplies taken up to last for a year or more. The Zealots thought they were safe – at least until the food ran out. The Roman Army arrived and the Commander studied the situation and gave his orders. The Roman Army began to build an enormous ramp – a great sloping causeway to run from the valley floor to the top of Masada. Despite the rain of missiles from above, the work steadily proceeded. When, finally, the ramp was near completion and it was obvious the Romans would be able to attack the top of the fortress in the next few days, the Zealots held a conference. They knew what was coming! They knew the Romans would spare no-one so they made a decision. Selected Zealots would kill all the rest, including women and children, as humanely as possible and then, finally, kill themselves. When the Roman Commander finally set foot on the summit of Masada there was nothing left to do, all around him was Death. The ramp to the top of the fortress of Masada still stands – to this day. Eventually, even the mighty Roman Empire, that had lasted for a thousand years, collapsed. To sum up – they became complacent, sloppy and finally ran out of good leaders.

In the Middle Ages, and through into the twentieth century, Europe developed and a number of European nations became great and powerful. England prospered and the British Isles became the United Kingdom of Great Britain. Throughout much of this time the rules, i.e. the laws of the land applying to the citizens of the UK, were harsh and were applied rigorously. In the Middle Ages the death penalty was prescribed and applied for a number of offences, including murder, highway robbery and sheep stealing. Treason was punishable by an especially dreadful death; hanging, drawing and quartering. The criminal was first hanged and allowed to strangle slowly. Then, as he began to lose consciousness, he was cut down and allowed to recover slightly. He was then disembowelled and, finally, hacked into four separate pieces. Witchcraft and heresy were punishable by being burned alive, lashed to a stake, on top of a pile of brushwood. Children were indoctrinated with all the rules of society at an early age and the slightest infringement could mean a brutal thrashing. People caught stealing quite minor items could be sentenced to deportation.

Fortunately we now live in a more enlightened age. However, we must be very careful in what we do. Civilisations must have rules, and the rules must be enforced, or chaos and anarchy will be the result. It is important, of course, when the rules (laws) are set out that they really are necessary, and make sense, and are genuinely for the good of the community or the individual. Having done this, it is then necessary to have some sort of sanctions to make sure the laws are adhered to. There are many different laws, covering every kind of human activity, and a very important sub-set of laws are the laws that deal with crimes against individual people. All laws, to be effective, must be backed by sanctions that work. At the present time, in many people's minds is the big question; are the sanctions adequate and are they working? What we are talking about is the question of Crime and Punishment. In a properly civilised Society, all law, abiding members should be able to enjoy the benefits of co-operating in that Society, including freedom from want, freedom from fear and anxiety, and freedom from violence.

Ideally, in a civilised Society, a deterrent or punishment should be the absolute minimum to achieve its purpose. One way to do this is to gradually increase the punishment until a satisfactory reduction in crime has been achieved. However nothing should be ruled out without consideration. There should be an acceptance that punishments, for any crime in any field, should be increased until they reach the level at which they are definitely effective and crime is minimised. The control of crime, in all its forms, should be accepted as a necessary requirement for a civilised Society, and that Society should be prepared to apply such punishments as are proved to be effective.

At the present time most of the Nations of the World are adopting relatively lenient and 'civilised' methods for correction and punishment of wrongdoers – from the gentle treatment of errant children to lenient treatment of serious criminals. As a civilised person I am naturally inclined to be in favour of this and, like most people, recoil at the harshness and brutality of the past. However, we cannot escape the fact that, whatever punishments Society chooses they must, in the end, work. It is up to Society to decide what level of crime and delinquency is acceptable and what is not, and then it is necessary to impose sanctions and punishments to maintain control at the accepted levels. This applies from the simple control of children all the way to control of serious crime. Having lived in the UK for 78 years I have seen considerable changes in Society – many for the better but some for the worse. For instance, when I was young, children were, in general, better behaved and, more importantly, teenage crime such as mugging, burglary, theft and shoplifting was far less. It was common for people to leave the doors of their houses unlocked, whether they were at home or not and very few people suffered burglary or were attacked on the street. Mugging (which is a euphemism for a form of Highway Robbery), bag snatching and shoplifting were rare despite the lower income and standard of living. I often wonder if the change over the last sixty years is related to the reduced control and discipline applied to children and teenagers. I will, therefore, describe the level of discipline and control I personally experienced when I was young. Bear in mind, it was a different age and Corporal Punishment was accepted as normal.

When I was a small child and badly misbehaved, at home or anywhere else, I received a smart slap on the legs or my backside. Very quickly I learned to take note of the warning look on my parents face and to believe them if I was told I would be smacked if I continued to annoy them. At five years old I started school and soon found I couldn't misbehave there either. Within a week I was caned on the hand – only a couple of whacks but it stung and I soon sat down and began to listen to what the teacher was saying. For various reasons my parents moved around the country and I went to no less than six different schools. I can only think of one where I was not caned. Usually I was caned for relatively minor things such as being unruly in class or elsewhere. As an example, I remember when I attended Wellington Boys Grammar School and, one day, we had a concert where girls from another school entertained us in the assembly hall. I can't say I was particularly interested in the music or the singing but it was better than Maths or Chemistry. I sat about six rows back from the stage. The Headmaster and some other teachers were on the front row. A youth, who was no great friend of mine, sitting immediately behind me, gradually became bored and decided to amuse himself by poking me in the back with a pencil. I put up with it for a time but, when it continued, turned and whispered – "Pack it in!" When the pencil came again I lost my temper, stood up, turned around and belted him in the teeth. He leapt to his feet, chairs went over and fists flailed. The girls, in the middle of playing and singing, faltered and everything ground to a halt. The Headmaster rose to his feet, saw the fight and thundered "STOP!"; then he simply pointed to the door. We knew what he meant so off we trundled to his study and waited. Eventually, he turned up, waved us inside, walked to his cupboard, brought out the cane, flexed it, pointed to me and then his desk. I duly bent over, took three on the backside and walked out, stiff legged, desperately trying to stop my eyes watering. The other youth followed me out. All this – without a word. The 'Head' was not in the least interested in who had started it.

I liked and respected the Headmaster who I thought was a great guy! If you behaved like an adult he would treat you like one and I used to chat to him about many things. If he caned my backside – or anyone else's – he did it only because it was necessary – to keep control and discipline. As soon as the punishment was over, the slate was cleared and everything was back to normal. He was not a sadist! He was a likeable, friendly, intelligent man, simply doing his job, which was to educate us; to do that efficiently, he had to maintain control and discipline. Not all the boys at the school were caned; most, I would say, were not. However, those of us who were, acted as a lesson to the remainder who then watched their step. Unruly behaviour is contagious. If a few 'tearaways' are allowed to get away with it then others will copy.

When I first went to the Grammar School it was run by a different Headmaster, who did not keep control. These days he would probably have been considered 'progressive'. As a result the boys ran riot and the teachers were messed about mercilessly. It wasn't chaos, but it was terribly slack. Then a new Headmaster – Mr Cloke – arrived to take over and immediately introduced a system. The school was a modern one with classrooms off long corridors. If any teacher had trouble, the boy was ordered to go out into the corridor, and stay there until told to come back in. The Headmaster occasionally did a patrol of all the corridors; it was random and unpredictable. If he caught you standing in the corridor you were caned. He never bothered to ask why you were there since the teacher who sent you out must have had his reasons! Very quickly discipline was established! We had a few bravados, however; tough boys who could take a caning. After a few sessions, even they were usually under control! I don't remember anybody being expelled. I had my hands caned and, sometimes, my backside but I usually deserved it. If mother noticed me sitting down a bit gingerly, she might say, "What have you been up to?". Dad just grunted!

Although I was moved from school to school – five times, before I went to Grammar school – I took my 11 plus exam before I was 10, passed and was awarded a Special Place, which meant I could go to Grammar School and my parents didn't have to pay. When I was twelve, anyone who couldn't read and write was a rarity. At sixteen, I didn't know anyone who couldn't read; everybody could read and write and do arithmetic. Please don't tell me corporal punishment doesn't work! Every time I see a film, showing a school in the old days where children were caned, I see a travesty of the truth, with brutal, sadistic, flogging maniacs delighting in inflicting pain. There may have been a few who were like that, of course, but I never met one. The teachers I met were ordinary people, simply doing their job – which was to keep discipline and educate us with maximum efficiency – which they did.

When, later, I was in the Army, I met some good men. The sort you can rely on; the sort you would like to have at your side if bullets started flying. One of my Army friends still visits me; another, who died a couple of years ago, had six children. I used to visit him, and his wife and children regularly. He was one of the most patient, good natured, affable men I have ever met. I never, ever, saw him lose his temper; but he used to chastise his children – if he thought it necessary. I remember being with him once – we were chatting and one of his little girls began to get up to mischief, "Stop doing that, Suzy!" He said. We carried on talking and Suzy carried on with the mischief. Again he turned to Suzy and said, "I've told you – stop doing that!" We carried on chatting but the little girl thought, because I was there, she could carry on. "Excuse me" my friend said. He walked over, picked up Suzy, put her over his knee and gave her bottom a sharp whack with a slipper. Ignoring the resulting squeals and screams, he turned back to me. "Now! What were we saying?" Suzy disappeared in tears. Five minutes later she was back and climbed on his lap; all cuddles and happiness. All his children loved him and respected him.

I was not a 'tough guy ' child; far from it! My motto was "Discretion is the better part of valour". Sometimes, however, my temper brought about mistakes. I remember losing my temper, and punching someone much tougher and stronger than I was and taking a hammering before I was allowed to back off. On another occasion I was involved in a fight and got a bloody nose; the nose wouldn't stop bleeding. Eventually, mother carted me off to the Doctor's. After looking at it he said, "Burst blood vessel in the nose. I'll send you to the hospital to have it cauterised." "OK." I said. Back home, I dug out a dictionary and looked up the word cauterise; it said – "To sear with a hot iron". Holy Saints! I went to the hospital full of foreboding. Sure enough, my worst fears were justified. A massive, fierce-looking nurse checked me out and stuffed wadding up my nose. I sat waiting for half an hour, a time which seemed to go on forever. Finally she took me into a cubicle and, in one corner, was a diabolical machine – with an extension cable and what looked like the tip of a thick knitting needle on the end. The nurse sat me in a chair (a wonder she didn't strap me in – my eyes must have been like saucers.) She pulled out the wadding and started the machine which buzzed and hummed menacingly. Then she took the handle of the knitting needle contraption and adjusted the machine until the tip was a dull glowing red. Meanwhile, I was trying to force myself through the back of the chair. She told me to hold a little tray in position under my chin – probably to catch the blood, I thought. She advanced, like an angel from hell and pushed the red hot 'knitting needle' up my nose. There was a smell like a blacksmiths shop, when he is burning the shoe on to the horses hoof, but there was, however, no real pain; the wadding had been loaded with anaesthetic. My head jerked slightly, "Now look what you've done" she said impatiently, "I shall have to do the other nostril now!". I decided she could have given the Gestapo a few lessons! For a long time after that I was careful to keep out of punch-ups, if at all possible.

In human society there are fashions; fashion in clothes, fashion in habits, fashion in thinking. The pendulum tends to swing, over time, from one extreme to the other. People scoff now at the prudery of the Victorians, when the public were brainwashed – sex before marriage is sin, all sex out of wedlock is sin and so on.

However if you stop to think – at that time there were a number of dreadful sexual diseases. Syphilis was lethal; there was no cure and it gradually drove sufferers insane, before it killed them. The best answer – and the one that was adopted at the time – was to create a taboo; no sex before marriage; no sex outside of marriage. It all made sense during the Victorian era even though we may find it ridiculous now.

The point I am trying to make in all this is – it seems to me that, with regard to Corporal Punishment, the pendulum of fashion of thinking has swung too far. The attitude now is – all Corporal Punishment is bad. There must be no caning, no slapping, no smacking of children, no physical punishment of any kind. Parents are told that they cannot even chastise their own children.

Think carefully! Education is not just the three 'R's. Children are children! They are not small adults; the mind is immature. They need to be taught self-control and consideration for others. They need to be controlled for their own good. You are doing children no favours if you let them run riot, be selfish, be uncontrolled. What sort of adults do you think they will become? Some children are naturally thoughtful, naturally self controlled, naturally considerate. They will not get chastised anyway. However, the majority need control. I am of the opinion that the most effective way to correct an errant child is a simple whack on the backside. By this, I only mean a 'whack' that will 'sting' – not injure. I speak from experience! It did not turn me into a resentful, thuggish delinquent; quite the opposite! In my opinion parents should have the right to smack a child, on its bottom or legs, as they see fit. No amount of legislation will stop the pervert who abuses children, or the drunken slob, who beats his children black and blue. I am talking about the right of decent, normal, people to occasionally chastise their children as they deem necessary – at home or on the street or anywhere else. I am talking of a sensible use of a cane, or other simple means of punishment – a ruler perhaps – to control unruly children at school. I am convinced that our generation learned more at school, by the time we were fourteen, than a lot of eighteen year olds know today.

Then there is the question of criminals. When I was a teenager I knew a youth who was uncontrolled. He became a thief and then a burglar. Finally he was caught and the magistrate sentenced him to several strokes of the Birch. The 'Birch' was a bundle of birch twigs bound together and used to flog the bare back. I spoke to him after the birching. He was honest; no bravado. He said he had given up "those games", i.e. the burglary, as he never wanted to experience the birch again.

In my late twenties, I lived in lodgings for several years with an elderly couple who were very good to me. After about two years the man died, and I continued for several more years to stay with his widow, who treated me more like a son than a lodger. She was a fairly fragile old lady, but not normally nervous. At this time I was working late nearly every night trying to start a business and it was her practice to leave the back door unlocked so that I could walk in when I returned. One night, when I arrived, I found the door locked and, when I knocked, a very anxious voice called to ask who it was. She let me in and I saw that she was very distressed, and shaking with fright. When I asked what on Earth was the matter, she told me she had heard noises in her bedroom, whilst she was watching the television. The building was a bungalow which meant the burglar had been very close. At first, I was inclined to think she had been imagining things but, when I looked, the next morning, sure enough there was a footprint on the ground under the window. I spent a little time thinking about the situation – it was November, with dark early nights, and my normal procedure was, after working in the day, to dash back home for a quick meal, then drive back to town and work until late in the evening. I knew that my landlady would be going to a meeting at the Women's Institute in the evening, so the bungalow would normally be deserted, with lights off. Having decided there was a very small chance the burglar might decide to call again, I said to her "I will drive out of the village as I usually do, and you go to the Women's Institute as normal and, before you go, switch off the lights. Then I will park the car at the other end of the village, walk back across the field, up the garden and go back into the house, in the dark, and wait – just in case your burglar returns." I must admit I didn't think there was much of a chance, but, you never know!

So, I carried out the plan. There was a central room, with the bedrooms leading off, so I chose an easy chair and settled down, with a hefty piece of wood handy, to wait and see what might happen, if anything. It was a pitch dark night, with no moon, and I was quite tired (normal in those days) and, after an hour or so, I was on the verge of dropping off to sleep when, suddenly, I heard a faint sound. I couldn't believe it! The burglar really had come back. I heard him entering the bedroom through the window. I waited until I was sure he was in the room, then I burst in, banging the door open, and switched on the light. The burglar, who was only a youth, was suddenly faced with a glaring-eyed maniac with a raised club! The lad was almost frightened out of his life. He was a teenager, from the village, and I recognised him at once. He screamed, "Don't hit me! Don't hit me!" (I couldn't possibly have hit him. I only had the club because the burglar might have turned out to be a big beefy thug, rather than a teenage lad!). I told him to come with me. I knew who he was, and where he lived, so there would be no point in trying to run away. We walked through the village to the Women's Institute where I told him to wait outside. I then went in and found my landlady and told her I had caught her burglar and he was waiting outside. As soon as she saw the youth, the fear and anxiety evaporated and she was simply angry. He was obviously not a serious, dangerous, burglar but just a stupid youth, probably burgling as an act of adolescent bravado. The question was, how could he be made to see the error of his ways, and induced to give up this stupid game which could possibly ruin his life, in addition to causing misery to others?

The three of us walked back to the bungalow, and I mulled things over as we walked. Firstly, I gave him a lecture on how much fear and anxiety burglary caused, in the minds of innocent people – particularly defenceless old ladies. I then insisted he write a confession, there and then, and promise to pay back the few pounds he had stolen the night before. He was told that if he paid back the cash over the next 6 months, and did not get into any more trouble, then neither the Police nor his parents would be informed. The ploy worked! My landlady received her cash back and, more importantly, the lad, to my knowledge, never got into trouble again. So he made a mistake, was corrected, and did not have a Police record.

I firmly believe in giving foolish youngsters, like this one, a chance – but only one. After that, treatment should get tougher. The second offence should justify a simple caning – as per my school experiences; a good six across the backside. Third time I would escalate to the birch and more birch again for the fourth; only after that extend to jail sentences. The curse of jail is that, there, youngsters are likely to be educated to become hardened criminals. Also, keeping criminals in jail is expensive. Try a little corporal punishment first. It will probably cure three out of four delinquents. At the present time the fashion in thinking is to be lenient, and I would be quite happy with that if it actually worked, but the evidence indicates it does not. Sooner or later, the groundswell of public opinion will demand tougher penalties – indeed the trend is already under way. Thirty years ago, the punishment for many crimes was derisory, and criminals were being jailed for mere weeks after committing horrendous crimes. Now, it is noticeable that sentences are much more severe. In due course the clamour for punishments that work will grow. Eventually, I think, be it twenty or a hundred years from now, corporal punishment will return.

THE KILLING OF
PRESIDENT KENNEDY

There has been intense controversy and speculation about a possible conspiracy, almost from the moment John Fitzgerald Kennedy was shot and killed at Dallas, Texas, in 1963. I suspect, however, most conspiracy theories are the result of someone's fertile imagination; the famous Roswell incident, for example, involving flying saucers and dead aliens. Then, there is the recent idea that, somehow, Princess Diana's accident had been planned and organised and, most remarkably, the idea that the Apollo Moon landings did not actually take place, and had been faked. It is amazing how many people have taken up this latter idea, in view of the fact that everything was televised at the time, and millions of people actually watched the Apollo 11 Moon rocket lift off the launch pad at Cape Canaveral.

Nevertheless, although many conspiracy theories are undoubtedly invalid, there is no doubt that there have been many real conspiracies. There was the unquestionably valid conspiracy that culminated in the Al Qa'eda attacks on the Twin Towers World Trade Centre. There was also the attempt to kill Pope John Paul (he was, after all, a great thorn in the side of the Communist countries at the time) and the recent assassination of Alexander Litvinenko, where the radio-active substance Polonium 210 was used. The murder of Litvinenko was almost certainly a conspiracy, because Polonium 210 is extremely difficult to obtain. (It is a substance that is made only in nuclear reactors and is extremely radioactive). Only a few people, with specialist contacts, would be able to obtain it and know how to handle it safely. Litvinenko had been a considerable nuisance to his old Russian spymasters, and the unlikely method of killing him was obviously intended as a message to other, would be, defectors.

I think, in the light of the evidence, there probably was a conspiracy to kill President Kennedy. Having been in the Army, and fired a rifle myself, (fortunately – not in anger) I was immediately sceptical that one man had done it. Kennedy was seated in a moving car, several rapid shots were fired, and it was not the first shot that killed the President. It was claimed that Lee Harvey Oswald, acting on his own, shooting with a relatively old, bolt action rifle from an upper floor window, a considerable distance from the moving car, had murdered President Kennedy. After firing the first shot, Oswald would have had to re-load the rifle by hand action, re-aim, fire, re-load, re-aim, and fire several times in rapid succession. The President was seen to clutch at his neck and lean forwards slightly. (He had probably been hit by Oswald's first bullet). A very short time after that – his wife barely had time to look at him – a second bullet hit him in the head and killed him instantly.

I know from experience that, when you fire a shot from an old fashioned bolt action rifle, the gun kicks, quite powerfully. If you were looking through a telescope (Oswald was using telescopic sights) you would be almost certain to lose the target. (The target would be lost from your field of view). I know I always lost the target when the gun kicked, even without a telescope. I wasn't a crack shot but I managed to score a few 'bulls' in my time. It is also difficult to keep on target whilst re-loading. The very act of re-loading shakes the rifle. In the case of President Kennedy, the target was moving, and this complicates the shooting further. Whether you have plain sights or a telescope, it is necessary to 'lead' a moving target. In other words it is necessary to aim, not directly at the target, but in front of it. You are, in fact, aiming at the place the target will be when the bullet arrives, having taken a definite time to get there after it has left the rifle barrel. Shooting at a moving target is quite difficult because the amount of 'lead' varies, depending on the range, the speed the target is moving and, also, the angle the target is moving relative to the marksman.

A sportsman shooting at a flying bird often has to 'lead' by a metre (3.25ft) or even up to 2 metres (6.5ft) in order to hit his bird. He has to see the bird, judge its distance and speed and the angle of flight, and 'lead' by the right amount. He is also assisted by the fact he is using a shotgun instead of a single shot rifle. The shotgun produces a blast of shot with a substantial spread which increases with distance. If the sportsman had to use a single shot rifle I don't think the birds would need to worry too much. Bird shooting is done at relatively short range. Even a high velocity bullet takes a finite time to travel the distance to the target and, the greater the distance, the greater the amount of 'lead' that has to be allowed. For example, if you are shooting at a man who is walking at right angles to you, at 200 metres (650ft) range, the lead would probably be about 1 foot (30 centimetres). So, if you were to place the telescope cross hairs in the centre of his head and fire – the bullet would whistle behind his neck, because he would have moved roughly one foot (30cm), in the time it took the rifle bullet to travel from the barrel of the gun to the target. If he was in a vehicle, moving at 10 miles (16km) an hour at right angles, the 'lead' could be as much as four feet (1.22 metres). If the target is moving at 10 miles (16km) an hour at an oblique angle – say 20 degrees – the 'lead' would be about 1 foot (30cm).

Maybe Oswald was clever, and worked out the 'lead' he would need beforehand. Admittedly, a crack shot judges the 'lead' instinctively, but was Oswald that good? I doubt it! Then it was announced that the actual bullet that killed President Kennedy was 'found' on the stretcher carrying him into hospital; it matched Oswald's gun. A pistol bullet might lodge in someone's head, but a rifle bullet is a high velocity projectile. When I was in the Army, I was informed the rifle was so powerful it could shoot a bullet through the bodies of three men, one behind the other. That is one of the reasons why, if soldiers in combat are advancing over open ground, the platoon spreads out – and the men zigzag as well, if the bullets are flying. It is, therefore, very unlikely a human head would stop a high velocity rifle bullet. How then did the rifle bullet come to be on the stretcher on which President Kennedy's body was carried into hospital?

Finally, at a later date, there came a crucial piece of evidence; the Zapruder Video Tape. A man named Abraham Zapruder had actually been filming the President's motorcade, and was focussed on the President in his car during the few seconds the assassination was carried out. The film showed the car approaching, then the President reaching towards his neck, and leaning forwards, after a bullet had wounded him. His wife turns towards him and then another bullet, the fatal bullet, strikes. The fact of supreme importance is – the tape clearly showed the President's head jerking violently backwards, i.e. towards the rear of the car, at the impact of the fatal bullet. Apart from the horror, I am of the opinion the Zapruder tape is the evidence that can decide if Oswald acted alone, or was part of a conspiracy.

If a target is struck by a projectile, the transfer of energy on impact always acts in the direction of travel of the projectile. In other words, if someone standing in front of you, shoots you, the bullet will always knock you backwards. In any film, acted or reality, where a person is shot, the impact always knocks the person away from the one who shoots. It is a law of nature, encapsulated in Newton's famous Laws of Motion. Therefore, the implication must be that it was not Oswald who fired the fatal bullet. The Zapruder tape clearly shows President Kennedy's head slamming back at the moment of impact. He was killed by a shot fired from in front of the motorcade, probably from the 'Grassy Knoll' frequently referred to.

It would be very easy to conduct experiments to check if this hypothesis is correct. Simply re-enact the killing! It does not need to be done on the exact spot in Dallas where the President was killed. Anywhere will do, and the car does not need to be moving. Set up the car, with a dummy in the car to represent the President. The head of the dummy must match a human head as closely as possible. Set up a marksman, with a rifle that matches Oswald's, on a platform that matches exactly the distance, height and angle that Oswald was from the car as he stood in the window of the Repository. Then ask the marksman to fire a bullet through the dummy's head, as closely as possible to the point of impact of the lethal bullet and carefully film what happens. The marksman can take all the time in the world to get the shot accurate – and the target is standing still. Then repeat the tests but, this time, with the marksman placed at a position which matches the position of the grassy knoll in front of the car. A comparison of the films of the impacts of the bullets will indicate whether I am right or wrong. It would also, if adequate equipment is set up, be possible to measure the exact residual momentum of the bullet as it came out of the head. If the bullet exits the head as I expect, still retaining most of its momentum, then it would demonstrate that it would not have been possible for President Kennedy's head to have stopped the bullet that killed him, in which case someone must have deliberately placed the bullet that was found on the stretcher. Finally, the tests would provide an indication as to whether the bullet that killed Kennedy was of a different type to Oswald's bullets. (Some ammunition is specially designed to maximise the amount of damage caused on impact. The Zapruder tape showed that President Kennedy's head was almost blown apart by the bullet that killed him. The car and Jackie Kennedy were splattered by some of the President's brain matter).

I am inclined to believe that Lee Harvey Oswald really was telling the truth when he said he was a "Patsy" – a "Fall Guy" – and had been "set up". It seems very convenient that Oswald was shot and killed by Jack Ruby before he could be brought to trial. At such a trial, perhaps a smart defending lawyer might have argued for just such a re-enactment as I have described. Jack Ruby could never be brought to trial; he was already dying of Cancer.

Personally, I am convinced the Zapruder tape indicates Lee Harvey Oswald did not fire the shot that actually killed Kennedy and, sometimes, wonder about the man who really fired the fatal shot. Maybe he is still walking about this Earth today, but I doubt it. If it really was a conspiracy he probably wouldn't last much longer than Oswald. I think someone organised the killing of President Kennedy, but I think it very unlikely we will ever know who it was.

WATER DIVINING AND DOWSING

With anything controversial and unproven it is, I think, difficult to approach the subject with an unbiased mind. As I have gone through life I have tried to strike the balance between being too gullible and, on the other hand, having a closed sceptic mind that dismisses anything strange without even bothering to consider the evidence or give the subject much thought. I have tried to consider everything and weigh the evidence and probabilities very carefully before coming to conclusions.

I heard about water divining when I was a child and, a few years later, read about it together with dowsing, which appears to be an extension of water divining (or you could say – the other way around).

Immediately we are up against a problem. It is amazing what can be faked as anyone who has seen a good magician can vouch for. By simple tricks, and some – not so simple- stage magicians can appear to do amazing things. They are not called magicians for nothing. But these people who are magicians on stage do not pretend that the remarkable things they do are anything but tricks and illusions. Imagine the problems if someone who is a really good magician pretends the effects you see are real. I have no doubt many witch doctors have been, and there are probably some around today who are accomplished magicians. Add to this the fact that many people are very easily fooled and a remarkable percentage actually want to believe. Sometimes it seems incredible to me that anyone can believe some of the outrageous ideas behind some of the cults. There was a cult just a few years ago that believed the world was soon coming to an end and that aliens would come to Earth in a space ship and rescue them – the only true believers. The space ship was out there waiting for the right moment to come in and, as they prayed, was relatively close by. It was undetected because it was hiding behind a large comet (Hale Bopp) which was in the sky at the time.

In the 1930's spiritualism was in vogue and, after the death of his mother, the great escapologist, magician and illusionist, 'Houdini' became interested. He went to a number of séances but, being an experienced illusionist himself, was not impressed. He offered a massive sum of money to any medium who would come forward and demonstrate, and whom he, Houdini, could not prove was a fake. No one took up Houdini's challenge. Before he died he made a pact with his friends that, if it was at all possible, after he died he would make contact. No contact was ever reported.

We also have the problem that some people will make something out of nothing if it will make money. The writer 'Von Daniken' wrote of all the weird things to be found all over the world and which he argued was evidence for the Earth having been visited by aliens in the past. I read a little of one of his books once and he claimed that in some cave in South America a substance unknown to man had been discovered. There is no element unknown to man these days. Unknown compounds yes – but take a sample to a modern analytical laboratory and they will tell you exactly what it is made of and in what proportions within days. So there are plenty of reasons to be sceptical. However we must also look at the other side of the coin. Many of the great scientific discoveries must have seemed like magic at the time. Electro-magnetism being the first to enter my mind. Many scientific discoveries are quite incredible at first and it can take quite a while to accept that they are true and really represent reality. Einstein's Relativity and nuclear energy being a classic example. So, in my mind, it is necessary to tread a fine line between scepticism and gullibility when confronted with anything strange and disconcerting. Whatever it is should not be dismissed out of hand. It should be subjected to thorough and rigorous scientific investigation. If perchance the phenomena were real who knows what remarkable things could come of the discovery of the principles that lay behind it.

When Faraday experimented with the phenomenon of electro magnetism – which at first, looked like a mere laboratory curiosity – who would realise it would lead to enormous power generating stations and the electrical marvels of modern life, or that Rutherford's and Hahn's playing around with the effects of radiation would lead to nuclear power stations or a single bomb capable of wiping a hundred square miles completely off the map.

I bear these things in mind. It does not seem to me that any serious scientific study has been carried out on dowsing and water divining. I read a book on water divining that treated it as a totally established, proven and well understood, technique for discovering underground water. Not only could they establish the exact position of the stream of water flowing underground but also the depth at which it ran and even the actual rate of flow of the water. I saw a film where a diviner walked about, pinpointed the exact spot to drill, and, lo and behold, in 12 months time there was the well and people extracting water from it as predicted. Very impressive! Unfortunately the water diviner who had pinpointed the well airily said that, not only could he do it on the ground but he could actually do it from a photograph. In other words, show him an aerial photograph of some country which might be 500 miles (805km) away and he would swing his little crystal, on a thread, over the photograph and show where to drill for water, accurately to within twenty yards (18.4 metres) or so. Then he could go to the place and pinpoint the spot with total precision.

At the mention of the business with the photograph my mind began to baulk; open mind or not! It occurred to me there are vast areas of the planet that could be said to be almost floating on water. What I mean is, there are aquifers where a layer of porous sand or rock is flooded with water. Such aquifers can be anything up to thousands of square miles in extent. There is a gigantic aquifer under the Sahara Desert, and another enormous one under vast areas of Australia. This means that you could drill anywhere in thousands of square miles of Australia and strike water just a few feet down. (Unfortunately the water in Australia is contaminated by minerals. It is fit for cattle to drink but not for irrigation of crops).

In parts of India and Bangladesh thousands of wells were sunk thirty years ago which tapped into an enormous aquifer. The idea was to supply villagers with clean, bacteria free, water for drinking and so slash the incidence of water borne diseases. At first it was thought to be very successful but, for some reason the water was never checked out perfectly, as it should have been, and now millions of people are suffering from chronic arsenic poisoning. The amount of arsenic in the water is very very small but, unfortunately, arsenic is a cumulative poison.

In the UK there are aquifers everywhere. In many old villages every house had its own well and pump. In the southern counties of the UK I believe 60% of the water people drink today is extracted from aquifers. I realised, therefore, that anyone who was inclined to do so might offer to find water, walk about with a divining stick or rods and say, "Drill here! You will find water.! And he would be right every time. I also read, however, that diviners could not only find water but they could find all sorts of other things. This was usually referred to as Dowsing. Apparently they could discover the whereabouts of buried electricity cables, gas pipes, boxes of treasure – you name it. So – with my open mind – I decided to go on a Dowsing and Divining course at a college in the UK. (You can study almost anything on a course – or even at University these days).

The course was for three days. The first day was mainly theory. The lecturer claimed there was some sort of field which was detectable by the subconscious mind. The field business sounded more than a little airy fairy to me but I know the subconscious can do remarkable things. The second day we went on to the practicalities – actual divining and dowsing. Divining was to be done with a pair of L shaped wires loosely held in the fingers so that the two long parts of the L projected forwards. We were told to start off with the rods parallel and then walk slowly ahead, at the same time concentrating your mind and thinking of what it was you wished to detect. When you passed over the desired substance or object the wires would swing and cross over.

After discussing this for a while we were then taken into a large room. An electric cable ran across the middle of the floor from a socket at one end of the room to a lamp at the other. The instructor said, to make it easier, he would first switch on the lamp. It would be easier to detect a live cable than an inert one. Everybody was issued with the L shaped wires (made from coat hangers) and shown how to hold them. We were then told to line up on one side of the room, hold our divining rods out, and walk slowly forward to pass over the cable in the middle of the room. Before this, during the preliminary lectures, the instructor had said he was convinced anyone could do divining, if they had a little practice, but, as with most things, some people were more gifted than others.

Firstly I stood back and watched the others to see how they progressed. People walked slowly forward, wires swung, some inward, some outward. "Oh Yes!" Said one person. "Definitely!" So I tried it. I tried to blank my mind, then concentrate on the electric cable, walk forward slowly, my wires held loosely, but with both wires parallel. Nothing! I walked slowly from one side of the room to the other. My wires never wavered. "Try it again", said the instructor. Second time – exactly the same as the first. "You have to believe", someone said. Obviously I had a catch 22 situation. If I don't believe – it won't work. But it has to work, for me to believe. I can't believe without evidence. I tried a third time. Somebody suggested, as I walked over the wire I, sort of, 'helped it a little'. I ignored that. Either it would work or it would not. It did not. The instructor then said maybe the wires weren't for me. What about a traditional divining device shaped like a Y. He gave me a device which was made up of two, T section, plastic strips bound together at one end and lying parallel to each other. He instructed me to separate the two loose ends, one in each hand, and force them apart to form a Y shape with the tip facing outwards horizontally – away from myself. This produced tension and strain in the fingers and wrists. If I relaxed my grip but still held the Y shape the device tended to flip up or down to release the stress in the sticks. I walked across the cable again. Nothing! I walked across the cable again and the thing flipped. Hooray! Success, or at least apparent success. Maybe my wrists were just tired. I was congratulated by one or two people.

After a while, when people had practised more – sometimes with the power switched off, and people could still apparently detect the inert cable – the instructor took us out to a large lawn. There were, he said, a number of drainage pipes under the lawn, the positions of which were indicated on a map he had in his pocket but which we were not allowed to see. We were each to take a batch of marker pegs and walk slowly over the lawn with our divining rods. Every time someone walked over a pipe and the rods gave an indication, push a peg in the ground. After a while, the line of a pipe would be indicated by a line of pegs. We all went out and wandered over the lawn with our divining rods, pushing little pegs in here and there. Most of us managed to produce lines of pegs. Then we went back and were allowed to have a look at the plan showing where the drains really were. I can't say I was particularly impressed with our performance. Oh Well! Perhaps we needed more practice.

Off we went indoors again, this time to try dowsing. For this we were each given a thread, a few centimetres long, with a crystal on the end. We were told to take the end of the thread, between thumb and forefinger, with the crystal dangling, extend our arms, and gently swing the crystal over a cup full of water. Then, verbally, ask the crystal to indicate if there was water in the cup. The crystal would either continue to swing in a straight line, backwards and forwards over the cup or it would slowly change until it was rotating in a circle. Whatever it did, and it varied from person to person, was the answer Yes! Since we already knew that there was water in the cup. Once you had established which movements indicated Yes! and No! for yourself, it should be possible to ask the crystal to give the answer to questions about which you could not know. (I believe, years ago, dowsers used this technique, swinging a crystal over the distended abdomen of a pregnant woman, to predict the sex of an unborn child). After everyone had satisfied themselves as to the response of their particular crystal to the cup of water, they went around practicing with the thread and crystal on anything they fancied. Everybody was very enthusiastic, I reserved judgement.

Finally there came the situation I was hoping for. The instructor said we would now check how good everyone was with a test. He led us into the next room, where, on a long table, were twenty cups and saucers. Saucers were on top of the cups. The cups and saucers were numbered 1 to 20, half the cups contained water, the other ten were empty, in random distribution. This was exactly what I wanted to see. An organised scientific test. Everybody was issued with a card numbered one to twenty. Simply tick the ones you were convinced held water. We then all did our stuff. I listened to some of the comments. "Oh! Yes! Definitely water in that one," "This one is empty." And so on. When we had all finished he asked us to signal our results with a show of hands. Did no.1 cup hold water? 14 hands went up, and the figures went in the columns on the blackboard. Number one cup – 14 yes and 6 no and so on. This was repeated with all the cups. When this was finished he then marked which cups had actually contained water and those which had not. Finally he totted up how many people had been right and how many wrong. The percentage number was 50/50. Exactly the figure you would expect if everything was total guesswork. If the figure had been 80:20 I would have been impressed. If it had been 60:40 I would have thought, "Maybe!" But at 50:50 I knew – everybody was just kidding themselves.

At this point I decided to call it a day. I approached the instructor and gently said it was all very interesting but I was going to leave at this point. He was a very pleasant engaging Gent. Said he hoped to see me again sometime. Obviously, not wanting to upset anyone, I did not comment on the results. I went on my way. I could not, of course, totally write off water divining as rubbish on such limited tests. I would like to see a properly conducted, in depth series of tests and evaluations, carried out with professional Water Diviners and Dowsers, to see if there is anything in dowsing and divining or not. But things didn't look too promising to me. Later I met a professional bore hole driller who went around the country drilling bore holes for water – Stately Homes and all that. I asked him if he used water diviners. "No!" He said, "I rely on British Geological Survey maps." He told me he had done drilling in Australia. "Ah!" I said, "Out there you could drill absolutely anywhere knowing you would hit water, couldn't you?" He smiled and there was a twinkle in his eye. "Of course!" He answered.

It is noticeable that people these days looking for buried treasure usually use a modern scientifically designed metal detector, not divining rods or a dangling crystal. But I would still like to see properly organised scientific tests. Water divining and dowsing is, of course, a form of ESP (Extra Sensory Perception). A few years ago it was suggested that Psychics were capable of a form of remote sensing that could threaten National Security. It was claimed they could mentally invade secure premises, enter locked filing cabinets and read top secret documents, all of course, without leaving any evidence and with no one having a clue that espionage had taken place. Recently a Ministry of Defence department admitted it had spent good money investigating such claims. They had carried out tests with marked cards (the usual circles, squares, wavy lines etc.) hidden in envelopes where subjects tried to mentally detect the content of the envelopes. It was stated the tests were inconclusive and had been discontinued. I congratulate the department concerned for having an open mind and bothering to undertake the study. Better safe than sorry! It is interesting to note that the department first invited at least a dozen known Psychics (people who advertise their abilities) to participate in the tests. Every single one refused.

DEVOLUTION OF SCOTLAND AND WALES

The age of Empire building Nations is now at an end. For thousands of years dominant nations conquered other countries and built Empires. At its height the Roman Empire encompassed much of Europe and the Middle East. Before that there was the Persian Empire and so it went on. The last great Empire on this Planet was the British Empire - the largest the world had ever seen.

At the end of the Second World War, Britain recognised that the world was changing rapidly. Attitudes were changing, communications were developing, World Industrialisation was on its way. Nations who previously had accepted their situation as part of the British Empire began to clamour for independence. Despite the denials of the Anti-Colonialists the British Empire was probably the most enlightened the world has known. The British built roads, railways, dams, and other infrastructure and introduced better methods of agriculture and new crops. The people of at least some of the countries in the British Empire were better off under British Rule than they were before. Naturally, the British exploited the conquered nations but not in a totally callous, uncaring way. Nevertheless, there is no substitute for freedom and, in 1945, the British decided the days of Empire were over. For the first time in the history of the world, Nations were offered their freedom and independence without the collapse or destruction of the dominant power.

As an example, India was offered its Independence but there were, however, ethnic problems. A free India was likely to explode into a riot of ethnic violence. The problem was solved by splitting India into three separate states; Pakistan, India and Bangladesh. To achieve a reasonably peaceful transition and future, Pakistan and Bangladesh were devolved from India. They became totally independent Sovereign States with their own governments, laws and economies, and separate military organisations. Malaya also was granted independence – with its golden economic legacy of rubber – introduced from South America by the British. In African states, such as Kenya and Zimbabwe, the British had introduced tobacco, coffee, cotton and maize. These states were also, later, granted independence.

I suppose the old USSR was a form of Empire because, although all its constituent Nations were supposed to be united under the Hammer and Sickle flag, a great many of them only remained in the USSR because of the constant threat of force if any nation attempted to break away. However, after the collapse of the Soviet Union, many states did break away – devolved – from the Union and became independent Sovereign States with their own governments, their own laws and their own economies. Ukraine is now totally independent of Russia, as are Georgia, Belarus, Latvia, Lithuania and others. All are now Nations, independent and standing on their own feet. The trend for independence and self determination continues - and so it should. This is the 21st century. The age of Industrialisation, Global Communication and the Free Association of Nations in a World Economy is approaching.

In the early days of expansion and conquest, England had warred with, and subdued, the Scots, Welsh and Irish, and later incorporated them in what could be called a compound state, The United Kingdom, before setting out to dominate half the world. It was an uneasy Union and Ireland was the first to call for, and fight for, freedom from English control. The Irish free state of Eire (Republic of Ireland) was created and became a totally separate Sovereign State, with its own government, laws and economy. Northern Ireland, mainly because of religious difficulties, remained as part of the United Kingdom of Great Britain.

The Scots and the Welsh have talked about independence for many years. If they wish it, they should be allowed to go ahead. Why not? This is an age of freedom! A move in this direction has already been made. Following Referendums, the Scots and the Welsh have been allowed to set up their own Parliament and Assembly respectively – with separate, but limited, powers over their own areas. In my mind this was a mistake. The Scots and the Welsh should hold further Referendums. Do they want devolution from the UK or not? Perfectly simple! If they vote 'yes' they should be allowed to become totally free Independent States – with their own Parliaments, laws, and economic controls. Everybody in the State of Scotland would be able to vote in Elections for a fully independent Scottish Parliament with absolutely no interference from England or anywhere else. What they chose to decide about votes for 'Expats' would be their business alone. The same for the Welsh; they could vote for a perfectly free and independent State of Wales. If either people voted 'no' then that would be it. They would be part of the Union and, as such, subject to all Laws and Rules, Taxes and Economic Constraints passed by the Government of the Union in Westminster.

Either the Scots and Welsh want Independence or they do not. You cannot be a little bit independent. Either a country is a separate Independent Sovereign State or it is not. Surely the Scots and the Welsh should make up their minds. They should be offered total freedom; a free Independent State for the asking! Surely, if all the other states on Earth that have taken independence have managed to make a go of it, the Scots and Welsh can. They don't need English 'apron strings' do they? The only point is, of course, that if the Scots and Welsh take independence then England automatically becomes independent in the same way Russia has become independent of Ukraine and Belarus. England will have been left on its own. In the same way that Welsh and Scottish Governments will be elected by people within their borders, the English parliament will only be elected by people within English borders – the English counties. This, of course, is the 'crunch' that Tony Blair and the present Government don't like at all. They granted Scotland and Wales their own Parliament and Assembly without thinking it through completely. In a moment of rational thought some of the politicians realised that total independence for Scotland and Wales would mean independence for England. In a frantic effort to head off this possibility, John Prescott suggested separate Assemblies for different parts of England – a classic case of the idea of 'divide and rule'. But it won't wash, Mr Prescott! If Scotland and Wales are to be independent then England must be too. The reason, of course, that the Government would not be happy to contemplate such a situation, is that they know the Labour Party would probably not be in power for long in an independent England.

On a number of occasions in the past, the English have had to accept a Government they did not, on a percentage basis, vote for. It was only the predominance of left-wing Scottish and Welsh MPs that decided the issue. Because of this, a verbal smoke screen is thrown up; John Prescott produces his 'Area Assemblies' idea for England and other Government Ministers insist the idea of a separate England is 'Unworkable'. How strange they think the 'halfway house' of the present Scottish Parliament and Welsh Assembly is workable! Of course an independent English State is workable. It would be far easier to set up a separate English State than, it was in, say, Ukraine or Belarus or Georgia. For heavens sake we are already three parts there. We already have our Parliament in Westminster. We already have our own laws, our own policing, our economic system, our own defence systems. The only thing England would need to do is to change its political system, so that only English citizens could vote, for an English parliament. Nothing could be simpler!

Basically, the Scots and the Welsh should be asked the simple question. Do you want a totally free Sovereign State completely independent of England or not? I would point out, that if they become, or remain, part of the European Union, they don't even need to worry about the economic subsidies they receive at present from England; they will get the subsidies from the EU. Look at Eire! It now has the highest level of income per capita in the entire world.

If I was Scottish or Welsh I would go for it. All to gain and nothing to lose and, as an Englishman, I would be happy in an independent England.

GREAT DISCOVERIES AND INVENTIONS

Many people, when they see this headline, will immediately think I have written of the great modern inventions of our time. I have, to a degree, but, if you think carefully, the greatest discoveries and inventions are the ones we would consider simple today but, nevertheless, gave the human race the means to survive and, not only survive, but to spread and eventually dominate and conquer the entire planet.

I remember the enthralling scene, in Stanley Kubrick's film '2001', which depicts the first breakthrough in the development of human beings from apes. The scene shows a primitive proto-human scavenging amongst the bones of a buffalo or wildebeest, searching in vain for some morsel the other scavengers may have left behind. He picks up a femur bone and idly scuffs and taps at the other bones, then notices the effect a minor impact has on the other bones. He strikes the loose bones littered around and we see portrayed, brilliantly, the dawning of the idea that the bone in his hand is a weapon. As realisation dawns, he thrashes and smashes at the other bones in excitement. The next scene shows a tapir, tumbling to Earth, its skull smashed by a blow from the weapon bone in the proto-human's hand and the family no longer go hungry. In the next scene all the proto-humans are armed and dangerous. To us, it all seems so straightforward and obvious. Once the recognition of the fact that the bone is a potential weapon has been grasped, it is a logical progression to using it to kill animals for food, the arming of other members of the group and, in one leap of imagination, the film takes us all the way to the creation of spacecraft in orbit. And Kubrick was right! From that first breakthrough, the progression, all the way to space travel, was an inevitable progression. In reality, however, maybe the recognition that the bone could be used as a weapon is not so obvious as it appears to us. Maybe the obviousness is a tribute to the capabilities of the human brain.

Chimpanzees are intelligent; no one today would doubt it. They are clever, have a form of communication with each other, and often co-operate in groups to catch and kill monkeys for food. They have been observed using twigs as tools, to dig grubs out of trees and, recently, a case has been reported where a chimpanzee deliberately sharpened a stick with its teeth, and used it as a stabbing tool, to jab into holes in trees to injure and kill small mammals and frogs hiding in the holes. They will even, occasionally, pick up stones and throw them. Yet, despite all this, the chimpanzee has not made the breakthrough to a full realisation of the potential of sticks and stones as weapons. We do not see roving bands of

453

chimpanzees armed with clubs or spears. They have not even grasped the fact that a chimpanzee with a stone in his hand, merely for striking a blow, is more dangerous than a chimpanzee who is empty handed. This failure of chimpanzees to recognise the potential of simple things to be used as weapons, is all the more remarkable because, over millions of years, they must have seen human beings using sticks and stones as weapons. It would be expected, if they are so bright, they would at least have copied us, even if they did not think it out for themselves. An armed, aggressive band of chimpanzees would be very dangerous. Perhaps it is as well for us they did not make this mental leap but the fact they did not is amazing nevertheless.

So the greatest single act of human discovery and invention must be the weapon – no matter how simple – be it stone, or bone, or club, or spear. It made us dangerous. It gave us power. It gave us food, and even the most dangerous animals would soon learn that an armed band of humans was best left alone.

I think the next most important invention must be clothing. Clothing gave us the world. With clothing humans could survive in far more extreme conditions than could ever be tolerated by a naked human being. Simply learning to take the skins off animals, and use them as crude clothing, must have at least tripled the areas of the Earth where humans could operate. The needle therefore, initially just a sliver of bone with a hole in it, which, using sinews as thread, allowed skins to be sewn together to create footwear and more elaborate clothes, must rank as one of the greatest inventions. The use of fire and the invention of the means to make fire must come next. Fire gives warmth, keeps away animals and, above all, cooked food is far safer to eat than uncooked food, which would mean an improvement in survival and the expectation of life. A little realised fact, is that the use of fire resulted in the shape of face we have today. In order to chew uncooked food, early man had massive jaws and a bony crest on top of the skull to act as an anchor for the muscles. The use of fire and the resulting softness of cooked food allowed a reduction in musculature, and bony structure, and resulted in the smaller jaws and chin and the more refined features of the face we see today.

The creation of pottery must have resulted from chance observation that fire converted what had been soft clay, or mud, into stone. Again we see the importance of the human gift of observation and imagination. Pottery vastly increased the potential of cooking and allowed storage of liquid and semi liquid items. It only remained for humans to learn how to create their own habitation – their own personal shelters – and the entire world was theirs, practically from pole to pole. In the wild, chimpanzees and gorillas make crude nests and, no doubt, early humans would do the same. Then, for millions of years, humans lived in natural caves – even to the present day. At some point humans began to create substantial shelters from Earth, rocks, trees, animal skins and even from snow and ice. In some parts of Russia – on the Steppes, where there were no trees – shelters were made from Mammoth bones and animal skins.

These initial discoveries and inventions gave Homo Sapiens freedom to roam and survive over the entire world. It could be said that everything else has merely added to the inventions that allowed human beings to conquer the planet. Certain of these additional inventions stand out of course; stone tools, the bow and arrow, the fishing net, metallic tools – bronze and iron, gunpowder, the internal combustion engine and, more recently, the atomic bomb.

A not so obvious great discovery and invention which we all take for granted and which greatly enhances life is soap. The Romans would definitely have classed this as one of the great discoveries. One of the Roman virtues was that they liked to be clean. Anywhere where we find ruins of Roman habitations we find very elaborate facilities for ablutions. Cold baths, warm baths, hot baths, steam rooms – all intended to loosen and sweat out dirt and grime which was finally removed from the body by scraping with a strigil. The strigil was a relatively blunt knife-like instrument that would scrape but not cut. To get yourself clean, in Roman times, was a laborious, time consuming and tedious business. Nowadays we can get ourselves just as clean or cleaner by taking ten minutes in the shower with a bar of soap.

On a recent visit to New Zealand I was surprised to learn that, when Tasman and Captain Cook arrived at New Zealand, the Maoris were still in the Stone Age. However, working purely with stone tools, they were able to fell trees over two metres (six and a half feet) in diameter and construct ocean-going boats, capable of transporting hundreds of settlers from Samoa. I saw a war canoe around a hundred feet (thirty metres) long, built from hollowed out trees, capable of carrying sixty or eighty warriors. They also constructed large timber houses and buildings. It is easy to underestimate what can be done with stone tools.

The ingenuity of man has manifested itself in the invention of many early weapons. The bow and arrow, the woomera, the boomerang and the sling come to mind. The woomera, or throwing stick, is not a weapon in itself, but it enables a spear to be thrown much further than is possible with the unaided human arm. How the aerodynamic throwing weapon – the boomerang – came to be invented by a primitive people is beyond my comprehension. Few people realise that a sling, in its right configuration and in the right hands, can be as dangerous as a bow and arrow. In Roman times slings were often used. To achieve greater power and accuracy slings-men did not use simple pebbles. Slingshot were made from clay, moulded to exact shape and weight, and fired in a kiln so that the shot were all identical, enabling accuracy and skill to be obtained by practice. A sling, with the right shot and in skilled hands, could be very dangerous. (I am inclined to think that sending the biblical Goliath, armed with a sword against the young David, with his sling, was about as fair as pitting a Samurai warrior against a soldier with a Kalashnikov). A few years ago, Archaeologists excavating the site of a Roman fortification, in the south of England, came upon a large cache of sling shot – large, fired clay, marbles – confirming that the Roman legions used slingsmen battalions as well as archers.

The largest version of the sling ever used, created in the Middle Ages, was a monstrous siege war machine called a Trebuchet. For many years, historians did not really grasp how a trebuchet worked, or its potential. Then, around 20 years ago, a group of scientists studied the old illustrations and descriptions and worked out how the things operated. It is, in effect, a gigantic sling. An enormous pivoting beam takes the place of the human arm and a massive counterweight provides the motive power. In the largest versions, the counterweight was a vast wooden box containing 20 tons or more of rocks. The arm was winched down and the missile (which could be anything from a great ball of stone to a dead horse) was placed in the sling. A restraining rope was released and the missile flung on its way to strike the walls or fall inside the enemy fortification. (Rotting dead horses or cows were, sometimes, flung into the enemy positions as an early form of biological warfare). If used to sling large stone balls the trebuchet was very effective. Because it was gravity operated, the trebuchet would throw the large stone missiles accurately, along the same trajectory and to the same point of impact time after time, providing the missiles were the same weight. Once the trebuchet had been set up in a suitable position and its range adjusted, castle walls could be methodically pounded and breached. Some enthusiasts in England, a few years ago, set to and built a medium sized trebuchet. I was amazed to see films of the contraption throwing small automobiles and pianos through the air for a distance of a couple of hundred yards (183 metres) or so. Heaven knows what the capabilities of the really large versions were.

The simple bow and arrow, which probably reached the peak of its development with the Medieval English Long Bow, was demonstrated with devastating effect at the battles of Crecy and Agincourt in France when thousands of French nobles and soldiers were slaughtered. I read an article a few years ago as to what would have happened if 500 English

Archers had faced 500 Musketeers. The musketeers would not have stood a chance. The archers could have aimed and released a lethal barrage of up to 15 arrows a minute whereas a trained musketeer would probably manage 3 shots a minute. The reason bows and arrows were supplanted by muskets is because it takes years of practice for an archer to become proficient. The ammunition – arrows – are difficult, laborious and slow to produce, whereas anyone can be trained to fire a musket in a few hours and the ammunition, simple lead spheres, can be easily cast by the ton. Extremely powerful versions of the bow, using steel springs, gears and ratchets were created. The Crossbow, almost like a hybrid between a bow and a gun – because it was aimed like a gun and fired with a trigger – was very dangerous and with a considerably longer range than the long bow. However, the crossbow had a similar disadvantage to the musket, in battle conditions, in that it took a long time to reload. Obviously, when firearms were developed to the level they are today – high-velocity, semi-automatic rifles – there was really nothing to compare them with.

I think it was probably the invention of the engine – first steam engines and then internal combustion engines – that has changed the modern world the most, by creating sources of power other than that produced by animal and human muscles. An intermediate stage was the use of water and wind power to run mills and simple equipment, but it was the creation of engines that really spurred industrial development and built the modern world. The invention of sailing ships and, later, steam ships, made it possible, slow but possible, for human beings to travel the world, but it is the invention of the aeroplane that has really made it possible for humans to get anywhere on the planet in a few days, and to most of it in a few hours. The key to modern high-speed aircraft and world travel was, of course, the invention of the turbo-jet engine. I am forever amazed at the incredible power produced by these relatively small devices. I remember, in the early days, the first jet engines produced around 500 kilograms (1,102 pounds) of thrust, which was enough to propel the first jet-powered aircraft. Then they were developed to produce 2000 (4409lbs), then 4000 (8818lbs), then 6000kg (13,227lbs) thrust, which seemed incredible at the time. However, there seems no limit yet in sight in the power to which they can be developed. The latest jet engines can produce up to 45,000kg (99,207lbs) of thrust which means an aircraft, to carry up to 800 or more people, thousands of miles, at a speed of nearly six hundred miles (966km) an hour, can be built using only four of these engines. As far as I am aware, the jet engine is the only modern propulsion device not predicted by science fiction writers.

The working of a jet engine is not obvious! I remember when the first engines were used, and drawings of the interiors of these engines became available, I studied a drawing and said to a friend of mine, "The question is – how does it work"? "Simple" he answered, "Air is pulled into the front, compressed by these blades and passed to the combustion chamber where fuel is added and burned. The combustion products and expanded air then pass through a turbine at the rear and, finally, the exhaust blasts out of the back". "I know all that" I said, "But how does it work"? I pointed out there were no valves and the compressor at the front was driven, directly, by the turbine at the rear. If a jet engine was standing still, and a firework was placed at the centre and set alight, the smoke could just as easily come out of the front as at the back. We know it works but it is not obvious how it works. In America in the 1930's, or early in World War Two, some Americans became aware of the idea of building a turbo jet engine to propel aircraft. One company designed and built an experimental jet engine as I have described. The turbine at the rear drove the turbo-compressor at the front and there was a combustion chamber in the centre. When the engine was started, using an electric motor to set the engine spinning, and the fuel turned on, the jet engine began to work. The electric motor was then disconnected, and it was hoped the engine would continue to run, and build up speed and thrust; but it did not. It gradually slowed down and stopped. The Engineers modified the design, and tinkered with it for a long time, but they could not get it to work. They eventually concluded that the compressor needed more power than the turbine could provide and, therefore, the engine was like a perpetual motion machine and could never work. Eventually the whole project was abandoned.

In England, the inventor Frank Whittle adopted a slightly different design, with a Centrifugal Compressor at the front. This arrangement was more efficient, and the turbine at the rear produced slightly more power than the compressor needed so, theoretically, the engine should, after being started, speed up 'ad infinitum'. When Whittle built his engine, and started it, that was exactly what happened and the engine speeded up until it exploded. There is a film showing Whittle and his team of engineers standing around the engine when it was started up. As the engine speed built up, higher and higher, the engineers can be seen, getting more and more anxious, until eventually they ran in all directions; all except Whittle, who continued to stick with, and attend to, his brainchild until the inevitable explosion occurred. Fortunately he escaped unscathed! Why nobody thought to simply switch off the fuel supply surprises me. The next design project, no doubt, was how to design a governor to stop the engine over-speeding.

In Germany a brilliant engineer – Hans Joachim Pabst Von Ohain – was also working on the design of a jet engine. He tackled it as the

Americans had done – with a turbo-compressor at the front. One of the key things in getting a jet engine to work is the shape – the variation in the cross section from front to rear – and Von Ohain was aware of this. Also, by improving the efficiency of the power turbine at the rear, and the efficiency of the compressor at the front (by better blade design and arrangement), he succeeded in creating a design where the power turbine produced slightly more power than the compressor needed and, thus, invented the first modern type turbo jet engine.

As proof of the importance of the internal shape, it is possible to design and run a jet engine without any turbines or compressor at all. In fact, just a shaped pipe will do, providing you have exactly the right shape and inject and burn the fuel at the right place. The device is then called a ramjet, or athodyd. The snag here is that you have to push the engine at 300 mph (483km) or so, through the air, before you can start it up; but it does work. In modern jet engines, engineers have so improved the efficiency of the compressors and the turbines that, now, the turbine produces far more power than is needed to drive the compressor. Sometimes this extra power is used to drive a propeller (prop jet), or the rotor of a helicopter. In the big engines that propel your 300 seat airliner on holiday, the extra power is used to drive a big fan at the front of the engine, and increase overall thrust. A trick is to use the slow moving fan air, to blanket the high-speed air coming out of the exhaust, in order to reduce the noise. All very clever! Modern jet engines are remarkably efficient, especially when the plane is cruising at 30,000 to 40,000 feet (9,230 to 12,308 metres). A lot of fuel is used climbing to that altitude but, nevertheless, a plane will fly you across the Atlantic and burn only a gallon of fuel for every 70 or so passenger miles. (Because there are 350 people travelling over 3,000 miles (4828km) this adds up to quite a few tons of fuel at take off). Some planes now being designed are expected to be capable of 100 passenger miles per gallon.

Another discovery that could be said to have changed the world was the discovery of Electro-Magnetism. The simple fact that passing a conductive wire through a magnetic field would induce electricity to flow in the wire has resulted, years later, in enormous multi-megawatt electricity generating stations, providing power and lighting to billions of people across the entire planet. One of the men who made this possible was the scientific and engineering genius – Nikola Tesla. Born in 1856 in Serbia he spent most of his adult life in the USA. Not as well known as he should be, he made brilliant innovations in the fields of electrical engineering and electronics. His most valuable contributions to modern life were the invention of the high efficiency, multi phase alternating current, long distance, power transmission system (the overhead power lines we see everywhere today) and the generators and induction motors to go with it. He also experimented with radio (before Marconi), Xrays, Radar and produced many other devices including the automobile petrol engine spark plug. Perhaps best known for his invention of the 'Tesla Coil' – a device to boost electrical voltages to phenomenal levels. He loved to demonstrate this device and astound observers by producing artificial lightning – electrical spark discharges up to 50 feet (15.2 metres) or more in length.

A deeper understanding of the nature of electricity and electro-magnetism – i.e. electrons and electro-magnetic waves – has led to the modern miracles of Electronic Computers and worldwide Communications Networks. The invention of the modern electronic computer has changed all our lives, in the last few years, to greater or lesser degree. Perhaps I am more aware of it than many since I am old enough to have lived in a time when they did not exist. There is no doubt of the remarkable improvements in communications, control systems and general efficiency they have made possible. (How can we now imagine a supermarket keeping track of sales of thousands of different products, or the Army organising the myriads of spare parts for all its equipment, without them?). However, I confess, I have an uneasy nervousness about our becoming so dependent and I wonder about the long term effects of children becoming so engrossed – particularly with computer games. Let us hope my anxieties are unjustified.

The most impressive human invention has to be the thermo-nuclear bomb. I have described how these devices work elsewhere (see Chapter on WAR AND NUCLEAR WEAPONS). What a fantastically long way the human race has advanced since they first ventured out onto the savannah armed only with clubs and spears. Now they have harnessed the very power of the sun to create the most incredible weapon the world has ever seen. Let us hope that the species that has the intelligence to create such a weapon, has the intelligence to recognise the danger, and the sense to abolish and dismantle such devices and consign them, as simply fantastic novelties, to the Museums.

THINK FOR YOURSELF

At first this headline may seem ridiculous. We are all individuals, we all have our own thoughts, we all think for ourselves don't we? However, in actual fact, it is far more unusual and difficult to really think for oneself, than it is to follow pre-set patterns of thinking and inculcated thoughts, almost akin to forms of brain-washing. Most people do not really bother to think for themselves. At first they are taught certain ideas as infants then, later, they read other people's thoughts in books, listen to other people speak, watch the TV, go to lectures and read the Newspapers. At best, they can end up believing minor fallacies and myths. At worst, they can have beliefs that beget wars, murder and strife.

As an example of minor fallacies, there are quite a number of people around who have been fooled into believing the Apollo Moon Landings were nothing more than a confidence trick, perpetrated by NASA at the behest of the US Government; and this – less than forty years after the amazing event. If these people just stopped to pause and think for a moment. The Russians, who were very keen to land men on the Moon first, would have been monitoring the radio signals emanating from the spacecraft, all the way to the Moon, while it was there, and all the way back. If the signals had not been coming from the Moon, the Russians would immediately have said so. They would have shouted it from the rooftops. What about the millions (including my brother) who watched the giant Saturn Five rocket lift off the pad at Cape Canaveral and head for the Moon. (My brother decided to go and see the launch because there is only, ever, one first time). People who came to believe the films of the Moon landing were faked, did so because they had seen a misleading programme on television. That such a thing can happen, so soon after the event, gives us a clue to the enormous power of the media, and propaganda in general, to influence public opinion.

It is amazing how many people actually believe in simple myths, such as the Loch Ness Monster. A lot more say they do but, living locally, they have a vested interest in the tourism generated. However, people have actually paid good money to mount expeditions, with special equipment, to dive and search for the creature. Normally the Monster is shown as being like a plesiosaur – a prehistoric marine reptile. No one has ever suggested it was a type of fish or squid or other water breathing animal. So – if we are to accept that the monster is supposed to be an animal like a plesiosaur – we can dismiss the idea, immediately, as a hoax or, much more likely, a tourist attraction; an invented novelty no more real then a Welsh Dragon.

Plesiosaurs breathed air. If a sperm whale, as an air breathing mammal, cannot hide from humans in forty million square miles of sea, in the Pacific Ocean, there is no way an air breathing plesiosaur could hide in the thirty to forty square miles (48 to 64 square kilometres) of Loch Ness. It would be seen every day – coming up for air. If it had been real it would, by now, be stuffed and adorning a museum, because somebody couldn't resist taking a pot shot at it with his rifle. Either that, or it would be cavorting near the shore, being fed with sardines by school children.

Other similar legends, like the 'Yeti' in the Himalayas or the 'Bigfoot' in Canada, are harder to pin down but, in the Himalayas, the Yeti would have to eat and therefore, sooner or later, it would be seen on hunting forays into the valleys. Bigfoot is the most difficult to dismiss entirely, because there are tens of thousands of square miles of forest in Canada. Since it is so easy to fake footprints, or even a film of a Bigfoot, I think its existence is very unlikely. If one should ever, in reality, be caught, it would be sad to see such a creature in a zoo - like the great apes. I shall, I admit, be extremely surprised if such an animal as Bigfoot actually turned out to be real.

I remember a television programme many years ago. As part of the presentation, a speaker claimed that, although millions of people ate spaghetti, in fact, what they were eating was only an imitation – cobbled up out of flour and water; the real spaghetti which, of course, the fake spaghetti manufacturers would never mention did in fact grow on trees or, to be precise, bushes. They then showed a film – with workers moving along a row of bushes, carefully picking off the ripe, hanging spaghetti and placing it gently in baskets. Most of us laughed! It was, of course, April the first. For people who are not British I will explain that April the first in England was, and is, called April Fool's Day. All sorts of pranks and tricks used to be played, sometimes even by the BBC. You would be amazed how many people ended up believing that, originally, spaghetti grew on bushes!

I was almost taken in myself once! In a Science Magazine I read where archaeologists, working on a Pacific island, had found some remarkable remains, indicating strange arrangements of ropes and pulley blocks, laid out flat on the ground. At first everybody had been baffled. Then a really bright student had worked out that it was a form of computer, invented hundreds of years ago, on an island in the Pacific! The article showed diagrams of various rope arrangements corresponding to components of a modern computer. Fascinating! However, somehow the name of the Island caught my attention again; the Island was called Aprafulia. I looked at the date of the magazine – April the first – of course!

I suppose the classic example of people being fooled was Orson Welles' presentation of 'The War of the Worlds', on the radio in the late 1930's. In order to make the story more dramatic, Welles decided to present it as if it was real, and happening right here and now. Without any explanation or preamble, the programme commenced with breathless announcers stating that strange objects, believed to be spacecraft from Mars, had fallen to Earth in the United States. Details of the Martian spacecraft, and the totally invincible fighting machines that emerged from them, were presented as though everything was a true, here and now, happening. The result was that millions of people believed that it was real, and a mass panic ensued. Thousands of people left their homes, jumped into their cars, and tried to escape what they thought was a genuine Martian invasion. When it was realised what was happening, the Producers frantically broadcast denials and said it was merely a dramatisation of a famous story. Gradually, things were sorted out, and Orson Welles was castigated for what he had done. Cynics suggested he knew perfectly well what he was doing, and had achieved his aim, Fame and Notoriety; publicity at any price. Maybe he was innocent, and simply did not realise what the public reaction might be.

So – we have a situation where all of us are indoctrinated – one way or another. In Universities, students listen to lecturers and read books. In Churches the congregations listen to preachers. A few years ago the Chinese were indoctrinated by Chairman Mao's 'Little Red Book'. Before that, millions read Karl Marx's 'Das Capital' and Hitler's 'Mein Kampf'. Whatever it is that you hear, or read, or have been taught, pause sometimes to ask yourself "Does this really make sense?" Is it just possible it could be wrong or, maybe, a distortion of the truth? Is there a motive or a vested interest? Is there a subtle reason why you should be misled? Or is someone making a simple, honest mistake? Is someone presenting the facts in a roundabout way, in order to give a false impression? In Politics this is called 'spin'. I personally am impressed by Science. The miracles of science today are the result of rational, logical, thinking producing theories confirmed by practical, repeatable, experiment. The great men of science come to mind – Newton, Einstein, Bohr, Hawking and so on. These are men of genius or, at least, brilliance. However, it should still be borne in mind they are, or were, human and, therefore, not infallible. Even they can, and do, occasionally make mistakes.

Einstein spent years thinking before he produced his 'Theory of Relativity'. It is a remarkable theory, and has been called 'The Greatest Intellectual Achievement of All Time' by some. I would not go quite so far; there have been other very clever people. If Einstein had not thought it up – someone else would. When followed through – one of the implications of Einstein's Theory was that the Equations as they stood, indicated the Universe would either be expanding or contracting; not static. Einstein decided that this was a problem. All the world knew, or thought they knew, at that time, that the Universe was static and had been for billions of years. So, to make the equations fit the facts, Einstein added a little extra – a Cosmological Constant. Add this in and, if the Constant was adjusted – just so, you could have a static Universe. Great man or not – Einstein had fudged it. (Let us not pretend differently). He wanted his equations to fit the obvious facts. Then, later, the astronomers found out the Universe was not static; it was, in fact, expanding. Einstein was mortified. He was basically an honest man – but he had succumbed to the temptation of fudging his equations, to fit what he, and everybody else, thought was reality. He said, quite openly, his addition of the Cosmological Constant was the greatest mistake of his life. In my mind – he was right. Think of it! If he had stuck to his guns – that the Universe must be expanding or contracting – in the face of all the evidence at the time showing otherwise, then what an accolade when they finally found that, even in this, he was right. Instead he demeaned himself, but he was 'big' enough to admit it. Surprisingly enough, now that scientists have discovered evidence indicating that the Universe appears to be expanding faster and faster, some are now saying Einstein was right after all. There is a Cosmological Constant. They do not like the idea that their hero stumbled a little as he climbed on to his pedestal. Of course, he wasn't right! When he did it – it was a simple fudge. Researchers do it all the time – if facts don't fit their pet theory. Sometimes they get caught out! Personally, I think Einstein was more than brilliant; a genius. However, he was, after all, human!

When Isaac Newton (a true genius if ever there was one) produced his 'Principia', the world was provided with all the Mathematics it needed to calculate Ballistics and Celestial Mechanics. (The trajectory and laws of motion of cannon balls, bullets, spacecraft, planets, etc). The mathematics allow you to calculate, absolutely precisely, the exact trajectory needed to get a spacecraft to Mars, or anywhere else in the Solar System. Newtonian mathematics are used by Engineers all the time. Then Einstein came along. What if we travelled very fast indeed; near, or at, the speed of light. It was found that Newton's mathematics would not hold. At these speeds Engineers have to use the mathematics of Einstein's 'Theory of Relativity'.

At CERN, near Geneva – where they are building the large Hadron Collider – scientists have to use Relativity maths. In their machine, protons will be accelerated until they are travelling at 99.9999%

of the speed of light. The protons will become many times heavier, time will be distorted (for the protons that is) and the protons will be foreshortened to flat discs, all in accordance with Einstein's 'Theory of Relativity'. When I was young, my mind was stunned by the Theory's implications. I remember an occasion when I climbed into a train standing at a railway station and sat down; checked my ticket, glanced out of the window and was surprised that we were starting to move. Then I had a slight shock. The train next to us pulled away, and I saw the station and realised we were still stationary. For a moment I had been convinced we were moving. Now imagine – out in space – three spaceships. One sees another approaching, at high speed. They pass at 50,000 miles an hour. One pilot says, "According to our instruments he was travelling at 50,000 miles an hour". The other pilot says exactly the same. The pilot of the third ship, close by, says, "That green craft passed us at a fair speed, 35,000 miles an hour; the red one was travelling at 15,000 miles an hour, in the opposite direction". They are all correct. It simply depends on the observer, and what he measures speed relative to. That seemed straight forward and understandable to me but, as I delved further, and found that, as you began to reach speeds near the speed of light, time was distorted, mass was distorted, distances were distorted, and furthermore, the implications were that mass and energy were two forms of the same thing and $E=MC^2$, my mind was bewildered.

According to the Theory of Relativity, any observer moving near the speed of light, relative to me, will have his time rate changed. At 99.99% of the speed of light, one hour of his time would be equal to maybe a week or more of mine. In addition, his mass would be building up towards infinity and he would be flattened to a wafer. (These effects actually occur in particle accelerators). But, I ask myself, what is the situation at very long distances away in space? Space is expanding. The further a Galaxy is away from us the faster it is receding. With their latest telescopes, Astronomers can now observe objects (Galaxies and Quasars) that are so far away that they are receding from us at nearly the speed of light. Soon they will be able to see objects at such a distance that they will be travelling away from us at over 99% of the speed of light. (There is then a visual barrier. We will never be able to see Galaxies that are travelling away from us at the speed of light or faster; the light will never reach us). I ask myself – would people on planets, out at this enormous distance, travelling away from me at nearly the speed of light, have their time rates changed? Would one hour of their time be equal to a week of mine? I realise the Universe carries on, beyond the limit we shall ever be able to see, so I imagine – what would an observer in one of the Galaxies at the limit of our vision see? He would see us, at the limit of his vision in one direction, travelling away from him at nearly the speed of light. If he looks in the other direction, he will see another galaxy at the limit of his vision, again travelling away from him at nearly the speed of light. Therefore, relative to us, the other galaxy would appear to be travelling at nearly twice the speed of light. However, these speeds are all due to the expansion of the Universe.

Considering the Universe as a whole, I feel it is reasonable to assume that any observer, anywhere in the Universe, if he bothers to work out the age of the Universe, from the evidence available, will come up with the same age as we do. In other words, there will be no time distortion between the galaxies although they are travelling at high speeds relative to each other, because the speed is caused by the expansion of space. If I am right, it would appear that Einstein's Theory of Relativity only applies to a local volume of space (cosmologically speaking). Speed simply caused by the expansion of space itself, would not be covered by the Theory of Relativity.

Many experiments, on this Earth and in space, have confirmed the validity of Einstein's Theory. However, when we need to consider the behaviour of the extremely small, i.e. atomic and sub atomic, particles it is necessary to use the mathematics of Quantum Theory. The behaviour of very small particles, at the quantum level, can be extremely strange and there is a property termed 'Entanglement'. It is possible to create pairs of particles which are linked in their behaviour; they are said to be 'entangled' and 'complementary'. For instance, it is possible to produce polarised photon pairs, where one particle is polarised one way and the other in a specifically different way. The word Entanglement only applies to the condition of the particles and they could, according to Quantum Theory, be separated by any distance – even as far as the other side of the Universe – but they would still retain the property of Entanglement. In addition, according to Quantum Theory, the two entangled particles must remain complementary at all times even if the condition of one particle is changed. The implication of this is that, the instant the condition of one of the particles is changed, the other must also change, in order to preserve complementarity. (A simple way to think of it is to imagine you have two tennis balls – one green and one red and some strange law says that, no matter where they are, one ball must be green and the other red. You can, if you like, change the colour of one ball from red to green but, if you do, the other must automatically change from green to red, even if something has carried the second ball to the moon or the far side of the Universe. The change will happen instantaneously even if it would take hours or even thousands of years for light to make the journey between the two. This implies instantaneous communication, i.e. faster than light, between the two particles. It is as though the two were permanently connected – through space and time. Einstein was extremely unhappy at this implication of Quantum Theory. He did not like the idea of, "Spooky action at a distance" as he called it, and spent a great deal of his time thinking, and trying to find a flaw in Quantum Theory. This was quite understandable, because one of the key tenets of the Theory of Relativity is that nothing could travel faster than light; nothing physical, not light itself and not even information. Einstein never was able to disprove this predicted property of quantum particles, even to his death. Recently, some ingenious scientists managed to conduct an experiment to confirm or refute the prediction of the effects of Entanglement. Their results confirm Entanglement is valid. The entangled particles do, indeed, seem to be able to communicate faster than the speed of light. Einstein himself once said that, if a single example were found that did not agree with the predictions of Relativity, the whole Theory of Relativity should be reconsidered. The business of instantaneous communication between entangled particles appears to me to be such a case.

Apparently Einstein's Relativity also runs into trouble in the most extreme gravitational conditions, such as may exist at, or inside, the Event Horizon of a Black Hole. Some scientists have a habit of saying, "The laws of nature break down in the conditions at, or near, a black hole". To me that sounds like a get out! They are really saying nobody yet understands the conditions at a black hole, and existing mathematics cannot handle the conditions. Before Einstein, somebody using Newtonian maths might equally have said, "The laws of nature break down when you approach the speed of light". I have a feeling that, one of these days, some bright young mathematician is going to say "Einstein's mathematics are brilliant – but they will not work in extreme circumstances – such as in, or very near to, a black hole. I have had an idea – and this is my new Theory". Incidentally, if the reader wishes to read and understand more about Relativity and Quantum Theory – look them up – there are plenty of books on these subjects. There is no question that, apart from these examples, the Theory of Relativity appears to be valid, and provides incredibly accurate predictions of the way Space and Time behave. One of the equations resulting from the Theory of Relativity was the famous $E=MC^2$, which implied there was an immense amount of energy in any form of matter. The idea that a simple pebble, held in my hand, represented enough energy to vaporise a city was hard to swallow when I was young, but the explosion that destroyed Hiroshima was very convincing!

The point I am trying to make in all this is that you should never assume anything anyone says, or writes, or, indeed, that anything that has ever been written, is necessarily the truth, or the very last word. Always be prepared to question and to think about things yourself; to ask yourself if something is logical, rational and makes sense – not some fixed, preconceived notion that has been put into your head by somebody else. Be prepared to think about, and question, Science, Politics, Religion and any established Dogma. You have a brain; use it; how else are we ever going to progress? Sometimes you may make mistakes, occasionally you may make a fool of yourself, but sometimes you will be right. So – don't be afraid – think for yourself!